Translations of Mathematical Monographs *Volume 10*

The Theory of

IRRATIONALITIES OF THE THIRD DEGREE

by

B. N. Delone and D. K. Faddeev

AMERICAN MATHEMATICAL SOCIETY
PROVIDENCE, RHODE ISLAND
1964

ТЕОРИЯ ИРРАЦИОНАЛЬНОСТЕЙ ТРЕТЬЕЙ СТЕПЕНИ

Б. Н. ДЕЛОНЕ и Д. К. ФАДДЕЕВ

Труды Математического Института
имени В. А. Стеклова XI.

Издательство Академии Наук СССР

Москва 1940 Ленинград

Translated from the Russian
by Emma Lehmer and Sue Ann Walker

Publication aided by a grant from the
NATIONAL SCIENCE FOUNDATION

Text composed on Photon, Partly subsidized by NSF Grant G21913

Library of Congress Card Number 63-21548

Printed in the United States of America

AUTHOR'S FOREWORD TO THE TRANSLATION

The initiative for writing this book came from Edmund Landau, who suggested it to me in Göttingen in 1928. The book was begun in collaboration with the Norwegian mathematician Nagell, but we soon realized that it would be much more convenient for me to have a coauthor living in Leningrad, where I resided at that time, in the person of my pupil, a very gifted algebraist, Dimitriĭ Konstantinovič Faddeev. The whole book was conceived by me, in a sense, as a framework for my investigations into indeterminate equations of the third degree, as developed in Chapter VI.

After the works of Lagrange and Gauss in the theory of indeterminate equations of the second degree in two unknowns, which used to occupy an important part of any course in the theory of numbers, there appeared on the one hand the works of Dirichlet, and on the other those of Hermite. Dirichlet generalized the work of Lagrange and Gauss to equations of the form $\Phi = m$, where Φ is a form of the nth degree in n variables, decomposable into irrational linear factors, and m is a given number, while Hermite considered the equation $\Psi = m$, where Ψ is a quadratic form in n variables. An interesting result concerning such equations was also obtained by Dickson. As to indeterminate equations of the third and higher degree in two unknowns, only the remarkable method of Thue was applicable. This method was brought to its ultimate conclusion by Roth without introducing anything new in principle. However, for the effective solution of such equations one must apparently look for new and deeper methods.

Around 1920 there appeared two series of papers on the indeterminate equations of the third degree in two unknowns: my papers, which are given here in Chapter VI, having to do with integer solutions, and those of Mordell on a finite basis for rational solutions, which form the culmination of an idea of Poincaré.

At the present time the following two problems in the theory of indeterminate equations are unquestionably the ones to which attention should now be turned: 1) To test the effectiveness of the method for finding integer solutions of binary equations, possibly by developing further my algorithm of ascent and at the same time probably solving the problem of incomplete quotients. 2) To obtain effectively the Poincaré basis for rational solutions. The second problem is being studied by some well-known modern mathematicians, such as Serre in Paris and Šafarevič in Moscow, but nobody has given any serious attention to the development of my method since I abandoned it in the 1930's. It should be pointed out that there is no algebraic irrational of degree higher than the second for which we know whether the partial quotients in its expansion in a continued fraction are bounded or not. However, an effective solution even of the equation $ax^3 + y^3 = \sigma$, with given integers a and σ, would apparently lead to the solution of this problem for $\sqrt[3]{a}$.

I hope that the publication of this book in the United States will serve as a stimulus to others to develop further the methods presented in Chapter VI.

B. Delone
Moscow,
July 30, 1962

Translators' note. The translators are deeply grateful to Professor Delone for his valuable assistance with certain details of the text and for his suggestions regarding the inclusion of recent or supplementary material.

TABLE OF CONTENTS

INTRODUCTION

A large part of the modern theory of algebraic numbers is concerned with problems whose simplest nontrivial examples can be found in the theory of quadratic irrationalities given by Gauss in his *Disquisitiones arithmeticae.* To this belong the theory of units, theory of ideals, laws of reciprocity and therefore, to a certain extent, class field theory.

A similar study of the theory of cubic irrationalities is interesting not only as the next case in complexity after the quadratic case, in which it is still possible to give solutions in terms of convenient algorithms, but primarily because it poses further problems that were so trivial in the quadratic case as to escape notice. To this belong in the first place the problem of classification of cubic irrationalities, the so-called inverse problem of the Galois theory for these irrationalities, and the problem of approximation of irrational numbers of higher degree by rationals, which is as yet not completely solved and which is closely connected with the problem of representing numbers by incomplete reducible forms (i.e., forms in which the number of variables is less than the degree). These two fundamental problems first appeared in a nontrivial way in the theory of cubic irrationalities, but they exist for irrationalities of any degree.

Until now there has appeared no monograph in the mathematical literature on the theory of cubic irrationalities. Our book fills this gap.

It is natural that this book should be published by the Academy of Sciences (U.S.S.R.), since many of the investigations in the theory of cubic irrationalities are due to mathematicians who are in one way or another connected with the Academy. They are: E. Zolotarev, A. Markov, G. Voronoĭ, myself, V. A. Tartakovskiĭ, D. K. Faddeev, E. A. Venkov, and O. K. Žitomirskiĭ. The most important contributions of foreign mathematicians to this subject are due to Eisenstein, Thue, Mordell, Nagell, A. Weil and C. L. Siegel, as well as to Dedekind and Hasse. The investigations of the last two mathematicians are not included in this monograph, since their methods are more in the nature of application of general class field theory to the special case of cubic fields.

One may hope that considerations similar to the ones discussed in Chapters I and III may lead to the construction of a theory, close to class field theory, but which will give solutions to problems now solved by class field theory without the use of the analytical theory of numbers.

D. K. Faddeev and I are equal coauthors of this book, and about half of the material contained in it belongs to D. K. Faddeev. Usually, the plan for each section was discussed by us jointly in advance, and subsequently each of us looked over the sections written by the other. Thus §§7–9, 12, 19, 22–25, 34, 35, 42–59, 64, 70, 72–74, 79–82 were written by D. K. Faddeev, while §§1–6, 10, 11, 13–18, 20, 21, 26–33, 36–41, 60–63, 65–68, 71, 75–78 were written by me. We are indebted to V. A. Tartakovskiĭ for §69.

The plan and the idea of the book are mine, but as a result of the invaluable cooperation of D. K. Faddeev, who gave all his enthusiasm to this work, it became possible to realize a much wider program than was first envisaged, when I began to write this book with Nagell. Faddeev and I have developed especially for this book many of the results in the theory of cubic irrationalities which were not available among the known results. This is particularly true of much of the material in Chapters I and III.

I shall give a brief account of the contents of the various chapters.

Chapter I contains the most complete step-by-step geometric development of the theory of algebraic irrationalities of any degree, considered, on my suggestion, as a theory of multiplicative lattices in n-dimensional complex space K_n. It serves as an introduction to the whole book. Such lattices are somewhat more general than algebraic fields and are connected with their direct sums. They are needed in Chapter III for the solution of the inverse problem of Galois theory for fields of the third and fourth degree. The geometrical character of the exposition in Chapter I was adopted because it was necessary in Chapter III and, even more so in Chapter IV. In the beginning of Chapter I (§2) will be found my proposed proof of the theorem about the existence of infinitely many independent irreducible algebraic irrationalities of a given dimension and signature. The idea of considering an affine dilation with coefficients $r, r^2, \cdots, r^n$ along the axes in calculating the volume $Q^*(r)$ is due to a student of the Moscow State University, E. Vegeman. Further, in §3, we give the geometry of Galois theory which was developed by me [19]. [1] §4 contains a purely geometrical interpretation of Dirichlet

---

1) Numbers in square brackets after an author's name refer to the bibliography. If there is no such reference, then the result appears for the first time in this book.

units. §5 contains the researches of Minkowski from *Diophantische Approximationen* of the geometry of the theory of ideals (this is the only mention of the proposed geometrical theory of algebraic numbers which has so far appeared in the literature). Theorem I of §5 is due to Faddeev. §6 is devoted to the development of the theory of n-dimensional auxiliary lattices proposed by Klein, which is somewhat deeper than ideal theory. The special case $n = 2$ was considered by Klein [27] in his famous lectures on the theory of numbers, while the case $n = 3$ was the subject of a Ph. D. dissertation by Furtwängler [63]. Both the theory of units and the theory of ideals are developed in Chapter I for a most general n-dimensional maximal lattice, which may be reducible. §§7, 8, and 9 contain the theory of various forms connected with the lattices in K_n. The suggestion of considering the generalized Bézoutiants arose in connection with my plan to tabulate, in common with I. Sominskiĭ and K. Billevič, the fields of the fourth degree [18] (see §40) by making use of the projection of a field parallel to a subfield. D. K. Faddeev [60] suggested the consideration of the lattice inverse to a given lattice and correspondingly the form polar to a given reducible form. This form presents a very useful algorithmic tool, as is evident in §64.

Chapter I may be useful to anyone wishing to study the theory of algebraic numbers, as it contains a sufficiently complete step-by-step exposition of the fundamental facts of the theory.

Chapter II contains the elements of algebraic fields of the third degree. Its exposition, in contrast to Chapter I, is purely algebraic and it can be read independently of Chapter I. In Chapter II we give everywhere the most useful arithmetical algorithms which we know for actually carrying out the calculations involved and sometimes we even give numerical examples. In §11 we give a formula for raising a cubic number to any power. The method of extracting roots was suggested by Faddeev. It is useful for checking whether a given unit is fundamental or not and is used in §49 to solve the problem inverse to the Tschirnhausen problem for two equations of the fourth degree. In §13 I give my solution [15] of the problem for two equations of the third degree. §15 contains the theory developed by F. Levi [28] and by me [15]. §16 contains my method [15] for solving the problem of equivalence of two binary cubic forms without the reduction theory of forms. §17 contains an exposition of the well known method of Voronoĭ [8] for calculating a basis of a cubic field, a method which was the main result of his Master's dissertation. §18 contains the algorithm for the decomposition of a prime into prime ideals in a field of the nth degree, and in particular for cubic fields according to Zolotarev [26].

Chapter III. §§26–30 and §§37–41 give an independent tabulation of multiplicative lattices and therefore also of fields of the third and fourth degree for all signatures. These sections close by giving tables of these lattices. The tabulation of rings of the third degree with positive discriminants was first achieved by Arndt [1–4] in 1852, using Eisenstein's idea [21], as a tabulation of clases of binary cubic forms. An analogous tabulation for negative discriminants was made by Mathews and Berwick [30, 31] and in a different manner by me [15]. The tabulation of rings of the fourth degree with signature $\tau = 0$ (number of pairs of complex roots) was made by I. Sominskiĭ and K. Billevič [18] and myself, while for $\tau = 1$ the table was calculated by Č. Poplavskiĭ. §§32–35 contain the geometry of binary cubic forms. The reduction theory was developed by Mathews [30, 31] and myself. The consideration of binary cubic forms as norms is due to Faddeev. The theorem in §36 was proved by Tartakovskiĭ in 1919 as a result of our conjecture, which arose from the study of a large table of discriminants of cubic units calculated for me in 1918 by students of the University of Kiev, using desk computers. This theorem remained unpublished up to now. As to the classification of cubic regions in terms of quadratic regions and of quartic regions in terms of cubic regions the following remarks are in order. Eisenstein [21] gave, in 1841, an interesting classification of binary cubic forms in terms of their quadratic covariants, which was later perfected by Arndt [1–4]. In my seminars at Leningrad University I often pointed out that Eisenstein's theory can be considered in the first place as a classification of cubic rings in terms of quadratic regions, in the second place it can be geometrized, and in the third place, it can be generalized to regions of higher degree. Subsequently B. A. Venkov [6] translated Eisenstein's classification into the language of algebraic number theory, while O. K. Žitomirskiĭ [24] completed its geometrization by showing how to select the axes in the projection space. Later I was able to discover the generalization of this theory to regions of the fourth degree. The detailed work on this generalization to the fourth degree was done by D. K. Faddeev [59]. At the present time Faddeev and I are constructing this theory, in [62], for fields of any degree. If by the direct problem of Galois theory we mean the problem of finding all the algebraic properties of a given field in terms of its Galois group and if by the inverse problem we mean that of finding all fields having a certain Galois group, then the theory developed in §§42–53 could be thought of as the solution of the inverse problem of Galois theory for fields of the third and fourth degree. We here give this theory (in a very careful and detailed account of Faddeev) also for fields of the fourth degree, since their classification is based on the consideration of the fields of the third degree and also, curiously enough, on the consideration of general three-dimensional multiplicative lattices (i.e., also reducible lattices) and their auxiliary lattices.

Chapter IV is devoted to Voronoĭ's algorithm for the calculation of multiplicative automorphisms of fields of the third degree. At first we considered giving all the algorithms existing for this purpose, such as those of Zolotarev [25], Minkowski [33], Charve [67], Voronoĭ [9], Berwick [5] and Uspensky [55], but finally we decided to give only Voronoĭ's algorithm, as being the most convenient one. The case $D > 0$ was written up by D. K. Faddeev, while the case $D < 0$ was done by me (see also my note [16]). In §64 we give a refinement of Voronoĭ's algorithm for $D > 0$ which was suggested by me at the Kharkov congress and perfected by D. K. Faddeev in such a way as to reduce the calculations to rational integers. I must add that Faddeev has very elegantly perfected my calculations by noting that it is best to transform in parallel the given reducible ternary cubic form and its polar form. He also introduced the symbolic triangular notation for reducible ternary cubic forms.

Chapter V contains the exposition of Thue's theorem. The main ideas in this exposition, given in §§65, 66, 68, are due to V. A. Tartakovskiĭ [17], who is responsible for the term "boundary series." The result given in §69 is also due to V. A. Tartakovskiĭ. This result, which materially supplements Thue's result, remained unpublished up to now.

In §70 Siegel's result [46], which was obtained by him from considerations similar to those of Thue, is given in a more geometrical and therefore more elementary form, developed by Faddeev without the use of hypergeometric expansions and their estimates. A more careful estimate enabled us to give a stronger result, namely fifteen solutions instead of eighteen. This result is a generalization of my theorem in §75 to the case of positive discriminant. One must suppose that Siegel's limit of eighteen as well as Faddeev's limit of fifteen solutions is not exact (my limit of five for the case of negative discriminant is exact).

Chapter VI contains in its first part, §§71, 75, and 76, my investigations [11–14] concerning the representation of numbers by binary cubic forms of negative discriminant, and secondly (at the end of §75) the addition of Nagell [42] to my paper [12]. In §§72, 73, 74 we give the continuation of my investigation [11] by D. K. Faddeev [57, 61]. Nagell's theorem [40] is contained as a special case of these investigations. The second part of Chapter VI contains a proof of the fundamental theorem of Mordell given by André Weil [7] and the investigations of D. K. Faddeev on the equation $x^3 + y^3 = Az^3$.

By the word "field" we mean throughout a finite algebraic extension of the field of rationals. From the point of view of multiplicative lattices considered in Chapter I the field consists of the totality of the coordinates of all the points of an irreducible multiplicative lattice, together with all the quotients of these coordinates obtained by dividing one point by another. The analogous totality of coordinates for a reducible multiplicative lattice will be called a "region."

B. Delone,
Moscow,
1940.

CHAPTER I

THE THEORY OF MULTIPLICATIVE LATTICES

§1. MULTIPLICATIVE LATTICES IN n-DIMENSIONAL COMPLEX SPACE

We shall consider an n-dimensional complex space K_n, i. e., by a *point* of K_n we shall mean a system of any n complex numbers $x^{(1)}, x^{(2)}, \cdots, x^{(n)}$, which shall be called the coordinates of the point, where the coordinate index is denoted by a superscript in parentheses. The same point may also be denoted by a single letter. Let $\omega_1, \omega_2, \cdots, \omega_n$ be n points of K_n that are linearly independent, i. e., they are noncoplanar with the origin, the determinant

$$\begin{vmatrix} \omega_1^{(1)} & \omega_2^{(1)} & \dots & \omega_n^{(1)} \\ \omega_1^{(2)} & \omega_2^{(2)} & \dots & \omega_n^{(2)} \\ \cdot & \cdot & \cdot & \cdot \\ \omega_1^{(n)} & \omega_2^{(n)} & \dots & \omega_n^{(n)} \end{vmatrix} \tag{1}$$

being not equal to zero. The *sum, difference, product,* and *quotient* of two given points of the space K_n will be the point each of whose coordinates is the sum, difference, product, or quotient of the corresponding coordinates of the two given points. By an n-dimensional *lattice* in K_n, or simply a lattice in K_n, we mean the collection of all points of the form $u_1\omega_1 + u_2\omega_2 + \cdots + u_n\omega_n$, where $u_1, u_2, \cdots, u_n$ are all possible systems of n rational integers, i. e., the collection of all points of K_n obtained from additions and subtractions of the points $\omega_1, \omega_2, \cdots, \omega_n$. Such a lattice will be denoted by $[\omega_1, \omega_2, \cdots, \omega_n]$ or $[\omega]$ and $\omega_1, \omega_2, \cdots, \omega_n$ will be called its *basis* or its basic *n-vectors*. There exist *multiplicative lattices*, that is, lattices having the property that the product of any two of their points is again one of their points. The goal of the present chapter is the construction of the complete theory of such lattices.

The fundamental points of this theory will be the following. In the present section we will show that each such lattice may be extended to some *maximal* one, i.e., to a lattice which can not be made any denser with preservation of the multiplicative property. Then we will show that every maximal lattice is either *irreducible* itself or is the direct sum of irreducible lattices, each of which cannot be further decomposed. In §2 we will show that for each dimension n and each *signature* τ there exist infinitely many irreducible lattices. In §3 we will construct the Galois theory of these lattices. In §4 we will study the theory of *multiplicative automorphisms* for arbitrary lattices in K_n, i.e., we will investigate the existence and properties of points in K_n such that when a given lattice of K_n is multiplied by one of them, the result is again the given lattice. In §§5 and 6 we will construct the theory of ideals for multiplicative lattices, which we need in Chapter III for the classification of fields of 3rd and 4th degrees. In §§7, 8, and 9, we will consider various forms connected with such lattices.[1]

A point of K_n, no two of whose coordinates are equal and none of whose coordinates are zero, will be called a *generic point* in K_n.

LEMMA 1. *There exists a generic point in each lattice constructed from n linearly independent vectors of K_n.*

In fact, let us consider the point $\omega = u_1\omega_1 + u_2\omega_2 + \cdots + u_n\omega_n$, lexicographically constructed from $\omega_1, \omega_2, \cdots, \omega_n$, that is, constructed so that the rational integer coefficients $u_1, u_2, \cdots, u_n$ grow rapidly, each successive coefficient being many times larger than its predecessor. The ith and kth coordinates of this point have the following forms:

$$\omega^i = u_1\omega_1^{(i)} + u_2\omega_2^{(i)} + \ldots + u_n\omega_n^{(i)}; \qquad \omega^k = u_1\omega_1^{(k)} + u_2\omega_2^{(k)} + \ldots + u_n\omega_n^{(k)}.$$

Let us assume that $\omega_n^{(k)} = \omega_n^{(i)}$, $\omega_{n-1}^{(k)} = \omega_{n-1}^{(i)}$, $\cdots$, $\omega_{l+1}^{(k)} = \omega_{l+1}^{(i)}$, but that $\omega_l^{(k)} \neq \omega_l^{(i)}$. It is impossible for all the ith and kth coordinates of the n vectors to be equal to each other, for then the determinant (1) would have two equal rows

---

1) Before reading this first chapter it is necessary to look at the supplement at the end of Chapter I which contains required lemmas from the theory of real lattices.

and would be zero, contrary to the assumption of linear independence. Thus $\omega^{(k)} \neq \omega^{(i)}$ for $u_l \omega_l^{(k)}$ and $u_l \omega_l^{(i)}$ are not equal and all the following terms after this term are correspondingly equal while the u_i may be chosen so that the lth terms are as many times as large as the sums of the preceding terms as desired. It is also impossible for a coordinate of the point ω to be zero. For if, say, the ith coordinate were zero, i.e., $\omega_n^{(i)} = 0$, $\omega_{n-1}^{(i)} = 0, \cdots,$ then $\omega_t^{(i)}$ would not be zero, for otherwise the determinant (1) would have a row consisting only of zeros, the determinant thus being zero, contrary to assumption. But now all the terms of $\omega^{(i)}$ following $u_t \omega_t^{(i)}$ are zero, while the sum of all the preceding terms may be as many times smaller than this tth term as desired. Hence the coordinate $\omega^{(i)}$ is not zero.

We will call a polynomial *primary* if it has rational integer coefficients and leading coefficient 1.

LEMMA 2. *The coordinate of a point* ω *in a multiplicative lattice in* K_n *are all roots of some* n*th degree primary polynomial. If* ω *is a generic point, then all the equations which are satisfied by the coordinates of other points in the lattice are obtainable from the polynomial which* ω *satisfies by a rational Tschirnhausen transformation.*

Since the lattice is multiplicative we have for each of its points whether genetic or not,

$$\begin{aligned}
\omega_1\omega &= a_{11}\omega_1 + a_{12}\omega_2 + \cdots + a_{1n}\omega_n,\\
\omega_2\omega &= a_{21}\omega_1 + a_{22}\omega_2 + \cdots + a_{2n}\omega_n,\\
&\cdots\cdots\cdots\cdots\cdots\cdots\\
\omega_n\omega &= a_{n1}\omega_1 + a_{n2}\omega_2 + \cdots + a_{nn}\omega_n,
\end{aligned}$$

where each a_{ik} is a rational integer. (Here $\omega_1, \omega_2, \cdots, \omega_n$ is a basis of the lattice.) From this it follows that

$$F(\omega) = \begin{vmatrix} a_{11} - \omega, & a_{12}, & \cdots & a_{1n} \\ a_{21}, & a_{22} - \omega, & \cdots & a_{2n} \\ \cdot & \cdot & \cdots & \cdot \\ a_{n1}, & a_{n2}, & \cdots & a_{nn} - \omega \end{vmatrix} = 0.$$

The polynomial $F(\omega)$ is primary. If ω is a generic point, then all n of its coordinates are distinct, and hence they constitute all of the roots of the nth degree polynomial $F(\omega) = 0$. This proves the first assertion of the lemma for a generic point.

For the proof of the second assertion, let ω be a generic point. Then the vectors $1, \omega, \omega^2, \cdots, \omega^{n-1}$ are linearly independent since the determinant consisting of their coordinates is the Vandermonde determinant for the coordinates of the point ω, no two of whose coordinates are equal, so that the determinant is not equal to zero.

All these vectors, except perhaps the vector 1, belong to the given lattice. The unit vector is, however, the integer part of some vector belonging to the lattice, for example the vector all of whose coordinates are equal to the constant a_n of the equation

$$F(\omega) = \omega^n + a_1\omega^{n-1} + \ldots + a_n = 0,$$

where ω is a root. Such a vector is the linear combination $-(\omega^n + a_1\omega^{n-1} + \cdots \cdots + a_{n-1}\omega)$ of the vectors $\omega, \omega^2, \cdots, \omega^n$ which all belong to the lattice. Hence any vector $\tilde{\omega}$ of the lattice is a certain linear combination of the vectors $1, \omega, \cdots, \omega^{n-1}$ with rational coefficients, i.e.,

$$\tilde{\omega} = \varphi(\omega) = b_1\omega^{n-1} + \ldots + b_{n-1}\omega + b_n.$$

Thus the coordinates of the vector $\tilde{\omega}$ are the roots of the equation $G(\tilde{\omega}) = 0$ which is obtained from $F(\omega) = 0$ by a Tschirnhausen transformation with rational coefficients where all the roots of the transformed equation, and only those, from the coordinates of the point $\tilde{\omega}$. If $\tilde{\omega}$ is a generic point, this equation does not differ from the equation $\tilde{F}(\tilde{\omega}) = 0$ (formed for $\tilde{\omega}$ exactly as $F(\omega)$ was for ω) since they have identical roots. Each point that is not generic may be considered as the limit of a sequence of generic point and therefore, from continuity considerations, the equation $\tilde{F}(\tilde{\omega}) = 0$ and $G(\tilde{\omega}) = 0$ coincide.

The lemma is thus proven in its entirety, since the polynomial is primary.

Now we introduce the concept of a *signature space*. If the equation $F(\omega) = 0$ has σ real roots and 2τ complex-conjugate roots, then the corresponding coordinates of any point $\tilde{\omega}$ of the given lattice are real and complex-conjugate. Thus the multiplicative lattices in K_n are of $[n/2] + 1$ signature types: without complex coordinates, with one pair of complex-conjugate coordinates, with two pairs, etc. All lattices of a given signature type, or of a given signature, whose points have the correspondingly determined real coordinates and pairs of complex-conjugate coordinates, lie in one and the same "section" of the space K_n, which characterizes the real or complex-conjugate nature of the corresponding coordinates. We will call this "section" the *signature section* of the space K_n. If the axes of K_n are numbered so that in the given signature section the first σ coordinates $\zeta^{(1)}, \zeta^{(2)}, \ldots, \zeta^{(\sigma)}$ of a point are the real ones and the complex-conjugate pairs are the next $n-\sigma = 2\tau$ coordinates

$$\xi^{(1)} + i\eta^{(1)}, \quad \xi^{(1)} - i\eta^{(1)}, \quad \xi^{(2)} + i\eta^{(2)}, \ \xi^{(2)} - i\eta^{(2)}, \\ \ldots, \quad \xi^{(\tau)} + i\eta^{(\tau)}, \quad \xi^{(\tau)} - i\eta^{(\tau)},$$

then each such point may be "associated" in the real n-dimensional space $R_{n,\tau}$ with the point having real coordinates $\zeta^{(1)}, \zeta^{(2)}, \ldots, \zeta^{(\sigma)}, \xi^{(1)}, \eta^{(1)}, \xi^{(2)}, \eta^{(2)}, \ldots, \xi^{(\tau)}, \eta^{(\tau)}$. We will call the space $R_{n,\tau}$ the corresponding *signature space* for the given signature section. The passage from the signature section to the corresponding real signature space really consists of a selection of the axes in K_n. We leave unchanged the coordinate axes corresponding to those σ coordinates of the signature subspace which are real, but we replace the pair of axes in K_n corresponding to the complex coordinates $x^{(i)}x^{(k)}$ by the pair $(x^{(i)} + x^{(k)})/2$, $(x^{(i)} - x^{(k)})/2i$. The sum, difference, product, and quotient of two points of the same signature section of the space K_n are again, as can easily be seen, points of the same signature section. In the corresponding real space $R_{n,\tau}$ the addition and subtraction of points is obviously made by the same law as in K_n, namely, simple addition or subtraction of the corresponding coordinates, i.e., the sum or difference of two points in K_n lying in this signature section will correspond in $R_{n,\tau}$ to points whose coordinates in $R_{n,\tau}$ are simply sums or differences of the corresponding coordinates of the combined points. To the point in K_n which is the product of the two points in K_n with coordinates in $R_{n,\tau}$

$$\zeta_1^{(1)}, \ \zeta_1^{(2)}, \ \ldots, \ \zeta_1^{(\sigma)}, \ \xi_1^{(1)}, \ \eta_1^{(1)}, \ \xi_1^{(2)}, \ \eta_1^{(2)}, \ \ldots, \ \xi_1^{(\tau)}, \ \eta_1^{(\tau)},$$

and

$$\zeta_2^{(1)}, \ \zeta_2^{(2)}, \ \ldots, \ \zeta_2^{(\sigma)}, \ \xi_2^{(1)}, \ \eta_2^{(1)}, \ \xi_2^{(2)}, \ \eta_2^{(2)}, \ \ldots, \ \xi_2^{(\tau)}, \ \eta_2^{(\tau)} \tag{1}$$

there corresponds in $R_{n,\tau}$ the point with coordinates

$$\zeta_1^{(1)}\zeta_2^{(1)}, \ \zeta_1^{(2)}\zeta_2^{(2)}, \ \ldots, \ \zeta_1^{(\sigma)}\zeta_2^{(\sigma)}, \ \xi_1^{(1)}\xi_2^{(1)} - \eta_1^{(1)}\eta_2^{(1)}, \ \xi_1^{(1)}\eta_2^{(1)} + \xi_2^{(1)}\eta_1^{(1)}, \\ \ldots, \ \xi_1^{(\tau)}\xi_2^{(\tau)} - \eta_1^{(\tau)}\eta_2^{(\tau)}, \ \xi_1^{(\tau)}\eta_2^{(\tau)} + \xi_2^{(\tau)}\eta_1^{(\tau)}. \tag{2}$$

Thus the multiplication of points in $R_{n,\tau}$ depends upon the signature τ.

The *norm* of points of the space K_n, namely, the product of its complex coordinates $N(\omega) = \omega^{(1)} \cdot \omega^{(2)} \cdot \dots \cdot \omega^{(n)}$, is a complex number: for the points of the signature section the norm is a real number and can be expressed by the real coordinates of the corresponding point in $R_{n,\tau}$ as

$$N(\omega) = \zeta^{(1)} \cdot \zeta^{(2)} \dots \zeta^{(\sigma)} \cdot (\xi^{(1)^2} + \eta^{(1)^2})\,(\xi^{(2)^2} + \eta^{(2)^2}) \dots (\xi^{(\tau)^2} + \eta^{(\tau)^2}). \tag{3}$$

If n arbitrary points $\omega_1, \omega_2, \cdots, \omega_n$ lie n-dimensionally with respect to the origin of coordinates, i. e., are linearly independent with respect to the complex numbers, then the nonzero determinant formed from their coordinates may be called the complex volume of the parallelepiped constructed on the n vectors connecting the origin with these points. The square of this determinant is called the *discriminant* of the collection of points $\omega_1, \omega_2, \cdots, \omega_n$ in the space K_n and is denoted by $D[\omega_1, \omega_2, \cdots, \omega_n]$; it is in general a complex number. If the points $\omega_1, \omega_2, \cdots, \omega_n$ lie in the same signature section, then we have formula (4) and consequently, if the vectors representing the points $\omega_1, \omega_2, \cdots, \omega_n$ in K_n are linearly independent with respect to the complex numbers, then their corresponding vectors in the space $R_{n,\tau}$ are linearly independent (with respect to the real numbers), and conversely. In particular, the collection of points in the corresponding $R_{n,\tau}$ which correspond to the points of some n-dimensional multiplicative lattice in K_n is an n-dimensional real lattice in the space $R_{n,\tau}$.

$$\begin{vmatrix} \zeta_1^{(1)}, & \zeta_2^{(1)} & \dots\dots & \zeta_n^{(1)} \\ \zeta_1^{(2)}, & \zeta_2^{(2)} & \dots\dots & \zeta_n^{(2)} \\ \vdots & \vdots & & \vdots \\ \zeta_1^{(\sigma)}, & \zeta_2^{(\sigma)} & \dots\dots & \zeta_n^{(\sigma)} \\ \xi_1^{(1)} + i\eta_1^{(1)}, & \xi_2^{(1)} + i\eta_2^{(1)} & \dots\dots & \xi_n^{(1)} + i\eta_n^{(1)} \\ \xi_1^{(1)} - i\eta_1^{(1)}, & \xi_2^{(1)} - i\eta_2^{(1)} & \dots\dots & \xi_n^{(1)} - i\eta_n^{(1)} \\ \vdots & \vdots & & \vdots \\ \xi_1^{(\tau)} + i\eta_1^{(\tau)}, & \xi_2^{(\tau)} + i\eta_n^{(\tau)} & \dots\dots & \xi_n^{(\tau)} + i\eta_n^{(\tau)} \\ \xi_1^{(\tau)} - i\eta_1^{(\tau)}, & \xi_2^{(\tau)} - i\eta_2^{(\tau)} & \dots\dots & \xi_n^{(\tau)} - i\eta_n^{(\tau)} \end{vmatrix} = (2i)^{\tau} \begin{vmatrix} \zeta_1^{(1)}, & \zeta_n^{(1)} & \dots\dots & \zeta_n^{(1)} \\ \zeta_1^{(2)}, & \zeta_2^{(2)} & \dots\dots & \zeta_2^{(2)} \\ \vdots & \vdots & & \vdots \\ \zeta_1^{(\sigma)}, & \zeta_2^{(\sigma)} & \dots\dots & \zeta_n^{(\sigma)} \\ \xi_1^{(1)}, & \xi_2^{(1)} & \dots\dots & \xi_n^{(1)} \\ \eta_1^{(1)}, & \eta_2^{(1)} & \dots\dots & \eta_n^{(1)} \\ \vdots & \vdots & & \vdots \\ \xi_1^{(\tau)}, & \xi_2^{(\tau)} & \dots\dots & \xi_n^{(\tau)} \\ \eta_1^{(\tau)}, & \eta_2^{(\tau)} & \dots\dots & \eta_n^{(\tau)} \end{vmatrix} \tag{4}$$

From formula (4) we see that the discriminant of the collection of n points in K_n that lie in the same signature space is a real number, and thus we have

$$D[\omega_1, \omega_2, \ldots, \omega_n] = (-1)^\tau \cdot 4^\tau \cdot V^2, \tag{5}$$

where V is the usual volume in the real space $R_{n,\tau}$ of the parallelepiped constructed from the vectors to the corresponding points of $R_{n,\tau}$. If $\omega_1, \omega_2, \cdots, \omega_n$ are points in K_n belonging to the same multiplicative lattice in K_n, then the discriminant

$$D(\omega_1, \omega_2, \ldots, \omega_n) = \begin{vmatrix} \omega_1^{(1)} \omega_2^{(1)} \ldots \omega_n^{(1)} \\ \omega_1^{(2)} \omega_2^{(2)} \ldots \omega_n^{(2)} \\ \ldots\ldots\ldots\ldots \\ \ldots\ldots\ldots\ldots \\ \omega_1^{(n)} \omega_2^{(n)} \ldots \omega_n^{(n)} \end{vmatrix}^2, \tag{6}$$

being a polynomial with rational integer coefficients in rational integers, is an algebraic integer. This expression, as is easily seen, is a rational symmetric combination of the roots of that equation with rational integer coefficients satisfied by some generic point ω in the given lattice. All the points $\omega_1, \omega_2, \cdots, \omega_n$ are expressible rationally in terms of this point (by Lemma 2), and hence this expression is a rational number. Thus the discriminant of n linearly independent points of a multiplicative lattice is a nonzero rational integer. It is positive if the τ corresponding to this lattice is even and it is negative if the τ is odd. Moreover, the volume of the parallelepiped constructed from its vectors is given by $V = \sqrt{|D|}/2^\tau$. The discriminant of the basic parallelepiped of the lattice is called the *discriminant of the lattice*.

LEMMA 3. *All the points of all multiplicative lattices of a given signature type in* K_n *form a discrete set of points* $W_{n,\tau}$ *in the corresponding* $R_{n,\tau}$.

Every point of all such lattices has coordinates in K_n which satisfy an nth degree primary polynomial (Lemma 2). Thus for every such point we have $x^{(1)} + x^{(2)} + \cdots + x^{(n)} = -a_1; \cdots; x^{(1)} \cdot x^{(2)} \cdot \ldots \cdot x^{(n)} = \pm a_n$, where $a_1, a_2, \cdots, a_n$ are rational integers, or if we use the coordinates

$$\varsigma^{(1)}, \varsigma^{(2)}, \ldots, \varsigma^{(\sigma)}, \xi^{(1)}, \eta^{(1)}, \xi^{(2)}, \eta^{(2)}, \ldots, \xi^{(\tau)}, \eta^{(\tau)}$$

of the same point in $R_{n,\tau}$ we get the equations

$$\begin{aligned}
&\zeta^{(1)} + \zeta^{(2)} + \ldots + \zeta^{(\sigma)} + 2\xi^{(1)} + 2\xi^{(2)} + \ldots + 2\xi^{(\tau)} = -a_1, \\
&\zeta^{(1)}\zeta^{(2)} + \zeta^{(1)}\zeta^{(3)} + \ldots + \xi^{(\tau-1)}\xi^{(\tau)} - \eta^{(\tau-1)}\eta^{(\tau)} + \xi^{(\tau-1)}\eta^{(\tau)} + \xi^{(\tau)}\eta^{(\tau-1)} = a_2, \\
&\cdots\cdots\cdots\cdots\cdots\cdots\cdots\cdots\cdots\cdots \\
&\cdots\cdots\cdots\cdots\cdots\cdots\cdots\cdots\cdots\cdots \\
&\zeta^{(1)}\cdot\zeta^{(2)}\ldots\zeta^{(\sigma)}\cdot(\xi^{(1)2} + \eta^{(1)2})(\xi^{(2)2} + \eta^{(2)2})\ldots(\xi^{(\tau)2} + \eta^{(\tau)2}) = \pm a_n,
\end{aligned} \tag{7}$$

i.e., all these points lie in $R_{n,\tau}$ in the points of intersection of the discrete family of surfaces (7). We will denote this collection of points in $R_{n,\tau}$ by $W_{n,\tau}$. By a *centering* of a lattice in K_n we shall mean a lattice consisting of all the points of the centered lattice plus some further points in K_n that have real coordinates with respect to the basic n-vectors of the centered lattice.

We will say that a multiplicative lattice is *maximal* if no centering of it is multiplicative.

LEMMA 4. *In each multiplicative lattice there is a point* $(a, a, \cdots, a)$ *whose coordinates are all the same rational integer; if the lattice is maximal it contains the point* $(1, 1, \cdots, 1)$.

For the proof, let ω be a generic point and let $\omega^n + a_1\omega^{n-1} + \cdots + a_{n-1}\omega + a_n = 0$ be the primary equation satisfied by its coordinates (see Lemma 2). In such a case the point $-(\omega^n + a_1\omega^{n-1} + \cdots + a_{n-1}\omega)$ has all of its coordinates equal to a_n. Let us assume now that our lattice is maximal. Let us consider the totality of all points in K_n which are obtained by additions and subtractions from the points of the given lattice and the point $(1, 1, \cdots, 1)$. This set $\omega + k$ consists of points of the same signature as that of the points in the given lattice, and if we consider it in the corresponding $R_{n,\tau}$, it consists of all points of the corresponding $W_{n,\tau}$. However, the set $\omega + k$ is obviously n-dimensional since the set ω is already n-dimensional and is additive and subtractive, i.e., it represents in the real space $R_{n,\tau}$ an n-dimensional lattice (see Lemma 1 of the supplement), and thus it also represents an n-dimensional lattice in K_n. Moreover, this lattice is multiplicative since the point

$$(\omega_1 + k_1)(\omega_2 + k_2) = \omega_1\omega_2 + \omega_1 k_2 + \omega_2 k_1 + k_1 k_2 = \omega + k_1 k_2$$

is again of the form $\omega + k$. Hence, if the given lattice is maximal it contains the point $(1, 1, \cdots, 1)$.

LEMMA 5. *Each multiplicative lattice in* K_n *is a sublattice of a unique maximal lattice.*

Each multiplicative lattice in K_n, and hence also each of its sublattices, belongs to a definite one of all the possible $[n/2]+1$ signature types according to the number of pairs of complex-conjugates of its coordinates. We will examine the following questions in the corresponding real space $R_{n,\tau}$: is a given multiplicative lattice maximal, is it contained in maximal lattices, and in what kind of maximal lattices can it be contained? From Lemma 3 it follows that each multiplicative lattice lies in a certain maximal lattice since if one could form successive centerings of it without limit while preserving the multiplicative property, then one would obtain points of $R_{n,\tau}$ arbitrarily close to the origin. However, there exists a certain small sphere about the origin which does not contain any nonzero points of $W_{n,\tau}$.

It remains to be shown that each multiplicative lattice is contained in only one maximal lattice. Let us suppose the contrary, that some lattice is contained in two maximal lattices, A_1 and A_2. By Lemma 4 both these lattices contain the point 1 and each of their bases will be rationally expressible in terms of the other since the basis of the initial lattice is rationally expressible in terms of both these bases. We denote by N the common denominator in the expression of the basis of the lattice A_2 in terms of the basis for A_1. If all points of the lattice A_1 are divisible by N, we obviously obtain a new lattice which we denote by A_1/N. The lattice A_2 is contained in A_1/N as a sublattice. Now we multiply the lattices A_1 and A_2, i.e., multiply all points in A_1 by all points in A_2 and form all the possible sums of such products. We get a new point set which we denote by A_1A_2. This set is obviously additive and multiplicative and contains the lattices A_1 and A_2 since each of them contains the point 1. This set is discrete since it is contained in the product of the lattice A_1 by A_1/N. But it is also equal to A_1/N since the lattice A_1 is multiplicative and therefore the product of any point from A_1/N by any point from A_1 belongs to A_1/N. Thus A_1A_2 is a multiplicative lattice and contains both A_1 and A_2. But this contradicts the original assumption, thus proving the lemma.

By a *zero-divisor* we shall mean any point of K_n that has some zero coordinates but is not the origin (all of whose coordinates are zero). For such a point there exist points different from the origin such that the product of the zero-divisor by these points gives zero, i.e., the origin. Every point of K_n such that its coordinates are zero when the corresponding coordinates of the zero-divisor are different from zero and such that at least one of its coordinates corresponding to a zero coordinate of the zero-divisor is different from zero, is such a cofactor of the zero-divisor.

We note that it follows from the theorem which we shall prove next that if a point of a maximal lattice is a zero-divisor, then its cofactors belong to the same lattice.

Lattices, multiplicative or nonmultiplicative, not containing zero-divisors, will be called *irreducible lattices.* Irreducible maximal lattices play an important role: they are the simplest lattices of which maximal lattices are composed, as described by the following basic theorem.

THEOREM. *Any maximal lattice is either itself irreducible or is uniquely decomposable into a direct sum of irreducible maximal lattices of lower dimension which are constructed on separate sets of coordinate axes.*

If there is no zero-divisor in the given maximal lattice $[\omega]$ the lattice is irreducible.

Let us now assume that there is some zero-divisor ψ in the given maximal lattice $[\omega]$, and suppose further that the axes of K_n are numbered so that the first n_1 coordinates $\psi^{(1)}, \psi^{(2)}, \cdots, \psi^{(n_1)}$ are not equal to zero, but the $n_2 = n - n_1$ remaining coordinates $\psi^{(n_1+1)}, \cdots, \psi^{(n)}$ are equal to zero. Let K_{n_1} be an n_1-dimensional complex space constructed from the first n_1 axes of K_n, and let K_{n_2} be the n_2-dimensional complex space constructed from the remaining axes. The point ψ will lie in the space K_{n_1}. The coordinates of the point ψ, as of each point of the given maximal lattice $[\omega]$, are all roots of some nth degree primary polynomial in which, since n_2 of the coordinates are equal to zero, the first n_2 coefficients are all zero while the $(n_2 + 1)$th coefficient is not zero. Hence the first n_1 (nonzero) coordinates of the point ψ, i.e., $\psi^{(1)}, \psi^{(2)}, \cdots$ $\cdots, \psi^{(n_1)}$, satisfy the equation $\psi^{n_1} + a_1\psi^{n_1-1} + \cdots + a_{n_1-t}\psi + a_{n_1} = 0$ with rational integer coefficients a_i. Since $a_{n_1} \neq 0$ the point $\theta = -\psi^{n_1} - a_1\psi^{n_1-1} - \cdots$ $\cdots - a_{n_1-1}\psi$, which obviously belongs to the given lattice $[\omega]$, has coordinates $(\overbrace{a, a, \cdots, a}^{n_1}, \overbrace{0, 0, \cdots, 0}^{n_2})$, where $a = a_{n_1}$ is a rational integer. Now consider the set of all points of the given maximal lattice $[\omega]$ of the form $\theta \cdot \omega$, where ω runs through all points of this lattice. All these points lie in the space

K_{n_1}; moreover, they clearly lie in the same signature section of K_{n_1} so that we may consider all of them in R_{n_1, r_1}. The equation which their coordinates satisfy in K_{n_1}, as well as that satisfied by ψ, will be an nth degree primary polynomial. Thus all these points $\theta \cdot \omega$ lie in W_{n_1, r_1}. However the set $\theta \cdot \omega$ is clearly additive and subtractive, and thus (by Lemma 1 of the Supplement) is a lattice in R_{n_1, r_1} and hence also a lattice in K_{n_1}.

This lattice is n_1-dimensional in K_{n_1}, since if a point ω were generic in K_{n_1}, then $\theta \cdot \omega$ would be generic in K_{n_1}. Hence the vectors $\theta \cdot \omega$, $(\theta \cdot \omega)^2$, $\cdots$, $(\theta \cdot \omega)^{n_1}$ are an n_1-dimensional set in K_{n_1} since the determinant of their coordinates is not zero. We denote by η the point of the space K_{n_1} that has coordinates $(\overbrace{1, 1, \cdots, 1}^{n_1}, \overbrace{0, 0, \cdots, 0}^{n_2})$. In view of the fact that $\theta[\omega]$, as we have just shown, is an n_1-dimensional lattice in K_{n_1}, obviously $\eta[\omega]$ is also an n_1-dimensional lattice in K_{n_1}, and consequently so is the lattice $a^{-1} \cdot \theta[\omega]$, where a is a given number.

The lattice $\eta[\omega]$ is obviously a multiplicative lattice, since $\eta\bar{\omega} \cdot \eta\bar{\bar{\omega}} = \eta\bar{\omega}\bar{\bar{\omega}} = \eta\bar{\bar{\bar{\omega}}}$. Denoting the point $\eta\omega$ by $\tilde{\omega}$, we see that $\tilde{\omega}$ is obtained from the corresponding point ω if the first n_1 coordinates of ω are left unchanged and the remaining n_2 coordinates are changed to zero. Therefore the point $\tilde{\omega}$ is the orthogonal projection of the point ω on the coordinate subspace K_{n_1}. Thus the totality of orthogonal projections of all points ω of the given lattice on the subspace K_{n_1} is an n_1-dimensional lattice $[\tilde{\omega}]$ in this subspace. The projections $\tilde{\omega}$ may not be points of the lattice $[\omega]$; however, we will show that if the lattice $[\omega]$ is maximal the projections $\tilde{\omega}$ are also points of $[\omega]$. In fact, let us consider the totality of all sums and differences of points ω and $\tilde{\omega}$. This set is obviously also a lattice in K_n, because all points ω, as well as points $\tilde{\omega}$, may be considered to lie in $R_{n,r}$ and in any case they are contained in the lattice $[\omega/a]$ (here we must consider the a in the denominator as a number). We will denote this lattice by $[\omega]^*$. It will be multiplicative since

$$\begin{aligned}(\omega_1 + \tilde{\omega}_2)(\omega_3 + \tilde{\omega}_4) &= \omega_1\omega_3 + \omega_1\tilde{\omega}_4 + \omega_3\tilde{\omega}_2 + \tilde{\omega}_2\tilde{\omega}_4, \\ &= \omega_1\omega_3 + \tilde{\omega}_1\tilde{\omega}_4 + \tilde{\omega}_3\tilde{\omega}_2 + \tilde{\omega}_2\tilde{\omega}_4,\end{aligned}$$

and $[\omega]$ and $[\tilde{\omega}]$ are multiplicative lattices. Hence, if $[\omega]$ is maximal it contains

$[\tilde{\omega}]$.

We denote by $\overset{\approx}{\omega}$ the difference $\omega - \tilde{\omega}$, where ω is any point of the lattice $[\omega]$ and $\tilde{\omega}$ is its orthogonal projection on the space K_{n_1}. All of the points $\overset{\approx}{\omega}$ clearly lie in the subspace K_{n_2} and in the same signature section, i.e., we may consider them in the corresponding real space R_{n_2, r_2}. Moreover, the set of all $\overset{\approx}{\omega}$ is obviously additive and subtractive and therefore is a sublattice of the lattice $[\omega]$, namely, an n_2-dimensional lattice of K_n consisting of all those points of $[\omega]$ whose first n_1 coordinates are equal to zero. Obviously each point of $[\omega]$ has the form $\tilde{\omega}_1 + \overset{\approx}{\omega}_2$, and conversely, i.e., the lattice $[\omega]$ is the direct sum $[\tilde{\omega}] \oplus [\overset{\approx}{\omega}]$ of the lattices $[\tilde{\omega}]$ and $[\overset{\approx}{\omega}]$ which are multiplicatives in K_{n_1} and K_{n_2}, respectively. Moreover, these lattices are maximal in the spaces K_{n_1} and K_{n_2}, for if one of them, for example $[\tilde{\omega}]$, were centered so that its centering $[\tilde{\omega}]^*$ is also multiplicative in K_{n_1}, then the lattice $[\tilde{\omega}]^* \oplus [\overset{\approx}{\omega}]$ would also be multiplicative in K_n since $(\tilde{\omega}_1^* + \overset{\approx}{\omega})(\tilde{\omega}_3^* + \overset{\approx}{\omega}_4) = \tilde{\omega}_1^* \tilde{\omega}_3^* + \tilde{\omega}_1^* \overset{\approx}{\omega}_4 + \tilde{\omega}_2 \overset{\approx}{\omega}_3^* + \overset{\approx}{\omega}_2 \overset{\approx}{\omega}_4 = \tilde{\omega}_1^* \tilde{\omega}_3^* + \overset{\approx}{\omega}_2 \overset{\approx}{\omega}_4$ (both the middle summands are equal to zero); however, the lattices $[\tilde{\omega}]^*$ and $[\overset{\approx}{\omega}]$ are multiplicative and hence $[\omega]$ would not be maximal.

By continuing to decompose the lattices $[\tilde{\omega}]$ and $[\overset{\approx}{\omega}]$ (if there are zero-divisors in the spaces K_{n_1} and K_{n_2}), we will arrive at the proof of the theorem.

This decomposition into a direct sum of irreducible lattices is unique, because if there were one decomposition with $K_{n_1}, K_{n_2}, \cdots, K_{n_k}$ as the spaces of its irreducible parts, then the coordinates corresponding to each of these spaces of any point of $[\omega]$ would either be all nonzero (this happens whenever a nonzero summand of this point appears in the corresponding irreducible part) or would be all zero (this happens whenever a zero summand of this point appears in the corresponding irreducible part) inasmuch as the points of the irreducible parts different from zero do not have any coordinates equal to zero. Let us assume that we have another decomposition into irreducible parts $K_{n_1}, K_{n_2}, \cdots, K_{n_l}$. Now take any point belonging, for example, to the ith of these irreducible parts and suppose that one of its coordinates belongs to the jth irreducible part of the first decomposition; then all coordinates of the jth irreducible part of the first decomposition are not zero, i.e., they are coordinates of the given ith irreducible part of the second decomposition. Thus if two irreducible parts of both decompositions have one common coordinate, then they have identical coordinates, i.e., the decompositions coincide. This completes the proof of the theorem. The theorem is not necessarily true for nonmaximal lattices.

LEMMA 6. *Each point ω whose coordinates are roots of an nth degree primary polynomial belongs to some maximal lattice.*

If the polynomial is irreducible, then the lattice $[1, \omega, \omega^2, \cdots, \omega^{n-1}]$ is multiplicative; on the other hand, if it is reducible then the direct sum of the lattices for its irreducible factors is multiplicative.

§2. THE EXISTENCE OF AN INFINITE NUMBER OF DIFFERENT IRREDUCIBLE MAXIMAL LATTICES FOR ANY GIVEN DIMENSION $n > 1$ AND ANY GIVEN SIGNATURE τ

We begin with the derivation of an important asymptotic formula.

By virtue of Lemma 3, all points of all multiplicative lattices in K_n of a given signature τ form in the corresponding space $R_{n,\tau}$ a discrete set (not a lattice) of points $W_{n,\tau}$. In the space $R_{n,\tau}$ we form the sphere with radius r and center at the origin and we will derive the asymptotic formula for the number $N_{r,n,\tau}$ of the points lying inside such a sphere for each r.

LEMMA. *The number $N_{r,n,\tau}$ is expressed by the asymptotic formula $\nu_{n,\tau} \cdot r^{n(n+1)/2}$ where $\nu_{n,\tau}$ is a constant depending only on n and τ, i.e.,*

$$\lim_{r \to \infty} \frac{N_{r,n,\tau}}{\nu_{n,\tau} \cdot r^{\frac{n(n+1)}{2}}} = 1. \text{[1)]}$$

For the proof we denote by $R_{n,\tau}$ the space of roots of nth degree algebraic equations of signature τ; we also consider the n-dimensional real space A_n of the coefficients of all algebraic equations of nth degree with real coefficients and with leading coefficients equal to 1, i.e., the space in which to each point corresponds such an equation having its coefficients as coordinates of this point and conversely. The coefficients of the primary nth degree equations form in the

1) Subsequently the authors obtained similar asymptotic formulas for equations with various Galois groups, such as the four-groups for cubic equations (transitive and intransitive) and the eleven groups for quartic equations (except the alternating group). For example, the quartic equations with the symmetric group S_4 have $N_{r,n,s} \cong C_s r^{10}$; with the four group V we have $N_{r,n,V} \cong C_V r^4 \ln^3 r$; with the cyclic group Z_4 we have $N_{r,n,z} \cong C_z r^4 \ln r$, etc.

space A_n an n-dimensional lattice of all points with integer coordinates, that is, a lattice whose basic parallelepiped is the unit cube. Only a part of this lattice gives the equations of a given signature τ. We will denote by A_n the region of the space A_n restricted by the well-known Borchard inequality and containing the points corresponding to equations of a given signature τ, and we will call it the region of signature τ. To each point of the space A_n there corresponds one equation of the nth degree, and conversely, to each equation of the nth degree there corresponds one point of the space A_n. To each point of the space $R_{n,\tau}$ there corresponds one equation of nth degree of signature τ, but to any such equation there corresponds not one, but $\sigma!\tau!2^\tau$ points of the space $R_{n,\tau}$. For if the real roots are laid off on the axes $\zeta^{(1)}, \zeta^{(2)}, \ldots, \zeta^{(\tau)}$ and the corresponding real and imaginary parts of the pairs of complex-conjugate roots, $\xi + i\eta$, $\xi - i\eta$, are laid off on the axes $\xi^{(1)}, \eta^{(1)}, \ldots, \xi^{(\tau)}, \eta^{(\tau)}$, then there are $\sigma!$ ways of laying off the σ real roots on the axes ζ and $\tau!$ ways of assigning the pairs of complex-conjugate roots on the pairs of axes ξ, η; moreover, for each pair of complex-conjugate roots we have two choices for the sign of η. In the space $R_{n,\tau}$ we consider the basic region $R^*_{n,\tau}$ consisting of all points of which an nth degree equation of signature τ corresponds uniquely. For this, for example, we can lay off on the axis $\zeta^{(1)}$ the largest root in absolute value, on $\zeta^{(2)}$ the next largest, etc.; analogously we assign the axes $\xi^{(1)}, \eta^{(1)}$ to the complex-conjugate pair with the largest $\xi^{(1)}$ in absolute value, etc.; finally, all η may be taken to be positive. Obviously the formulas of Vieta

$$\begin{aligned} -a_1 &= \rho^{(1)} + \rho^{(2)} + \ldots + \rho^{(n)}, \\ a_2 &= \rho^{(1)} \cdot \rho^{(2)} + \rho^{(1)} \cdot \rho^{(3)} + \ldots + \rho^{(n-1)} \cdot \rho^{(n)}, \\ &\ldots\ldots\ldots\ldots\ldots\ldots \\ \pm a_n &= \rho^{(1)} \cdot \rho^{(2)} \cdot \ldots \cdot \rho^{(n)}, \end{aligned}$$

where $\rho^{(1)}, \rho^{(2)}, \ldots, \rho^{(n)}$ are the roots, give a one-to-one transformation of the region $R^*_{n,\tau}$ of the space $R_{n,\tau}$ into the region $A^*_{n,\tau}$ of the space A_n except for the boundary points of this region, which do not play any significant role in what follows.

We consider in the space $R_{n,\tau}$ the sphere with radius 1 centered at the origin. The body forming a common part of this sphere and the region $R^*_{n,\tau}$ is denoted by $P^*(1)$. Now assume this body is transformed by the Vieta transformation into some body $Q^*(1)$ of the space A_n. We denote the volume of the body

$Q^*(1)$ by $v_{n,\tau}$. We now increase r-fold the radius of this sphere centered at the origin in the space $R_{n,\tau}$ and denote by $P^*(r)$ the body which is the intersection of this sphere of radius r with the region $R^*_{n,\tau}$. Since the region $R^*_{n,\tau}$, as is easily seen, is a cone with vertex at the origin, the body $P^*(r)$ is obtained from the body $P^*(1)$ by a dilation relative to the origin with coefficient r. But such a dilation may be considered also as the totality of the uniform dilation of all n axes of $R_{n,\tau}$ with the same coefficient r for each axis. From the form of the Vieta transformation, such dilations of the axes of $R_{n,\tau}$ with the same coefficient r correspond to the dilations of the n axes in A_n with coefficients r, $r^2, r^3, \cdots, r^n$; therefore the volume of the body $Q^*(r)$ obtained from $P^*(r)$ by the Vieta transformation is equal to $v_{n,\tau} \cdot r \cdot r^2 \cdot \ldots \cdot r^n = v_{n,\tau} \cdot r^{n(n+1)/2}$. As the radius r increases, the number of points of the space A_n corresponding to primary equations and lying in the body $Q^*(r)$ is asymptotically equal to the volume of this body, since the collection of all points of A_n corresponding to primary equations represents a simple lattice whose basic parallelepiped is the unit cube.

The remainder term of this asymptotic formula does not exceed some multiple independent of r of the surface area of $Q^*(r)$. The surface area of $Q^*(r)$ in turn does not exceed the surface area of $Q^*(1)$ multiplied by $r^{2+3+\cdots+n} = r^{n(n+1)/2-1}$. Indeed, if we denote the differential of surface area of the body $Q^*(1)$ by dP and its orthogonal projections on the coordinate planes by $dP_1, dP_2, \cdots, dP_n$ (likewise $dQ, dQ_1, \cdots, dQ_n$ for the body $Q^*(r)$), then we have

$$dP=\sqrt{dP_1^2+\ldots+dP_n^2},$$

$$dQ=\sqrt{dQ_1^2+\ldots+dQ_n^2}.$$

Moreover, we have

$$|dQ_i|=\left|\frac{rr^2\ldots r^n}{r^i}\,dP_i\right|\leqslant\frac{1}{r}\cdot r^{\frac{n(n+1)}{2}}\,dP_i,$$

from which it follows that

$$dQ<r^{\frac{n(n+1)}{2}-1}\cdot dP,$$

and hence

$$Q<r^{\frac{n(n+1)}{2}-1}\cdot P.$$

Thus the remainder term of the asymptotic equation is of order $r^{n(n+1)/2-1}$, so that in each case the order of the remainder term is less than the order of the principal term. But the number of points of A_n inside $Q^*(r)$ is the same as the number of points corresponding to the primary equations, i.e., the points of the net $W_{n,\tau}$ lying in the body $P^*(r)$ of the space $R_{n,\tau}$: and this latter number is asymptotically equal to $v_{n,\tau}r^{n(n+1)/2}$.

Now it is easy to see that the number of points of $W_{n,\tau}$ in the r-sphere is simply $\sigma!\,\tau!\,2^\tau$ times that in the body $P^*(r)$ and hence, if we put $v_{n,\tau}\sigma!\tau!2^\tau = \nu_{n,\tau}$, then the number of points of $W_{n,\tau}$ in the r-sphere is asymptotically equal to $\nu_{n,\tau}r^{n(n+1)/2}$, which is what was to be proven.

By introducing the asymptotic formula we have shown that the set of points $W_{n,\tau}$ becomes, so to speak, denser away from the origin in the sense that the number of points of the system inside the sphere with center at the origin does not grow as the volume of the sphere (i.e., not proportional to r^n) but grows faster, namely is proportional to $r^{n(n+1)/2}$, and thus the "density" of the points of $W_{n,\tau}$ in the sphere (the ratio of this number to the volume) is not constant but grows like $r^{n(n-1)/2}$

By employing this asymptotic formula it is easy to prove the following basic theorem of the theory of multiplicative lattices.

THEOREM 1. *There exist infinitely many different irreducible maximal lattices for any given dimension* n *and signature* τ.

For the proof we will consider the set $W_{n,\tau}$ and show that if we exclude from it all points which belong to at least one of the irreducible maximal lattices in its decomposition, then there remains the set $W^*_{n,\tau}$, which, like the set $W_{n,\tau}$, is infinitely more dense away from the origin in the sense that the number of its points in the sphere of radius r with center at the origin grows faster than the volume of this sphere.

If this is shown, then further reasoning preceeds as follows: We pick some point ω_1 in $W^*_{n,\tau}$; from Lemma 6 it belongs to some maximal lattice appearing in $W_{n,\tau}$. If we remove all points in $W^*_{n,\tau}$ which belong to this irreducible maximal lattice, then there remains a set of points $W^{*\prime}_{n,\tau}$, which also is infinitely denser away from the origin since a lattice does not become denser but is everywhere uniformly dense. Let ω_2 be any point in this set; then it belongs to some different irreducible maximal lattice appearing in $W_{n,\tau}$. If we remove all points in $W^*_{n,\tau}$ belonging either to the first or second of these two irreducible lattices, then the remaining set $W^{*\prime\prime}_{n,\tau}$ is also infinitely denser away from the origin, etc. In such a manner we will get infinitely many different irreducible maximal lattices included in $W_{n,\tau}$; moreover, such a process yields all of them.

Now it remains to show that the set $W^*_{n,\tau}$ is infinitely denser away from the origin. Let us consider all those reducible maximal lattices included in $W_{n,\tau}$ which can be decomposed into two coordinate subspaces K_{n_1} and K_{n_2}, the direct sum of which is equal to K_n (i. e., $n_1 + n_2 = n$), where it makes no difference whether the parts of these lattices lying in K_{n_1} and K_{n_2} are reducible or irreducible. All these lattices appear in the direct sum $W_{n_1,\tau_1} \oplus W_{n_2,\tau_2}$ of the sets of $W_{n,\tau}$ lying in K_{n_1} and K_{n_2} (which are the sets of points of $W_{n,\tau}$ lying in K_{n_1} and K_{n_2}). The number of points of W_{n_1,τ_1} lying in the n_1-dimensional r-sphere (centered at the origin and contained in the intersection of the n-dimensional r-sphere in $R_{n,\tau}$ with the n_1-dimensional plane of $R_{n,\tau}$ containing the set W_{n_1,τ_1}) is equal to $N_{rn_1\tau_1} \approx \nu_{n_1\tau_1} r^{n_1(n_1+1)/2}$. The number of points of the set W_{n_2,τ_2} lying in the n_2-dimensional r-sphere which is contained in the intersection of the n-dimensional sphere with the n_2-dimensional plane R_{n_2,τ_2}, and containing the set W_{n_2,τ_2}, is equal to $N_{rn_2\tau_2} \approx \nu_{n_2\tau_2} r^{n_2(n_2+1)/2}$. The product of these two mutually orthogonal n_1-dimensional and n_2-dimensional spheres of radii r forms a certain body containing the n-dimensional sphere of radius r under consideration (here by "product" we understand the set of points which are the endpoints of the sums of all possible vectors from the origin to the points of the "multiplied" spheres). The number of points in the direct sum $W_{n_1\tau_1} \oplus W_{n_2\tau_2}$ of this "product" is equal to $N_{rn_1\tau_1} \cdot N_{rn_2\tau_2} \approx \nu_{n_1\tau_1} \nu_{n_2\tau_2} r^{(n_1(n_1+1)+n_2(n_2+1))/2}$, and hence, if we remove from the n-dimensional r-sphere all those points of $W_{n,\tau}$ which are contained in the irreducible maximal lattices corresponding to the decomposition $K_n = K_{n_1} \oplus K_{n_2}$, then it is necessary to subtract from $N_{r,n,\tau}$ a number less than $N_{rn_1\tau_1} \cdot N_{rn_2\tau_2}$. The number of all possible representations of K_n in the form of a direct sum of two complementary coordinate subspaces K_{n_1} and K_{n_2} is bounded. Here we need take only those partitions which are consistent with the given signature section, since it is impossible to separate the coordinates corresponding to the complex-conjugate roots. If we subtract from $N_{rn\tau}$ the product $N_{rn_1\tau_1} \cdot N_{rn_2\tau_2}$ corresponding to all these decompositions, the difference will be even less than the number of points of $W_{n,\tau}$ included in the n-dimensional r-sphere but not belonging to any reducible maximal lattice contained in $W_{n,\tau}$.

To see this note that if $n_1 + n_2 = n$, then

$$n_1(n_1+1)+n_2(n_2+1)<n(n+1);$$

in fact,

$$n_1^2+n_1+n_2^2+n_2<(n_1+n_2)(n_1+n_2+1)=n_1^2+n_1+n_2^2+n_2+2n_1n_2$$

by $2n_1n_2$.

The difference thus has the form

$$ar^{\frac{n(n+1)}{2}} - b_1r^{m_1} - b_2r^{m_2} - \ldots, b_kr^{m_k},$$

where the number k of subtracted terms is bounded, the coefficients $a, b_1, \cdots$ $\cdots, b_k$ are constants, and all the exponents $m_1, m_2, \cdots$ are less than $n(n+1)/2$ by at least $2(n-1)$ since, if n_1 and n_2 are positive integers and $n_1 + n_2 = n$, then $n_1 n_2$ is not less that $n - 1$. The ratio of this number to the volume of the n-dimensional sphere $\Gamma_n r^n$ consequently tends to infinity as r increases, i.e., the set $W^*_{n,\tau}$ is denser away from the origin. This completes the proof of the theorem.

The following theorem, which supplements Theorem 1, is due to Hermite.

THEOREM 2. *There is only a finite number of multiplicative lattices whose basic parallelepiped have volumes less in absolute value than a given fixed number.*

Since each multiplicative lattice is a sublattice of some maximal multiplicative lattice, it is sufficient to prove the theorem only for maximal lattices. But each maximal lattice is a direct sum of irreducible lattices, for we may take as the basic n-vectors of the given lattice n vectors composed from the n_1 vectors of the first summand, n_2 vectors of the second summand, etc.; the spaces $K_{n_1}, K_{n_2}, \cdots, K_{n_k}$ are mutually orthogonal. It is sufficient, consequently, to prove the theorem only for irreducible multiplicative lattices of a given signature type. Let us consider a parallelepiped centered at the origin, one of whose vertices is a point of the space $R_{n,\tau}$ whose first $n-1$ coordinates (in $R_{n,\tau}$) $y^{(1)}, y^{(2)}, \cdots, y^{(n-1)}$ are positive and less than $1/\sqrt{2}$ and whose nth coordinate $y^{(n)}$ is positive and so large that the product $y^{(1)} \cdot y^{(2)} \cdot \cdots \cdot y^{(n-1)} \cdot y^{(n)}$ is larger than the given value L, and whose sides are parallel to the coordinate planes in $R_{n,\tau}$. Then this parallelepiped is a convex body with center at the origin and with volume more than 2^n times the volume of the basic parallelepiped of any lattice in $R_{n,\tau}$ that has one of its points at the origin and the volume of its basic parallelepiped not larger than L. Each such lattice, by the lemma of the Supplement to Chapter I, has at least two points other than the origin inside this parallelelpiped. (The points will be symmetric with respect to the origin.) Hence each irreducible (multiplicative) lattice in K_n of a given type, the volume of whose basic parallelepiped is not larger than L, has at least one point different from the origin lying in this parallelepiped. But since for this point the product $\zeta^{(1)}\zeta^{(2)} \cdots \zeta^{(\sigma)} \cdot (\xi^{(1)2} + \eta^{(1)2}) \cdots (\xi^{(\tau)2} + \eta^{(\tau)2}) = \pm a_n$ is a nonzero integer, i. e., greater than or equal to unity in absolute value, therefore the nth coordinate in $R_{n,\tau}$ is certainly greater than $1/\sqrt{2}$ and this point in K_n has all its other coordinates in absolute value less than 1 and one coordinate (or two complex conjugate coordinates, if the nth coordinate is the imaginary part of the complex coordinate) larger than 1, i. e., this point is a generic point in K_n, since the coordinates of each point of an irreducible lattice decomposes into ν complexes of δ equal coordinates (where $\delta > 1$ and $n = \nu \cdot \delta$), as will be proved in the next section. But all points of all multiplicative lattices in K_n of a given type are points of the set $W_{n,\tau}$ which lies in the corresponding $R_{n,\tau}$; this set is discrete and has only a finite number of points in the given parallelepiped. If two multiplicative lattices have in common a generic point ω, then they have an n-dimensional sublattice in common, for example, one constructed from the vectors $\omega, \omega^2, \cdots, \omega^n$. But there exists in general only a finite number of distinct centerings of such a lattice composed of points of a discrete set $W_{n,\tau}$.

§3. THE GEOMETRY OF GALOIS THEORY

1. Maximal sublattices of a maximal lattice. We divide the n axes of K_n into ν complexes, each having no axes in common with the others and each having exactly δ axes. For each complex we equate the coordinates corresponding to the axes included in the given complex. In this manner we obtain a system of equations defining a ν-dimensional *bisectrix* of the space K_n or, more simply, the selected set of axes of the space K_n. If n is a prime, then K_n has only one 1-dimensional bisectrix $x^{(1)} = x^{(2)} = \cdots = x^{(n)}$; if n is not a prime, then there are bisectrices of dimension ν for each divisor ν of n. There are as many bisectrices of dimension ν dividing n as there are ways of partitioning n coordinates into ν complexes of δ coordinates each. If we consider a partition in which all the coordinates of one of the complexes are equal while the coordinates of the remaining complexes are zero, this will give ν 1-dimensional straight lines in K_n which clearly are mutually orthogonal. We call these straight lines the axes of the corresponding bisectrix.

If a sublattice O_1 of dimension ν (smaller than n) of an n-dimensional maximal lattice O in K_n is multiplicative in K_n and cannot be centered so that its centering (which by definition is also of dimension ν) is also multiplicative in K_n, then we will call it a *maximal sublattice*.

THEOREM 1. *The dimension* ν *of a maximal sublattice* O_1 *of an irreducible maximal n-dimensional lattice* O *must be a divisor of n. Moreover, such a maximal sublattice is the* ν*-dimensional collection of all the points of the lattice* O *that lie in some* ν*-dimensional bisectrix, and conversely, if the lattice* O *has a* ν*-dimensional collection of points lying in some* ν*-dimensional bisectrix, then this collection is its* ν*-dimensional maximal sublattice. Such a maximal lattice, if we look at it in the space of the bisectrix and take the axes of the bisectrix for axes and* $\sqrt{\delta}$ *for a scalar unit on the axes, where* $\nu \cdot \delta = n$, *then the given maximal sublattice is a* ν*-dimensional maximal lattice in these axes.*

Let us look at an arbitrary point of the irreducible maximal lattice; the coordinates $\omega^{(1)}, \omega^{(2)}, \ldots, \omega^{(n)}$ of this point are the roots of an nth degree primary equation $f(x) = 0$. We will show that this equation is either irreducible or is the power of an irreducible equation. That is, any point of the irreducible lattice is either a generic point or a point of some bisectrix. In fact, if $f(x) = g_1(x) \cdot g_2(x) \cdot \ldots \cdot g_k(x)$, where $g_1(x), g_2(x), \ldots, g_k(x)$ are irreducible, and if $g_1(x)$ is the irreducible factor of lowest degree (if the degrees of the factors are not all equal), we consider the point $\theta = g_1(\omega)$ as the point with coordinates $g_1(\omega^{(1)}), g_1(\omega^{(2)}), \ldots, g_1(\omega^{(k)})$. Then the coordinates of θ corresponding to the $\omega^{(i)}$ (which are roots of $g_1(x)$) are zero, and thus, since the lattice is assumed to be irreducible (it has no zero-divisors), this point θ is the origin and all its remaining coordinates are also zero: in other words, the roots of all the remaining irreducible factors $g_2(x), \cdots, g_k(x)$ are the roots of $g_1(x)$. But since an irreducible equation cannot have multiple roots, it follows that, in the first place, the degree of each of the g's is ν, the degree of the first factor g_1, and secondly, that each of the g's is the same as g_1.

Now let O_1 be some sublattice of the lattice O. The sublattice O_1 cannot have a generic point in K_n, for if all n of its coordinates were different, it would be contrary to the assumption that it is n-dimensional. Thus all the points of O_1 are points of some bisectrix.

Let ω_1 be a point of the sublattice O_1 having the least multiplicity δ_1 of its coordinates in K_n; in view of what has just been proved, $\delta_1 \neq 1$.

Let us consider any other point ω_2 of the lattice O_1; those coordinates that are equal for ω_1 must also be equal for this point, since otherwise the point $q \cdot \omega_1 + \omega_2$, where q is a very large rational integer, would have more unequal coordinates than ω_1, since the coordinates of that complex in which they are equal for ω_1 but not equal for ω_2 would be unequal and the coordinates of the complexes of ω_1 would still be unequal, since their difference would be larger in absolute value than any difference of coordinates of ω_2.

Thus all the points of the sublattice O_1 lie in the bisectrix determined by the point ω_1. If the bisectrix is ν-dimensional, then the powers of the point ω_1 clearly lie in it ν-dimensionally. Let us consider the collection of all the points of the n-dimensional maximal lattice O which lie in this bisectrix; this collection represents a ν-dimensional sublattice of the lattice O, as may be seen if one goes over to the signature space of O. This ν-dimensional sublattice is obviously multiplicative; for on the one hand, the product of any two of its points will be again a point of the lattice O, and on the other, the product of any two points lying in some bisectrix will evidently lie in the same bisectrix. Thus, if O_1 is maximal, it coincides with this lattice. The last assertion of the theorem follows from the fact that if we take $\sqrt{\delta}$ as a scalar unit on the axes of the bisectrix, then the lattice O will be an irreducible, ν-dimensional, maximal lattice that is multiplicative in these axes (i. e., it will be the collection of all integer points of some algebraic field of order ν).

2. Normal lattices. We will define an *axial permutation* of K_n to be any orthogonal transformation of the first or second kind of the space K_n that leaves the origin invariant and transforms semiaxes of K_n with positive coordinates into themselves. We will call the axial permutation that leaves the lattice O invariant and axial permutation of O into itself. It is easy to see that an irreducible

n-dimensional lattice cannot have more than n axial permutations into itself. To show this, let $\omega^{(1)}, \omega^{(2)}, \cdots, \omega^{(n)}$ be the coordinates of some generic point of this lattice; then the coordinates of those points into which this point may be transformed under axial permutations will be the same numbers, but in a different order. No two different axial permutations can carry this point into the same point, for the given point is generic and thus has no equal coordinates, while different axial permutations must permute at least two axes. If there were more than n axial permutations taking the given lattice into itself, then there would be two different points in this lattice which would have the same, say first, coordinates; but then the difference of these points, while different from zero, would have the first coordinate zero, i.e., would be a zero divisor, and the lattice could not be irreducible. We will call an irreducible lattice that has exactly n axial permutations into itself a *normal lattice*.

THEOREM 2.[1] *Any n-dimensional multiplicative lattice* Ω *of* K_n *that is irreducible and maximal is either a normal lattice or is a maximal sublattice of least dimension of some normal m-dimensional lattice, where* m *is an integer multiple of* n.

For the proof we will first construct a certain auxiliary $n!$-dimensional lattice Ω as follows. We will write in columns the numbers $1, 2, \cdots, n$ of the coordinates of the points of Ω in all possible arrangements, and we will examine the rectangular matrix of numbers that we obtain:

$$\left.\begin{array}{cccccc}
1 & 1 & \cdots & \cdots & \cdots & n \\
2 & 2 & \cdots & \cdots & \cdots & n-1 \\
\cdot & \cdot & \cdots & \cdots & \cdots & \cdot \\
\cdot & \cdot & \cdots & \cdots & \cdots & \cdot \\
n-1 & n & \cdots & \cdots & \cdots & 2 \\
n & n-1 & \cdots & \cdots & \cdots & 1
\end{array}\right\}. \qquad (*)$$

Each of its rows will characterize an n-dimensional bisectrix plane of the space $K_{n!}$. The matrix $(*)$ thus gives n completely determined n-dimensional bisectrix planes in $K_{n!}$. Consider in $K_{n!}$ the points whose coordinates correspond to the rows of the matrix $(*)$, written in order for all the points of Ω. Thus we will obtain in the n bisectric planes of $K_{n!}$ the lattices $\Omega_1, \Omega_2, \cdots$ $\cdots, \Omega_n$ which are similar to the lattice Ω but $\sqrt{n!/n}$ times larger than it. Let us look at the collection Ω^* of all points of $K_{n!}$ that can be obtained by multiplication, addition, and subtraction of any of the points of any of the n

1) In this section the symbols Ω, Ω, Ω have distinct meanings.

lattices. If $\theta^{(1)}, \theta^{(2)}, \cdots, \theta^{(n)}$ are the coordinates of some generic point of Ω in K_n, then any point of Ω^* has for its first coordinate $\Phi(\theta^{(1)}, \theta^{(2)}, \cdots, \theta^{(n)})$, where Φ is some polynomial function of $\theta^{(1)}, \theta^{(2)}, \cdots, \theta^{(n)}$ (perhaps with fractional coefficients since the coordinates of some of the points of Ω may be expressed in terms of the corresponding coordinates of θ integrally, but with fractional coefficients). It will have as its second coordinate the same function Φ but of the second ordering $\theta^{(1)}, \theta^{(2)}, \cdots, \theta^{(n)}, \theta^{(n-1)}$, and so on. The coordinates of any point of Ω^* are, by the fundamental theorem on symmetric functions, the roots of a primary equation $F(x) = 0$ of degree $n!$. But since these roots are obtained by the addition, subtraction, and multiplication of whole algebraic numbers, the coefficients of F are rational integers. The coordinates $\theta^{(1)}, \theta^{(2)}, \cdots, \theta^{(n)}$ fall into complex-conjugate pairs, and thus, independently of the choice of the Φ's, all $n!$ of them will also fall into complex-conjugate pairs. In fact, those Φ will be complex-conjugate that may be obtained from each other by a substitution of the coordinates θ^i in all complex-conjugate pairs. Thus all the points of Ω^* lie in the corresponding $W_{n!,r}$, i.e., the set of points Ω^* is discrete. But the point $V = A_1\theta_1 + A_2\theta_2 + \cdots + A_n\theta_n$, where $\theta_1, \theta_2, \cdots, \theta_n$ denote the location of θ in the lattices $\Omega_1, \Omega_2, \cdots, \Omega_n$ which have been introduced, and the A_i are lexicographically chosen rational integers, is a generic point in $K_{n!}$, for its distinct coordinates in $K_{n!}$ are obtained from $A_1\theta^{(1)} + A_2\theta^{(2)} + \cdots + A_n\theta^{(n)}$ by making here all $n!$ permutations of $\theta^{(1)}, \theta^{(2)}, \cdots, \theta^{(n)}$. Thus the set Ω^* is $n!$-dimensional. By the construction of the set Ω^*, it is additive and subtractive, i.e., it is an $n!$-dimensional lattice, multiplicative in $K_{n!}$.

Let us denote by Ω the maximal lattice for Ω^* in $K_{n!}$ if Ω^* is not itself maximal. The lattice Ω^* has $n!$ axial permutations in $K_{n!}$, which correspond to the $n!$ permutations of the columns of the matrix (*). These are obtained from all $n!$ permutations of its rows since each of its $n!$ axial permutations in $K_{n!}$ only interchange the lattices $\Omega_1, \Omega_2, \cdots, \Omega_n$ from which Ω^* was constructed. Obviously these $n!$ axial permutations will leave Ω^* invariant.

Now let $\Omega_1, \Omega_2, \cdots, \Omega_k$ be the irreducible parts of the direct sum which constitutes the maximal lattice Ω, and let $K_{m_1}, K_{m_2}, \cdots, K_{m_k}$ be the coordinate spaces in which they lie. We will show that all the irreducible parts are not only of the same dimension, but are even identical. For this purpose we take from the axial permutations under consideration an axial permutation s of the lattice Ω into itself which matches some coordinate K_{m_1} with some other coordinate K_{m_i}; among our $n!$ axial permutations such axial permutations exist for any two given coordinates (for otherwise there would exist two different axial permutations which would transform the same coordinate into the same place, contrary to the construction of these axial permutations from the permutations of the rows of the matrix (*)). Any point ω of the lattice Ω is either included in some nonzero vector of the irreducible part of Ω_i, in which case all the coordinates of this point which correspond to K_{m_i} are not zero, since in Ω_i only the point 0 has coordinates in K_{m_i} equal to zero, or the point ω is included in no vector of the irreducible part, in which case all the coordinates corresponding to K_{m_i} are equal to zero.

Let us suppose that $m_1 \leq m_2 \leq \cdots \leq m_k$; then the permutation s transforms a point of Ω_1 into some point of Ω, one of whose coordinates is the coordinate in K_{m_i} such that it has $m_1 \leq m_i \neq 0$ coordinates; but in view of what has been said above about the points of Ω, this is possible only if $m_i = m_1$ and if all the coordinates of the point Ω_1 go into coordinates of K_{m_i} under the axial permutation s. Moreover, we see that Ω_1 coincides with Ω_i after the axial permutation since Ω_i is the collection of the points of Ω that lie in K_{m_i}. We thus see that all of the Ω_i are one-dimensional and identical. This argument also shows that Ω_1 has m axial permutations into itself, for if the coordinates of K_{m_1} are $1, 2, \cdots, m_1$, then all the $n!$ axial permutations of Ω into itself which take the 1st coordinate onto the 2nd, 3rd, $\cdots$, or m_1st place will, by what was proved above, coincide with one another. Thus each of the irreducible parts of Ω is normal. Finally, it is not difficult to see that Ω is "imbedded" in any Ω_i.

To show this, let θ_1 be a generic point of Ω_1 in Ω. Then θ_1, like any point of Ω, has the form $\theta_{11} + \theta_{12} + \cdots + \theta_{1k}$, where the θ_{1i} are points in the the corresponding irreducible parts; if θ_{1i} is not the origin, then there is in Ω_i a point θ_{1i} which has all the distinct coordinates of the point θ_1, for if it had only some of the distinct coordinates of the point θ_1, then θ_1 could not be a generic point in the irreducible Ω, which is what we wanted to show.

We will call the group G of all m axial permutations of Ω into itself the *Galois group* of the irreducible maximal lattice Ω and also the Galois group of the irreducible maximal lattice Ω. The normal lattice Ω will be called the norm of the lattice Ω. In the case that Ω is an irreducible maximal lattice, we may repeat the previous argument, but we cannot assert that the lattice Ω will itself be a maximal sublattice of the normal irreducible lattice Ω; we can only prove that each of its irreducible parts is such a sublattice. In this case, when the maximal lattice is not irreducible, its Galois group will be defined to be the group G of all m axial permutations of the normal irreducible lattice Ω into itself, where Ω is constructed from Ω as in the above case when Ω was irreducible; we will also call this lattice Ω the norm of the lattice Ω. When Ω is irreducible, the dimension m of the lattice Ω is divisible by $n(m = n \cdot d)$, the dimension of the multiplicative lattice Ω, since the lattice Ω is in this case a multiplicative sublattice of lowest dimension of the lattice Ω. Hence its dimension is equal to the dimension of some bisectrix K_m; if Ω is reducible, then m may not be divisible by n, and may even be smaller than n.

3. Subgroups of the group G and maximal sublattices of the lattice Ω. Let H be a subgroup of the group G of order δ, so that $m = \mu\delta$, where μ is an integer. We will investigate the axes into which the first axis of K_m goes under all the permutations in H. In view of the fact that the group of permutations of the axes $1, 2, \cdots, m$ of the space K_m is regular, there will be δ distinct axes $1, 2, \cdots, \delta$. Thus the 2nd axis will be transformed by the permutations of H into only the 1st, 2nd, $\cdots$ and so on to the δth axis. Hence these axes will be permuted only among themselves by the permutations in H. Analogously, if we start from the $(\delta + 1)$st axis with the next δ arrangements of the numbers of the axes of K_m corresponding to H, we will obtain a square with δ elements constructed for the numbers of the next δ axes of K_m permuted only among themselves by the subgroup H, and so on.

$$G\left\{\begin{array}{l} H\left\{\begin{array}{l}\begin{pmatrix} 1, 2, 3 \; . \; . \; . \; . \; \delta \\ 2, \; . \; . \; . \; . \; . \; . \\ 3, \; . \; . \; . \; . \; . \; . \\ \cdot \qquad \qquad \cdot \\ \cdot \qquad \qquad \cdot \\ \cdot \qquad \qquad \cdot \\ \delta, \; . \; . \; . \; . \; . \; . \end{pmatrix} \begin{pmatrix} \delta+1 \; . \; . \; . \; 2\delta \\ . \; . \; . \; . \; . \\ . \; . \; . \; . \; . \\ . \; . \; . \; . \; . \\ . \; . \; . \; . \; . \\ \\ \\ \end{pmatrix} \begin{matrix} . \; . \; . \; . \\ . \; . \; . \; . \\ . \; . \; . \; . \\ . \; . \; . \; . \\ \\ \\ \\ \end{matrix} \begin{pmatrix} (\mu-1)\delta+1 \; . \; . \; . \; m \\ . \; . \; . \; . \; . \\ . \; . \; . \; . \; . \\ . \; . \; . \; . \; . \\ \\ \\ \\ \end{pmatrix}\end{array}\right. \\ \delta+1 \\ \cdot \\ \cdot \\ \cdot \\ \cdot \\ \cdot \\ \cdot \\ m \end{array}\right\}.$$

Obviously, the collection of all permutations of the subgroup H will leave invariant those and only those points of the space K_m which correspond to the μ-dimensional bisectrix plane of K_m which is obtained by equating the coordinates in the separate squares of the subgroup H.

THEOREM 3. *Each subgroup H of the group G corresponds to a μ-dimensional maximal sublattice of the lattice Ω, and conversely.*

If we consider any point of Ω and evaluate at it all δ axial permutations of H, and then add together all δ of the points obtained, we get a point of Ω lying in the bisectrix plane corresponding to the subgroup H. If we do this for every point of Ω, we will obtain a μ-dimensional lattice in this bisectrix plane, since it is possible to take points of Ω such that the sums of the coordinates in the different complexes will be all distinct and nonzero, i. e., so as to obtain a generic point in the corresponding bisectrix.

Thus to each subgroup H there corresponds a sublattice, and hence a maximal sublattice of the lattice lying in the bisectrix corresponding to H and having the same dimension as this bisectrix. The dimension of this sublattice is equal to the index of the subgroup H relative to the group G.

Let us now assume conversely that in a normal lattice Ω there is a μ-dimensional sublattice Ω that is multiplicative, and let α be a generic point of the sublattice. Let H be the subgroup of the group of all permutations G that leave α fixed. The number of permutations in H is not larger than δ since, for example, the 1st coordinate of the point α may go to at the most δ places under the permutations, namely, those places where the first coordinates are equal to the first coordinate of α. But G does not contain different permutations leaving a given coordinate fixed. On the other hand, the number of permutations in H is not less than δ; for otherwise the images of α under all the elements of G would constitute more than μ different points, and, for example, the 1st coordinate of these points would have to have more than μ different values, which is impossible since α has only μ different coordinates. Each permutation in H thus permutes coordinates only within complexes where the coordinates are equal. The sublattice Ω therefore belongs to the subgroup H in the above-mentioned sense, and the proof of the theorem is complete.

Let us see what points are zero-divisors in the lattice Ω. Rational relations between the roots may be written in the form $\Phi(x^{(1)}, x^{(2)}, \cdots, x^{(n)}) = 0$ and this form includes all the rational relations between roots. If there are no divisors in Ω, i.e., if there are no rational relations between the roots due to at least one of the $n!$ permutations, then Ω is an irreducible lattice and the Galois group of the lattice Ω is symmetric.

§4. MULTIPLICATIVE AUTOMORPHISMS (UNITS) OF LATTICES IN K_n

If we multiply all the points of some lattice in K_n by the same arbitrary fixed point ω of K_n that is not a zero-divisor, then it is obvious that there will correspond to the sum or difference of two points of the original lattice the sum or difference of the corresponding points (i.e., the points obtained from multiplication of the given points by ω) of the multiplicative lattice. The complex volume (i.e., the value of the determinant of the coordinates in K_n) of the points obtained from some n basic points of the initial lattice after multiplication by ω will be equal to the corresponding complex volume of the initial lattice multiplied by the norm of the point ω. From this it follows that multiplication of an n-dimensional lattice of K_n by a point of K_n that is not a zero-divisor will yield another n-dimensional lattice of K_n.

Any point ϵ of K_n which, when multiplied by a given lattice, yields the same lattice is said to be a point of K_n giving a *multiplicative automorphism* of the given lattice. We will call such a point a unit of the given lattice since such a point plays the same role for the given lattice as the points $(1, 1, \cdots, 1)$ and $(-1, -1, \cdots, -1)$, multiplication by which will obviously give a multiplicative automorphism for any lattice in K_n. (The above is true for $(-1, -1, \cdots \cdots, -1)$ in consequence of the symmetry of any lattice in K_n with respect to the point 0.) It is obvious that any multiplicative automorphism is not a zero-divisor and has a norm of ± 1. Moreover, we see that under multiplication by a point, the complex volume of a parallelepiped is multiplied by the norm of that point.

In this section we will show that any multiplicative lattice, and also any lattice rationally related to such a lattice (even if it is not multiplicative), will in general have infinitely many multiplicative automorphisms different from 1 and -1, and that conversely if a lattice in K_n has generic multiplicative automorphisms, then it is either a multiplicative lattice, or a sublattice of some multiplicative lattice, or is obtained from such a lattice by multiplication by some point of K_n. It will be seen that if a lattice is not maximal, its multiplicative automorphisms may fail to belong to it.

THEOREM 1. *If* $[\omega_1, \omega_2, \cdots, \omega_n]$ *is an irreducible maximal lattice which is neither one-dimensional nor complex two-dimensional (i. e., the number* $\sigma + \tau - 1 > 0$*), then the lattice has infinitely many multiplicative automorphisms* ϵ*, which are all points of the lattice and which are expressed by the formula* $\epsilon = E_i \cdot \epsilon_1^{m_1} \cdot \epsilon_2^{m_2} \cdot \cdots \cdot \epsilon_{\sigma+\tau-1}^{m_{\sigma+\tau-1}}$, *where* $\epsilon_1, \epsilon_2, \cdots, \epsilon_{\sigma+\tau-1}$ *are the so-called "basic multiplicative automorphisms" of our lattice,* $m_1, m_2, \cdots, m_{\sigma+\tau-1}$ *are all possible rational integer exponents, and the* E_i *are certain special multiplicative automorphisms of our lattice which are a finite number of roots of unity.*

Let M be some point in the lattice $R_{n,\tau}$ that corresponds to our given lattice. The coordinates of the point M in $R_{n,\tau}$ are $\zeta', \zeta'', \cdots, \zeta^{(\sigma)}, \xi', \eta', \xi'', \eta'', \cdots, \xi^{(\tau)}, \eta^{(\tau)}$. Let us call the positive numbers $|\zeta'|, |\zeta''|, \cdots, |\zeta^{(\sigma)}|$, $\rho' = |\xi'^2 + \eta'^2|$, $\rho'' = |\xi''^2 + \eta''^2|, \cdots, \rho^{(\tau)} = |\xi^{(\tau)2} + \eta^{(\tau)2}|$ the parameters of the point M. The collection of all points of $R_{n,\tau}$ whose parameters are not larger than the corresponding parameters of the point M form a convex body in $R_{n,\tau}$ with center at the origin, since the vector sum of convex bodies is a convex body. We will call this collection the *normed body* of the point M. For $\sigma = 3$, $\tau = 0$, for example, this will be a rectangular parallelepiped in the corresponding $R_{3,0}$ with one of its verticies at the point M, its center at the origin, and its faces parallel to the coordinate planes. For $\sigma = 3$, $\tau = 1$ this will be a right circular cylinder with center at the origin, with axis along the axis ζ', and with the point M lying on the circumference of one of the bases.

We will call a point M of the lattice a *relative minimum* of the lattice if it is not zero and if within its normed body there are no points of the given lattice other than zero which are at its center. The point $1 = (1, 1, \cdots, 1)$ of the lattice $[\omega_1, \omega_2, \cdots, \omega_n]$ is its relative minimum, for the norm of any point of this lattice is a rational integer, and the norm of a point lying inside the normed body of the point 1 is obviously less than 1 in absolute value. The norm is equal to 0 only at the point 0, since the lattice $[\omega_1, \omega_2, \cdots, \omega_n]$, being irreducible, does not have zero-divisors.

We will show that there exists in the lattice $[\omega_1, \omega_2, \cdots, \omega_n]$ an infinite sequence of relative minima such that one of their parameters, say the kth, grows infinitely large in absolute value with the number of the minima while the remaining parameters all decrease with the number of the minima. We will call such a collection a chain of relative minima increasing in the kth parameter. We will show that for any value $k = 1, 2, \cdots, \sigma + \tau$ of a parameter, there exists such a chain. The point 1 is a relative minimum all of whose parameters are equal to 1. We will not change the parameters of the normed body of the point 1 except for the kth, which we will begin to increase. When we do this, the volume of the body will increase, and by Lemma 3 of the Supplement (the lemma of Minkowski), when the volume increases beyond 2^n times the volume in $R_{n,\tau}$ of the basic parallelepiped of the given lattice, then within this body will lie at least two points of the lattice that are symmetric to each other with respect to the origin. Let ϕ_1 be one of the points of the first pair of points which intersects the surface of the normed body as the kth parameter increases, and which has the smallest norm among all such pairs (or is one of those points of smallest norm if there are several of them). Since our lattice does not have zero-divisors, the volume of the normed body of the point ϕ_1 is not zero, and thus the product of its parameters is not zero. The kth parameter is greater than 1 in absolute value, while the remaining parameters are less than 1 in absolute value; for if, while leaving the other parameter fixed, the kth parameter by an arbitrarily small amount, we cause the point ϕ_1 to be within the normed body thus obtained. The point ϕ_1 is also a relative minimum, for if there were a point of the lattice inside its normed body, then all of the parameters of the point would have to be less in absolute value than the parameters of ϕ_1, i.e., all its parameters would be smaller than the parameters of the point 1, and the kth parameter would be smaller than the kth parameter of the point ϕ_1. But then ϕ_1 would not be the first point of the lattice which is intersected by the given extended normed body. Moreover, the point ϕ_1 is even the first point adjacent to the point 1 in the chain from the point 1 in the direction of growth of the kth parameter, or is one of the first, if there are several of them. Hence it is the first relative minimum from 1 in the direction of growth of the kth parameter whose remaining parameters are less in absolute value than the corresponding parameters of the point 1.

In view of the required minimality of the norm of the point ϕ_1, only points with the same norm can lie on the surface of its normed body; but then their parameters must be equal to the corresponding parameters of the point ϕ_1, for if even one were smaller, then this point would have a smaller norm than ϕ_1. Let us now fix all the parameters of the normed body of the point ϕ_1 except the kth, which we will increase as before; then a point of the lattice will not immediately enter the extended normed body. Let ϕ_2 be the first point of the lattice which intersects this extended body. As before, we can show that ϕ_2 is the first relative minimum adjacent to ϕ_1 in the direction of the growth of the kth parameter, and so on. In view of the possibility of having on each body several suitable points the question of uniqueness of such a construction remains open.

It is easy to see that the volume of the normed body of a given point is $\pm 2^{\sigma}\pi^{\tau}$ times the norm of the point. Since by the above lemma of Minkowski the volume inside a convex body with center in a point of the lattice cannot be more than 2^n times as large as the volume of the basic parallelepiped of this lattice, the norms of all the relative minima of the given lattice are bounded in absolute value. Thus if we multiply our lattice $[\omega_1, \omega_2, \cdots, \omega_n]$ by the relative minima $\phi_1, \phi_2, \phi_3, \cdots,$ we will obtain sublattices whose indices are bounded, since the lattice is multiplicative. But as there are only finitely many sublattices (cf. Supplement) and infinitely many relative minima, there will be among the relative minima infinitely many that will give the same sublattice $[\psi_1, \psi_2, \cdots, \psi_n]$ when multiplied into our lattice $[\omega_1, \omega_2, \cdots, \omega_n]$. For example, let $\phi_\lambda \cdot [\omega_1, \omega_2, \cdots, \omega_n] = [\psi_1, \psi_2, \cdots, \psi_n]$ and $\phi_\mu \cdot [\omega_1, \omega_2, \cdots, \omega_n] = [\psi_1, \psi_2, \cdots, \psi_n]$; then $(1/\phi_\mu)[\psi_1, \psi_2, \cdots, \psi_n] = [\omega_1, \omega_2, \cdots, \omega_n]$, and it follows that $(\phi_\lambda/\phi_\mu)[\omega_1, \omega_2, \cdots, \omega_n] = [\omega_1, \omega_2, \cdots, \omega_n]$.

Thus the point $\epsilon = \phi_\lambda/\phi_\mu$ is a multiplicative automorphism of our lattice. But 1 is in our lattice, since it is a maximal lattice, and thus the point $1 \cdot \epsilon$ is a point of our lattice, i.e., the point ϵ is itself a point of our lattice. If ϕ_λ is the minimum following ϕ_μ in the given k-chain, then, since the parameters of the product or quotient of two points are the corresponding parameters of the product or quotient of the parameters of the points, the kth parameter of ϵ is greater than unity, while the remaining parameters are less than unity. The powers $\epsilon, \epsilon^2, \epsilon^3, \cdots$ thus give successively different automorphisms, since the kth parameter of these powers grows in absolute value with the growth of the exponent, while the remaining parameters decrease.

We have thus proven the existence of an infinite number of distinct multiplicative automorphisms for any irreducible maximal lattice for which $\sigma + \tau - 1 > 0$, since in this case the number of parameters of the normed body of a point is greater than 1. If the number of these parameters is 1, which will occur when $n = 1$, or when $n = 2$, and $\sigma = 1$ (i.e., the coordinates are complex-conjugates), it is impossible to extend the normed body of the point 1 without bringing the point within the body. When the number of the parameters is greater than 1, it is possible to do this by leaving all but one parameter fixed. Thus the point 1 does not become an interior point of the extended normed body, but is on its surface.

Any multiplicative automorphism (i.e., unit) of our lattice $[\omega_1, \omega_2, \cdots, \omega_n]$ is one of its points with norm ± 1, for under multiplication by such a point the volume of the basic parallelepiped of the lattice is not changed since it is taken into itself. Conversely, any point of the lattice $[\omega_1, \omega_2, \cdots, \omega_n]$ with a norm of ± 1 is a multiplicative automorphism (unit) of the given lattice. This follows from the fact that since the lattice is multiplicative, we obtain a sublattice when we multiply it by such a point; but since the norm of the point is ± 1, the index of the sublattice is 1 and it must be the whole lattice $[\omega_1, \omega_2, \cdots, \omega_n]$. We have thus shown that there are infinitely many points of the norm ± 1 in a maximal irreducible sublattice if $\sigma + \tau - 1 > 0$.

Let us now turn to the second part of the theorem, namely to the question of basic multiplicative automorphisms by means of which all the others can be expressed.

We first remark that two distinct points of the lattice $[\omega_1, \omega_2, \cdots, \omega_n]$ may none the less have the same parameters. More specifically, because of the irreducibility of the lattice, i.e., because of the absence of zero divisors, no two of the first σ parameters of two different points can be equal, for then the difference of these points would have a zero coordinate without being the origin. However, two of the last τ parameters, i.e., two (and possibly even all) of the parameters ρ, may be identical in two different points.

Thus we see that if $\sigma = 0$, i.e., $n = 2\tau$, there may exist in $[\omega_1, \omega_2, \cdots, \omega_n]$ distinct points having the same set of parameters $\rho', \rho'', \cdots, \rho^{(\tau)}$. Examples show that such cases do occur. Let us consider when two multiplicative automorphisms of our lattice can have identical sets of parameters if $\sigma = 0$. For example, let the parameters of the automorphisms ϵ_1 and ϵ_2 be equal, i.e., $\rho_1' = \rho_2'$, $\rho_1'' = \rho_2''$, $\cdots$, $\rho_1^{(\tau)} = \rho_2^{(\tau)}$. Let us consider the point $E = \epsilon_1 / \epsilon_2$; obviously it is also a multiplicative automorphism of our lattice. All its parameters are 1. If there exists in our lattice points E, whose parameters are all equal to 1, there are in any case only a finite number of them, since they lie on the sphere $\xi'^2 + \eta'^2 + \xi''^2 + \eta''^2 + \cdots + \xi^{(\tau)2} + \eta^{(\tau)2} = \tau$ in $R_{n,\tau}$. The product of two such points $E_1 \cdot E_2$ is again such a point E_3, and, in particular, any power E^m of such a point with a positive integer exponent m is such a point. From this it follows, because of the finiteness of the number of such points in our lattice, that $E^{m_1} = E^{m_2}$ for some positive integers $m_1 > m_2$, and thus that $E^{m_1 - m_2} = 1$, i.e., that this point has coordinates which are roots of unity.

Thus we see that two multiplicative automorphisms of our lattice have identical parameters if and only if they differ by one of the members of the finite set of the factors E. The units 1 and -1 always occur among the units E.

Let us now look at the $(\sigma+\tau)$-dimensional real space $R_{\sigma+\tau}$, whose coordinates we will denote by the letter y. We will associate with the multiplicative automorphism ϵ of the given irreducible maximal lattice $[\omega_1, \omega_2, \cdots, \omega_n]$ the point with coordinates $y', y'', \cdots, y^{(\sigma+\tau)}$, which are the parameters $|\zeta'|$, $|\zeta''|, \cdots, |\zeta^{(\sigma)}|, \rho', \rho'', \cdots, \rho^{(\tau)}$ of the automorphism ϵ. The set of points $\bar{\epsilon}$ lies in $R_{\sigma+\tau}$ on the surface $y' \cdot y'' \cdot \cdots \cdot y^{(\sigma+\tau)} = +1$, and is obviously multiplicative if the product of two points of R is understood to be the point whose coordinates are simply the products of the corresponding coordinates of the points being multiplied, for the set of points ϵ in $R_{n,\tau}$ is multiplicative and the product of two ϵ's corresponds to the product of the corresponding $\bar{\epsilon}$. Let us now consider, corresponding to all the $\bar{\epsilon}$, the points $\bar{\bar{\epsilon}}$ in $R_{\sigma+\tau}$ whose coordinates are logarithms of the corresponding coordinates of the $\bar{\epsilon}$. In view of the fact that the product of the coordinates of any point $\bar{\epsilon}$ is $+1$, the set of all points $\bar{\bar{\epsilon}}$ lies in a $(\sigma+\tau-1)$-dimensional plane P, which passes through the origin in $R_{\sigma+\tau}$ and has the equation $y' + y'' + \cdots + y^{(\sigma+\tau)} = 0$. Here the point $\bar{\bar{\epsilon}}$ for $\epsilon = 1$ is the origin of coordinates in the plane P. The product of two points $\bar{\epsilon}$ corresponds to the sum of the two points $\bar{\bar{\epsilon}}$ in the plane P, for when numbers are multiplied, their logarithms are added; thus to say that the set of $\bar{\epsilon}$ is multiplicative is the same as to say that the set of $\bar{\bar{\epsilon}}$ is additive. From the fact that among the points ϵ there are points having any one coordinate large and the remaining coordinates small it follows that the points $\bar{\bar{\epsilon}}$ lie in a plane of dimension $\sigma+\tau-1$.

For example, let us look at the case when the plane P is 3-dimensional, i.e., when $\sigma+\tau-1=3$. The coordinate planes of the space $R_{\sigma+\tau}$, which in this case is 4-dimensional, intersect P in four 2-dimensional planes which form the sides of a right tetrahedron passing through one point in P, namely the origin of coordinates O. We will translate these planes very slightly in P parallel to themselves and in a negative direction, to form around the origin a small right tetrahedron T; we will denote by the numbers 1, 2, 3, and 4 the trihedral angles perpendicular to the trihedral angles of this tetrahedron. If there are points ϵ which have any one of their parmaeters large (larger than 1), i.e., the logarithm is larger than 0, while the remaining parameters are small (smaller than 1), i.e., their logarithms are less than zero, then it is obvious that there are points $\bar{\bar{\epsilon}}$ inside each of the trihedral angles 1, 2, 3, and 4. It is necessary to show that in such a case the set of points $\bar{\bar{\epsilon}}$ in P is 3-dimensional. To show this, let us take a point inside each of the trihedral angles 1, 2, 3, 4 and call them $\bar{\bar{\epsilon}}_1, \bar{\bar{\epsilon}}_2, \bar{\bar{\epsilon}}_3$ and $\bar{\bar{\epsilon}}_4$. Let us turn the planes of the lateral surfaces of the tetrahedron T around the edges of its base so that they will pass through the point $\bar{\bar{\epsilon}}_4$. We obtain a tetrahedron T_4 containing the tetrahedron T and such that the points $\bar{\bar{\epsilon}}_1, \bar{\bar{\epsilon}}_2, \bar{\bar{\epsilon}}_3$ lie, as before, inside the trihedral angles perpendicular to the trihedral angles of its corresponding vertices, while the point $\bar{\bar{\epsilon}}_4$ is one of its vertices. Analogously, rotating the planes of the faces of the tetrahedron T_4, we obtain a tetrahedron $T_{3,4}$ containing T and such that two of the given points are vertices. Next we can get a tetrahedron containing T with three of the given points as vertices, and finally such a tetrahedron $T_{1,2,3,4}$ with all four of our points as vertices. But the tetrahedron $T_{1,2,3,4}$ contains all the preceding tetrahedra, and thus also the tetrahedron T, i.e., it is 3-dimensional, and therefore the points $\bar{\bar{\epsilon}}_1, \bar{\bar{\epsilon}}_2, \bar{\bar{\epsilon}}_3, \bar{\bar{\epsilon}}_4$ lie 3-dimensionally.

If P is of dimension greater than 3, the argument is completely analogous.

The set of points $\bar{\bar{\epsilon}}$ is discrete, since each part of the logarithmic space with finite diameter is a transform of a finite part of the space $R_{n,\tau}$, and from Lemma 1 of the Supplement it follows that the $\bar{\bar{\epsilon}}$ form a $(\sigma + \tau - 1)$-dimensional lattice. Let $\bar{\bar{\epsilon}}_1, \bar{\bar{\epsilon}}_2, \cdots, \bar{\bar{\epsilon}}_{\sigma+\tau-1}$ be basic points of this lattice. Then any point $\bar{\bar{\epsilon}}$ of this lattice has the form $\bar{\bar{\epsilon}} = m_1\bar{\bar{\epsilon}}_1 + m_2\bar{\bar{\epsilon}}_2 + \cdots + m_{\sigma+\tau-1}\bar{\bar{\epsilon}}_{\sigma+\tau-1}$ where $m_1, m_2, \cdots, m_{\sigma+\tau-1}$ are rational integers.

Returning to the points $\bar{\epsilon}$, we see that any point $\bar{\epsilon}$ has the form $\bar{\epsilon} = \bar{\epsilon}_1^{m_1}\bar{\epsilon}_2^{m_2}\cdots\bar{\epsilon}_{\sigma+\tau-1}^{m_{\sigma+\tau-1}}$. In addition, it is necessary to take into consideration that the correspondence of points ϵ with points $\bar{\epsilon}$ is carried out only up to the multiples E_i, i.e., that all the points $\epsilon \cdot E_i$ correspond to the same point $\bar{\epsilon}$, and hence the general form of the point ϵ is $\epsilon = E_i \cdot \epsilon_1^{m_1} \cdot \epsilon_2^{m_2} \cdots \epsilon_{\sigma+\tau-1}^{m_{\sigma+\tau-1}}$, as the theorem asserts. When there is only one real coordinate, the points E_i are just the points $+1$ and -1.

THEOREM 2. *If* $[\omega_1, \omega_2, \cdots, \omega_n]$ *is a reducible maximal lattice where* κ *is the number of its irreducible parts and* $\sigma + \tau - \kappa > 0$, *then the lattice has infinitely many multiplicative automorphisms which are points of the lattice and are expressible by the formula*

$$\varepsilon = E_1 \cdot \varepsilon_1^{m_1} \cdot \varepsilon_2^{m_2} \cdots \varepsilon_{\sigma_1+\tau_1-1}^{m_{\sigma_1+\tau_1-1}} \cdot E_2 \cdot \varepsilon_{(\sigma_1+\tau_1-1)+1}^{m_{(\sigma_1+\tau_1-1)+1}} \cdots \varepsilon_{\sigma+\tau-\varkappa}^{m_{\sigma+\tau-\varkappa}},$$

where the exponents $m_1, m_2, \cdots, m_{\sigma+\tau-\kappa}$ *are all possible rational integers, the* E_i *and* ϵ_k *are the basic automorphisms of the preceding theorem for the irreducible parts, and the unit* 1 *is written for all those coordinates of* K_n *which are not in the given irreducible part.*

As in the preceding theorem we see that each multiplicative automorphism ϵ of the given reducible lattice is a point of the lattice with norm 1, and conversely. Any such automorphism obviously takes into itself any linear subspace that is spanned by some complex of the axes of K_n and thus takes into itself the individual irreducible parts of the given lattice, i.e., if the coordinates of ϵ are x, $x', \cdots, x^{(n-1)}$, then $(x, x', \cdots, x^{(n_1-1)})$ is a multiplicative automorphism of the first irreducible part, $(x^{n_1}, x^{n_1+1}, \cdots, x^{n_1+n_2-1})$ is a multiplicative automorphism of the second irreducible part, and so on; conversely, if these are the coordinates of multiplicative automorphisms of the individual irreducible parts, then $(x, x', \cdots, x^{(n-1)})$ is a multiplicative automorphism of the whole given lattice, since this point has norm ± 1 and lies in the given lattice. Designating by $E_1, \epsilon_1, \epsilon_2, \cdots, \epsilon_{\sigma_1+\tau_1-1}$ points of our lattice whose first n_1 coordinates coincide with the coordinates of the corresponding basic multiplicative automorphisms of the first irreducible part and whose remaining $n - n_1$ coordinates are 1 (such points exist in our lattice since they can be obtained by adding to the corresponding multiplicative automorphisms of the first irreducible part the trivial multiplicative automorphisms $(00\cdots0\overbrace{11\cdots1}^{n_2}00\cdots0)$, $(00\cdots\cdots0\overbrace{11\cdots1}^{n_3}00\cdots0), \cdots (00\cdots00\cdots0\overbrace{11\cdots1}^{n_k})$ of the remaining irreducible parts), then similarly letting $E_2, \varepsilon_{(\sigma_1+\tau_1-1)+1}, \cdots, \varepsilon_{(\sigma_1+\tau_1-1)+(\sigma_2+\tau_2+1)}$ have the same meaning for the second irreducible part, and so on, we obtain the theorem.

We will say that two lattices in K_n are *similar* if one can be obtained from the other by multiplication by some point in K_n that is not a zero-divisor.

THEOREM 3. *Any n-dimensional lattice in* K_n *that is rational with respect to a multiplicative lattice of* K_n, *or is similar to such a rational lattice has, if* $\sigma + \tau - \kappa > 0$, *infinitely many multiplicative automorphisms, which in general may not be points of the lattice.*

Such a lattice differs only by a factor from a lattice that is rational with respect to a maximal lattice with the same $\sigma + \tau - \kappa$, namely from that lattice in which the given multiplicative lattice lies. We will multiply the given lattice by all the multiplicative automorphisms of this maximal lattice; the result will be lattices that are similar to lattices that are rational with respect to the maximal lattice with the same index and denominator. But there are infinitely many different multiplicative automorphisms of the maximal lattice under consideration, while there are only a finite number of lattices of given denominator and index that are rational with respect to a given lattice (cf., Lemma III^{II} of the Supplement), and hence there will be infinitely many multiplicative automorphisms giving the same lattice. The quotient of any two such automorphisms will again be a multiplicative automorphism of the given lattice.

THEOREM 4. *An arbitrary n-dimensional lattice in* K_n *having a multiplicative automorphism* ϵ *that is a generic point in* K_n *is either rational with respect to some maximal multiplicative lattice for which* $\sigma+\tau-\kappa>0$, *or is similar to such a rational lattice.*

Let ϵ be a multiplicative automorphism of some lattice $[\omega_1, \omega_2, \cdots, \omega_n]$ for which $\sigma+\tau-\kappa>0$ in K_n where the ϵ chosen is a generic point in K_n. Then we have:

$$\begin{aligned}
\omega_1\varepsilon &= a_{11}\omega_1 + a_{12}\omega_2 + \dots + a_{1n}\omega_n\\
\omega_2\varepsilon &= a_{21}\omega_1 + a_{22}\omega_2 + \dots + a_{2n}\omega_n\\
&\cdots\cdots\cdots\cdots\cdots\cdots\\
\omega_n\varepsilon &= a_{n1}\omega_1 + a_{n2}\omega_2 + \dots + a_{nn}\omega_n
\end{aligned}$$

where the coefficients a_{ik} are rational integers. Thus the coordinates of the point ϵ (since it is a generic point, i.e., all its coordinates are different) are all the roots of the primary equation

$$F(\varepsilon) = \begin{vmatrix} a_{11}-\varepsilon, & a_{12}, & \dots, & a_{1n}\\ a_{21}, & a_{22}-\varepsilon, & \dots, & a_{2n}\\ \cdot & \cdot & \cdot & \cdot\\ a_{n1}, & a_{n2}, & \dots, & a_{nn}-\varepsilon \end{vmatrix} = 0.$$

If the point ϵ is generic, then the vectors $1, \epsilon, \epsilon^2, \cdots, \epsilon^{n-2}$ lie n-dimensionally in K_n, and hence the determinant of the matrix with rational integer coefficients b_{ik} of the system

$$\left.\begin{aligned}
\omega_1 &= \omega_1\\
\omega_1\varepsilon &= b_{21}\omega_1 + b_{22}\omega_2 + \dots + b_{2n}\omega_n\\
&\cdots\cdots\cdots\cdots\cdots\cdots\\
&\cdots\cdots\cdots\cdots\cdots\cdots\\
\omega_1\varepsilon^{n-1} &= b_{n1}\omega_1 + b_{n2}\omega_2 + \dots + b_{nn}\omega_n
\end{aligned}\right\}$$

is not equal to zero, from which it follows that at least one of the minors of elements of the 1st column of this matrix has a nonzero determinant. Taking the corresponding $n-1$ equations and dividing them by ω_1 (ω_1 by assumption is not a zero-divisor, so it is possible to divide), we find that $\omega_2/\omega_1, \omega_3/\omega_1, \cdots$ $\cdots, \omega_n/\omega_1$ are expressible linearly and homogeneously by means of rational coefficients in terms of $1, \epsilon, \epsilon^2, \cdots, \epsilon^{n-1}$, i.e., the lattice $[1 = \omega_1/\omega_1, \omega_2/\omega_1, \omega_3/\omega_1, \cdots, \omega_n/\omega_1]$ is rational with respect to the lattice $[1, \epsilon, \epsilon^2, \ldots, \epsilon^{n-1}]$, and hence rational with respect to the maximal lattice in which this lattice lies, i.e., to the maximal lattice defined by the equation $F(\epsilon) = 0$. It follows that the lattice $[\omega_1, \omega_2, \cdots, \omega_n]$ is either rational with respect to this maximal lattice, or is proportional to such a rational lattice.

§5. IDEALS OF A MAXIMAL LATTICE, THE GROUP OF THEIR CLASSES, UNIQUENESS OF DECOMPOSITION

1. Definition of the notion of ideals. By the product of two arbitrary lattices L_1 and L_2 in K_n is meant the collection of points obtained as follows: all the points of L_1 are multiplied by all the points of L_2 and all possible sums and differences are taken among the resulting products. This collection may in general not be a lattice; if the collection is also a lattice L_3 in K_n and if L_1 and L_2 are n-dimensional lattices in K_n, then L_3 is also n-dimensional, for after multiplication of the lattice L_1 by even only one generic point of the lattice L_2 we already obtain an n-dimensional lattice in K_n. We will call the lattice L_3 the product of the lattices L_1 and L_2. If the lattice L_2 is such that the product $L_1 \cdot L_2$ is either the complete lattice L_2 or one of its sublattices, then we will call the lattice L_2 an ideal of the lattice L_1. If the lattice L_1 contains the point $(1, 1, \cdots, 1)$ and L_2 is an ideal of the lattice L_1, then $L_1 \cdot L_2 = L_2$. Every maximal multiplicative lattice O contains the point $(1, 1, \cdots, 1)$, and thus every lattice L that is an ideal of O has the property of being fixed under multiplication by O. In this section we will consider ideals only of maximal lattices. As before, we will say that two lattices in K_n are similar if one can be obtained from the other by multiplication by a point of K_n; this point, of course, must not be a zero-divisor, for otherwise after multiplication the lattice would no longer be n-dimensional, and we have agreed that, if nothing is said to the contrary, the words "lattice in K_n" will always denote an n-dimensional lattice in K_n. We will call a collection of all lattices similar to one another a *class of lattices*; in particular, we will call a collection of ideals similar to one another a class of ideals. It is obvious that if L is an ideal of O and ϕ is any point of K_n that is not a zero-divisor, then $\phi \cdot L$ is also an ideal of O; we thus see that an ideal of the lattice O may be irrational with respect to the lattice O. In general, an ideal of the lattice O may be *integral*, i.e., composed of points of O (a sublattice of the lattice O), may be *fractional* with respect to O, i.e., be a lattice rational with respect to O, or may be *irrational* with respect to O. If ω is a point of O that is not a zero-divisor, then the sublattice $\omega \cdot O$ of the lattice O is an ideal of the lattice O; we call such an ideal a *principal ideal* and denote it (ω). If $\omega = \epsilon$, where ϵ is some unit of O, then $\epsilon \cdot O = O$. Thus the lattice O itself is a principal ideal in O, and is called a *unit ideal.*

2. THEOREM 1. *If O is reducible, then any ideal j of O is the direct sum of ideals of the irreducible parts of O.*

For the proof let $\phi_1, \phi_2, \cdots, \phi_n$ be a basis for the given ideal. We will construct the product $O \cdot j$ as follows: multiply O first by ϕ_1, then by ϕ_2 and so on, and finally by ϕ_n, obtaining the n lattices $O \cdot \phi_1, O \cdot \phi_2, \cdots, O \cdot \phi_n$. If O is the direct sum of the sublattices $O_1, O_2, \cdots, O_\kappa$ lying in the coordinate subspaces $K_{n_1}, K_{n_2}, \cdots, K_{n_\kappa}$, then each of the n lattices thus obtained is also the direct sum of certain lattices lying in these subspaces. To show this, we see that each point ψ of the lattice O has the form $\psi = \psi_1 + \psi_2 + \cdots + \psi_\kappa$, where $\psi_1, \psi_2, \cdots, \psi_\kappa$ are certain points of these sublattices. Hence we may multiply by ϕ_i by ψ in the following manner: $\psi\phi_i = \psi_1\phi_{i_1} + \psi_2\phi_{i_2} + \cdots + \psi_\kappa\phi_{i_\kappa}$, where $\phi_{i_1}, \phi_{i_2}, \cdots, \phi_{i_\kappa}$ are points of K_n lying in the subspaces $K_{n_1}, K_{n_2}, \cdots, K_{n_\kappa}$ such that their sum is equal to ϕ_i, i.e., the coordinates of these points that correspond to the given subspace K_{n_i} are the same as the corresponding coordinates of ϕ_i and their remaining coordinates are zero. Thus the product $O\phi_i$ is the direct sum of the lattices $O_1\phi_{i1}, O_2\phi_{i2}, \cdots, O_\kappa\phi_{i_\kappa}$ lying in these subspaces. Since the lattice j may be obtained by addition and subtraction of the points $\phi_1, \phi_2, \cdots, \phi_n$, we can obtain the product $O \cdot j$ if we take the sums and differences of all the points of the lattices $O\phi_1, O\phi_2, \cdots, O\phi_n$. But each of them is the direct sum of lattices lying in the subspaces $K_{n_1}, K_{n_2}, \cdots, K_{n_\kappa}$ and thus the product is also the direct sum of lattices lying in these subspaces. But O contains the point $(1, 1, \cdots, 1)$ and thus the product $O \cdot j$ is j; that is, j is the direct sum of lattices lying in the subspaces $K_{n_1}, K_{n_2}, \cdots, K_{n_\kappa}$.

For example, let $j = j_1 + j_2 + \cdots + j_K$ where $j_1, j_2, \cdots, j_K$ are these lattices. We then have $O_i \cdot j_i = j_i$, since $O_i \cdot j_i$ consists of points of $O \cdot j$, i.e., of points of j lying in the subspace K_{n_i}; all such points of j constitute the lattice j_i in K_{n_i} and hence all the points of $O_i \cdot j_i$ lie in j_i; but O_i contains the point $\overbrace{(1, 1, \ldots, 1)}^{n_i}$ and thus $O_i \cdot j_i$ coincides with j_i, i.e., j_i is an ideal of O_i.

3. THEOREM 2. *Every ideal of O is similar to some sublattice of the lattice O.*

Let ϕ be a point of the ideal j of the lattice O that is a generic point in K_n. Let us divide j by the point ϕ; we obtain the lattice $j' = j/\phi$ which contains the point $(1, 1, \cdots, 1)$. Since j is an ideal, j' is an ideal of O, and hence j' contains all the points of $j' \cdot O$, in particular all the points of $1 \cdot O$, i.e., j' is a centering of O. Multiplying j' by the common denominator Q of this centering, we obtain the lattice $j'' = j' \cdot Q$, which is a sublattice of O and to which j is similar. Thus, any ideal of O, even an irrational one, is an integer ideal of O multiplied by some point of K_n.

4. THEOREM 3. *The number h of the classes of ideals of a given maximal lattice O is finite.*

In view of the preceding theorem it is obvious that it is sufficient to prove the statement only for ideals that are sublattices of the lattice O, i.e., that are integer ideals of O. For brevity, we will call such ideals of the lattice O ideals in O. Let j be some ideal in O; then (Theorem 1) $j = j_1 + j_2 + \cdots + j_K$, where $j_1, j_2, \cdots, j_K$ are ideals in the irreducible parts $O_1, O_2, \cdots, O_K$. If V_j is the volume of the basic parallelepiped of j considered in the signature space $R_{n,\tau}$ corresponding to O, and $V_{j_1}, V_{j_2}, \cdots, V_{j_K}$ are the volumes of the basic parallelepipeds of the ideals $j_1, j_2, \cdots, j_K$ considered in the signature spaces $R_{n_1,\tau_1}, R_{n_2,\tau_2}, \cdots, R_{n_K,\tau_K}$ corresponding to the irreducible parts of O, then obviously $V_j = V_{j_1} \cdot V_{j_2} \cdot \cdots \cdot V_{j_K}$.

Let ψ_1 be a relative minimum of the lattice j_1 considered in the space R_{n_1,τ_1}, ψ_2 a relative minimum of the lattice j_2 considered in the space R_{n_2,τ_2}, and so on. Then the norm of ψ_1, by the lemma of Minkowski about a convex body, is not larger than $(2/\pi)^{\tau_1} V_{j_1}$, the norm of ψ_2 is not larger than

$(2/\pi)^{\tau_2} V_{j_2}$, and so on. Hence the norm of the point $\psi = \psi_1 + \psi_2 + \cdots + \psi_K$ (which lies in j and is not a zero-divisor) is not larger than $(2/\pi)^\tau V_j$. The lattice $\psi \cdot O$ is a sublattice of j, the volume of its basic parallelepiped being equal to $N_\psi \cdot V_O$ (where V_O is the volume of the basic parallelepiped of O), i.e., not larger than $(2/\pi)^\tau V_j \cdot V_O$, or in other words j/ψ is a centering of O with index not less than $[(2/\pi)^\tau \cdot V_O]^{-1}$. But there are only a finite number of different centerings with index greater than a given number, and hence our arbitrary ideal j in O is similar to one of the lattices in the finite set.

5. **Multiplication of ideals and composition of classes.** Let $\mathfrak{a}$ and $\mathfrak{b}$ be ideals of O; then they are similar to sublattices $\bar{\mathfrak{a}}$ and $\bar{\mathfrak{b}}$ of the lattice O since O is multiplicative and additive; the product of the lattices $\bar{\mathfrak{a}}$ and $\bar{\mathfrak{b}}$ will consist of points of O and thus will also be a sublattice $\bar{\mathfrak{c}}$ of the lattice O. The lattice is again an ideal in O, for if ω is any point of O, then $\omega\bar{\mathfrak{b}}$ are points in $\bar{\mathfrak{b}}$ since $\bar{\mathfrak{b}}$ is an ideal in O; thus $\bar{\mathfrak{a}} \cdot \bar{\mathfrak{b}}\omega$ consists of points of $\bar{\mathfrak{a}} \cdot \bar{\mathfrak{b}}$, i.e., of points of $\bar{\mathfrak{c}}$ and therefore multiplication of $\bar{\mathfrak{c}}$ by any point of O gives again a point of $\bar{\mathfrak{c}}$. Thus if we multiply the lattices $\mathfrak{a}$ and $\mathfrak{b}$, we obtain some lattice $\mathfrak{c}$ (similar to the ideal $\bar{\mathfrak{c}}$) which is hence also an ideal of O.

The ideal $\mathfrak{c}$ will be called the product of the ideals $\mathfrak{a}$ and $\mathfrak{b}$.

If one takes two different ideals $\mathfrak{a}^*$ and $\mathfrak{b}^*$ from the same classes as $\mathfrak{a}$ and $\mathfrak{b}$, i.e., so that $\mathfrak{a}^* = \mathfrak{a} \cdot \lambda$ and $\mathfrak{b}^* = \mathfrak{b} \cdot \mu$ where λ and μ are points of K_n that are not zero-divisors, then $\mathfrak{a}^* \cdot \mathfrak{b}^* = \mathfrak{c}^*$ where $\mathfrak{c}^* = \mathfrak{c} \cdot \lambda\mu$ so that $\mathfrak{c}^*$ is of the same class as $\mathfrak{c}$; thus the multiplication of ideals leads to the concept of the composition of classes.

We will call any lattices of K_n that are similar to lattices of ideals of O lattices of classes; then we have the following theorem.

THEOREM 4. *The product of two classes is a well-defined class.*

It is easy to see that multiplication of lattices is associative, from which follows:

THEOREM 5. *The composition of classes is associative.*

Let us multiply any ideal j of the lattice O by the lattice O, which is, as we have seen, also an ideal of O, namely a so-called unit ideal.

In view of the fact that j is an ideal of O, the multiplication of the points of O by the points of j gives only points of j, and since O contains the point $1 = (1, 1, \cdots, 1)$ we thus obtain all the points of j, so that we have $jO = j$, i.e., the following theorem.

THEOREM 6. *The principal class, i. e., the lattices similar to the lattice O (and thus to the lattices of any principal ideal), plays the role of a unit in the composition of classes.*

We will prove the following theorem.

THEOREM 7. *Any class of ideals of O has a reciprocal class, i. e., a class whose product by the given class yields the principal class.*

We will first show that the maximal lattice O is a unit ideal such that multiplication by it does not change the first factor. For the proof let

$$\mathfrak{a}\mathfrak{b} = \mathfrak{a}.$$

Let us consider the collection of all points of the space K_n such that multiplication by any one of them takes $\mathfrak{a}$ into itself. Such points are obviously additive, subtractive, and multiplicative and form a discrete set lying n-dimensionally in K_n, since all the points of the lattice O are part of the collection. It follows that this collection of points is a multiplicative lattice. In view of the fact that the collection contains all the points of O it must coincide with O since O is maximal. Since the ideal $\mathfrak{a}$ goes into itself under multiplication by any point of the ideal $\mathfrak{b}$, all the points of the ideal $\mathfrak{b}$ must be included in O, i.e., $\mathfrak{b}$ is an integer ideal.

We will now show that the ideal $\mathfrak{b}$ contains the point 1, for which it will obviously be necessary to show only that $\mathfrak{b} = O$, since we have already shown that $\mathfrak{b}$ is contained in O; but $\mathfrak{b}$, being an ideal of O, will contain, together with the point 1, all the points of O. Let us denote by $\alpha_1, \alpha_2, \cdots, \alpha_n$ a basis of the ideal $\mathfrak{a}$.

Each of the points of the basis of $\mathfrak{a}$ must belong to the lattice $\mathfrak{a}\mathfrak{b}$ and thus be a sum of product of points in $\mathfrak{a}$ and $\mathfrak{b}$; such a sum can obviously be written as $\beta_1\alpha_1 + \beta_2\alpha_2 + \cdots + \beta_n\alpha_n$, where $\alpha_1, \alpha_2, \cdots, \alpha_n$ are points of the basis of $\mathfrak{a}$ and $\beta_1, \beta_2, \cdots, \beta_n$ are points of $\mathfrak{b}$.

Applying this argument to the points of the basis of $\mathfrak{a}$, we get:

$$\begin{aligned} \alpha_1 &= \beta_{11}\alpha_1 + \beta_{12}\alpha_2 + \ldots + \beta_{1n}\alpha_n, \\ \alpha_2 &= \beta_{21}\alpha_1 + \beta_{22}\alpha_2 + \ldots + \beta_{2n}\alpha_n, \\ &\ldots\ldots\ldots\ldots\ldots \\ \alpha_n &= \beta_{n1}\alpha_1 + \beta_{n2}\alpha_2 + \ldots + \beta_{nn}\alpha_n, \end{aligned}$$

from which we see that

$$\begin{vmatrix} \beta_{11}-1, & \beta_{12}, & \ldots, & \beta_{1n} \\ \beta_{21}, & \beta_{22}-1, & \ldots, & \beta_{2n} \\ \cdot & \cdot & \cdot & \cdot \\ \beta_{n1}, & \beta_{n2}, & \ldots, & \beta_{nn}-1 \end{vmatrix} = 0.$$

From this equation we conclude that the point 1 is obtained as the result of the operations of multiplication, addition, and subtraction on the points of the ideal $\mathfrak{b}$, and thus is included in $\mathfrak{b}$. Hence $\mathfrak{b} = O$.

Now let $\mathfrak{c}$ be an ideal of some class. In view of the fact that the number h of the number of classes is finite, among the powers of the ideal $\mathfrak{c}$ with positive exponents, there will be infinitely many belonging to the same class. Let $\mathfrak{c}^m$ and $\mathfrak{c}^{m+k}$ belong to the same class, and let γ be a point of K_n such that $\gamma \cdot \mathfrak{c}^m = \mathfrak{c}^{m+k}$. Let us consider the ideal $\mathfrak{b} = \mathfrak{c}^k/\gamma$. It is obvious that

$$\mathfrak{c}^m \mathfrak{b} = \frac{1}{\gamma} \mathfrak{c}^{m+k} = \mathfrak{c}^m .$$

From this it follows that $\mathfrak{b} = O$ and hence $\mathfrak{c}^k = \gamma O$ lies in the principal class. Obviously $\mathfrak{c}^{k-1}$ belongs to the reciprocal class of the class containing $\mathfrak{c}$, for

$$\mathfrak{c}^{k-1} \cdot \mathfrak{c} = \mathfrak{c}^k = \gamma O .$$

Theorems 4, 5, 6, and 7 show that the lattices of classes form a group under composition. In consequence of the theorem about the finiteness of the number h of classes, this group is finite, and since the commutativity of the multiplication of ideals follows directly by definition, the group is abelian. Thus we have the following theorem:

THEOREM 8. *The lattices of classes form a finite abelian group under consideration.*

Begining with subsection 6, the present section will deal only with ideals in O.

6. THEOREM 9. *Every divisor is a centering ideal and conversely.*

Let the ideal $\mathfrak{a}$ be the product of the ideals $\mathfrak{m}$ and $\mathfrak{t}$; then, as we have seen in the proof of the previous theorem, any point of $\mathfrak{a}$ may be expressed linearly in terms of the basis of $\mathfrak{t}$ with coefficients which are points of $\mathfrak{m}$, i.e., in view of the fact that $\mathfrak{t}$ is an ideal in O, the lattice $\mathfrak{a}$ is a sublattice of the lattice $\mathfrak{t}$ and it follows that $\mathfrak{t}$ is a centering of $\mathfrak{a}$.

Let us assume conversely that the ideal $\mathfrak{t}$ is a centering of the ideal $\mathfrak{a}$, and let $\mathfrak{t}^*$ be some ideal of the class that is reciprocal to the class of the ideal of $\mathfrak{t}$ and such that $\mathfrak{t}\mathfrak{t}^* = \tau O$, where τ is some point of O. In such a case the ideal $\tau O = \mathfrak{t} \cdot \mathfrak{t}^*$ is a centering of the ideal $\mathfrak{a}\mathfrak{t}^*$, since from the fact that each point α of the ideal $\mathfrak{a}$ is simultaneously a point of the ideal $\mathfrak{t}$ it follows that all the points $\alpha_i \cdot t_k^*$, where the α_i are points of the basis of $\mathfrak{a}$ and the t_k^* are points of the basis of $\mathfrak{t}^*$, are points of the ideal $\mathfrak{t}\mathfrak{t}^*$, and thus any sum or difference of such points is also a point of the ideal $\mathfrak{t} \cdot \mathfrak{t}^*$. Hence all the points of the ideal $\mathfrak{a} \cdot \mathfrak{t}^*$ are included among the points of the ideal $\mathfrak{t} \cdot \mathfrak{t}^* = \tau O$, and it follows that $\mathfrak{a} \cdot \mathfrak{t}^* = \tau \mathfrak{m}$, where $\mathfrak{m}$ is some lattice of O which is an ideal in O since it is similar to the ideal $\mathfrak{a}\mathfrak{t}^*$.

If we multiply both parts of the last equality by the ideal $\mathfrak{t}$, we obtain $\mathfrak{a}\mathfrak{t}^*\mathfrak{t} = \mathfrak{t}\mathfrak{m}\mathfrak{t}$ or, since $\mathfrak{t}^*\mathfrak{t} = \tau O$ and $\mathfrak{a}O = \mathfrak{a}$, we get $\mathfrak{a}\tau = \tau\mathfrak{m}\mathfrak{t}$, and dividing both lattices by τ we finially have $\mathfrak{a} = \mathfrak{m}\mathfrak{t}$.

7. Finiteness of the number of divisors of an ideal; prime ideals.

THEOREM 10. *The number of different divisors of a given ideal is finite.*

Since there are only finitely many centerings of any given sublattice of O that are composed only of points of O, it follows from the preceding theorem that there are also only finitely many distinct lattices which are lattices of ideals of divisors of a given ideal.

Let some given ideal in O be different from O and not have proper divisors, i.e., divisors different from itself and the unit ideal O; we call such an ideal prime; if an ideal has such divisors it is said to be not prime.

Let us consider an arbitrary ideal in O. If it is not prime, it has a proper divisor. Let us consider this divisor; if it is not prime, it has in turn a proper divisor, and so on. We thus obtain a chain of ideals that form a chain of successive centerings of the initial ideal, each consisting of points of O and such that the volume of the basic parallelepipeds is continually decreasing. Since the number of such different centerings is finite, the chain must break off; i.e., eventually one of the successive ideals will not contain proper divisors and will be prime. Dividing this prime ideal factor out of the given ideal, we obtain an ideal which is also a centering of the given ideal, i.e., has a basic parallelepiped of smaller volume than that of the given ideal. We can perform the same process with this ideal, and the remaining factor will have an even smaller volume. In view of the finiteness of the number of different centerings of a given sublattice of

O consisting of points of O, we may thus divide out prime factors only a finite number of times, and the initial ideal is obviously their product. Hence any ideal is the product of a finite number of prime ideals.

8. The uniqueness of the decomposition of an ideal into prime ideals.

THEOREM 12. *If the ideals* $\mathfrak{a}$ *and* $\mathfrak{b}$ *do not have a common divisor other than* O, *then there exists a point* α *in* $\mathfrak{a}$ *and a point* β *in* $\mathfrak{b}$ *such that* $\alpha + \beta = 1$.

Let $\alpha_1, \alpha_2, \cdots, \alpha_n$ be the basis of the ideal $\mathfrak{a}$, and $\beta_1, \beta_2, \cdots, \beta_n$ be the basis of the ideal $\mathfrak{b}$. Let us form the collection of points $\lambda_1\alpha_1 + \lambda_2\alpha_2 + \cdots + \lambda_n\alpha_n + \mu_1\beta_1 + \mu_2\beta_2 + \cdots + \mu_n\beta_n$, where λ_i and μ_i are arbitrary points of O. Obviously this will be an n-dimensional lattice in O such that the product of any of its points by a point ω of O will be again one of its points, i.e., it is an ideal in O. Since O contains the point 1, this lattice must contain all the points $\alpha_1, \alpha_2, \cdots, \alpha_n$, and all the points $\beta_1, \beta_2, \cdots, \beta_n$, i.e., the whole lattice $\mathfrak{a}$ and the whole lattice $\mathfrak{b}$. This ideal is thus both a centering of $\mathfrak{a}$ and a centering of $\mathfrak{b}$.

Let us now assume that the ideals $\mathfrak{a}$ and $\mathfrak{b}$ are relatively prime, i.e., that they have no common divisor other than O. Then the above ideal is O. But in that case the point 1 also has such a form, i.e., $1 = \alpha + \beta$, where α and β are certain points of the ideals $\mathfrak{a}$ and $\mathfrak{b}$.

THEOREM 13. *If the product of two ideals is divisible by a prime ideal* $\mathfrak{p}$, *then at least one of the factors is divisible by* $\mathfrak{p}$.

Let the product of two ideals $\mathfrak{a} \cdot \mathfrak{b}$ be divisible by the prime ideal $\mathfrak{p}$. Let us assume that $\mathfrak{a}$ is not divisible by $\mathfrak{p}$, or in other words, that $\mathfrak{a}$ and $\mathfrak{p}$ are relatively prime, since $\mathfrak{p}$ has no divisors other than O and itself. In such a case, there is a point α and $\mathfrak{a}$ and a point π in $\mathfrak{p}$ such that $\alpha + \pi = 1$. If β is any point of $\mathfrak{b}$, then the point $\alpha \cdot \beta$ is included in $\mathfrak{a} \cdot \mathfrak{b}$ and since $\mathfrak{p}$, being a divisor of $\mathfrak{a} \cdot \mathfrak{b}$, is a centering of $\mathfrak{a} \cdot \mathfrak{b}$, the point $\alpha \cdot \beta$ is also included in $\mathfrak{p}$. But since $\mathfrak{p}$ is an ideal, the point $\pi \cdot \beta$ is included in $\mathfrak{p}$. Then the point $\alpha \cdot \beta + \pi \cdot \beta$ is also included in $\mathfrak{p}$, and since $\alpha\beta + \pi\beta = (\alpha + \pi)\beta = \beta$, we see that any point of $\mathfrak{b}$, and thus the whole lattice $\mathfrak{b}$, is included in the lattice $\mathfrak{p}$, i.e., $\mathfrak{p}$ is a centering, and hence, by Theorem 9, is a divisor of the ideal $\mathfrak{b}$. Thus if the product of the two ideals is divisible by the ideal $\mathfrak{p}$, then at least one of the factors is itself divisible by the prime ideal.

THEOREM 14. *Any ideal decomposes into prime factors in only one way.*

Let us assume to the contrary that some ideal has two decompositions into prime factors: $\mathfrak{a} = \mathfrak{p}_1\mathfrak{p}_2 \cdots \mathfrak{p}_k = \mathfrak{q}_1\mathfrak{q}_2 \cdots \mathfrak{q}_l$. Only one of the $\mathfrak{q}$ can be divisible by $\mathfrak{p}_1$, and since all the $\mathfrak{q}$ are prime, it must coincide with $\mathfrak{p}_1$. Moreover, at least one of the $\mathfrak{q}$ must be divisible by $\mathfrak{p}_1$, for otherwise, in view of the preceding theorem, the whole product $\mathfrak{a} = \mathfrak{q}_1\mathfrak{q}_2 \cdots \mathfrak{q}_l$ then could not be divisible by $\mathfrak{p}_1$, which it is by assumption. Let us choose an enumeration of the factors $\mathfrak{q}$ such that $\mathfrak{q}_1 = \mathfrak{p}_1$; in that case the ideals $\mathfrak{p}_2 \cdots \mathfrak{p}_k$ and $\mathfrak{q}_2 \cdots \mathfrak{q}_l$ are the same, since whenever $\mathfrak{b}\mathfrak{c} = \mathfrak{b}\mathfrak{d}$ it follows that $\mathfrak{c} = \mathfrak{d}$, as we will now show.

Let us multiply both sides of the equation by an ideal $\mathfrak{b}^*$ belonging to the class that is reciprocal to the class of $\mathfrak{b}$. Then $\mathfrak{b}\mathfrak{b}^* = \tau O$, where τ is a point of O; thus we obtain $\tau O\mathfrak{c} = \tau O\mathfrak{d}$ or, dividing both lattices by τ, we have $O\mathfrak{c} = O\mathfrak{d}$. But $O\mathfrak{c} = \mathfrak{c}$ and $O\mathfrak{d} = \mathfrak{d}$ so $\mathfrak{c} = \mathfrak{d}$.

Repeating the same argument with the products $\mathfrak{p}_2 \cdots \mathfrak{p}_k$ and $\mathfrak{q}_2 \cdots \mathfrak{q}_l$ and assuming $k \le l$, we obtain $O = \mathfrak{q}_{k+1} \cdots \mathfrak{q}_l$, i.e., that $l = k$ and that if the original products differ, they differ only in the order of the factors.

9. THEOREM 15. *In any two classes of ideals there exist integer relatively prime ideals.*

Proof. Let the two classes K_1 and K_2 be given. Let us select an arbitrary integer ideal $\mathfrak{a}$ from the class K_1 and an arbitrary integer ideal $\mathfrak{b}$ from the class K_2^{-1}. Let $\mathfrak{v}_1, \mathfrak{v}_2, \cdots, \mathfrak{v}_k$ be all the different prime ideals included in $\mathfrak{a}$. Let π_1 be a point in the ideal $\mathfrak{b}\mathfrak{v}_2\mathfrak{v}_3 \cdots \mathfrak{v}_k$ which is not in the ideal $\mathfrak{b}\mathfrak{v}_1$. Such a point exists, since otherwise the ideal $\mathfrak{b}\mathfrak{v}_2\mathfrak{v}_3 \cdots \mathfrak{v}_k$ would be contained in the ideal $\mathfrak{b}\mathfrak{v}_1$ and thus be divisible by it, in which case the ideal $\mathfrak{v}_2\mathfrak{v}_3 \cdots \mathfrak{v}_k$ would be divisible by $\mathfrak{v}_1$, which is impossible. In the same way we find a point π_2 belonging to the ideal $\mathfrak{b}\mathfrak{v}_1\mathfrak{v}_3 \cdots \mathfrak{v}_k$ and not belonging to $\mathfrak{b}\mathfrak{v}_2$, and so on.

The point $\beta = \pi_1 + \pi_2 + \cdots + \pi_k$ will obviously belong to the ideal $\mathfrak{b}$, but not belong to any of the ideals $\mathfrak{b}\mathfrak{v}_1, \mathfrak{b}\mathfrak{v}_2, \cdots, \mathfrak{b}\mathfrak{v}_k$. Since β belongs to $\mathfrak{b}$, the ideal $\mathfrak{c} = \beta\mathfrak{b}^{-1}$ will be an integer ideal and will not be divisible by any of the ideals $\mathfrak{v}_1, \mathfrak{v}_2, \cdots, \mathfrak{v}_k$, i.e., it will be relatively prime to $\mathfrak{a}$. The ideal $\mathfrak{c}$ belongs to the class K_2. Thus, in any two classes K_1 and K_2, we can find relatively prime ideals. With this the theorem is proved in full.

We will note one corollary of the above theorem. *Any integer ideal is the greatest common divisor of two principal ideals.* To show this, let $\mathfrak{a}$ be an ideal of some class K. Let α be an arbitrary point in this ideal. Then the ideal $[\alpha]$ will be divisible by $\mathfrak{a}$, i.e., $[\alpha] = \mathfrak{a}\mathfrak{b}$. Let $\mathfrak{c}$ be an ideal in the class K^{-1} that is relatively prime to $\mathfrak{b}$. The ideal $\mathfrak{a}\mathfrak{c}$ will be principal, $\mathfrak{a}\mathfrak{c} = [\beta]$, and the greatest common divisor of the ideals $[\alpha]$ and $[\beta]$ will be $\mathfrak{a}$, since the ideals $\mathfrak{b}$ and $\mathfrak{c}$ are relatively prime.

10. A theorem on norms of ideals. The index of a lattice of an integer ideal with respect to the lattice O (i.e., the number of multiples of the volume of the basic parallelepiped of the lattice in the volume of the basic parallelepiped of the lattice of the ideal) is called the *norm* of the ideal. Since the lattice of any ideal in O is a sublattice of the lattice O, the norm of any ideal is a positive rational integer.

THEOREM 16. *The norm of the product of two ideals is equal to the product of the norms of the factors.*

We first note that it is sufficient to prove this theorem for any pair of representatives of two given classes in order to see that it is valid for all pairs of ideals from these classes.

To see this, assume the theorem valid for the ideals $\mathfrak{a}$ and $\mathfrak{b}$, and let $\mathfrak{a}_1$ and $\mathfrak{b}_1$ be ideals equivalent, respectively, to the ideals $\mathfrak{a}$ and $\mathfrak{b}$. Since the lattices of the ideals $\mathfrak{a}$ and $\mathfrak{a}_1$, and of $\mathfrak{b}$ and $\mathfrak{b}_1$ are similar we can write $\mathfrak{a}_1 = \alpha\,\mathfrak{a}$, $\mathfrak{b}_1 = \beta\,\mathfrak{b}$ where α and β are points of K_n. Hence $\mathfrak{a}_1\mathfrak{b}_1 = \alpha\beta\,\mathfrak{a}\mathfrak{b}$.

It is also obvious that after multiplication by some point of K_n the norm of an ideal increases by a factor equal to the absolute value of the norm of the point by which it is multiplied, for it varies as the volume of the basic parallelepiped of the lattice. Hence,

$$N(\mathfrak{a}_1\mathfrak{b}_1) = |N(\alpha\beta)|\,N(\mathfrak{a}\mathfrak{b}) = |N(\alpha)|\cdot|N(\beta)|\cdot N(\mathfrak{a})\,N(\mathfrak{b}) =$$
$$= |N(\alpha)|\,N(\mathfrak{a})\cdot|N(\beta)|\,N(\mathfrak{b}) = N(\mathfrak{a}_1)\,N(\mathfrak{b}).$$

From this remark the validity of the theorem already follows in the case where one of the ideals is principal, since it holds when one of the factors is the unit ideal O.

On the basis of Theorem 15, the proof of the theorem in general is reduced to the case of relatively prime ideals, for it is possible to find relatively prime representatives in any two classes.

We will now prove the theorem for two relative prime ideals $\mathfrak{a}$ and $\mathfrak{b}$. Their sum $(\mathfrak{a}, \mathfrak{b})$ is equal to O. It is easy to see that their product is equal to their intersection. This is because each point of the product of the ideals $\mathfrak{a}$ and $\mathfrak{b}$ lies in both of them and is thus in their intersection. Conversely, let γ be a point belonging to the intersection of the ideals $\mathfrak{a}$ and $\mathfrak{b}$. Since $\mathfrak{a}$ and $\mathfrak{b}$ are relatively prime, there exists a point α in $\mathfrak{a}$ and a point β in $\mathfrak{b}$ such that $\alpha + \beta = 1$.

Hence $\gamma = \alpha\gamma + \beta\gamma$. The point $\alpha\gamma$ belongs to the ideal $\mathfrak{a}\mathfrak{b}$, since α belongs to $\mathfrak{a}$ and γ belongs to $\mathfrak{b}$. The point $\beta\gamma$ also belongs to $\mathfrak{a}\mathfrak{b}$, since β belongs to $\mathfrak{b}$ and γ belongs to $\mathfrak{a}$. Thus γ belongs to $\mathfrak{a}\mathfrak{b}$. Applying Lemma 4 of the Supplement to the lattices O, $\mathfrak{a}$, $\mathfrak{b}$, and $\mathfrak{a}\mathfrak{b}$, we obtain:

$$\frac{N(\mathfrak{a}\mathfrak{b})}{N(\mathfrak{a})} = \frac{N(\mathfrak{b})}{N(O)},$$

and it follows that $N(\mathfrak{a}\mathfrak{b}) = N(\mathfrak{a})\,N(\mathfrak{b})$.

The theorem is now completely proved.

§6. A BASIC FIGURE CONSISTING OF THE PRINCIPAL LATTICE O AND $h-1$ AUXILIARY LATTICES

Let us choose one ideal from each of the h classes. Let us take the ideal O from the principal class, and let us normalize the ideals of the remaining $h-1$ classes by multiplication with points of K_n that are not zero-divisors so that the volume of each of the lattices thus obtained will be made the same as the volume V_O of the lattice O.

After this normalization, these $h-1$ lattices will in general no longer be sublattices of O.

Let $g_1 = O,\ g_2, g_3, \cdots, g_h$ be the lattices obtained in this way. We will show that the multiplication of two such lattices g_i, g_k will give a lattice $\bar{g}_l$ with the same volume.

For the proof, let $\lambda g_i = j_i$ and $\mu g_k = j_k$, where j_i and j_k are those ideals in O from which we obtain the lattices g_i and g_k, and the points λ and μ are the points reciprocal to those factors which were used to normalize the ideals to obtain the lattices. In this case $N(\lambda)$ and $N(\mu)$ are the norms of the ideals j_i and j_k. But $N(j_i j_k) = N(j_i)\,N(j_k) = N(\lambda)\,N(\mu) = N(\lambda\mu)$, and hence $\bar{g}_l$ has the same volume V_O as g_i and g_k. These normalized lattices of classes $g_1, g_2, \cdots, g_h$ form, under composition, a group of classes which, up to multiples of the points of K_n have norm 1. We will say that such multiples are *rotating factors.*

We will now normalize our lattice further, namely by multiplication with certain rotating factors chosen in a specific manner. After this second normalization the $h-1$ lattices will in general no longer lie in the same signature space of K_n as O does; for example, O may be purely real, while the coordinate of these lattices may become complex. We proceed as follows: we leave $g_1 = O$ unchanged; each of the remaining g_i which are elements of a basis for the abelian group of classes will be multiplied by a factor e_i such that, if the order of g_i is q (g_i^q is a lattice similar to g_1), after multiplication the qth power of the product will coincide with g_1, i.e., such that $(g_i e_i)^q = g_1$. If λ_i is a point in K_n by which it is necessary to multiply g_i^q in order to obtain g_1, then it is obviously necessary and sufficient that $e_i^q = \lambda_i$, i.e., that $e_i = \sqrt[q]{\lambda_i}$. In general, the point e_i may not lie in the signature space corresponding to O. For example, when all the coordinates of O are real, it may occur (as is shown by examples) that not all the coordinates of the points are positive, and moreover when q is even (which also occurs) not all the coordinates e_i will be real.

After such an additional normalization of the lattices g_i that form a basis of the group of classes, that is, after the replacement of them by the lattices $e_i g_i$, they are already so "rotated" in the space K_n that corresponding powers of them will not only be similar to the lattice $g_1 = O$ of the principal class, but will coincide with it. If we now express the remaining g_i in terms of the basic g_i, then all the g_i thus obtained will already be properly oriented in the sense that if $g_i g_k$ is similar to g_l, then it coincides with it, i.e., $g_i g_k = g_l$. The collection of all these h *properly* oriented lattices g_i will be called a *basic figure* corresponding to the given maximal multiplicative lattice O.

From the construction of a basic figure we see that we can construct it in more than one way for a given O. Let us see how the basic figures obtained in different ways differ from one another. In the first place, if λ_i is a point that, when multiplied by g_i^q, gives $g_1 = O$, then $\lambda_i \cdot \epsilon$, where ϵ is any automorphism of O, is also such a point; conversely, if $\bar{\lambda}_i$ is another such point and $\bar{\lambda}_i = \lambda_i \cdot \bar{\epsilon}$, then $\bar{\epsilon}$ is an automorphism of O. Thus the general form of the points by which it is necessary to multiply g_i^q in order to obtain g_1 is $\lambda_i \cdot \epsilon$ where ϵ is any automorphism of O. From this we see that if there are infinitely many automorphisms of O, then $e_i = \sqrt[q]{\lambda_i \epsilon}$ has infinitely many values. But two different e_i and $\bar{e}_i$ which differ only by a multiplicative automorphism of O will give the same lattice with a given g_i; for if $\bar{e}_i = e_i \cdot \epsilon$, then $g_i \bar{e}_i = g_i e_i \epsilon$.

It is easy to see this latter fact if we note that $g_i = j_i \cdot \mu_i$, where μ_i is some point of K_n; then $g_i e_i = j_i \mu_i e_i$, and $g_i e_i \epsilon = j_i \mu_i e_i \epsilon$. But $j_i \epsilon = j_i$, since multiplication of any point of an ideal by a point ϵ from O will yield another point in the ideal (since the norm of ϵ is equal to ± 1 we obtain all the points of the ideal). Thus different completely normalized lattices g_i will be obtained from a preliminarily normalized lattice g_i only by means of factors that do not differ simply by a multiplicative automorphism of the lattice O. Thus, if $\epsilon_1, \epsilon_2, \cdots, \epsilon_{\sigma+\tau-\kappa}$ are the basic multiplicative automorphisms of the lattice O, then it is sufficient to take for a factor ϵ under the radical in e_i only factors of the form $E_1 E_2 \cdots E_\varkappa \varepsilon_1^{q_1} \varepsilon_2^{q_2} \cdots \varepsilon_{\sigma+\tau-\varkappa}^{q_{\sigma+\tau-\varkappa}}$, where all the powers $q_1, q_2, \cdots, q_{\sigma+\tau-\kappa}$ are greater than or equal to zero and less than q, and the E_i are the different automorphisms of finite order discussed in §4. Moreover, it is possible to choose any of the values of the radical $\sqrt[q]{\ }$.

Let us consider any one member of the finite set of different possible basic figures for the given maximal multiplicative lattice O.

THEOREM 1. *A basic figure is multiplicative.*

This is true, for if θ_i is a point belonging to the lattice g_i of the basic figure, and θ_j belongs to its lattice g_j (where j may be equal to i) and $g_i g_j = g_k$, then the point $\theta_i \theta_j = \theta_k$ belongs to the lattice g_k.

REMARK. It is easy to show by examples that if $h > 1$ (if $h = 1$, the basic figure is O itself), the basic figure is not a lattice, i.e., it is not additive.

THEOREM 2. *The absolute value of the norm of any point of a basic figure is a rational integer.*

If a point of the lattice is a zero-divisor its norm is zero, and conversely. Now let θ be a point of the lattice g_i that is not a zero-divisor. Multiplying this point by all the points of the lattice g_i^{-1} that corresponds to the class reciprocal to g_i, we obtain some sublattice of the lattice $g_1 = O$. Hence the volume of the basic parallelepiped of the lattice g_i^{-1}, which is equal to the volume of the basic parallelepiped of $g_1 = O$, increases by an integer factor. But under multiplication by a point the volume of a basic parallelepiped of a lattice increases by a factor that is equal to the absolute value of the norm of this point, i.e., the absolute value of the norm of the point is a rational integer.

THEOREM 3. *Any multiplicative automorphism ϵ of the whole basic figure is an automorphism of any of its lattices and hence is an automorphism of the principal lattice. The converse holds.*

If ϵ is a multiplicative automorphism of $g_1 = O$, then the ϵg_k are the points g_k, since ϵ belongs to the principal lattice. But its norm is ± 1 and hence the volume of the basic parallelepiped of $\epsilon \cdot g_k$ is equal to the volume of the basic parallepiped of g_k, i.e., $\epsilon g_k = g_k$. Hence any multiplicative automorphism ϵ of the principal lattice is a multiplicative automorphism of the collection of all h lattices $g_1, g_2, \cdots, g_h$, and is even a multiplicative automorphism of each of them separately. Conversely, if ϵ is a multiplicative automorphism of the set of all h lattices $g_1, g_2, \cdots, g_h$, then the absolute value of its norm is 1. The point ϵ is a point of a basic figure, since the point 1 is in a basic figure, and $\epsilon \cdot 1$ must be a point of a basic figure. The point ϵ lies in the principal lattice, for if it lay in an auxiliary lattice g_k, then the lattice $g_k^{-1} \cdot \epsilon$ would consist of points of the principal lattice g_1 and would coincide with it, since the volumes of the lattices g_k^{-1} and g_1 are the same and the absolute value of the norm of the point ϵ is 1; but an auxiliary lattice cannot be similar to the principal lattice. Thus any automorphism ϵ of the basic figure is a point of the principal lattice with norm ± 1, i.e., is an automorphism of the principal lattice.

We will say that two points of a basic figure are associated if they can be obtained from each other by multiplicative automorphisms of the basic figure, i.e., by multiplicative automorphisms of the lattice O. The collection of all points of the basic figure associated with a certain one of its points that is not a zero-divisor will be called a *net of associated points*. Obviously, all points of a net of points associated to some point in the basic figure that belongs to its lattice g_i will also belong to the same lattice g_i, since all the automorphisms ϵ belong to the principal lattice.

THEOREM 4. *Any point θ of the basic figure that is not a zero-divisor (together with all the points of the net of points associated with the point θ) corresponds uniquely to some ideal of the lattice O, and conversely; moreover, the product of two such points will correspond to the product of the corresponding ideals, and conversely.*

Let θ_i be some point of the lattice g_i. The lattice $\mathfrak{a}_i = g_i^{-1}\theta_i$ lies in $g_1 = O$ and is an ideal of O. Let ω be some point of O. Then the points $g_i^{-1}\theta_i\omega$ are again points of O and lie in the same lattice $\mathfrak{a}_i$; for, when we multiply by ω that ideal of O which was used in the normalization to get the lattice g_i^{-1}, we get points of the same ideal, and thus when we multiply the lattice g_i^{-1} by ω we obtain points of the same lattice, and consequently, when we multiply the lattice $\mathfrak{a}_i = g_i^{-1}\theta_i$ by ω, we will get points of the same lattice $\mathfrak{a}_i$. We will say that the ideal $\mathfrak{a}_i$ corresponds to the point θ_i of the basic figure. Obviously, any point $\theta_i\epsilon$, where ϵ is any automorphism of O (and thus of the basic figure), corresponds to the same ideal $\mathfrak{a}_i$; for ϵ is an automorphism of the ideal in O used in the normalization to get g_i^{-1}. Thus ϵ is also an automorphism of g_i^{-1}, i.e., $g_i^{-1}\epsilon\theta_i = g_i^{-1}\theta_i$. Conversely, if $\mathfrak{a}$ is an ideal of the ith class of the lattice O, $\mathfrak{a}$ thus being $g_i^{-1}\mu$, where μ is some point of K_n that is not a zero-divisor, then $\mathfrak{a}g_i = g_1\mu$, and since $g_1 = O$ contains the point 1, the point μ is in $\mathfrak{a}g_i$, i.e., μ is in g_i.

The product of the points $\theta_i\theta_j\cdots\theta_k$ of a basic figure lying in the ith, jth, $\cdots$, kth lattices g, where $i, j, \cdots, k$ may be either equal or distinct, obviously corresponds in the above sense to the ideal $\mathfrak{a} = g_i^{-1}\theta_i \cdot g_j^{-1}\theta_j \cdots g_k^{-1}\theta_k$, i.e., the ideal $g_e^{-1}\cdot\theta_i\theta_j\cdots\theta_k$.

THEOREM 5. *In any class of ideals in O there exists an ideal whose norm is* $<(2/\pi)^\tau\sqrt{|D|}$.

Any auxiliary lattice g of the principal lattice $g_1 = O$ is obtained from some ideal j in O by multiplication by some normalizing point whose norm is equal in absolute value to $1/N(j)$. Let $\bar{O}$ be the lattice in $R_{n,\tau}$ corresponding to O, and let $\bar{j}$ be the ideal in $\bar{O}$ corresponding to j. As we have shown in subsection 4 of §5, there exist in $\bar{j}$ points $\bar{\omega}$ that are not zero-divisors, and are relative minima in $\bar{j}$, in the sense that inside the normed body of such a point $\bar{\omega}$ there are no points of $\bar{j}$ other than the point O. The volume of the normed body of such a point is $2^\sigma\pi^\tau N(\omega)$ and is in this case, by the Minkowski lemma on convex bodies, less than the volume $(\sqrt{|D|}/2^\tau)N(j)$ of the basic paralellepiped of $\bar{j}$ taken 2^n times, i.e., $N(\omega) < (2/\pi)^\tau\sqrt{|D|}N(j)$. After the normalization of the ideal j into the corresponding auxiliary lattice g, we see that there is a point $\bar{\bar{\omega}}$ in g with norm $N(\bar{\bar{\omega}}) < (2/\pi)^\tau\sqrt{|D|}$. If we multiply the auxiliary lattice g^{-1} by the point $\bar{\bar{\omega}}$, then by the preceding theorem we obtain an ideal in O with norm equal to $N(\bar{\bar{\omega}})$, i.e., its norm is $<(2/\pi)^\tau\sqrt{|D|}$.

For the irreducible lattices of the chain given in Theorem 5, there is the further refinement, given in the following theorem.

THEOREM 6. *In any class of ideals in an irreducible lattice, there is an ideal whose norm is less than*

$$\frac{n!}{n^n}\left(\frac{4}{\pi}\right)^\tau\sqrt{|D|}.$$

PROOF. Let K be some class of ideals, and K^{-1} its reciprocal class. Let $\mathfrak{a}$ be some ideal from the class K^{-1}. The ideal $\mathfrak{a}$ is a lattice in the space $R_{n,\tau}$ whose basic parallelepiped has volume $(1/2^{\tau})\sqrt{|D|}\,N(\mathfrak{a})$.

Let us consider the body

$$|x^{(1)}|+|x^{(2)}|+\ldots+|x^{(\sigma)}|+2\sqrt{\xi^{(1)2}+\eta^{(1)2}}+\ldots+2\sqrt{\xi^{(\tau)2}+\eta^{(\tau)2}}\leqslant T.$$

It is easy to see that this body is convex and has the origin as center of symmetry. Its volume is

$$2^{\sigma}\left(\frac{\pi}{2}\right)^{\tau}\cdot\frac{1}{n!}T^{n}.$$

Let us choose T so that the volume will be equal to the volume of the basic parallelepiped of the ideal $\mathfrak{a}$ multiplied by 2^{n}.

$$2^{\sigma}\left(\frac{\pi}{2}\right)^{\tau}\cdot\frac{1}{n!}T^{n}=2^{n}\cdot\frac{1}{2^{\tau}}\sqrt{|D|}\,N(\mathfrak{a}).$$

Then by Lemma 5 of the Supplement there exists, either inside or on the surface of the body, at least one nonzero point α of the ideal $\mathfrak{a}$. Since the lattice $\mathfrak{a}$ does not have zero-divisors, $N(\alpha)\neq 0$. The geometric mean of positive numbers is less than or equal to their arithmetic mean. Thus

$$N(\alpha)=|x^{(1)}|\cdot|x^{(2)}|\cdot\ldots\cdot|x^{(\sigma)}|\cdot(\sqrt{\xi^{(1)2}+\eta^{(1)2}})^{2}\cdot\ldots\cdot(\sqrt{\xi^{(\tau)2}+\eta^{(1)2}})^{2}\leqslant$$
$$\leqslant\left(\frac{|x^{(1)}|+|x^{(2)}|+\ldots+|x^{(\sigma)}|+2\sqrt{\xi^{(1)2}+\eta^{(1)2}}+\ldots+2\sqrt{\xi^{(\tau)2}+\eta^{(\tau)2}}}{n}\right)^{n}\leqslant$$
$$\leqslant\frac{T^{n}}{n^{n}}=\frac{2^{n-\sigma}}{\pi^{\tau}}\cdot\frac{n!}{n^{n}}\sqrt{|D|}\,N(\mathfrak{a})=\left(\frac{4}{\pi}\right)^{\tau}\frac{n!}{n^{n}}\sqrt{|D|}\,N(\mathfrak{a}).$$

The principal ideal $[\alpha]$ is divisible by the ideal $\mathfrak{a}$, $[\alpha]=\mathfrak{a}\mathfrak{b}$. The quotient $\mathfrak{b}$ is an integer ideal from the class K. From the fact that $|N(\alpha)|=N(\mathfrak{a})\cdot N(\mathfrak{b})$ we conclude

$$N(\mathfrak{b})\leqslant\left(\frac{4}{\pi}\right)^{\tau}\frac{n!}{n^{n}}\sqrt{|D|},$$

which is what we wanted to show.

From the proof of the theorem it follows that

$$\left(\frac{4}{\pi}\right)^{\tau}\frac{n!}{n^{n}}\sqrt{|D|}\geqslant 1,$$

since $N(\mathfrak{b})\geq 1$, and thus

$$\sqrt{|D|} \geqslant \frac{n^n}{n!} \cdot \left(\frac{\pi}{4}\right)^{\tau}.$$

This inequality shows, in the first place, that $\sqrt{|D|} > 1$, and secondly, that the smallest discriminant of an irreducible multiplicative lattice of a given number of dimensions increases with the growth of the number of dimensions n.

THEOREM 7. *Any point of a basic figure decomposes uniquely (up to automorphisms of* O*) into a product of its prime points.*

For points that are not zero-divisors this theorem follows directly from the uniqueness of the decomposition of ideals of O into prime ideals and from Theorem 5. We can obtain the same result for a zero-divisor by considering, instead of O, the partial direct sum of the irreducible part of O corresponding to this zero-divisor, i.e., that sum which lies in the same coordinate space as the given zero-divisor.

§7. QUADRATIC FORMS OF A LATTICE IN K_n

1. Forms associated with a lattice in K_n. With each n-dimensional lattice of the space K_n, whether multiplicative or not, there may be associated certain forms in n variables, whose introduction is sometimes useful in the investigation of certain products of lattices. We now turn to the consideration of the most important form of this kind.

First we will associate lattices with systems of linear forms. Let a lattice be given by the coordinates of the points of the basis

$$\begin{gathered}\Phi_1 (\varphi_1^{(1)}, \varphi_1^{(2)}, \ldots, \varphi_1^{(n)}),\\ \Phi_2 (\varphi_2^{(1)}, \varphi_2^{(2)}, \ldots, \varphi_2^{(n)}),\\ \cdots\cdots\cdots\cdots\\ \Phi_n (\varphi_n^{(1)}, \varphi_n'^{(2)}, \ldots, \varphi_n^{(n)}).\end{gathered}$$

The coordinates of any point $(\omega^{(1)}, \omega^{(2)}, \ldots, \omega^{(n)})$ of the lattice may be expressed by means of the coordinates of the points of the basis as linear covariant (i.e., depending on the same system of variables) forms

$$\begin{aligned}\omega^{(1)} &= x_1\varphi_1^{(1)} + x_2\varphi_2^{(1)} + \ldots + x_n\varphi_n^{(1)},\\ \omega^{(2)} &= x_1\varphi_1^{(2)} + x_2\varphi_2^{(2)} + \ldots + x_n\varphi_n^{(2)},\\ &\cdots\cdots\cdots\cdots\cdots\\ \omega^{(n)} &= x_1\varphi_1^{(n)} + x_2\varphi_2^{(n)} + \ldots + x_n\varphi_n^{(n)},\end{aligned}$$

with rational integer values of the variables $x_1, x_2, \cdots, x_n$. Thus with each basis of the lattice there is uniquely associated a system of n covariant linear forms in n variables. Conversely, with each system of n covariant linear forms in n variables we can associate a basis of some lattice so that the values of the forms for all possible integer values of the variable will give the coordinates of all the points of the lattice. It is necessary to require only that the determinant of the coefficients of the system of forms be different from zero.

We will now consider the relations between the systems of covariant forms corresponding to different bases of the same lattice of the space.

Let $(\varphi_1, \varphi_2, \ldots, \varphi_n)$ and $(\psi_1, \psi_2, \ldots, \psi_n)$ be two set of n vectors that are related to each other by the permutation

$$\psi_i = a_{i1}\varphi_1 + a_{i2}\varphi_2 + \ldots + a_{in}\varphi_n \quad (i = 1, 2, \ldots, n)$$

with matrix $A = \| a_{ik} \|$. If the two sets of n vectors $(\varphi_1, \varphi_2, \ldots, \varphi_n)$ and $(\psi_1, \psi_2, \ldots, \psi_n)$ are bases of the same lattice, then the matrix A is composed of integers, and its determinant is ± 1.

The systems of linear forms corresponding to these sets of n vectors are

$$(\omega^{(1)}, \omega^{(2)}, \ldots, \omega^{(n)}) \text{ and } (\tau^{(1)}, \tau^{(2)}, \ldots, \tau^{(n)}),$$

where

$$\omega^{(s)} = x_1\varphi_1^{(s)} + x_2\varphi_2^{(s)} + \ldots + x_n\varphi_n^{(s)}$$

and

$$\tau^{(s)} = x_1'\psi_1^{(s)} + x_2'\psi_2^{(s)} + \ldots + x_n'\psi_n^{(s)}. \quad (s = 1, 2, \ldots, n).$$

Expressing $\tau^{(s)}$ directly in terms of $\phi^{(s)}$, we obtain

$$\begin{aligned}\tau^{(s)} = &(a_{11}x_1' + a_{21}x_2' + \dots + a_{n1}x_n')\,\varphi_1^{(s)} + \\ &+ (a_{12}x_1' + a_{22}x_2' + \dots + a_{n2}x_n')\,\varphi_2^{(s)} + \\ &+ \dots\dots\dots\dots\dots + \\ &\dots\dots\dots\dots\dots \\ &+ (a_{1n}x_1' + a_{2n}x_2' + \dots + a_{nn}x_n')\,\varphi_n^{(s)}, \qquad (s = 1, 2, \dots, n)\end{aligned}$$

from which it follows that the form $(\tau^{(1)}, \tau^{(2)}, \dots, \tau^{(n)})$ may be obtained from the forms $(\omega^{(1)}, \omega^{(2)}, \dots, \omega^{(n)})$ by a linear transformation of the variables

$$\begin{aligned}x_1 &= a_{11}x_1' + a_{21}x_2' + \dots + a_{n1}x_n', \\ x_2 &= a_{12}x_1' + a_{22}x_2' + \dots + a_{n2}x_n', \\ &\dots\dots\dots\dots\dots \\ x_n &= a_{1n}x_1' + a_{2n}x_2' + \dots + a_{nn}x_n',\end{aligned}$$

whose matrix A^* is the transpose of the matrix A of the permutation taking the coordinates of the set of n vectors $[\varphi_1, \varphi_2, \dots, \varphi_n]$ into the coordinates of the set $[\psi_1, \psi_2, \dots, \psi_n]$. When the sets of n vectors are bases of the same lattice, the matrix A^* also consists of integers and has a discriminant equal to ± 1.

The converse is obvious: if one takes two systems of covariant linear forms $(\omega^{(1)}, \omega^{(2)}, \dots, \omega^{(n)})$ and $(\tau^{(1)}, \tau^{(2)}, \dots, \tau^{(n)})$ with nonzero determinants and such that $(\tau^{(1)}, \tau^{(2)}, \dots, \tau^{(n)})$ can be obtained from $(\omega^{(1)}, \omega^{(2)}, \dots, \omega^{(n)})$ by a linear transformation of the variables with an integer matrix whose determinant is ± 1, then these systems will be bases of the same lattice.

We will say that systems of covariant forms that are thus related are *equivalent*, and the set of all equivalent systems of forms will be called a *class* of the systems of covariant forms. Thus each lattice corresponds to a completely determined class of systems of covariant forms with nonzero determinants and, conversely, each class of systems of covariant forms with nonzero determinants corresponds to a completely determined lattice.

Let $(\omega^{(1)}, \omega^{(2)}, \dots, \omega^{(n)})$ be a system of covariant forms corresponding to some basis of a lattice, and let $\varphi(u^{(1)}, u^{(2)}, \dots, u^{(n)})$ be some form in n variables. Obviously

$$\varphi(\omega^{(1)}, \omega^{(2)}, \dots, \omega^{n}) = F(x_1, x_2, \dots, x_n)$$

will be a form of the same degree in the variables $x_1, x_2, \cdots, x_n$. To different bases of the same lattice with the same form ϕ will correspond equivalent forms

F, i.e., forms which go into one another by linear transformations with rational integer coefficients, and with determinants of ± 1, so that in this manner the whole lattice corresponds to a class of equivalent forms F.

Moreover, if the lattice under consideration is rational with respect to a multiplicative lattice, and the form ϕ is a symmetric function of $u^{(1)}, u^{(2)}, \cdots$ $\cdots, u^{(n)}$, then the form $F(x_1, x_2, \cdots, x_n)$ will have rational coefficients, since the coefficients will be symmetric functions of the coordinates of any generic point of the lattice under consideration, and the coordinates of each such point are the roots of some nth degree equation with rational coefficients.

The most important forms associated with such lattices are the forms

$$B_0(x_1, x_2, \cdots, x_n) = u^{(1)2} + u^{(2)2} + \cdots + u^{(n)2}$$

and

$$N(x_1, x_2, \cdots, x_n) = u^{(1)} u^{(2)} \cdots u^{(n)}.$$

We will call the first of these forms the Hermitian, and the second the Dirichlet form. If a given lattice is rational with respect to some multiplicative lattice, then both of these forms have rational coefficients; moreover, if the lattice is a rational integer with respect to some multiplicative lattice, then the coefficients of the forms will be rational integers.

2. The Hermitian is a quadratic form in n variables. It is positive definite if the lattice is situated in a purely real subspace of the space K_n, and otherwise it will be indefinite with the number of negative squares in a classical decomposition being equal to the number of pairs r of complex coordinates of points in the lattice, i.e., equal to the number which is called the signature of the lattice.

In the purely real case the given Hermitian completely defines a lattice, but does not define its orientation with respect to the axes, so that one Hermitian can correspond to infinitely many lattices that may be obtained from each other by rotation as a rigid body, or by rotation and reflection with respect to some $(n-1)$-dimensional plane.

In the case when the Hermitian has rational integer coefficients, one could expect that among the infinite set of lattices corresponding to it there would always be one multiplicative lattice, or a sublattice of such a lattice. In fact, however, this is not the case. Namely, it may happen that a given integral quadratic form is not the Hermitian of any multiplicative lattice nor of any sublattice of any multiplicative lattice. Thus, for example, for $n = 3$, $x_1^2 + x_2^2 + 2x_3^2$ is such a form, as is easy to see. It is also possible that two or several lattices have the same Hermitian. Thus the lattices constructed on the bases $[1, \lambda, \lambda^2 - 9\lambda + 7]$ and $[1, \mu, (\mu^2 - 9\mu + 10)/2]$, where $\lambda^3 = 9\lambda^2 - 6\lambda - 1$ and $\mu^3 = 9\mu^2 - 6\mu - 8$, have the same Hermitian

$$x_1^2 + 69x_2^2 + 69\,x_3^2 + 18x_1x_2 + 18x_1x_3 + 12x_2x_3.$$

Analogous cases also occur for lattices situated in other signature spaces.

3. Bezoutians. Besides the association of a quadratic form with the whole lattice, it is useful in some cases to associate in the same way quadratic forms with projections of the lattice, parallel to the n-dimensional "bisectrices" of K_n, onto spaces of lower dimension $n - m$ (where m is some divisor of n) that are supplementary to the spaces of these bisectrices.

Let us consider a multiplicative lattice S in the space K_n (or a part of a multiplicative lattice) having an m-dimensional sublattice R, situated on the "bisectrix"

$$\begin{aligned} u^{(1)} = u^{(2)} &= \ldots = u^{(\mu)}, \\ u^{(\mu+1)} = u^{(\mu+2)} &= \ldots = u^{(2\mu)}, \\ &\cdots\cdots\cdots \\ u^{(n-\mu+1)} = u^{(n-\mu+2)} &= \ldots = u^{(n)} \qquad \left(\mu = \frac{n}{m}\right). \end{aligned}$$

We will show that if the lattice S is projected parallel to the bisectrix and onto the $(n - m)$-dimensional space complementary to it:

$$\begin{aligned} u^{(1)} + u^{(2)} &+ \ldots + u^{(\mu)} = 0, \\ u^{\mu+1} + u^{(\mu+2)} &+ \ldots + u^{(2\mu)} = 0, \\ &\cdots\cdots\cdots \\ u^{(n-\mu+1)} + u^{(n-\mu+2)} &+ \ldots + u^{(n)} = 0, \end{aligned}$$

then we obtain a lattice whose quadratic form, constructed in the same way, will have rational integer coefficients after multiplication by μ.

So as not to complicate the discussion, let us assume that S is taken to be a maximal multiplicative lattice. This can be done without loss of generality, since any other multiplicative lattice is contained in a maximal multiplicative lattice.

We first remark that if there exists an m-dimensional sublattice of S on the bisectrix, then if ω is any point of the lattice S with coordinates

$$(\omega^{(1)}, \omega^{(2)}, \ldots, \omega^{(\mu)}, \ldots, \omega^{(n-\mu+1)}, \omega^{(n-\mu+2)}, \ldots, \omega^{(n)})$$

and $\psi(u^{(1)}, u^{(2)}, \ldots, u^{(\mu)})$ is a whole symmetric function of μ variables with whole coefficients, then the point with coordinates $(\psi^{(1)}, \psi^{(1)}, \ldots, \psi^{(1)}, \ldots \ldots, \psi^{(m)}, \psi^{(m)}, \ldots, \psi^{(m)})$, where

$$\begin{aligned}
\psi^{(1)} &= \psi(\omega^{(1)}, \omega^{(2)}, \ldots, \omega^{(\mu)}),\\
\psi^{(2)} &= \psi(\omega^{(\mu+1)}, \omega^{(\mu+2)}, \ldots, \omega^{(2\mu)}),\\
&\cdots\cdots\cdots\cdots\cdots\cdots\\
&\cdots\cdots\cdots\cdots\cdots\cdots\\
\psi^{(m)} &= \psi(\omega^{(n-\mu+1)}, \omega^{(n-\mu+2)}, \ldots, \omega^{(n)}),
\end{aligned}$$

will be a point of the lattice R.

From Galois theory it is known that this point is rationally related with a generic point of the lattice R and thus also with a generic point of the lattice S. Moreover, its coordinates are algebraic integers, since they come from algebraic operations on integers. Hence it belongs to the lattice S, since S was assumed to be a maximal multiplicative lattice and thus must contain all points with algebraic integer coordinates that are rationally related to a generic point. Finally, it lies on the bisectrix and thus belongs to the lattice R.

With the lattice R let us associate the lattice $\overline{R}$ in the space K_m whose points have coordinates that are coordinates of the points in R taken once from each group of different coordinates. The lattice $\overline{R}$ will be a maximal multiplicative lattice in K_m.

Let $(\omega^{(1)}, \omega^{(2)}, \cdots, \omega^{(\mu)}, \cdots, \omega^{(n-\mu+1)}, \cdots, \omega^{(n)})$ be a point in K_m. The point σ of the space K_m with coordinates

$$(\sigma^{(1)}, \sigma^{(2)}, \ldots, \sigma^{(m)}),$$

where

$$\begin{aligned}
\sigma^{(1)} &= \omega^{(1)} + \omega^{(2)} + \ldots + \omega^{(\mu)},\\
\sigma^{(2)} &= \omega^{(\mu+1)} + \omega^{(\mu+2)} + \ldots + \omega^{(2\mu)},\\
&\cdots\cdots\cdots\cdots\cdots\cdots\\
&\cdots\cdots\cdots\cdots\cdots\cdots\\
\sigma^{(m)} &= \omega^{(n-\mu+1)} + \omega^{(n-\mu+2)} + \ldots + \omega^{(n)},
\end{aligned}$$

will, by the above remark, belong to the lattice $\overline{R}$. We will call the point σ the *trace* of the point ω relative to the bisectrix under consideration. Obviously, if the point ω can be represented by means of a basis of S and its trace σ by means of a basis of $\overline{R}$, then the coefficients of the second representation will be linear integer forms with coefficients of the first representation.

Let us now find the projection of the point ω on the space complementary to the bisectrix. For this, we represent ω as the sum of two points, one of them τ belonging to the bisectrix, and the second ϕ to the complementary space. The point ϕ will be the desired projection.

It is easy to verify that τ must have the coordinates

$$\tau^{(1)}, \tau^{(2)}, \ldots, \tau^{(\mu)}, \ldots, \tau^{(n-\mu+1)}, \ldots, \tau^{(n)},$$

where

$$\tau^{(1)} = \tau^{(2)} = \ldots = \tau^{(\mu)} = \frac{\omega^{(1)} + \omega^{(2)} + \ldots + \omega^{(\mu)}}{\mu} = \frac{\sigma^{(1)}}{\mu},$$

$$\tau^{(\mu+1)} = \tau^{(\mu+2)} = \ldots = \tau^{(2\mu)} = \frac{\omega^{(\mu+1)} + \omega^{(\mu+2)} + \ldots + \omega^{(2\mu)}}{\mu} = \frac{\sigma^{(2)}}{\mu},$$

$$\cdots\cdots\cdots\cdots\cdots\cdots\cdots\cdots$$

$$\tau^{(n-\mu+1)} = \tau^{(n-\mu+2)} = \ldots = \tau^{(n)} = \frac{\omega^{(n-\mu+1)} + \omega^{(n-\mu+2)} + \ldots + \omega^{(n)}}{\mu} = \frac{\sigma^{(m)}}{\mu}.$$

To see this, the relative trace of the point τ thus taken is equal to the relative trace of the point ω, and it follows that the relative trace of the point ϕ is zero; this means that the point ϕ lies in the space complementary to the bisectrix.

Let us represent the point ω by the basis of S.

$$\omega = x_1\omega_1 + x_2\omega_2 + \ldots + x_m\omega_m + x_{m+1}\omega_{m+1} + \ldots + x_n\omega_n.$$

The basis may be chosen so that its first m points belong to the lattice R. The projection of the point ω on the space complementary to the bisectrix will have the form

$$\varphi = x_{m+1}\varphi_{m+1} + \ldots + x_n\varphi_n,$$

where $\phi_{m+1}, \ldots, \phi_n$ are the projections of the points $\omega_{m+1}, \ldots, \omega_n$. The projections of the points $\omega_1, \omega_2, \ldots, \omega_m$ will obviously be zero. Thus the projection of the lattice S will in fact be $(n-m)$-dimensional.

Let us compute its quadratic form, first multiplying the latter by μ.

$$B_m(x_{m+1}, x_{m+2}, \dots, x_n) = \mu \sum_{i=1}^{n} (\varphi^{(i)})^2 = \mu \sum_{i=1}^{n} (\omega^{(i)} - \tau^{(i)})^2 =$$

$$= \mu \sum_{i=1}^{n} (\omega^{(i)})^2 - 2\mu \sum_{i=1}^{n} \omega^{(i)}\tau^{(i)} + \mu \sum_{i=1}^{n} (\tau^{(i)})^2 =$$

$$= \mu \sum_{i=1}^{n} (\omega^{(i)})^2 - 2\mu \sum_{j=1}^{m} \sigma^{(j)} \frac{\sigma^{(j)}}{\mu} + \mu^2 \sum_{j=1}^{m} \left(\frac{\sigma^{(j)}}{\mu}\right)^2 =$$

$$= \mu \sum_{i=1}^{n} (\omega^{(i)})^2 - \sum_{j=1}^{m} (\sigma^{(j)})^2 =$$

$$= \mu \cdot B_0(x_1, x_2, \dots, x_n) - B_0'(y_1, y_2, \dots, y_m).$$

Here B_0 denotes the Hermitian of the lattice S, B_0' denotes the Hermitian of the lattice $\overline{R}$, and $y_1, y_2, \cdots, y_m$ are the linear forms of $x_1, x_2, \cdots, x_n$ which are the coefficients in the representation of the relative trace of the point ω by the basis of the lattice $\overline{R}$.

Since Hermitians for multiplicative lattices are represented by quadratic forms with integer coefficients, we can conclude from the formulas we have obtained that the form B_m has integer coefficients.

We will call the form B_m the *generalized Bezoutian* of the lattice S, namely the Bezoutian relative to the given bisectrix. The generalized Bezoutian B_1 of the lattice with the power basis $[1, \rho, \cdots, \rho^{n-1}]$ relative to the unique one-dimensional bisectrix, i.e., relative to the "rational straight line" $u^{(1)} = u^{(2)} = \cdots$ $\cdots = u^{(n)}$, is represented by a quadratic form that is usually called simply the Bezoutian of the number ρ, or the Bezoutian of the equation $f(\rho) = 0$, which is satisfied by the number ρ.

§8. FACTORABLE FORMS OF A LATTICE IN K_n

The Dirichlet form, i.e., the form $N(x_1, x_2, \dots, x_n) = u^{(1)} \cdot u^{(2)} \cdot \dots \cdot u^{(n)}$, for a lattice is an nth degree form in n variables that may be decomposed into linear factors which are linearly independent. We will say that forms that have this property are factorable forms.

Each factorable form may be considered as the Dirichlet form for some lattice, although the representation of the factorable form does not completely determine the basis of the lattice for which it is the Dirichlet form, since the decomposition of the form into factors is not unique. Namely, in the decomposition of the form into factors

$$F(x_1 x_2 \ldots x_n) = \prod_{i=1}^{n} (x_1\omega_1^{(i)} + x_2\omega_2^{(i)} + \cdots + x_n\omega_n^{(i)})$$

it is possible to multiply each respective factor by constants $\lambda^{(i)}$ where $\Pi_{i=1}^{n} \lambda^{(i)} = 1$. This means that it is possible simultaneously to multiply the points of the basis of the lattice $\omega_1, \omega_2, \cdots, \omega_n$ for which the form F is the Dirichlet form by the arbitrary point $(\lambda^{(1)}, \lambda^{(2)}, \cdots, \lambda^{(n)})$ with norm 1. The "complex volumes" of the basic parallelepipeds of all such lattices will obviously be the same. The square of the volume, i.e., the discriminant of the lattice, is called the discriminat of the factorable form. It is obvious, furthermore, that similar lattices, under a corresponding choice of bases, will correspond to Dirichlet forms that differ by a constant factor equal to the norm of the coefficient of similarity; and conversely, factorable forms that differ by a constant factor correspond to similar lattices. From this it follows that discriminants of factorable forms that differ by a factor e, will differ by a factor e^2, i.e., the discriminant of a form is a homogeneous quadratic function of the coefficients of the form.

In view of what was said at the begining of the preceding section, a Dirichlet form for a lattice which is similar to a lattice that is rationally situated with respect to a multiplicative lattice, will be, up to a factor, a form with rational coefficients.

We will now show conversely that a factorable form with rational coefficients determines a lattice that is similar to a lattice that is rationally situated with respect to some multiplicative lattice.

Let

$$F(x_1, x_2 \ldots x_n) = \sum_{i_1+i_2+\cdots+i_n=n} A_{i_1, i_2 \ldots i_n} \cdot x_1^{i_1} \cdot x_2^{i_2} \cdots x_n^{i_n} =$$

$$= \prod_{s=1}^{n} (x_1\omega_1^{(s)} + x_2\omega_2^{(s)} + \cdots + x_n\omega_n^{(s)}) \qquad (*)$$

be a factorable form with rational coefficients.

Without loss of generality one can assume that the coefficient $A_{n,0,0\cdots 0}$ of x_1^n is 1 and that $\omega_1^{(1)} = \omega_1^{(2)} = \cdots = \omega_1^{(n)} = 1$. This is true because there is a generic point in the lattice of the given form F which may be taken as the first point in the basis. Thus changing the basis and dividing by the first point of the basis we obtain a similar lattice that satisfies the above requirement. Its factorable form differs from the given equivalent form only by a rational factor. By the same argument it is possible to assume that the point $(\omega_2^{(1)}, \omega_2^{(2)}, \ldots, \omega_2^{(n)})$ is a generic point.

We will now show that the coordinates of the point ω_2 are the roots of an algebraic equation with rational coefficients and that all the remaining points of the basis $\omega_3, \omega_4, \ldots, \omega_n$ may be rationally expressed in terms of ω_2. With this the main assertion will be proved.

Let us assume that in the equality (*), $x_2 = -1$, $x_3 = x_4 = \cdots = x_n = 0$. We obtain

$$\prod_{s=1}^{n} (x_1 - \omega_2^{(s)}) = x_1^n - A_{n-1,\,1,\,0\cdots 0}\, x_1^{n-1} + A_{n-2,\,2,\,0\cdots 0}\, x_1^{n-2} - \cdots = \varphi(x_1).$$

From this it follows that the coordinates of the point ω_2 are roots of an nth degree equation with rational coefficients.

Further, we write out the expression for some of the coefficients by means of the coordinates of the points of the basis. To shorten the writing, we introduce the following notation. The symbols $\lambda_1^{(1)}, \lambda_2^{(1)}, \ldots, \lambda_{n-1}^{(1)}$ will denote the elementary symmetric functions of the coordinates of the point ω_2 other than $\omega_2^{(1)}$. Similarly, the symbols $\lambda_1^{(2)}, \lambda_2^{(2)}, \ldots, \lambda_{n-1}^{(2)}$ will denote the elementary symmetric functions of the coordinates of the point ω_2 other than $\omega_2^{(2)}$, and so on.

We obtain:

$$\begin{aligned}
&\omega_3^{(1)} + \omega_3^{(2)} + \cdots + \omega_3^{(n)} = A_{n-1,\,0,\,1,\,0\ldots 0} = a_1\\
&\omega_3^{(1)}\lambda_1^{(1)} + \omega_3^{(2)}\lambda_1^{(2)} + \cdots + \omega_3^{(n)}\lambda_1^{(n)} = A_{n-2,\,1,\,1,\,0\ldots 0} = a_2\\
&\omega_3^{(1)}\lambda_2^{(1)} + \omega_3^{(2)}\lambda_2^{(2)} + \cdots + \omega_3^{(n)}\lambda_2^{(n)} = A_{n-3,\,2,\,1,\,0\ldots 0} = a_3\\
&\cdots\cdots\cdots\cdots\cdots\cdots\cdots\cdots\\
&\cdots\cdots\cdots\cdots\cdots\cdots\cdots\cdots\\
&\omega_3^{(1)}\lambda_{n-1}^{(1)} + \omega_3^{(2)}\lambda_{n-1}^{(2)} + \cdots + \omega_3^{(n)}\lambda_{n-1}^{(n)} = A_{0,\,n-1,\,1,\,0\ldots 0} = a_n.
\end{aligned}$$

We multiply the first equation by $\omega_2^{(1)n-1}$, the second by $\omega_2^{(1)n-2}$, the third by $\omega_2^{(1)n-3}$, and so on, and add:

$$\omega_3^{(1)}(\omega_2^{(1)^{n-1}} - \lambda_1^{(1)}\omega_2^{(1)^{n-2}} + \lambda_2^{(1)}\omega_2^{(1)^{n-3}} - \cdots) +$$
$$+ \omega_3^{(2)}(\omega_2^{(2)^{n-1}} - \lambda_1^{(2)}\omega_2^{(1)^{n-2}} + \lambda_2^{(2)}\omega_2^{(1)^{n-3}} - \cdots) +$$
$$+ \cdots\cdots\cdots\cdots\cdots$$
$$\cdots\cdots\cdots\cdots\cdots$$
$$+ \omega_3^{(n)}(\omega_2^{(n)^{n-1}} - \lambda_1^{(n)}\omega_2^{(1)^{n-2}} + \lambda_2^{(n)}\omega_2^{(1)^{n-3}} - \cdots) =$$
$$= a_1\omega_2^{(1)^{n-1}} - a_2\omega_2^{(1)^{n-2}} + a_3\omega_2^{(1)^{n-3}} - \cdots.$$

Obviously, the coefficient of $\omega_3^{(1)}$ on the left side of the equation is equal to $(\omega_2^{(1)} - \omega_2^{(2)})(\omega_2^{(1)} - \omega_2^{(3)}) \cdots (\omega_2^{(1)} - \omega_2^{(n)}) = \phi'(\omega_2^{(1)})$, which is different from zero and rationally expressible in terms of $\omega_2^{(1)}$. The coefficients of $\omega_3^{(2)}, \cdots$ $\cdots, \omega_3^{(n)}$ are all equal to zero. Hence

$$\omega_3^{(1)} = \frac{a_1\omega_2^{(1)^{n-1}} - a_2\omega_2^{(1)^{n-2}} + a_3\omega_2^{(1)^{n-3}} - \cdots}{\varphi'(\omega_2^{(1)})}.$$

In the same way, the numbers $\omega_3^{(2)}, \omega_3^{(3)}, \ldots, \omega_3^{(n)}$ may be expressed in terms of $\omega_2^{(2)}, \omega_2^{(3)}, \ldots, \omega_2^{(n)}$:

$$\omega_3^{(i)} = \frac{a_1\omega_2^{(i)^{n-1}} - a_2\omega_2^{(i)^{n-2}} + a_3\omega_2^{(i)^{n-3}} - \cdots}{\varphi'(\omega_2^{(i)})}.$$

We obtain by the same method rational expressions for the remaining points of the basis in terms of the point ω_2.

The assertion is now proved.

As we have seen, similar lattices correspond to proportional factorable forms, and conversely. It is natural to ask the question of possible normalization of the factorable forms with rational coefficients, i.e., the question of the possibility of selecting one form from the collection of all proportional factorable forms that is most naturally associated with a given multiplicative lattice. The problem of normalization is solved by means of the so-called ring of multipliers of a lattice.

Let the lattice S be given in the space K_n. Let us consider the collection of all the points λ of the space K_n with the property that the product of a point λ with any point of the lattice S will again be in the lattice S. The collection of points λ obviously contains all rational integer points and is additive, subtractive and multiplicative. We will call this collection the *ring of multipliers* of the lattice S.

We will show that if the lattice S is similar to a lattice that is rationally oriented with respect to some multiplicative lattice, then the ring of multipliers will be a lattice of the space K_n, i.e., it will be n-dimensional and discrete.

To see this, let us assume that the lattice S is similar to a lattice that is rational with respect to some multiplicative lattice. Without loss of generality we can assume that the lattice S is itself rational with respect to a multiplicative lattice and contains the identity. In fact, we can obtain a lattice similar to S satisfying the above condition by dividing S by one of its generic points, and similar lattices obviously have the same ring of multipliers.

Let $[\omega_1, \omega_2, \ldots, \omega_n]$ be a basis of the lattice S and let ω be some point of the lattice S. The products of the points of the basis multiplied by ω may be expressed in terms of the basis :

$$\begin{aligned}
\omega\omega_1 &= a_{11}\omega_1 + a_{12}\omega_2 + \cdots + a_{1n}\omega_n \\
\omega\omega_2 &= a_{21}\omega_1 + a_{22}\omega_2 + \cdots + a_{2n}\omega_n \\
&\cdots\cdots\cdots\cdots\cdots \\
&\cdots\cdots\cdots\cdots\cdots \\
\omega\omega_n &= a_{n1}\omega_1 + a_{n2}\omega_2 + \cdots + a_{nn}\omega_n,
\end{aligned}$$

where the coefficients are rational numbers, since the lattice S is rational with respect to a multiplicative lattice. We will denote by d the common denominator of the coefficients a_{ik}. It is obvious that the point $d\omega$ belongs to the ring of multipliers, for when we multiply this point by the points of the basis of the lattice S, we obtain linear combinations of these points with rational integer coefficients, i.e., points of the lattice S. Thus we see that there exist points of the ring of multipliers on any ray connecting the origin with any points of the lattice S. Hence the ring of multipliers is n-dimensional. The discreteness can be shown more simply. Namely, the ring of multipliers must be completely included in the lattice S, since the latter contains the identity. The lattice S is discrete, so the ring of multipliers must be discrete.

Thus the ring of multipliers of a lattice that is rationally oriented with respect to some maximal multiplicative lattice is itself a multiplicative lattice, obviously contained in the same multiplicative lattice.

The converse is quite obvious: if the lattice S has as its ring of multipliers an n-dimensional lattice, then the lattice S is similar to a lattice that is rationally oriented with respect to a multiplicative lattice, namely, relative to the ring of multipliers.

It may be proved in exactly the same way as we proved the finiteness of the number of classes of ideals that the number of lattices having a given ring of multipliers which are not similar is finite. Thus all lattices similar to a lattice rationally oriented with respect to a multiplicative lattice may be classified by their ring of multipliers, where each ring corresponds to only a finite number of lattices that are not similar to each other.

We will now show that the collection of proportional factorable forms with rational coefficients contains a form with discriminant equal to the discrimant of the ring of multipliers and with rational integer coefficients.

Let $[\omega_1, \omega_2, \ldots, \omega_n]$ be a basis of the lattice S' whose Dirichlet form is equal to the given factorable form $N(x_1, x_2 \ldots x_n)$ and let $[\lambda_1, \lambda_2, \ldots, \lambda_n]$ be a basis of the ring of multipliers of this lattice. Let us multiply the ring of multipliers by the point $\omega = x_1\omega_1 + x_2\omega_2 + \cdots + x_n\omega_n$.

We obtain a new lattice which is contained in the lattice S. The basis of this lattice will be the set of points

$$[\omega\lambda_1, \omega\lambda_2, \ldots, \omega\lambda_n] =$$
$$= [l_{11}\omega_1 + l_{12}\omega_2 + \cdots + l_{1n}\omega_n, \ldots, l_{n1}\omega_1 + l_{n2}\omega_2 + \cdots + l_{nn}\omega_n],$$

where l_{ik} are linear forms in $x_1, x_2, \ldots, x_n$, with rational integer coefficients. Let us consider the volume (complex) of the basic parallelepiped of this lattice in two ways.

On the one hand, it is obviously equal to

$$N(x_1, x_2, \ldots, x_n) \cdot V[\lambda_1, \lambda_2, \ldots, \lambda_n],$$

where $V[\lambda_1, \lambda_2, \ldots, \lambda_n]$ is the volume of the basic parallelepiped of the ring of multipliers. On the other hand, it is equal to

$$V[\omega_1, \omega_2, \ldots, \omega_n] \cdot \begin{vmatrix} l_{11}, & \ldots, & l_{1n} \\ \cdot & \cdot & \cdot \\ \cdot & \cdot & \cdot \\ l_{n1}, & \ldots, & l_{nn} \end{vmatrix} = V[\omega_1, \omega_2, \ldots, \omega_n] \cdot F(x_1, x_2, \ldots, x_n).$$

Here $V[\omega_1, \omega_2, \ldots, \omega_n]$ denotes the volume of the basic parallelepiped of the lattice S. The form

$$F(x_1, x_2, \ldots, x_n) = \begin{vmatrix} l_{11}, & \ldots, & l_{1n} \\ \cdot & \cdot & \cdot \\ l_{n1}, & \ldots, & l_{nn} \end{vmatrix}$$

obviously has rational integer coefficients.

Equating the results, we obtain:

$$N(x_1, x_2, \ldots, x_n) = \frac{V[\omega_1, \omega_2, \ldots, \omega_n]}{V[\lambda_1, \lambda_2, \ldots, \lambda_n]} \cdot F(x_1, x_2, \ldots, x_n).$$

We will now show that the discriminant of the form F is equal to the discriminant of the ring of multipliers. Denoting by D_N and D_F the discriminants of the forms N and F, we obtain from the relationship between the forms:

$$D_N = \left(\frac{V[\omega_1, \omega_2, \ldots, \omega_n]}{V[\lambda_1, \lambda_2, \ldots, \lambda_n]}\right)^2 \cdot D_F.$$

But D_N, by definition, is equal to $(V[\omega_1, \omega_2, \ldots, \omega_n])^2$, and thus $D_F = (V[\lambda_1, \lambda_2, \cdots, \lambda_n])^2$, i.e., in fact the discriminant of the form F is equal to the discriminant of the ring of multipliers.

Thus we have succeeded in choosing for a given factorable form $N(x_1, x_2, \cdots$ $\cdots, x_n)$ a form $F(x_1, x_2, \ldots, x_n)$ proportional to it with integer coefficients and with a discriminant equal to the discriminant of the ring of multipliers.

§9. INVERSE LATTICES AND FACTORABLE INVERSE FORMS

In the theory of quadratic forms and in crystallography it is sometimes useful to consider along with a given lattice its inverse lattice. In 3-dimensional real space we mean by this the collection of the ends of vectors perpendicular to each pair of vectors of the initial lattice and of length equal to the area of the parallelogram constructed on the pair. We recall some properties of inverse lattices.

Let S be 3-dimensional real space with basis $(\omega_1^{(1)}, \omega_1^{(2)}, \omega_1^{(3)})$, $(\omega_2^{(1)}, \omega_2^{(2)}, \omega_2^{(3)})$ and $(\omega_3^{(1)}, \omega_3^{(2)}, \omega_3^{(3)})$. We will write the basis of the lattice in the form of a matrix

$$\begin{pmatrix} \omega_1^{(1)} \omega_1^{(2)} \omega_1^{(3)} \\ \omega_2^{(1)} \omega_2^{(2)} \omega_2^{(3)} \\ \omega_3^{(1)} \omega_3^{(2)} \omega_3^{(3)} \end{pmatrix},$$

where each line contains the coordinates of a point of the basis.

Let us consider the pair of vectors ending in points of the lattice:

$$\tau = x_1\omega_1 + x_2\omega_2 + x_3\omega_3 \quad \nu = y_1\omega_1 + y_2\omega_2 + y_3\omega_3.$$

Let us denote by $(\mu^{(1)}, \mu^{(2)}, \mu^{(3)})$ a point of the reciprocal lattice corresponding to the pair (τ, ν). Its coordinates are obviously computed by the formulas:

$$\mu^{(1)} = \begin{vmatrix} x_1\omega_1^{(2)} + x_2\omega_2^{(2)} + x_3\omega_3^{(2)}, & x_1\omega_1^{(3)} + x_2\omega_2^{(3)} + x_3\omega_3^{(3)} \\ y_1\omega_1^{(2)} + y_2\omega_2^{(2)} + y_3\omega_3^{(2)}, & y_1\omega_1^{(3)} + y_2\omega_2^{(3)} + y_3\omega_3^{(3)} \end{vmatrix} =$$

$$= \begin{vmatrix} x_2, & x_3 \\ y_2, & y_3 \end{vmatrix} \cdot \begin{vmatrix} \omega_2^{(2)}, & \omega_3^{(2)} \\ \omega_2^{(3)}, & \omega_3^{(3)} \end{vmatrix} + \begin{vmatrix} x_3, & x_1 \\ y_3, & y_1 \end{vmatrix} \cdot \begin{vmatrix} \omega_3^{(2)}, & \omega_1^{(2)} \\ \omega_3^{(3)}, & \omega_1^{(3)} \end{vmatrix} + \begin{vmatrix} x_1, & x_2 \\ y_1, & y_2 \end{vmatrix} \cdot \begin{vmatrix} \omega_1^{(2)}, & \omega_2^{(2)} \\ \omega_1^{(3)}, & \omega_2^{(3)} \end{vmatrix};$$

$$\mu^{(2)} = \begin{vmatrix} x_2, & x_3 \\ y_2, & y_3 \end{vmatrix} \cdot \begin{vmatrix} \omega_2^{(3)}, & \omega_3^{(3)} \\ \omega_2^{(1)}, & \omega_3^{(1)} \end{vmatrix} + \begin{vmatrix} x_3, & x_1 \\ y_3, & y_1 \end{vmatrix} \cdot \begin{vmatrix} \omega_3^{(3)}, & \omega_1^{(3)} \\ \omega_3^{(1)}, & \omega_1^{(1)} \end{vmatrix} + \begin{vmatrix} x_1, & x_2 \\ y_1, & y_2 \end{vmatrix} \cdot \begin{vmatrix} \omega_1^{(3)}, & \omega_2^{(3)} \\ \omega_1^{(1)}, & \omega_2^{(1)} \end{vmatrix};$$

$$\mu^{(3)} = \begin{vmatrix} x_2, & x_3 \\ y_2, & y_3 \end{vmatrix} \cdot \begin{vmatrix} \omega_2^{(1)}, & \omega_3^{(1)} \\ \omega_2^{(2)}, & \omega_3^{(2)} \end{vmatrix} + \begin{vmatrix} x_3, & x_1 \\ y_3, & y_1 \end{vmatrix} \cdot \begin{vmatrix} \omega_3^{(1)}, & \omega_1^{(1)} \\ \omega_3^{(2)}, & \omega_1^{(2)} \end{vmatrix} + \begin{vmatrix} x_1, & x_2 \\ y_1, & y_2 \end{vmatrix} \cdot \begin{vmatrix} \omega_1^{(1)}, & \omega_2^{(1)} \\ \omega_1^{(2)}, & \omega_2^{(2)} \end{vmatrix}.$$

From these formulas it follows that the inverse lattice is in fact a lattice with a basis whose points have coordinates which form an inverse matrix (in the usual sense) of the matrix consisting of the coordinates of the original basis. Such a basis of the inverse lattice is said to be inverse with respect to the basis of the original lattice.

The inverse lattice of a lattice in the space K_n will be taken to be the lattice constructed on the basis whose coordinates form an inverse matrix of the matrix consisting of the coordinates of the points of the basis of the given lattice. The geometrical meaning of the inverse lattice for a real n-dimensional lattice is the same as in the 3-dimensional case, except that the perpendiculars are constructed for all collections of $(n-1)$ linearly independent vectors of the lattice.

The introduction of the inverse lattice also turns out to be very useful in the theory of multiplicative lattices. As usual, the scalar volume of the basic parallelepiped of the lattice divides the inverse lattice. In what follows, we will mean by the inverse lattice one that has already been divided by the volume of the basic parallelepiped.

We note several properties of such inverse lattices.

1. The inverse lattice of the inverse lattice is the given lattice.

To see this, if (ω) is a matrix consisting of the coordinates of a basis of the given lattice, then the corresponding inverse matrix for the lattice is $(\overline{\omega})^{-1}$ (the bar denotes the transpose), and the one for the inverse of the inverse is $(\overline{(\overline{\omega})^{-1}})^{-1} = \omega$.

2. If the two bases $(\tau_1, \tau_2, \ldots, \tau_n)$ and $(\omega_1, \omega_2, \ldots, \omega_n)$ are related by the

transformation with matrix A:

$$\begin{aligned}\tau_1 &= a_{11}\omega_1 + a_{12}\omega_2 + \cdots + a_{1n}\omega_n,\\ \tau_2 &= a_{21}\omega_1 + a_{22}\omega_2 + \cdots + a_{2n}\omega_n,\\ &\cdots\cdots\cdots\cdots\cdots\cdots\\ \tau_n &= a_{n1}\omega_1 + a_{n2}\omega_2 + \cdots + a_{nn}\omega_n,\end{aligned}$$

then the inverse bases are related by a transformation with matrix $\overline{A}^{-1}$.

In fact, the coordinate matrix gives

$$(\tau) = A(\omega),$$

from which it follows that

$$(\overline{\tau})^{-1} = (\overline{A\cdot(\omega)})^{-1} = ((\overline{\omega})\cdot\overline{A})^{-1} = \overline{A}^{-1}\cdot(\overline{\omega})^{-1}.$$

3. If the lattice S is multiplied by the point $(\lambda^{(1)}, \lambda^{(2)}, \ldots \lambda^{(n)})$, then the inverse lattice is multiplied by the point $(1/\lambda^{(1)}, 1/\lambda^{(2)}, \ldots, 1/\lambda^{(n)})$.

To see this let us multiply the lattice S by the point $(\lambda^{(1)}, \lambda^{(2)}, \ldots, \lambda^{(n)})$, which we may do by multiplying the coordinate matrix of the basis by the matrix

$$\Lambda = \begin{Vmatrix} \lambda^{(1)}, 0, 0 \ldots 0 \\ 0, \lambda^{(2)}, 0 \ldots 0 \\ \cdot\ \cdot\ \cdot\ \cdot\ \cdot\ \cdot \\ \cdot\ \cdot\ \cdot\ \cdot\ \cdot\ \cdot \\ 0,\ 0,\ 0, \ldots \lambda^{(n)} \end{Vmatrix}$$

from the right; then

$$((\overline{\omega)\ \Lambda})^{-1} = (\overline{\omega})^{-1}\overline{\Lambda}^{-1} = (\overline{\omega})^{-1}\Lambda^{-1},$$

since

$$\overline{\Lambda} = \Lambda.$$

4. Let λ belong to the ring of multipliers of a lattice with basis $(\omega_1, \omega_2, \cdots, \omega_n)$, where the basis undergoes a transformation with the matrix L under multiplication by λ. Then the inverse basis will undergo a transformation with matrix $\overline{L}$ under multiplication by λ.

PROOF. We will write in matrix form the property that the basis undergoes a transformation with matrix L under multiplication by λ.

We see that multiplication of the basis by λ is equivalent to multiplication of the coordinate matrix of the basis by the matrix

$$\Lambda = \begin{pmatrix} \lambda^{(1)} & & & \\ & \lambda^{(2)} & & \\ & & \ddots & \\ & & & \lambda^{(n)} \end{pmatrix}$$

from the right, and that the transformation of the basis by a matrix L is equivalent to multiplication of the coordinate matrix by L on the left. Thus

$$(\omega)\Lambda = L(\omega).$$

Multiplication by Λ^{-1} from the right and by L^{-1} from the left gives:

$$(\omega)\Lambda^{-1} = L^{-1}(\omega).$$

Transposing and taking inverses, we get

$$(\bar{\omega})^{-1}\Lambda = \bar{L}\,(\bar{\omega})^{-1}.$$

This equation contains the proof of the assertion.

5. A matrix and its inverse have the same ring of multipliers.

In view of the preceding property, each point of the ring of multipliers for a lattice S is a point of the ring of multipliers for the inverse lattice S^*, since together with L the matrix $\bar{L}$ consists of integers. Further, each point of the ring of multipliers for the lattice S^* is a point of the ring of multipliers for its inverse lattice, i.e., for S. Thus the rings of the multipliers for S and S^* are the same.

From the last property it follows that if the lattice S is an ideal of the maximal lattice O, then the inverse lattice S^* is also an ideal of O.

In particular, the lattice O^* is the ideal of O that plays a very important role in the theory of algebraic numbers.

We will now prove several theorems that concern lattices that are inverse to the ideals of a maximal ring.

THEOREM 1. *The norm of an ideal* $\mathfrak{a}^*$ *is equal to*

$$\frac{1}{|D|\,N(\mathfrak{a})},$$

where D *is the discriminant of the maximal lattice.*

PROOF. By definition

$$N(\mathfrak{a}) = \left|\frac{V(\mathfrak{a})}{V(O)}\right|,$$

where $V(\mathfrak{a})$ is the volume of the basic parallelepiped of the ideal $\mathfrak{a}$, and $V(O)$ is the volume of the basic parallelepiped of the maximal ring O.

Similarly

$$N(\mathfrak{a}^*) = \left|\frac{V(\mathfrak{a}^*)}{V(O)}\right|.$$

It clearly follows from the definition of the inverse lattice that

$$V(\mathfrak{a})\,V(\mathfrak{a}^*) = 1.$$

Thus,

$$N(\mathfrak{a})\,N(\mathfrak{a}^*) = \left|\frac{V(\mathfrak{a})\,V(\mathfrak{a}^*)}{[V(O)]^2}\right| = \frac{1}{D},$$

which is what we wanted to show.

COROLLARY.

$$N(O^*) = \frac{1}{D}.$$

THEOREM 2. *The trace of the product of any point* α *of* $\mathfrak{a}$ *by any point* α^* *of* $\mathfrak{a}^*$ *is an integer. Conversely, any point* α^* *that has the property that the trace of* $\alpha\alpha^*$ *is an integer for any point* α *of* $\mathfrak{a}$, *is in* $\mathfrak{a}^*$.

PROOF. Let $[\alpha_1, \alpha_2, \ldots, \alpha_n]$ be a basis of the ideal $\mathfrak{a}$ and let $[\alpha_1^*, \alpha_2^*, \ldots, \alpha_n^*]$ be a basis of the inverse ideal $\mathfrak{a}^*$. On the basis of the definition of the inverse lattice, it is obvious that $S(\alpha_i\,\alpha_j^*) = 0$, if $i \neq j$ and is equal to 1 if $i = j$.

Let

$$\alpha = x_1\alpha_1 + x_2\alpha_2 + \ldots + x_n\alpha_n \quad \text{be a point of } \mathfrak{a},$$

and

$$\alpha^* = y_1\alpha_1^* + y_2\alpha_2^* + \ldots + y_n\alpha_n^* \quad \text{be a point of } \mathfrak{a}^*.$$

The numbers $x_1, x_2, x_3, \ldots, x_n$ and $y_1, y_2, y_3, \ldots, y_n$ are rational integers. Then

$$S(\alpha\alpha^*) = x_1y_1 + x_2y_2 + \ldots + x_ny_n$$

is a rational integer.

Conversely, assume that $S(\alpha^*\,\alpha)$ is an integer for any point α of $\mathfrak{a}$, in particular for $\alpha = \alpha_1, \alpha_2, \ldots, \alpha_n$. Then representing α^* in the form

$$\alpha_1^*y_1 + \alpha_2^*y_2 + \ldots + \alpha_n^*y_n,$$

we get that

$$y_1 = S(\alpha^*\,\alpha_1),\quad y_2 = S(\alpha^*\,\alpha_2),\ \ldots,\ y_n = S(\alpha^*\,\alpha_n)$$

are all rational integers, and hence

$$\alpha^* = y_1\alpha_1^* + y_2\alpha_2^* + \ldots + y_n\alpha_n^*$$

belongs to the lattice $\mathfrak{a}^*$.

COROLLARY. *The lattice* O^* *is an ideal, all of whose points have integer* *traces. Conversely, every ideal having this property is in* O^*. *In particular,* $O \subset O^*$, *and thus* $\mathfrak{D} = O^{*-1}$ *is an integer ideal. This ideal is called the different of the maximal ring* O.

On the basis of the first theorem, the norm of the different is equal to the discriminant of the maximal ring O.

THEOREM 3.

$$\mathfrak{a}\mathfrak{a}^* = O^*.$$

PROOF. On the basis of the first theorem,

$$N(\mathfrak{a}\mathfrak{a}^*) = N(\mathfrak{a}) \cdot N(\mathfrak{a}^*) = \frac{1}{|D|} = N(O^*).$$

On the other hand, $\mathfrak{a}\mathfrak{a}^*$ is an ideal whose points all have rational integer traces. Thus

$$\mathfrak{a}\mathfrak{a}^* \subset O.$$

On the basis of this inclusion and the equality of the norms we conclude that

$$\mathfrak{a}\mathfrak{a}^* = O^*,$$

which is what we wanted to show.

THEOREM 4. *The product of the different of any point of a maximal lattice* O *by the lattice* O^* *is an integer ideal.*

The different of the point $(\lambda^{(1)}, \lambda^{(2)}, \ldots, \lambda^{(n)})$ is defined to be the point with coordinates

$$\begin{array}{l}[(\lambda^{(1)} - \lambda^{(2)})(\lambda^{(1)} - \lambda^{(3)}) \ldots (\lambda^{(1)} - \lambda^{(n)}), \\ (\lambda^{(2)} - \lambda^{(1)})(\lambda^{(2)} - \lambda^{(3)}) \ldots (\lambda^{(2)} - \lambda^{(n)}), \\ \cdots\cdots\cdots\cdots\cdots \\ (\lambda^{(n)} - \lambda^{(1)})(\lambda^{(n)} - \lambda^{(2)}) \ldots (\lambda^{(n)} - \lambda^{(n-1)})].\end{array}$$

PROOF. Let λ be a point of the maximal lattice; let us multiply all the points of the basis by it:

$$\begin{array}{l}\lambda\omega_1 = l_{11}\omega_1 + l_{12}\omega_2 + \ldots + l_{1n}\omega_n, \\ \lambda\omega_2 = l_{21}\omega_1 + l_{22}\omega_2 + \ldots + l_{2n}\omega_n, \\ \cdots\cdots\cdots\cdots\cdots \\ \lambda\omega_n = l_{n1}\omega_1 + l_{n2}\omega_2 + \ldots + l_{nn}\omega_n.\end{array}$$

In view of the fact that λ belongs to the lattice O, all the numbers $l_{i,k}$ are rational integers. The point 1 belongs to the lattice. Hence

$$1 = t_1\omega_1 + t_2\omega_2 + \ldots + t_n\omega_n$$

with rational integers $t_1, t_2, \cdots, t_n$. Let us consider the point μ_1 whose coordinate $\mu_1^{(1)}$ has the form:

$$\begin{vmatrix} t_1, & t_2, & \ldots, & t_n \\ l_{21}, & l_{22}-\lambda^{(1)}, & \ldots, & l_{2n} \\ \cdot & \cdot & \cdot & \cdot \\ l_{n1}, & l_{n2}, & \ldots, & l_{nn}-\lambda^{(1)} \end{vmatrix}$$

while its remaining coordinates are expressed in terms of $\lambda^{(2)}, \cdots, \lambda^{(n)}$ in the same way that $\mu_1^{(1)}$ is expressed in terms of $\lambda^{(1)}$. The point μ_1 belongs to the lattice O, since λ belongs to it and all the $l_{i,k}$ and t_i are rational integers.

Let us multiply μ_1 by the scalar volume of the basic parallelepiped of the lattice O. By the rule of multiplication of determinants, we obtain

$$\begin{vmatrix} t_1, & t_2, & \ldots, & t_n \\ l_{21}, & l_{22}-\lambda^{(1)}, & \ldots, & l_{2n} \\ \cdot & \cdot & \cdot & \cdot \\ l_{n1}, & l_{n2}, & \ldots, & l_{nn}-\lambda^{(1)} \end{vmatrix} \cdot \begin{vmatrix} \omega_1^{(1)}, & \omega_1^{(2)}, & \ldots, & \omega_1^{(n)} \\ \omega_2^{(1)}, & \omega_2^{(2)}, & \ldots, & \omega_2^{(n)} \\ \cdot & \cdot & \cdot & \cdot \\ \omega_n^{(1)}, & \omega_n^{(2)}, & \ldots, & \omega_n^{(n)} \end{vmatrix} =$$

$$= \begin{vmatrix} t_1\omega_1^{(1)}+t_2\omega_2^{(1)}+\ldots+t_n\omega_1^{(1)}, & t_1\omega_1^{(2)}+t_2\omega_2^{(2)}+\ldots+t_n\omega_n^{(2)}, \\ l_{21}\omega_1^{(1)}+l_{22}\omega_2^{(1)}+\ldots+l_{2n}\omega_1^{(1)}-\lambda\omega_1^{(1)}, & l_{21}\omega_1^{(2)}+\quad+\ldots+l_{2n}\omega_n^{(2)}-\lambda\omega_n^{(2)}, \\ \cdots\cdots & \cdots\cdots \\ l_{n1}\omega_1^{(1)}+l_{n2}\omega_2^{(1)}+\ldots+l_{nn}\omega_n^{(1)}-\lambda\omega_n^{(1)}, & l_{n1}\omega_1^{(2)}+\quad+\ldots+l_{nn}\omega_n-\lambda\omega_n^{(2)}, \end{vmatrix}$$

$$\begin{matrix} t_1\omega_1^{(n)}+t_2\omega_2^{(n)}+\ldots+t_n\omega_n^{(n)} \\ l_{21}\omega_1^{(n)}+\ldots\quad+l_{2n}\omega_n^{(n)}-\lambda\omega_2^{(n)} \\ \cdots\cdots \\ l_{n1}\omega_1^{(n)}+\ldots\quad+l_{nn}\omega_n^{(n)}-\lambda\omega_n^{(n)} \end{matrix}\Bigg| =$$

$$= \begin{vmatrix} 1, & 1, & \ldots & 1 \\ 0, & \omega_2^{(2)}(\lambda^{(2)}-\lambda^{(1)}), & \ldots & \omega_2^{(n)}(\lambda^{(n)}-\lambda^{(1)}) \\ \cdot & \cdot & \cdot & \cdot \\ 0, & \omega_n^{(2)}(\lambda^{(2)}-\lambda^{(1)}) & \ldots & \omega_n^{(n)}(\lambda^{(n)}-\lambda^{(1)}) \end{vmatrix} =$$

$$= (\lambda^{(2)}-\lambda^{(1)}) \ldots (\lambda^{(n)}-\lambda^{(1)}) \cdot \begin{vmatrix} \omega_2^{(2)}, & \ldots & \omega_2^{(n)} \\ \cdot & \cdot & \cdot \\ \cdot & \cdot & \cdot \\ \omega_n^{(2)}, & \ldots & \omega_n^{(n)} \end{vmatrix}.$$

Dividing again by the volume, we obtain

$$\mu_1^{(1)} = (\lambda^{(2)} - \lambda^{(1)}) \ldots (\lambda^{(n)} - \lambda^{(1)})\, \omega_1^{*(1)},$$

where ω_1^* is the first point of the basis of the inverse lattice of the lattice O.

Taking

$$\mu_2 = \begin{vmatrix} l_{11} - \lambda, & l_{12}, & \ldots & l_{1n} \\ t_1, & t_2, & \ldots & t_n \\ \cdot & \cdot & \cdot & \cdot \\ l_{n1}, & l_{n2}, & \ldots & l_{nn} - \lambda \end{vmatrix},$$

we obtain

$$\mu_2^{(1)} = (\lambda^{(2)} - \lambda^{(1)}) \ldots (\lambda^{(n)} - \lambda^{(1)})\, \omega_2^{*(1)},$$

and so on.

Thus the products of the points of the basis of the lattice O^* by the different of the point λ are the points $\mu_1, \mu_2, \cdots, \mu_n$ belonging to the lattice O. Therefore the product of O^* by the different of λ is an integer ideal, which is what we wanted to prove.

Theorem 4 may also be formulated as follows: *The differents of all the points of a maximal ring O are divisible by the different of the ring O.*

In conclusion we note certain properties of factorable forms corresponding to a lattice S and its inverse lattice S^*. Normalizing the lattices S and S^* in the sense of the preceding section, we obtain for them integral factorable forms with the same discriminant equal to the discriminant of their common ring of multipliers. We will call such a factorable form of the lattice S^* the Cayley form of the lattice S.

Properties of inverse lattices imply the following properties of the Cayley form:

1. The Cayley form of a Cayley form is the original form.
2. If a factorable form undergoes a linear transformation, then the Cayley form undergoes a contravariant transformation.

For 3-dimensional lattices, the Cayley form in the above sense differs only by a constant factor from the form that is known in the literature as the Cayley contravariant.

SUPPLEMENT.

SOME USEFUL LEMMAS ON LATTICES IN REAL EUCLIDEAN SPACE

By the sum (difference) of two points in the n-dimensional real euclidean space R_n, we will understand the point each of whose rectangular Cartesian coordinates is the sum (difference) of the corresponding coordinates of the points being added (subtracted). We will say that a set of points is additive (subtractive) if the sum (difference) of any two of its points is again one of its points. Since the addition of a point to all the points of a set is equivalent to a parallel translation of the set, such a set may be called a parallel translation set. A set of points will be called discrete if there exists nonzero distance r such that no two points of the given set lie closer to each other than the distance r. By a parallelepiped system of points, or a point lattice, or as we will later say, simply a lattice, we will mean the set of all points having rational integer components with respect to some set of n linearly independent vectors, which we will consider as coordinate set. We will call this set of n vectors the basic n-vectors of a given parallelepiped system, and the parallelepiped constructed on these vectors, its basic parallelepiped.

LEMMA I. *Any discrete set of points that is additive and subtractive is a lattice.*

Let there be given a discrete set of points E that is additive and subtractive. We assume that all the points of E lie in some m-dimensional plane in R_n, but do not all lie simultaneously in any $(m-1)$-dimensional plane.

Then there are m points $A, B, C, \cdots, L$ in E which together with the origin of coordinates O (which we shall consider a point of the set) determines an m-dimensional space containing all the rest of the points of E. Let $\overline{A}$ be the point of E that is nearest to O on the interval OA. (Such a point exists, since in a region of any finite diameter in R_m there lie only a finite number of points of E. The latter statement follows from the fact that if we circumscribe spheres of radius $r/2$ around all the points, then, in view of the assumption of discreteness, these spheres will not intersect each other.) If A is the nearest such point, we will take for the point $\overline{A}$ the point A itself. Let $\overline{B}$ be the point of E that is closest to the straight line $O\overline{A}$ and which belongs to the parellelogram $O\overline{A}B$. If that point is B, we will take for $\overline{B}$ the point B itself. Let $\overline{C}$ be the point closest to the plane $O\overline{A}\overline{B}$ that belongs to the parallelepiped

$O\overline{ABC}$, and so on to $\overline{L}$. In view of the additivity of E, all of the vertices of the parallelepiped $O\overline{ABC}\cdots\overline{L}$ are points of E, and in view of the choice of the points $\overline{A}, \overline{B}, \cdots, \overline{L}$, no other points of E lie inside the parallelepiped or on its boundary. Let us construct on the parallelepiped $O\overline{AB}\cdots\overline{L}$ a parallelepipedal system of points and denote it by $\overline{E}$. In view of the additivity and subtractivity of the set E, all the points of $\overline{E}$ belong to the set E but no other points belong to E. In fact, if a point of E were either inside or on the boundary of a parallelepiped of $\overline{E}$, homologous to the parallelepiped $O\overline{AB}\cdots\overline{L}$ (we say two figures are homologous to each other with respect to a given lattice $\overline{E}$ if one can be obtained from the other by a parallel translation by a vector of $\overline{E}$, i.e., by a vector connecting two points of that lattice), then, in view of the additivity and subtractivity of the set E, some point of E would lie inside or on the boundary (not in a vertex) of the parallelepiped $O\overline{AB}\cdots\overline{L}$, which is impossible.

LEMMA II. *The volumes of all the basic parallelepipeds of a given lattice are the same.*

Let us assume from now on that $m = n$. Let $OAB\cdots L$ be the basic n-vectors of a lattice, and let $OA'B'\cdots L'$ be another set of n vectors, i. e., $A', B', \cdots, L'$ are points of the lattice. In such a case the coordinates of the points $A', B', \cdots, L'$ relative to the basic n-vectors of this lattice are rational integers. It follows from the geometry of the matrices that the volume of the n vectors $OA'B'\cdots L'$ is Δ times as large as the volume of the n vectors $OAB\cdots L$, where Δ is the determinant of the coordinates. Thus the volume of any set of n vectors of the lattice is an integer multiple of the volume of the basic n-vectors. If $OA'B'\cdots L'$ is also a set of basic n-vectors for the given lattice, then the volume of this set of n vectors and that of the n vectors $OAB\cdots L$ may both be obtained from each other by multiplication by an integer, which may occur only if the two volumes are equal.

We will say that we have centered a lattice if we have added new points to the space R_n in which it lies so that the new collection is also a lattice, which is, of course, denser. (This term is taken from crystallography, where three special centerings play an important role: the addition of one point in the center of each parallelepiped of which the lattice is composed; the addition of one point each in the centers of all the faces of these parallelepipeds; and the addition of one point each in the centers of both bases of each of these parallelepipeds. As it is easy to see, such additions of points take lattices into lattice and make them denser by a factor of 2, 4, and 2. The three lattices thus obtained are said to be, with respect to the original lattice: simply centered, centered with respect to the faces, and centered with respect to the bases.)

LEMMA III. *The number of different centerings of a lattice with given index* δ *is finite.*

The index of a centering is defined to be the number $\delta = 1/\Delta$ by which it is necessary to multiply the volume of the basic parallelepiped of the given lattice to obtain the volume of the basic parallelepiped of the centering, where for brevity, we call the lattice obtained when we center, a centering of the given lattice. That the index of a centering will always be equal to 1 divided by a rational integer follows from the fact that the parallelepiped system thus obtained is a parallel translation set. In each basic parallelepiped of a given lattice, the same number of added points, $\Delta = 1/\delta$, is equal to the number of points assed to one parallelepiped, increased by 1. Since to give a means of finding all the centerings of given index and a precise formula for their number is not much more difficult than merely to prove that their number is finite, we will do the former.

We will first note that the points $\bar{A}, \bar{B}, \cdots, \bar{L}$ of Lemma I have coordinates

$$\begin{matrix} (x_{11} & 0 & 0 & \ldots & 0) \\ (x_{21} & x_{22} & 0 & \ldots & 0) \\ (x_{31} & x_{32} & x_{33} & \ldots & 0) \\ \cdot & \cdot & \cdot & \cdot & \cdot \\ (x_{n1} & x_{n2} & & \ldots & x_{nn}) \end{matrix}$$

with respect to the basic n-vectors $OAB \cdots L$. The lattice $\bar{E}$ is considered as a centering of the lattice E constructed on the n vectors $OAB \cdots L$. Denoting by Δ the integer which is the reciprocal of the index δ of this centering and which shows how many times the volume of the parallelepiped $\overline{OAB} \cdots \bar{L}$ is smaller than the volume of the parallelepiped $OAB \cdots L$, we see that $\Delta = \Delta_1 \cdot \Delta_2 \cdot \cdots \cdot \Delta_n$, where Δ_1 is a positive rational integer showing how many times the point $\bar{A}$ is closer to O than the point A, Δ_2 is a positive rational integer showing how many times the point $\bar{B}$ is closer to the straight line $O\bar{A}$ than the point B, and so on. The fact that the numbers are positive rational integers follows simply from the fact that all the points of $\bar{E}$ lying on the straight line $O\bar{A}$ have all their coordinates relative to the n vectors $\overline{OAB} \cdots \bar{L}$ equal to zero other than the first, and if the point A of the parallelepiped system E lying on the straight line $O\bar{A}$ has this coordinate equal to Δ_1, then Δ_1 is a rational integer, and so on. Moreover, we see that $x_{11} = 1/\Delta_1$, $x_{22} = 1/\Delta_2, \cdots, x_{nn} = 1/\Delta_n$. Thus, each centering of index δ corresponds uniquely (the order is also taken into consideration) to a definite decomposition of Δ into positive integer factors, where some of the factors may be equal to 1. Let us consider one of these decompositions, i.e., let us fix the numbers Δ_1, $\Delta_2, \cdots, \Delta_n$. As may be seen in Figure 1, where $\Delta_1 = 4$, $\Delta_2 = 3$, $\Delta_3 = 5$ (i.e., $\Delta = 60$), the vector $O\bar{B}$, extended Δ_2 times, has its end B' in an integer point of $\bar{E}$ that lies on the edge of the base of the centering parallelepiped $OAB \cdots L$ opposite OA, and the vector $O\bar{C}$, extended by a factor of Δ_3, has its end C' in an integer point of a plane of the base of the centering parallelepiped opposite OAB, and so on.

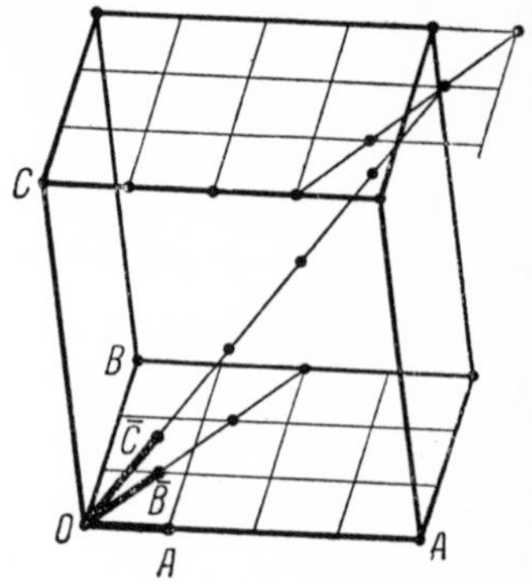

Figure 1

Let the point B' on the edge BB' be obtained from the point B by the addition of γ_{21} times the vector $O\bar{A}$, and the point C' on the upper base of the centering parallelepiped be obtained from the point C by the addition of γ_{31} times the vector $O\bar{A}$ and γ_{32} times the vector $O\bar{B}$, and so on. Then it is obvious that the coordinates of the points $\bar{A}, \bar{B}, \bar{C}, \cdots, \bar{L}$ with respect to the n vectors $OAB \cdots L$ are obtained by the following rule: write on the diagonal of a matrix the numbers $1/\Delta_1$, $1/\Delta_2, \cdots, 1/\Delta_n$ and write zero above the diagonal; then to the right of the square matrix put the columns of numbers γ_{21}; γ_{31}; γ_{32}; γ_{41}; γ_{42}; γ_{43}; ...; where we may suppose that the numbers of these columns are non-negative and smaller than the corresponding $\Delta_2, \Delta_3, \Delta_4 \ldots$; then each such possible listing corresponds uniquely to a specific centering with decomposition $\Delta_1 \cdot \Delta_2 \cdot \cdots \cdot \Delta_n$, and conversely,

$$\begin{pmatrix} \frac{1}{\Delta_1} & & & & \\ & \frac{1}{\Delta_2} & & & \\ & & \frac{1}{\Delta_3} & & \\ & & & \ddots & \\ & & & & \frac{1}{\Delta_n} \end{pmatrix} \quad \begin{matrix} \gamma_{21} & \gamma_{31} & \gamma_{41} & \cdots & \gamma_{n1} \\ & \gamma_{32} & \gamma_{42} & \cdots & \gamma_{n2} \\ & & \gamma_{43} & \cdots & \gamma_{n3} \\ & & & \cdots & \\ & & & & \gamma_{n(n-1)}. \end{matrix}$$

For the computation of the coordinates of the points $\bar{B}, \bar{C}, \cdots, \bar{L}$ that are beneath the diagonal, it is necessary to do the following: first compute the

the coordinates of $\bar{B}$, and then, when this coordinate is obtained, compute the coordinates of $\bar{C}$, etc., forming them as linear combinations of those alraedy occuring in the matrix of the corresponding coordinates and using as coefficients the numbers in the columns, and then dividing by the corresponding Δ_i.

EXAMPLE.

$$\begin{pmatrix} \frac{1}{4} & & & \\ \frac{1}{6} & \frac{1}{3} & & \\ \frac{13}{60} & \frac{2}{15} & \frac{1}{5} & \\ \frac{53}{180} & \frac{7}{45} & \frac{1}{15} & \frac{1}{3} \end{pmatrix} \begin{matrix} 2\ 3\ 2 \\ 2\ 1 \\ 1 \\ \ \end{matrix} \qquad \frac{2\cdot\frac{1}{4}}{3}=\frac{1}{6};$$

$$\frac{3\cdot\frac{1}{4}+2\cdot\frac{1}{6}}{5}=\frac{13}{60}; \qquad \frac{2\cdot\frac{1}{3}}{5}=\frac{2}{15};$$

$$\frac{2\cdot\frac{1}{4}+1\cdot\frac{1}{6}+1\cdot\frac{13}{60}}{3}=\frac{53}{180}; \quad \frac{1\cdot\frac{1}{3}+1\cdot\frac{2}{15}}{3}=\frac{7}{45}; \quad \frac{1\cdot\frac{1}{5}}{3}=\frac{1}{15}.$$

The number $I_{n,\Delta}$ of all possible different centerings of an n-dimensional lattice of index $\delta = 1/\Delta$ is equal, therefore, to $\Sigma\Delta_2 \cdot \Delta_3^2 \cdot \Delta_4^3 \cdot \dots \cdot \Delta_n^{n-1}$ where Σ extends over all possible different decompositions of the number Δ into n factors $\Delta_1, \Delta_2, \dots, \Delta_n$, the order of factors being taken into consideration. For example, $I_{3,6} = 91$ since $6 = 6\cdot1\cdot1 = 3\cdot2\cdot1 = 3\cdot1\cdot2 = 2\cdot3\cdot1 = 2\cdot1\cdot3 = 1\cdot6\cdot1 = 1\cdot1\cdot6 = 1\cdot2\cdot3 = 1\cdot3\cdot2$; $1\cdot1^2 + 2\cdot1^2 + 1\cdot2^2 + 3\cdot1^2 + 1\cdot3^2 + 6\cdot1^2 + 1\cdot6^2 + 3\cdot2^2 + 2\cdot3^2 = 1+2+4+3+9+6+36+12+18 = 91$.

LEMMA III′. *The number of different n-dimensional sublattices of a given n-dimensional lattice of index* Δ *is finite and is also equal to* $I_{n,\Delta}$.

We call any lattice that is a part of a given lattice a sublattice of the given lattice. If the lattice E_2 is a sublattice of the lattice E_1, then E_1 is a centering of the lattice E_2. By the index of a sublattice we again mean the number δ by which it is necessary to multiply the volume of the basic parallelepiped of the given lattice in order to obtain the volume of the basic parallelepiped of the sublattice under consideration.

The index δ of a sublattice is always, in view of Lemma II, a rational integer Δ. In view of the fact that the given lattice E_1 may be looked upon as a centering of its sublattice E_2 with the index $1/\Delta$, and that, if the different sublattices with the index Δ can be affinely transformed into the same lattice, then the given lattice obviously is transformed into different centerings of this lattice with index $1/\Delta$ (for otherwise the inverse transformations would not give different sublattices), we see that the number of different sublattices with index Δ is equal to $I_{n,\Delta}$.

LEMMA III″. *There are only finitely many different n-dimensional lattices that are rational with a fixed denominator with respect to a given n-dimensional lattice of given index.*

We say a lattice is rational with respect to a given lattice if the coordinates of all n of its basic points (and thus of all its points) are rational with respect to the basic n-vectors of the given lattice. Any sublattice or centering of a given lattice is rational with respect to the given lattice, but a lattice that is rational with respect to a given lattice may be neither a sublattice nor a centering of the given lattice.

By the index of such a lattice, we will again mean the number δ, by which it is necessary to multiply the volume of the basic parallelepiped of the given lattice to obtain the volume of the basic parallelepiped of this lattice. In this case the index may be either a whole number or a fraction. The denominator Q of such a lattice is defined to be the common denominator of all the coordinates of the n basic (and hence in general of all) points of this lattice, taken with respect to the basic n-vectors of the given lattice. All lattices that are rational with respect to a given lattice with a given denominator Q are obviously sublattices of the centering of the given lattice with index $\delta = 1/Q^n$, which can be obtained by simply increasing each of the basic vectors by a factor of Q. If a lattice that is rational with respect to the given lattice with denominator Q has an index δ with respect to it, then its index with respect to the lattice under consideration, being linearly Q times smaller, is an integer equal to $\delta_1 = Q^n/\delta$, and hence the number of such lattices that are different is not larger than I_{n,δ_1}. In general this number is smaller, since some of the centerings may have a denominator with respect to the given lattice that is not Q but rather some divisor of Q.

In view of the fact that the denominators Q are rational integers, it follows, from the fact that the number of different lattices that are rational with respect to a given lattice with given index and given denominator is finite, that this number is also finite for a given index and bounded denominator.

LEMMA IV. *Let R_1 and R_2 be two rationally related n-dimensional lattices. Let us denote by $T = [R_1, R_2]$ the intersection of these lattices, i. e., the collection of all common points. By $S = (R_1, R_2)$ let us denote the sum of the lattices R_1 and R_2, i. e., the collection of all the points of R_1 and of R_2 and of their sums. Then the index with which the lattice R_1 centers T is equal* *to the index with which the lattice S centers R_2.*

PROOF. First we show that S and T are actually lattices. Both these collections are obviously additive and subtractive. Let us denote by N the common denominator of the coefficients by means of which the basis of the lattice R_2 may be expressed in terms of the basis of R_1; then $R_2 \subset (1/N) R_1$, $R_1 \supset NR_2$. The collection T is n-dimensional, since it contains the n-dimensional lattice NR_2. The collection S is n-dimensional, since it contains the n-dimensional lattices R_1 and R_2. The collection T is discrete, since it is contained in the discrete lattices R_1 and R_2. The collection S is discrete, since it is contained in the lattice $(1/N) R_1$. By Lemma I, both collections S and T are lattices. We will say that two points of a lattice are congruent with respect to a sublattice if their difference belongs to this sublattice, and that they are incongruent otherwise. A collection of points that are pairwise incongruent with respect to a sublattice but are such that each point of the lattice is congruent to one of them, will be said to be a complete residue system of the lattice modulo the sublattice. An example of a complete residue system is the collection of all points of a lattice that lie inside and on the nonhomologous part of the boundary of a basic parallelepiped of a sublattice. The number of points forming a complete residue system is obviously equal to the index with which the lattice centers the sublattice.

For the proof of our lemma, we compare a complete residue system of the lattice R_1 with respect to T, and of the lattice S with respect to R_2.

Let $(\alpha_1, \alpha_2, \ldots, \alpha_k)$ be a complete residue system of the lattice R_1 with respect to T. We will show that it is also a complete residue system of S with respect to R_2. For this it is necessary to prove three things: first, that the points $(\alpha_1, \alpha_2, \ldots, \alpha_k)$ belongs to S, secondly, that they are pairwise incongruent modulo R_2, and finally, that each point of the lattice S is congruent to one of the points $(\alpha_1, \alpha_2, \ldots, \alpha_k)$ modulo the lattice R_2.

The first is obvious, since all the points of the lattice R_1, including the points $(\alpha_1, \alpha_2, \ldots, \alpha_k)$, belongs to the lattice S.

Let us now assume that $\alpha_i \equiv \alpha_j \pmod{R_2}$ for $i \neq j$. Then the difference $\alpha_i - \alpha_j$ belongs simultaneously to the lattice R_2 and to the lattice R_1, and thus to the intersection T, which contradicts the fact that the $(\alpha_1, \alpha_2, \ldots, \alpha_k)$ form a complete residue system modulo the lattice T. Thus the points

$(\alpha_1, \alpha_2, \ldots, \alpha_k)$ are pairwise incongruent modulo the lattice R_2. Now let σ be some point of the lattice S. Obviously σ may be represented in the form $\sigma = \alpha + \beta$ where α is a point of R_1 and β is a point of R_2; thus $\sigma \equiv \alpha(R_2)$. But $\alpha \equiv \alpha_i(T)$, since $(\alpha_1, \alpha_2, \ldots, \alpha_k)$ is a complete residue system of the lattice R_1 with respect to T, and hence $\sigma - \alpha_i = (\sigma - \alpha) + (\alpha - \alpha_i)$ belongs to the lattice R_2, for both $\sigma - \alpha$ and $\alpha - \alpha_i$ belong to R_2. Thus $\sigma \equiv \alpha_i \ (R_2)$ and it follows that $(\alpha_1, \alpha_2, \ldots, \alpha_k)$ is actually a complete residue system of the lattice S with respect to R_2. In view of the fact that the lattice R_1 with respect to T has the same complete residue system as the lattice S with respect to R_2, the indices of the centerings R_1 with respect to T, and S with respect to R_2, are the same, which is what we wanted to prove.

LEMMA V (MINKOWSKI). *A convex body with center at a point of a lattice, whose volume is more than 2^n times the volume of the basic parallelepiped of the lattice, has in it at least two points of the lattice (that are aymmetric with respect to the center).*

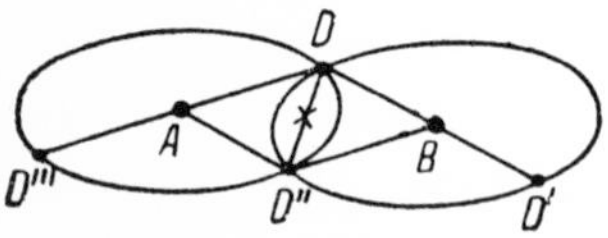

Figure 2

A body is said to be convex if, given any two of its points, any point on the interval connecting the points again belongs to the body. A point O will be called the center if, given any point of the body, there exists another point of the body that is symmetric to the original point with respect to O, i.e., so that O will be the midpoint of the interval connecting the two points. Let us take a convex body M that has its center at a point O of the lattice E and that contains no other points of E inside it or on its boundary. We will diminish this body M linearly by half, shrinking it homothetically towards the point O, and we will denote the body so obtained by M_1. We will construct bodies equal and parallel to M_1 around all the points of E as centers. Such bodies M_1 cannot have common points, for if there were two such bodies with centers at the points A and B of the lattice that had common points, then in view of the fact that they are convex, they would have centers of symmetry at the points A and B, equal and in parallel distribution, and the midpoint C of the interval AB would be another common point of the bodies. In fact, since the point D is a common point of the two bodies it follows that the point D' is a point of the body B, and that the point D'' is a point of the body A; analogously it follows that the point D''' is a point of the body A, and thus that the point D'' is a point of the body B. Thus the point D'' is also a common point of both bodies, but then the point C, which is the midpoint of the interval DD'' and hence also the midpoint of the interval AB, is also, in view of the convexity of the body, a common point of these bodies.

The volumes of the bodies M_1 is thus not larger than the volume of the basic parallelepiped.

Thus, if a convex body with center at some point O of a lattice E contains no other points of the lattice E, neither within it nor on its boundary, then its volume is not larger than 2^n times the volume of the basic parallelepiped of the lattice E.

Consequently, if the volume of a convex body M' is more than 2^n times larger than the volume of the basic parallelepiped of the lattice, then within the body M' there are at least two points of the lattice other than the center O.

CHAPTER II

SOME CALCULATIONS WITH NUMBERS IN CUBIC FIELDS

§10. CUBIC FIELDS, TSCHIRNHAUSEN TRANSFORMATIONS, INTEGERS IN THE FIELD

Let the numbers s, q, and n be rational integers and suppose that the equation

$$x^3 = sx^2 + qx + n \tag{1}$$

has no rational integer root, i.e., that none of the divisors of its constant term is a root. Then this equation is irreducible in the rational field and its roots ρ, ρ', ρ'' are called *cubic numbers*. If the coefficients of the equation are rational fractions instead of integers, then there exists a rational integer k such that it is possible to multiply the coefficients of the equation by k, k^2 and k^3, respectively, to make them integers. Therefore, every equation of type (1) with rational fractional coefficients is closely connected with a similar equation with rational integer coefficients.

In the case under consideration, where equation (1) is irreducible, the totality of all numbers ω which are rational functions of one of its roots, say ρ (i.e., they can be obtained from ρ by a finite number of combinations of ρ with itself by means of addition, subtraction, multiplication and division), forms the so-called field of the root ρ, which will be denoted by Ω_ρ. It is obvious that the combination of any finite number of numbers in the field by means of a finite number of additions, subtractions, multiplications and divisions (except division by zero) is again a number in the field. The fields

$$\Omega_\rho, \quad \Omega_{\rho'}, \quad \Omega_{\rho''}$$

are in general distinct.

Every rational function of ρ can be, as is well known, reduced to a polynomial of the second degree in ρ in both the numerator and denominator by dividing by $\rho^3 - s\rho^2 - q\rho - n$. By rationalizing the denominator it can be brought into the form

$$\omega = \frac{u\rho^2 + v\rho + w}{\Delta}, \tag{2}$$

where the numbers u, v, w, and Δ are rational integers. A practical rule for rationalizing the denominator, based on the method of indeterminate coefficients, will be given later.

It is easily seen that if the integers u, v, w and Δ are assumed to have no common factor, then the number ω is uniquely represented by the form (2), since two distinct representations, when equated to each other would produce an equation of the second degree satisfied by ρ; but this is impossible, since ρ satisfies by assumption the irreducible equation (1) of the third degree.

The field Ω_ρ is therefore nothing but the totality of all numbers of the form (2).

It is not difficult to construct an equation of the third degree satisfied by $z = u\rho^2 + v\rho + w = \phi(\rho)$, in other words to make a *Tschirnhausen transformation.* In fact it is sufficient to write z, $z \cdot \rho$ and $z \cdot \rho^2$ as polynomials of the second degree in ρ and to set the determinant of the coefficients of 1, ρ and ρ^2 equal to zero.

EXAMPLE. We let $\rho^3 = \rho + 1$, and it is required to form the equation satisfied by $z = 2\rho^2 + 3\rho + 1$. We write

$$\begin{aligned} z &= 2\rho^2 + 3\rho + 1, \\ z \cdot \rho &= 3\rho^2 + \rho + 2(\rho + 1) = 3\rho^2 + 3\rho + 2, \\ z \cdot \rho^2 &= 3\rho^2 + 2\rho + 3(\rho + 1) = 3\rho^2 + 5\rho + 3, \end{aligned}$$

and hence

$$\begin{vmatrix} z - 1, & -3, & -2 \\ -2, & z - 3, & -3 \\ -3, & -5, & z - 3 \end{vmatrix} = 0$$

or, expanding this determinant we obtain:

$$(z^2 - 6z + 9)(z - 1) - 27 - 20 - 6(z - 3) - 6(z - 3) - 15(z - 1) = 0$$

or finally

$$z^3 - 7z^2 - 27z - 5 = 0.$$

If the coefficients of the equation (1) and of the transformation function $\phi(\rho)$ are integers, then the coefficients of the transformed equations are also integers. The equation which is satisfied by ω is obtained from the equation satisfied by z by dividing its coefficients by Δ, Δ^2, Δ^3. If there is divisibility in each case, then the equation satisfied by ω will also have integer coefficients. The numbers in the field Ω_ρ which satisfy equations of type (1) with integer coefficients s, q, n will be called *integers* in the field. It is obvious that if ρ itself is an integer, then all the numbers of type (2) having $\Delta = \pm 1$ are integers. However, it is possible that the number ω is an integer even when the denominator Δ of ω is not equal to ± 1, because of the above-mentioned possibility that the coefficients of the equation satisfied by $z = u\rho^2 + v\rho + w$ happen to be divisible by Δ, Δ^2, Δ^3.

The roots of the equation obtained from (1) by the Tschirnhausen transformation $z = u\rho^2 + v\rho + w$ are

$$z = u\rho^2 + v\rho + w; \quad z' = u\rho'^2 + v\rho' + w; \quad z'' = u\rho''^2 + v\rho'' + w.$$

If this equation were reducible, then one of these roots would be a rational number r. Suppose, for example, that $u\rho'^2 + v\rho' + w = r$; then because of the uniqueness of the form (2) we must have $u = v = 0$, $w = r$. Therefore $z = w$, and the equation satisfied by z is of the form $(z - w)^3 = 0$. Therefore every number in a cubic field either satisfies an irreducible equation of the third degree and is a cubic number, so that at least one of the coefficients u, v is different from zero, or it is a rational number (this happens when $u = v = 0$). The numbers in the field Ω_ρ which satisfy irreducible equations of the third degree are called *primitive* numbers in the field.

All primitive numbers in the field can be rationally expressed in terms of one another, so that any primitive number in the field can be chosen instead of ρ to generate the same cubic field. In fact, let z be any primitive number and let

$$z = u\rho^2 + v\rho + w, \tag{3}$$

$$z^2 = u_1\rho^2 + v_1\rho + w_1; \tag{4}$$

then $\begin{vmatrix} u & v \\ u_1 & v_1 \end{vmatrix} \neq 0$, for otherwise we would have $u_1 = \delta \cdot u$, $v_1 = \delta \cdot v$, where δ is a rational integer or fraction, and therefore we would have $z^2 = \delta \cdot z + (w_1 - \delta w)$ and z would satisfy an equation with rational coefficients of degree lower than 3, which is contrary to assumption. But if $\begin{vmatrix} u & v \\ u_1 & v_1 \end{vmatrix} \neq 0$, then from (3) and (4), considered as a pair of linear equations, we can express ρ rationally in terms of z.

EXAMPLE. To express ρ in terms of $z = 2\rho^2 + 3\rho + 1$ if $\rho^3 = \rho + 1$. We have $z^2 = 4\rho^4 + 9\rho^2 + 1 + 12\rho^3 + 4\rho^2 + 6\rho = 4(\rho+1)^2 + 13\rho^2 + 6\rho + 1 + 12(\rho+1) = 17\rho^2 + 26\rho + 17$, so that we have for the determination of ρ the system

$$3\rho + 2\rho^2 = z - 1,$$
$$26\rho + 17\rho^2 = z^2 - 17,$$

from which $\rho = 2z^2 - 17z - 17$.

The totality of all integers in the field Ω_ρ forms a ring; that is, it can be generated by addition, subtraction and multiplication. In fact, let $\omega_1 = (u_1\rho^2 + v_1\rho + w_1)/\Delta_1$ and $\omega_2 = (u_2\rho^2 + v_2\rho + w_2)/\Delta_2$ be two integers in the field Ω_ρ. We construct the equation

$$F(x) = [x - (\omega_1 + \omega_2)]\,[x - (\omega_1' + \omega_2')]\,[x - (\omega_1'' + \omega_2'')], \tag{5}$$

where ω_1', ω_2'; ω_1'', ω_2'' are conjugate to ω_1, ω_2, i.e., they can be obtained by replacing ρ by ρ' and ρ''. By a theorem on symmetric functions the coefficients of equation (5), being symmetric functions of S, S', S'', are rational. We now construct a polynomial of the 9th degree:

$$F'(x) = [x - (\omega_1 + \omega_2)]\,[x - (\omega_1 + \omega_2')]\,[x - (\omega_1 + \omega_2'')]\,[x - (\omega_1' + \omega_2)]\,[x - (\omega_1' + \omega_2')]\cdot$$
$$\cdot[x - (\omega_1' + \omega_2'')]\,[x - (\omega_1'' + \omega_2)]\,[x - (\omega_1'' + \omega_2')]\,[x - (\omega_1'' + \omega_2'')]. \tag{6}$$

All the coefficients of this equation are rational integer symmetric functions both in $\omega_1, \omega_1', \omega_1''$ and in $\omega_2, \omega_2', \omega_2''$ and therefore are expressible rationally in terms of the coefficients of those equations of type (1) which are satisfied by the numbers ω_1 and ω_2. But by assumption these numbers are integers and therefore the coefficients of (6) are integers. Hence the polynomial $F'(x)$ with leading coefficient unity and the remaining coefficients rational integers is divisible by a polynomial $F(x)$, whose leading coefficient is unity, and whose other coefficients are rational. But then, by a well-known lemma of Gauss, the coefficients of $F(x)$ must be rational integers. Hence it follows that if ω_1 and ω_2 are integers in the field Ω_ρ, then $\omega_1 + \omega_2$ is also an integer in the field. An analogous proof can be given for the difference $\omega_1 - \omega_2$ and for the product $\omega_1 \cdot \omega_2$. If an integer in the field is rational, then it must be an ordinary rational integer, since as we have seen, the equation which it satisfies is of the form $(x - w)^3 = 0$, and hence w^3 and therefore w is an integer.

§11. THE OPERATIONS OF ADDITION, SUBTRACTION, MULTIPLICATION, DIVISION, RAISING TO POWERS AND TAKING ROOTS OF NUMBERS IN A CUBIC FIELD, AND THE CALCULATION OF NORMS AND DISCRIMINANTS

If $\omega_1 = u_1\rho^2 + v_1\rho + w_1$ and $\omega_2 = u_2\rho^2 + v_2\rho + w_2$, then $\omega_1 \pm \omega_2 = (u_1 \pm u_2)\rho^2 + (v_1 \pm v_2)\rho + (w_1 \pm w_2)$. In the product $\omega_1 \cdot \omega_2$ the number ρ enters to the 3rd and 4th degree. Therefore, for performing multiplications, it is convenient to prepare the identities lowering the degree, namely if

$$\rho^3 = s\rho^2 + q\rho + n,$$

then

$$\rho^4 = (s^2 + q)\rho^2 + (sq + n)\rho + sn.$$

Making use of these identities we can perform multiplications with greater facility.

EXAMPLES. Let $\rho^3 = 3\rho^2 + \rho + 2$; then $\rho^4 = 10\rho^2 + 5\rho + 6$ and the product is performed as follows:

$$\begin{aligned}(5\rho^2 + 2\rho - 1)(2\rho^2 - 3\rho + 2) &= 10(10\rho^2 + 5\rho + 6) + 4(3\rho^2 + \rho + 2) - 2\rho^2 - \\ &- 15(3\rho^2 + \rho + 2) - 6\rho^2 + 3\rho + 10\rho^2 + 4\rho - 2 = \\ &= 69\rho^2 + 46\rho + 36.\end{aligned}$$

The operation of division is carried out most readily by means of indeterminate coefficients; for example, let

$$\frac{5\rho^2 + 2\rho - 1}{2\rho^2 - 3\rho + 2} = A\rho^2 + B\rho + C.$$

Then

$$\begin{aligned}&2A\rho^4 - 3A\rho^3 + 2A\rho^2 + \\ &+ 2B\rho^3 - 3B\rho^2 + 2B\rho^2 + \\ &+ 2C\rho^2 - 3C\rho + 2C = 5\rho^2 + 2\rho - 1\end{aligned}$$

and using the degree-reducing identities we get

$$\begin{aligned}&2A(10\rho^2 + 5\rho + 6) - 3A(3\rho^2 + \rho + 2) + 2A\rho^2 + \\ &+ 2B(3\rho^2 + \rho + 2) - 3B\rho^2 + 2B\rho + \\ &+ 2C\rho^2 - 3C\rho + 2C = 5\rho^2 + 2\rho - 1.\end{aligned}$$

Identifying coefficients of the powers of ρ gives

$$\left.\begin{aligned}13A + 3B + 2C &= 5 \\ 7A + 4B - 3C &= 2 \\ 6A + 4B + 2C &= -1\end{aligned}\right\},$$

and hence $A = 121/172$, $B = -185/172$, $C = -79/172$.

This type of calculation is the most convenient way to eliminate the irrationality in the denominator.

It is also possible to perform the division by multiplying the numerator and denominator by the product of the two expressions which are the cubic conjugates of the denominator, and for this purpose it is convenient to have a ready-made formula for this product. If $\omega = u\rho^2 + v\rho + w$, then the product of the conjugates has the form

$$\omega'\omega'' = (-u^2q + uvs - uw + v^2)\rho^2 + (u^2sq + u^2n - uvs^2 - v^2s - vw)\rho + \\ + (u^2q^2 - u^2sn - uvsq - uvn + uws^2 + 2uwq - v^2q + vws + w^2).$$

We now consider raising to powers. If it is required to raise a cubic number $\omega = u\rho^2 + v\rho + w$ to powers, or to calculate a table of successive powers, it is best to establish a recursive formula which leads from ω^m to ω^{m+1}. For example, let $\rho^3 = \rho^2 + 2\rho + 2$ and let $\omega = -\rho^2 + \rho + 3$. We have in this case $\rho^4 = 3\rho^2 + 4\rho + 2$, and therefore if $\omega^m = A\rho^2 + B\rho + C$, then $\omega^{m+1} = (A\rho^2 + B\rho + C) \times (-\rho^2 + \rho + 3) = (A - C)\rho^2 + (-2A + B + C)\rho + (-2B + 3C)$. In this way we obtain a table of coefficients of the successive powers.

m	A	B	C
1	-1	1	3
2	-4	6	7
3	-11	21	9
4	-20	52	-15
5	-5	77	-149
....	....	....	....
			etc.

This method is unquestionably the most convenient one for calculating successive powers of a cubic number. There exists, however, a direct formula for writing down the coefficients of any power without going through the intermediate steps. In fact, suppose that we want to find a power of $\omega = u\rho^2 + v\rho + w$. By means of the Tschirnhausen transformation we can find the equation $\omega^3 = S\omega^2 + Q\omega + N$ satisfied by ω. Then if

$$\omega^m = U_m \cdot \omega^2 + V_m \cdot \omega + W_m, \tag{1}$$

we have the following formula:

$$U_m = \Sigma \frac{(\alpha + \beta + \gamma)!}{\alpha!\,\beta!\,\gamma!} \cdot S^\alpha \cdot Q^\beta \cdot N^\gamma, \tag{2}$$

where the sum goes over all the non-negative integers α, β, γ satisfying the relation $\alpha + 2\beta + 3\gamma = m - 2$.

The proof of this formula is by induction. In order to calculate V_m and W_m it is sufficient to note that $\omega^{m+1} = (U_m S + V_m)\omega^2 + \cdots$; $\omega^{m+2} =$

$[(U_m S + V_m) S + U_m Q + W_m]\omega^2 + \cdots$ (where we have omitted the terms not containing ω and those containing ω to the first degree). Therefore

$$V_m = U_{m+1} - U_m \cdot S;\ \ W_m = U_{m+2} - U_{m+1} \cdot S - U_m Q.$$

From these formulas V_m and W_m can be easily calculated after U_m, U_{m+1}, U_{m+2} have been obtained from formula (2). It remains to substitute into (1) the expression of ω in terms of ρ.

When it comes to extracting a root we propose the following method. Let

$$\omega^3 = S\omega^2 + Q\omega + N \tag{3}$$

be the equation satisfied by ω, and let $\omega = \rho^k$, where ρ is also a cubic number, given by the equation

$$\rho^3 = s\rho^2 + q\rho + n. \tag{4}$$

The elementary symmetric functions S, Q, N of the roots of (3) are also symmetric functions of the roots of (4) and are therefore expressible rationally in terms of the elementary symmetric functions s, q, n. In particular, it is clear that $N = n^k$.

The expressions for S and Q are more complicated but they can be written down for any given integer k.

Therefore the problem of finding the kth root of ω is reduced to finding s, q, n from given S, Q, N and k, or to the solution of a system of three equations in three unknowns in the case when this system admits a rational solution. Moreover, one of the equations of the system is solved independently.

Obviously, it is sufficient to be able to extract the root for a prime power.

We first consider the case $k = 2$. In this case

$$\begin{aligned} S &= s^2 + 2q, \\ Q &= 2sn - q^2, \\ N &= n^2. \end{aligned} \tag{5}$$

From the last equation, $n = \sqrt{N}$. The sign on this square root can be always taken as positive. In doing so we will get that value of $\sqrt{\omega}$ whose norm is positive.

We then eliminate q from the first two equations and obtain

$$(s^2 - S)^2 - 8ns + 4Q = 0.$$

We take for s a rational root of this equation, if such exists, and then find q from the first equation in (5).

In considering the question for other values of k we will limit ourselves to rational *integers* for S, Q, and N. In this case s, q, n are also rational integers. We shall show that the solution of the system of equations for determining s and q can be reduced to a finite number of trials. It will be seen from examples that this number is relatively small.

Let $k = p$ be an odd prime. We write a system of equations for s and q:

$$\begin{aligned} \Phi_p(s, q) &= S, \\ \Psi_p(s, q) &= Q. \end{aligned} \tag{6}$$

We consider the number $1 + \omega = 1 + \rho^p$. This number when divided by $(1 + \rho)$ gives an algebraic integer for a quotient. Therefore $N(1 + \omega)$ is divisible by $N(1 + \rho)$. Moreover, it can be easily seen that these norms must be of the same sign. Similarly $N(1 - \omega)$ must be divisible by $N(1 - \rho)$ and must be of the same sign. Expressing $N(1 \pm \omega)$ and $N(1 \pm \rho)$ in terms of the coefficients of the equations satisfied by ω and ρ we obtain:

$$\begin{aligned} &1 + S - Q + N \text{ is divisible by } 1 + s - q + n \text{ and is of the same sign;} \\ &1 - S - Q - N \text{ is divisible by } 1 - s - q - n \text{ and is of the same sign.} \end{aligned} \tag{7}$$

Considering all the divisors of $1 + S - Q + N$ and $1 - S - Q - N$ we obtain a finite number of trial values for s and q, which must then be substituted back into (6).

The number of trials can be reduced by the following considerations. It is obvious that $N = n^p \equiv n \pmod p$ by Fermat's theorem. We shall show that $S \equiv s \pmod p$.

In fact, $S = \omega^p + \omega'^p + \omega''^p = (\omega + \omega' + \omega'')^p - pA$, where A is a symmetric function of $\omega, \omega', \omega''$ with rational integer coefficients, since all the binomial coefficients in the expansion of $(\omega + \omega' + \omega'')$ are divisible by p. Therefore A is a rational integer and

$$S \equiv s^p \pmod p$$

and again by Fermat's theorem

$$S \equiv s \pmod p.$$

Similarly we can show that $Q \equiv q \pmod{p}$. Hence

$$\left.\begin{aligned} 1+s-q+n &\equiv 1+S-Q+N \\ 1-s-q-n &\equiv 1-S-Q-N \end{aligned}\right\} \pmod{p}. \tag{8}$$

These congruences reduce the number of combinations of s and q that need to be tried.

In the case of extracting a cube root, the system (6) becomes

$$S = s^3 + 3sq + 3n,$$
$$Q = q^3 - 3nsq - 3n^2.$$

The solution in this case is simplified by the fact that s divides $S - 3n$ while q divides $Q + 3n^2$. The relation $Q + nS = q^3 + ns^3$ is also helpful and should be noted.

The above considerations enable us to solve in a finite number of steps the following problem.

Given a cubic number ω, find whether or not this number is a perfect power of some other cubic number and if so find the exponent of this power and the corresponding root.

In fact if $N \neq 1$, then the exponent is greatly restricted because N must be a perfect power of a rational integer with the same exponent. If $N = 1$, we can begin by taking square roots as long as this is possible. After this has been accomplished the exponent will be divisible only by odd primes.

From the divisibility properties in (7) we will obtain a finite number of combinations of s and q, and for each pair a finite number of values of the exponent p. In fact by (8), p must divide the greatest common divisor of $S - s$ and $Q - q$.

We shall clarify the above by examples.

EXAMPLE 1. $\omega^3 = 22\omega^2 - 89\omega + 484$. Find $\sqrt{\omega}$.

First of all we find $n = \sqrt{484} = 22$.

Then we have the system

$$s^2 + 2q = 22,$$
$$q^2 - 44s = 89.$$

Eliminating q we obtain

$$s^4 - 44s^2 - 176s + 128 = 0,$$

from which $s = 8$, $q = -21$.

Hence $\omega = \rho^2$, where ρ satisfies the equation

$$\rho^3 = 8\rho^2 - 21\rho + 22.$$

EXAMPLE 2. $\omega^3 = -6\omega^2 - 29\omega + 1$. Find $\sqrt[3]{\omega}$.

We write down the system (6), taking into account that $n = 1$:

$$s^3 + 3sq = -9,$$

$$q^3 - 3sq = -26,$$

from which it follows that

$$q^3 + s^3 = -35,$$

and $q + s = -1, -5, -7, -35$.

But $q + s \equiv q^3 + s^3 = -35 \equiv 1 \pmod 3$. Hence there remains $q + s = -5$ or $q + s = -35$.

The first of these leads to the solution of the problem

$$q = -2; \quad s = -3.$$

Therefore $\omega = \rho^3$, where $\rho^3 = -3\rho^2 - 2\rho + 1$.

EXAMPLE 3. $\epsilon^3 = 7\epsilon^2 - 68\epsilon + 1$. Find whether or not ϵ is a perfect power of another cubic number.

SOLUTION. First of all we check whether or not ϵ is a square of a cubic number. Let $\epsilon = \rho^2$; then

$$\rho^3 = s\rho^2 + q\rho + 1, \; s^2 + 2q = 7, \; q^2 - 2s = 68.$$

Eliminating q we obtain

$$s^4 - 14s^2 - 8s - 223 = 0.$$

This equation has no rational roots; therefore $\epsilon \neq \rho^2$. Now let $\epsilon = \rho^p$, where p is an odd prime and let $\rho^3 = s\rho^2 + q\rho + 1$.

From (7) we obtain that

$$61 \text{ is divisible by } -q-s,$$

$$77 \text{ is divisible by } -q+s+2.$$

We make a table of all possible values of $s + q$ and the corresponding values of p, using the relation $S + Q \equiv s + q \pmod p$ and a similar table of $s - q + 2$ as follows:

$s+q$	-1	-61
p	3, 5	arbitrary,

$s-q+2$	1	7	11	77
p	19	5, 7	3, 11	arbitrary.

Combining the cases with the same p we get the following possibilities:

$-q$	5	38	3	30	33	35
s	4	37	2	-31	-28	-26
p	3	3, 5	5	19	5, 7	3, 11.

Trying the first case gives a positive result. We obtain

$$\epsilon = \rho^3, \text{ where } \rho^3 = 4\rho^2 - 5\rho + 1.$$

Repeating the process:

s_1+q_1	-1
p_1	arbitrary,

s_1-q_1+2	1	11
p_1	5	arbitrary.

The only possibility is $q_1 = 0$, $s_1 = -1$, $p_1 = 5$. This gives

$$\rho = \rho_1^5, \text{ where } \rho_1^3 = -\rho_1^2 + 1.$$

Repeating the process once more:

s_2+q_2	-1
p_2	arbitrary,

s_2-q_2+2	1
p_2	arbitrary.

There are no solutions and hence ρ_1 is not a power. Hence $\epsilon = \rho_1^{15}$.

The calculation of the norm and the discriminant. An explicit formula for the norm of $\omega = u\rho^2 + v\rho + w$ is rather complicated and not very convenient.

The discriminant of ρ has the following form:

$$D\rho = [(\rho-\rho')(\rho-\rho'')(\rho'-\rho'')]^2 = \begin{vmatrix} 1 & \rho & \rho^2 \\ 1 & \rho' & \rho'^2 \\ 1 & \rho'' & \rho''^2 \end{vmatrix}^2 = s^2q^2 - 18sqn + 4q^3 - 4s^3n - 27\,n^2.$$

It is convenient to calculate the norm and the discriminant as follows. In order to calculate the norm we begin with the Tschirnhausen transformation from ρ to ω. Then the determinant consisting only of the coefficients of 1, ρ and ρ^2 is the norm of ω. The discriminant of ω taken with the opposite sign is the norm of its "different" $\delta(\omega) = (\omega - \omega')(\omega - \omega'') = F'(\omega)$, where $F(\omega) = 0$ is the equation satisfied by ω, that is, $-D_\omega = N(F'(\omega))$. The calculation of the norm of $F'(\omega)$ can be carried out by the above method of a Tschirnhausen transformation.

§12. A LINEAR FRACTIONAL REPRESENTATION OF NUMBERS IN A CUBIC FIELD

We have seen earlier that every integer in the cubic field Ω_ρ can be represented by a quadratic polynomial in ρ with rational coefficients and that such a representation is unique. In some cases it is more convenient to have a linear fractional representation of a cubic number, namely,

$$\omega = \frac{\alpha\rho + \beta}{\gamma\rho + \delta}$$

with rational integer coefficients. We shall prove the existence of such a representation.

Let $\omega = a\rho^2 + b\rho + c$ be a number in the field Ω_ρ. The conjugate numbers $\omega' = a\rho'^2 + b\rho' + c$ and $\omega'' = a\rho''^2 + b\rho'' + c$ are obviously in the field Ω_ρ as well as the product of ω' and ω''. If we represent $\omega'\omega''$ in the canonical form

$$\omega'\omega'' = A\rho^2 + B\rho + C,$$

then

$$\omega''\omega = A\rho'^2 + B\rho' + C,$$

$$\omega\omega' = A\rho''^2 + B\rho'' + C.$$

It is obvious that

$$\omega = \frac{\omega\omega' - \omega\omega''}{\omega' - \omega''} = -\frac{A(\rho''^2 - \rho'^2) + B(\rho'' - \rho')}{a(\rho''^2 - \rho'^2) + b(\rho'' - \rho')} = -\frac{A(\rho'' + \rho') + B}{a(\rho'' + \rho') + b}.$$

Taking into consideration that $\rho'' + \rho' = s - \rho$, we obtain

$$\omega = \frac{A\rho - As - B}{-a\rho + as + b} = \frac{\alpha'\rho + \beta'}{\gamma'\rho + \delta'}.$$

The numbers α', β', γ', and δ' are rational. Multiplying numerator and denominator by an appropriate rational number we get the representation

$$\omega = \frac{\alpha\rho + \beta}{\gamma\rho + \delta},$$

in which the numbers $\alpha, \beta, \gamma, \delta$ are rational integers, whose common divisor is unity.

Such a representation is unique up to signs on $\alpha, \beta, \gamma, \delta$. In fact if

$$\frac{\alpha\rho + \beta}{\gamma\rho + \delta} = \frac{\alpha_1\rho + \beta_1}{\gamma_1\rho + \delta_1},$$

then

$$(\alpha\gamma_1 - \alpha_1\gamma)\rho^2 + (\beta\gamma_1 - \beta_1\gamma + \alpha\delta_1 - \alpha_1\delta)\rho + \beta\delta_1 - \beta_1\delta = 0,$$

from which

$$\alpha\gamma_1 - \alpha_1\gamma = 0,\ \beta\gamma_1 - \beta_1\gamma + \alpha\delta_1 - \alpha_1\delta = 0,\ \beta\delta_1 - \beta_1\delta = 0, \tag{1}$$

since the cubic number ρ cannot be a root of a quadratic equation with nonzero rational coefficients. Writing the first and third equations of (1) in the form

$$\frac{\alpha_1}{\alpha} = \frac{\gamma_1}{\gamma} = t,\ \frac{\beta_1}{\beta} = \frac{\delta_1}{\delta} = u$$

and substituting into the second equation $\alpha_1 = \alpha t$, $\gamma_1 = \gamma t$, $\beta_1 = \beta u$, $\delta_1 = \delta u$, we obtain

$$(\alpha\delta - \beta\gamma)\ (t - u) = 0.$$

Obviously $\alpha\delta - \beta\gamma \neq 0$, for otherwise ω would be rational. Therefore $t = u$ and the numbers $\alpha_1, \beta_1, \gamma_1, \delta_1$ are proportional to $\alpha, \beta, \gamma, \delta$.

If it is required that the numbers $\alpha_1, \beta_1, \gamma_1, \delta_1$ as well as $\alpha, \beta, \gamma, \delta$ have no common divisor different from 1, then the only possibility is

$$\frac{\alpha_1}{\alpha} = \frac{\beta_1}{\beta} = \frac{\gamma_1}{\gamma} = \frac{\delta_1}{\delta} = \pm 1,$$

which completes the proof.

In practice it is simpler to find a linear fractional representation by the method of indeterminate coefficients.

EXAMPLE. Represent as a linear fraction the number $\omega = \rho^2 - 3\rho + 1$, where ρ satisfies the equation $\rho^3 = \rho + 1$.

Let

$$\omega = \frac{\alpha\rho + \beta}{\gamma\rho + \delta} = \rho^2 - 3\rho + 1.$$

Multiplying by $\gamma\rho + \delta$ and replacing in the right-hand side ρ^3 by $\rho + 1$, we obtain

$$\alpha\rho + \beta = (\delta - 3\gamma)\,\rho^2 + (2\gamma - 3\delta)\,\rho + \delta + \gamma,$$

from which

$$\delta - 3\gamma = 0; \;\; 2\gamma - 3\delta = \alpha; \;\; \delta + \gamma = \beta,$$

and therefore $\delta = 3\gamma$, $\alpha = -7\gamma$, $\beta = 4\gamma$.

Substituting these values into the expression for ω we obtain

$$\omega = \frac{-7\gamma\rho + 4\gamma}{\gamma\rho + 3\gamma} = \frac{-7\rho + 4}{\rho + 3}.$$

§13. THE SOLUTION OF THE PROBLEM INVERSE TO THE TSCHIRNHAUSEN PROBLEM FOR A PAIR OF CUBIC EQUATIONS

Given two irreducible cubic equations the problem is to determine whether or not they generate the same cubic field. The most natural approach is to transform one of the equations by a Tschirnhausen transformation with the transformation function $\phi(z) = \alpha z^2 + \beta z + \gamma$, whose coefficients α, β, γ are left indeterminate, and then to see whether these coefficients can be chosen in such a way that the resulting transformed equation coincides with the second given equation. The problem reduces to finding a rational root of a certain equation of the 6th degree or in showing that this equation has no rational root. Unfortunately, the coefficients of this equation are expressed in a complicated way in terms of the coefficients of the two given equations and therefore can be quite large even if the given coefficients of the two cubics are quite small. It is possible nevertheless to modify this method so as to obtain a convenient practical solution of the problem.

We shall assume first of all that both given equations have been transformed so as to eliminate the term containing z^2, so that

$$z^3 = qz + n, \tag{1}$$

$$z^3 = \bar{q}z + \bar{n}, \tag{2}$$

where we shall assume that q, n, $\bar{q}$, $\bar{n}$ are rational integers and that both equations are irreducible. We transform equation (1) using the transformation function $\phi(z) = \alpha z^2 + \beta z + \gamma$, whose coefficients α, β, γ are as yet unknown, and equate the coefficients of the transformed equation with the coefficients of (2). We obtain $2\alpha q + 3\gamma = 0$ and two other equations. If we now substitute $\gamma = -(2/3)\alpha q$ in these remaining equations, we obtain

$$(3q\cdot\beta^2 + 9n\alpha\beta + q^2\alpha^2) - 3\bar{q} = 0, \tag{3}$$

$$[27n\beta^3 + 18q^2\beta^2\alpha + 27qn\beta\alpha^2 + (27n^2 - 2q^2)\alpha^3] - 27\bar{q} = 0, \tag{4}$$

where the expressions in parentheses are the quadratic and cubic covariants $H(x, y)$ and $Q(x, y)$ of the binary cubic form $f(x, y) = x^3 - qxy^2 - ny^3$ with $x = \beta$ and $y = \alpha$. But, as is well known (Cayley), there exists an identity (in (x, y)):

$$27\, Df^2 = -4H^3 - Q^2,$$

where $D = 4q^3 - 27n^2$ is the discriminant of the form f, and of equation (1). By (3) and (4) we obtain from this that $D\cdot[f(\beta, \alpha)]^2 = \bar{D}$, where $\bar{D} = 4\bar{q}^3 - 27\bar{n}^2$ is the discriminant of (2). This gives the well-known result that if two equations (1) and (2) form the same field, then their discriminants can differ only by a square factor.

If this is not the case, then there is no rational transformation of (1) into (2). If a transformation exists we have $D = D_1\cdot\Delta^2$ and $\bar{D} = D_1\cdot\bar{\Delta}^2$, where D_1 contains no square factors and Δ and $\bar{\Delta}$ are positive rational integers. In this case

$$f(\beta, \alpha) \mp \frac{\bar{\Delta}}{\Delta} = 0. \tag{5}$$

We eliminate β from (3), (4) and (5) by forming the combination $-(4) + 27n\,(5) + 6\alpha q\,(3)$, which is equal to zero. This combination is $8\alpha^3q^3 - 54\alpha^3n^2 - 18\alpha q\bar{q} + 27\bar{n} \mp 27\,(\bar{\Delta}/\Delta)\,n$; therefore if we let $\alpha = 3u_1/\Delta$ we get

$$D_1u_1^3 - q\bar{q}u_1 + \frac{\Delta\bar{n} \mp \bar{\Delta}n}{2} = 0. \tag{*}$$

On the other hand the combination $[\beta\,(3) - 3q\,(5)]\,q - 3\alpha n\,(3)$, which is also zero, works out to be $\beta(\alpha^2\Delta^2D_1 - 3q\bar{q}) + 9\alpha q\bar{n} \mp 3(\bar{\Delta}/\Delta)\,q^2 = 0$, and therefore if we let $\beta = v/\Delta$ and $\gamma = w/\Delta$ we obtain

$$u = 3u_1;\quad v = \frac{\mp q^2\bar{\Delta} \mp 9\bar{q}nu_1}{3D_1u_1^2 - q\bar{q}};\quad w = -2qu_1. \tag{**}$$

Here $3D_1u_1^2 - q\bar{q}$ is zero only if u_1 is a multiple root of (*). But in this case the third root of (*) is also rational and is not equal to the double root u_1 because (*) does not have three equal roots. (Since the coefficient of its square term is zero, it is not a perfect cube.) Therefore, if (*) has a rational double root, then it must have another rational root, which we denote by u_1, and then $3D_1u_1^2 - q\bar{q}$ is different from zero and the formulas (**) give the Tschirnhausen transformation.

The possibility remains that the equation (*) is of the form $D_1u_1^3 = 0$, but this can only happen if $q = \bar{q} = 0$; that is, if equations (1) and (2) are of the form $z^3 = n$ and $z^3 = \bar{n}$; but in this case they form the same field if and only if either $n\bar{n}$ or $\bar{n}/n$ is a perfect cube.

Hence equations (1) and (2) form the same field if and only if their discriminants are the same except for square factors and if at least one of the equations (*) has a rational root u_1 (we have here two equations because of $\mp$ signs on $\bar{\Delta}n$). This root u_1 must be a rational integer, since D_1 is not divisible by a square factor, and hence if p is a prime divisor of the denominator of u_1 which appears there to the degree κ, then in the first term, after cancellation, it would remain at least to the degree $3\kappa - 1$, and in the second and third terms when they are combined with a common denominator, it would appear to a degree not greater than κ. The number $(\Delta\bar{n} + \bar{\Delta}n)/2$ must therefore also be a rational integer. The coefficients α, β, γ of the transformation function ϕ are u/Δ, v/Δ, w/Δ, where u, v, w are rational integers obtained from (**). The fact that v is an integer is a good check on the calculations.

We have not discovered a simple criterion to decide a priori which of the two equations (*) has a rational root.

EXAMPLE. Given the cubic equations $z^3 = -3z - 2$ (I) and $116z^3 + 219z^2 + 138z + 29 = 0$. The first equation is of the required form, while the second one needs to be transformed. It is of the form $z^3 = -(219/116)\,z^2 - (138/116)\,z - 29/116$; letting $z' = 116z + 73$ we obtain for z' the equation $z'^3 = -21z' + 326$ (II). We look for a transformation from (I) to (II). We have $q = -3$, $n = -2$, $\bar{q} = -21$, $\bar{n} = 326$, $D = -216$, $\bar{D} = -216 \cdot 116^2$. Since D and $\bar{D}$ are the same except for a square factor the first condition is satisfied. We have $D_1 = -6$, $\Delta = 6$, $\bar{\Delta} = 696$ and (*) is therefore $-6u_1^3 - 63u_1 + (6 \cdot 326 \pm 696 \cdot 2)/2 = 0$, from which $u_1 = 6$ with the upper sign and from (*) we obtain $\alpha = 3$, $\beta = 2$, $\gamma = 6$, so that the transformation function from (I) to (II) is $\phi(z) = 3z^2 + 2z + 6$.

§14. A BASIS FOR INTEGERS IN A FIELD

A field Ω_ρ always contains three integers $\omega_0, \omega_1, \omega_2$ (in the case of a cubic field we will denote the first integer by ω_0 instead of ω_1 and the other two correspondingly by ω_1, ω_2 instead of ω_2, ω_3) such that every number ω in the field Ω_ρ can be expressed in terms of them as a homogeneous linear combination with rational integer coefficients as follows:

$$\omega = u\omega_0 + v\omega_1 + w\omega_2, \tag{1}$$

where u, v, w are rational integers. This triplet of numbers is called a basis of the field. If we approach this question geometrically, then the existence of a basis for the totality of integers in an algebraic field of any order n needs no demonstration because this totality of integers can be introduced, as in Chapter I, as a multiplicative lattice K_n, provided it is established that the following is true in the corresponding signature space R_n. First of all, the totality of all points whose coordinates are these numbers and their conjugates (if two of the conjugates $\omega^{(i)}, \omega^{(k)}$ are complex conjugates so that $\omega^{(i)} = \xi + i\mu$, $\omega^{(k)} = \xi - i\mu$, then we take for the corresponding coordinates the numbers ξ, μ) is an additive and multiplicative lattice (this follows from the fact that the sum and difference of two integers in a field is again an integer of the field). Secondly, these points lie in n-dimensions. This follows from the fact that all the conjugates of ω are distinct since the irreducible equation has no multiple roots, but then the points $1, \omega, \omega^2, \cdots, \omega^{n-1}$, together with the origin, are situated n-dimensionally, since the determinant

$$\begin{vmatrix} 1, \omega, \omega^2 \ldots\ldots \omega^{n-1} \\ 1, \omega', \omega'^2 \ldots\ldots \omega'^{n-1} \\ \cdots\cdots\cdots\cdots\cdots \\ \cdots\cdots\cdots\cdots\cdots \\ 1, \omega^{(n-1)}, \omega^{(n-1)2} \ldots \omega^{(n-1)n-1} \end{vmatrix} \neq 0$$

is a Vandermonde determinant and is equal to $(\omega - \omega')(\omega' - \omega'') \cdots (\omega^{(n-2)} - \omega^{(n-1)})$. Thirdly, all these points are discrete. For instance, there are no points in the neighborhood of the origin, because if all the coordinates of the point ω in R_n are very small in absolute value, then the coefficients of the equation which is satisfied by ω would also be very small, but the constant term, for instance, is a rational integer, different from zero and therefore at least 1 in absolute value.

From these three facts and from Lemma 1 of the Supplement to Chapter I about lattices in a real euclidean space, it follows that the totality of all the integers of a given field forms an n-dimensional lattice, i.e., it contains n numbers $\omega_1, \omega_2, \cdots, \omega_n$ such that any number ω in the field can be expressed in the form $\omega = u_1\omega_1 + u_2\omega_2 + \cdots + u_n\omega_n$, where $u_1, u_2, \cdots, u_n$ are rational integers.

We will give here, however, a purely arithmetical proof for a cubic field, although the argument could be made with equal ease for a field of any degree. We shall consider the denominators of the rational coefficients α, β, γ in the expression of ω in terms of ρ, namely $\omega = \alpha\rho^2 + \beta\rho + \gamma$. We have the three equations $\omega = \alpha\rho^2 + \beta\rho + \gamma$; $\omega' = \alpha\rho'^2 + \beta\rho' + \gamma$; $\omega'' = \alpha\rho''^2 + \beta\rho'' + \gamma$. Adding these equations, multiplying them respectively by ρ, ρ', ρ'' and then adding, and multiplying them by $\rho^2, \rho'^2, \rho''^2$ and adding, we obtain

$$\begin{aligned} S(\omega) &= \alpha\cdot s_2 + \beta\cdot s_1 + \gamma\cdot 3, \\ S(\omega\rho) &= \alpha\cdot s_3 + \beta\cdot s_2 + \gamma\cdot s_1, \\ S(\omega\rho^2) &= \alpha\cdot s_4 + \beta\cdot s_3 + \gamma\cdot s_2, \end{aligned} \tag{2}$$

where the coefficients of S and of s are symmetric functions of algebraic integers and therefore are rational integers. The determinant of the unknowns α, β, γ of the system (2) is the square of the determinant

$$\begin{vmatrix} 1 & \rho & \rho^2 \\ 1 & \rho' & \rho'^2 \\ 1 & \rho'' & \rho''^2 \end{vmatrix},$$

that is the discriminant D_ρ of ρ (see §11) and therefore the denominators of α, β, γ are divisors of D_ρ. Therefore every integer in the field Ω_ρ is of the form

$$\omega = \frac{a\rho^2 + b\rho + c}{D_\rho}, \tag{3}$$

where a, b, c are rational integers. The converse is not always true, i.e., a number of the form (3) with rational integers a, b, c may not be an algebraic integer.

Among the numbers in Ω_ρ there are three distinct types:

Type 1. Constant with respect to ρ, $\omega = c/D_\rho$.

Type 2. Linear with respect to ρ, $\omega = (b'\rho + c')/D_\rho$.

Type 3. Quadratic with respect to ρ, $\omega = (a''\rho^2 + b''\rho + c'')/D_\rho$.

In fact, the numbers 1, ρ, ρ^2 are themselves of these three types.

As a representative of the numbers of the first type, i.e., rational integers, we take the one with the least in absolute value nonzero c, namely $D_\rho/D_\rho = 1$ and call it ω_0. We denote by b'_0 the least b' among numbers of type 2 and call one of these numbers ω_1. Similarly we denote the least a'' found among the numbers of type 3 by a''_0 and take one of these numbers for ω_2. In other words let

$$\begin{aligned}\omega_0 &= 1,\\ \omega_1 &= \frac{b'_0\rho + c'_0}{D_\rho},\\ \omega_2 &= \frac{a''_0\rho^2 + b''_0\rho + c''_0}{D_\rho}\end{aligned} \tag{4}$$

We now show that every integer ω in the field Ω_ρ can be represented in the form (1) with rational integer coefficients u, v, w.

In fact, suppose that we are given an integer ω, then it has the form (3). The coefficient a of this number is either zero or is divisible by a''_0, for otherwise by adding or subtracting from ω multiples of ω_2 we could obtain an integer in Ω_ρ of type 3 with an a smaller than a''_0, which contradicts our assumption that a''_0 is the smallest a''.

Now let $a = w \cdot a''_0$. Then the integer $\omega - w\omega_2$ has $a = 0$ and therefore is either of the first or second type. Again adding to or subtracting from $\omega - w\omega_2$ an appropriate number of multiples of ω_1 we see that $b = v \cdot b'_0$, where v is a rational integer or zero. Then the integer $\omega - w\omega_2 - v\omega_1$ has $a = b = 0$, and therefore is a rational integer or zero. Letting it be equal to u, we have $\omega = u \cdot 1 + v\omega_1 + w \cdot \omega_2$, where u, v, and w are rational integers, so that the numbers $1, \omega_1, \omega_2$ form a basis.

If $\omega_0, \omega_1, \omega_2$ form a basis, then the integers in the field

$$\bar{\omega}_0 = u_0\omega_0 + v_0\omega_1 + w_0\omega_2;\ \bar{\omega}_1 = u_1\omega_0 + v_1\omega_1 + w_1\omega_2;\ \bar{\omega}_2 = u_2\omega_0 + v_2\omega_1 + w_2\omega_2$$

also form a basis of the field if and only if

$$\begin{vmatrix} u_0 & v_0 & w_0 \\ u_1 & v_1 & w_1 \\ u_2 & v_2 & w_2 \end{vmatrix} = \pm 1.$$

In fact if this determinant is ± 1, then the original basis elements and all the integers in the field are expressible as homogeneous linear combinations with integer coefficients of $\omega_0, \omega_1, \omega_2$. Conversely, if $\bar{\omega}_0, \bar{\omega}_1, \bar{\omega}_2$ form a basis in the field, that is if $\omega_0, \omega_1, \omega_2$ are each expressible as a homogeneous linear combination with integer coefficients of $\bar{\omega}_0, \bar{\omega}_1, \bar{\omega}_2$, then the determinant is equal to ± 1, since if the coefficients in the transformation of $\bar{\omega}_0, \bar{\omega}_1, \bar{\omega}_2$ into $\omega_0, \omega_1, \omega_2$ are $\bar{u}_0, \bar{v}_0, \bar{w}_0$; $\bar{u}_1, \bar{v}_1, \bar{w}_1$; $\bar{u}_2, \bar{v}_2, \bar{w}_2$, then the determinant of the transformation of $\omega_0, \omega_1, \omega_2$ into $\omega_0, \omega_1, \omega_2$ (that is the determinant of the identity transformation) is the product of the determinants

$$\begin{vmatrix} u_0 v_0 w_0 \\ u_1 v_1 w_1 \\ u_2 v_2 w_2 \end{vmatrix} \cdot \begin{vmatrix} \bar{u}_0 & \bar{v}_0 & \bar{w}_0 \\ \bar{u}_1 & \bar{v}_1 & \bar{w}_1 \\ \bar{u}_2 & \bar{v}_2 & \bar{w}_2 \end{vmatrix}$$

and is equal to ± 1. But each of the determinants, having for elements rational integers, is itself a rational integer and is therefore equal to ± 1.

The square of the determinant

$$\begin{vmatrix} \omega_0 \omega_1 \omega_2 \\ \omega_0' \omega_1' \omega_2' \\ \omega_0'' \omega_1'' \omega_2'' \end{vmatrix}$$

is invariant for any basis of the field. It is called the discriminant of the field and is denoted by D_Ω.

The discriminant of the field, being a symmetric function of ρ, ρ', ρ'', is a rational number, and since it is a rational function of algebraic integers it must be a rational integer.

For a geometric interpretation of all this see Chapter I.

§15. THE CONNECTION BETWEEN RINGS OF INTEGERS IN CUBIC FIELDS CONTAINING 1 AND CLASSES OF IRREDUCIBLE BINARY CUBIC FORMS WITH RATIONAL INTEGER COEFFICIENTS

In this section we shall consider rings of integers in a cubic field containing 1 and some primitive numbers of the cubic field under consideration. The totality of all integers in the field is, for example, such a ring. The totality of all numbers of the form $u\rho^2 + v\rho + w$, where u, v, w go over all rational integers is also an instance of such a ring. Let ρ be a primitive number in a cubic field, which is contained in some ring of this type. Then the numbers 1, ρ and ρ^2 are contained in this ring O, and therefore if we express all the numbers in the field Ω in terms of 1, ρ, and ρ^2, then O will contain numbers of the three types discussed in the derivation of a basis in the preceding section, and hence we can show exactly in the same way that the ring O has a basis $\omega_0, \omega_1, \omega_2$, where ω_0, in particular, can be taken as 1. We shall call such a basis of the ring O a *unitary* basis. The totality of all numbers which can be expressed homogeneously as a linear combination with rational integer coefficients of the three numbers $\omega_0, \omega_1, \omega_2$ will be called a *module* with basis $\omega_0, \omega_1, \omega_2$ and will be denoted by $[\omega_0, \omega_1, \omega_2]$. The ring having the basis $[\omega_0, \omega_1, \omega_2]$ will be denoted by $O[\omega_0, \omega_1, \omega_2]$.

It is not true that any two numbers ω_1, ω_2 of the field Ω together with 1 form a basis of a ring. In fact, for example, the module $[1, \rho, 2\rho^2]$, where ρ is some primitive integer in Ω, is not a ring, since the product $\rho \cdot \rho = \rho^2$ does not lie in it. In order to ascertain whether the module $[1, \omega_1, \omega_2]$ is a ring it is sufficient to ascertain whether all the products of its numbers lie in it. For this to be true, it is necessary and sufficient that the numbers ω_1^2, ω_2^2 and $\omega_1\omega_2$ lie in $[1, \omega_1, \omega_2]$. We express these three numbers in Ω as a linear combination of $1, \omega_1, \omega_2$ with rational coefficients, which can always be done if the determinant of the transformation from the basis of the field Ω to the triple $1, \omega_1, \omega_2$ is different from zero (which we shall assume about the proposed module).

Let

$$\begin{aligned} \omega_1^2 &= A_0 + A_1\omega_1 + A_2\omega_2, \\ \omega_2^2 &= B_0 + B_1\omega_1 + B_2\omega_2, \\ \omega_1\omega_2 &= C_0 + C_1\omega_1 + C_2\omega_2. \end{aligned} \tag{1}$$

If the nine numbers $A_0, A_1, A_2, B_0, B_1, B_2, C_0, C_1, C_2$ are integers, then the module $[1, \omega_1, \omega_2]$ is a ring; in the opposite case it is not. These nine numbers, which it is sufficient to know in order to perform all the multiplications in the ring, we will call "multiplication" coefficients.

The multiplication coefficients are not independent. In fact

$$\begin{aligned} A_0 &= A_2(C_1 - B_2) - C_2(A_1 - C_2), \\ B_0 &= B_1(C_2 - A_1) - C_1(B_2 - C_1), \\ C_0 &= A_2B_1 - C_1C_2, \end{aligned} \tag{2}$$

which can be easily seen by calculating $\omega_1^2 \cdot \omega_2$ and $\omega_1\omega_2 \cdot \omega_1$ and equating the coefficients after reducing them to the first degree in ω_1, ω_2 using (1).

The square of the determinant $\begin{vmatrix} 1 & \omega_1 & \omega_2 \\ 1 & \omega_1' & \omega_2' \\ 1 & \omega_1'' & \omega_2'' \end{vmatrix}$, where ω', ω'' are the conjugates of ω in the cubic field Ω and where $1, \omega_1, \omega_2$ is a basis of the ring O, is called the discriminant of the ring O and is denoted by D_O. If $1, \theta_1, \theta_2$ is another unitary basis of the same ring O, and

$$\begin{aligned} \theta_1 &= u_1 + v_1\omega_1 + w_1\omega_2, \\ \theta_2 &= u_2 + v_2\omega_1 + w_2\omega_2, \end{aligned}$$

then $\begin{vmatrix} v_1 w_1 \\ v_2 w_2 \end{vmatrix} = \pm 1$. Conversely if $u_1, v_1, w_1, u_2, v_2, w_2$ are rational integers and if $\begin{vmatrix} v_1 w_1 \\ v_2 w_2 \end{vmatrix} = \pm 1$, then $1, \theta_1, \theta_2$ forms another unitary basis of the same ring. If ρ is a number of the ring O and if $\rho = a_0 + a_1\omega_1 + a_2\omega_2$, $\rho^2 = b_0 + b_1\omega_1 + b_2\omega_2$,

then the discriminant $D_\rho = \begin{vmatrix} 1 & \rho & \rho^2 \\ 1 & \rho' & \rho'^2 \\ 1 & \rho'' & \rho''^2 \end{vmatrix}^2$ of the number ρ is obviously the discriminant of the ring D_O, multiplied by the square of the determinant $\Delta = \begin{vmatrix} a_1 a_2 \\ b_1 b_2 \end{vmatrix}$. We find ω_1, ω_2 from ρ and ρ^2,

$$\omega_1 = \frac{-a_2\rho^2 + b_2\rho + a_2 b_0 - a_0 b_2}{\Delta},$$

$$\omega_2 = \frac{a_1\rho^2 - b_1\rho + a_0 b_1 - a_1 b_0}{\Delta},$$

and therefore any number ω of the ring O is of the form $(u\rho^2 + v\rho + w)/\Delta$, where u, v, w are rational integers.

Every number of the ring O is therefore expressed as a homogeneous linear form in $1, \rho, \rho^2$ with rational coefficients, whose common denominator is Δ. The determinant Δ is called the *index* of ρ with respect to the ring O. In particular if O is the maximal ring of all integers in the field, then Δ is simply called the index of ρ.

We next calculate the index Δ of the number ρ with respect to the ring O in terms of the coefficeints a_1, a_2 of the number ρ and in terms of the multiplication coefficients (1). We obtain

$$\Delta = a_1^3 A_2 + a_1^2 a_2 (2C_2 - A_1) + a_1 a_2^2 (B_2 - 2C_1) - a_2^3 B_1.$$

We see that the index of ρ with respect to the ring O is the value of the binary cubic form

$$(A_2, 2C_2 - A_1, B_2 - 2C_1, -B_1) = f(x, y) \tag{3}$$

for $x = a_1$, $y = a_2$. We shall call this form the *index-form* of the basis $1, \omega_1, \omega_2$ of the ring O and we shall denote it by $f[1, \omega_1, \omega_2]$.

We shall call the bases $1, \omega_1, \omega_2$ and $1, \omega_1 + c_1, \omega_2 + c_2$, where c_1 and c_2 are any rational integers, *parallel* unitary bases, and the totality of all bases parallel to each other we shall call a *parallel* of unitary bases. If the product $\omega_1\omega_2$ is a rational number, then we shall call the unitary basis $1, \omega_1, \omega_2$ *normal.*

THEOREM I. *There is one and only one normal basis among all the parallel unitary bases of the ring O.*

In fact, consider the product

$$(\omega_1+c_1)(\omega_2+c_2)=\omega_1\omega_2+\omega_1 c_2+\omega_2 c_1+c_1c_2= \\ =(C_1+c_1)\omega_1+(C_2+c_2)\omega_2+C_0+c_1c_2.$$

We see that if we put $c_1=-C_1, c_2=-C_2$, we will obtain the normal basis 1, $\omega_1+c_1, \omega_2+c_2$.

THEOREM II. *The same index-form corresponds to all parallel unitary bases of the ring O.*

Let the multiplication coefficients of a parallel basis be

$$\overline{A}_0,\ \overline{A}_1,\ \overline{A}_2,\quad \overline{B}_0,\ \overline{B}_1,\ \overline{B}_2,\quad \overline{C}_0,\ \overline{C}_1,\ \overline{C}_2.$$

Then

$$\overline{A}_1=A_1+2C_1;\ \overline{B}_1=B_1;\ \overline{C}_1=C_1+C_2; \\ \overline{A}_2=A_2;\ \overline{B}_2=B_2+2C_2;\ \overline{C}_2=C_2+C_1.$$

Writing the index-form corresponding to this basis, we see that

$$f[1, \omega_1+c_1, \omega_2+c_2]=f[1, \omega_1, \omega_2].$$

THEOREM III. *To every irreducible binary cubic form with integer coefficients corresponds a parallel of unitary bases of some ring of integers in a cubic field, containing* 1.

Let $f=(A_2, -A_1, B_2, -B_1)$ be an irreducible binary cubic form with integer coefficients. Consider the numbers ω_1 and ω_2 such that ω_1 is a root of the equation

$$z^3-A_1z^2+A_2B_2z-A_2^2B_1=0, \qquad (4)$$

and ω_2 is a root of

$$z^3-B_2z^2+A_1B_1z-A_2B_1^2=0. \qquad (5)$$

Then $1/\omega_2$ is a root of the equation

$$-z^3A_2B_1^2+z^2A_1B_1-zB_2+1=0, \quad \text{or} \quad z^3-\frac{A_1}{A_2B_1}z^2+\frac{B_2A_2}{A_2^2B_1^2}z-\frac{A_2^2B_1}{A_2^3B_1^3}=0,$$

that is

$$\frac{A_2B_1}{\omega_2}=\omega_1, \quad \text{or} \quad \omega_1\omega_2=A_2B_1.$$

Therefore $1, \omega_1, \omega_2$ is a normal basis of some module.

It is not hard to see that the module $[1, \omega_1, \omega_2]$ is a ring. In fact, let $\omega_1^2 = \overline{A}_0 + \overline{A}_1\omega_1 + \overline{A}_2\omega_2$, $\omega_2^2 = \overline{B}_0 + \overline{B}_1\omega_1 + \overline{B}_2\omega_2$, $\omega_1\omega_2 = \overline{C}_0 + \overline{C}_1\omega_1 + \overline{C}_2\omega_2$, which can always be done if the discriminant of the basis $1, \omega_1, \omega_2$ is not equal to zero. But it is easily seen that it is different from zero if the form is irreducible. Taking into consideration that $\omega_2 = A_2B_1/\omega_1$, we obtain

$$\omega_1^3 - \overline{A}_1\omega_1^2 - \overline{A}_0\omega_1 - \overline{A}_2B_1A_2 = 0.$$

Comparing this with (4) we have

$$\overline{A}_0 = -A_2B_2;\ \overline{A}_1 = A_1;\ \overline{A}_2 = A_2.$$

Analogously we get

$$\overline{B}_0 = -A_1B_1;\ \overline{B}_1 = B_1;\ \overline{B}_2 = B_2, \text{ and } \overline{C}_0 = A_2B_1;\ \overline{C}_1 = 0;\ \overline{C}_2 = 0.$$

We see in this way by (1) and (2) that $[1, \omega_1, \omega_2]$ is a ring and that the index-form of its unitary normal basis $1, \omega_1, \omega_2$ is in fact $(A_2, -A_1, B_2, -B_1)$.

THEOREM IV. *To equivalent unitary bases of the ring O correspond equivalent index-forms and conversely, where* $f[1, \theta_1, \theta_2] = f[1, \omega_1, \omega_2]\binom{v_1 w_1}{v_2 w_2}$.

In fact, let $1, \omega_1, \omega_2$ be a normal unitary basis of a given ring, then

$$\begin{aligned}\omega_1^2 &= -A_2B_2 + A_1\omega_1 + A_2\omega_2,\\ \omega_2^2 &= -A_1B_1 + B_1\omega_1 + B_2\omega_2,\\ \omega_1\omega_2 &= A_2B_1.\end{aligned} \tag{6}$$

Let $\theta_1 = u_1 + v_1\omega_1 + w_1\omega_2$; $\theta_2 = u_2 + v_2w_1 + w_2\omega_2$ be another unitary basis of the same ring, that is $\begin{vmatrix} v_1 w_1 \\ v_2 w_2 \end{vmatrix} = \pm 1$. Since the index-forms corresponding to parallel bases are identical we can suppose that $u_1 = u_2 = 0$. Making use of (6), we obtain

$$\theta_1^2 = -v_1^2A_2B_2 - w_1^2A_1B_1 + 2v_1w_1A_2B_1 + (v_1^2A_1 + w_1^2B_1)\omega_1 + (v_1^2A_2 + w_1^2B_2)\omega_2.$$

Making the substitutions

$$\omega_1 = w_2\theta_1 - w_1\theta_2;\ \omega_2 = v_1\theta_1 - v_2\theta_2,$$

which express ω_1, ω_2 in terms of θ_1, θ_2, we can calculate the multiplication coefficients of the basis $1, \theta_1, \theta_2$ and from them by (3) the coefficients of the index-form $f[1, \theta_1, \theta_2]$.

If, on the other hand, we transform the form $f[1, \omega_1, \omega_2]$ by the substitution $\begin{pmatrix} v_1 w_1 \\ v_2 w_2 \end{pmatrix}$, we obtain $f[1, \omega_1, \omega_2]_{\begin{pmatrix} v_1 w_1 \\ v_2 w_2 \end{pmatrix}} = f[1, \theta_1, \theta_2]$.

We have therefore established a one-to-one correspondence between classes of irreducible binary cubic forms with integer coefficients and the ring O of integers in cubic fields containing 1, or more precisely, with triplets of such conjugate rings, that is, with irreducible three-dimensional multiplicative lattices containing the point 1.

If we write the form f as $f = (a, b, c, d)$ and if ω_1, ω_2 are, respectively, roots of equations (4) and (5) corresponding to this form, namely,

$$z^3 + bz^2 + acz + a^2 d = 0, \tag{4'}$$

$$z^3 - cz^2 + dbz - d^2 a = 0, \tag{5'}$$

then we shall call ω_1 and ω_2 the left and right roots of the form f. We see that $1, \omega_1, \omega_2$ form a normal unitary basis of the ring O corresponding to the form (a, b, c, d), where the multiplication coefficients are as follows:

$$\begin{aligned} \omega_1^2 &= -ac - b\omega_1 + a\omega_2, \\ \omega_2^2 &= -bd - d\omega_1 + c\omega_2, \\ \omega_1\omega_2 &= -ad. \end{aligned} \tag{7}$$

THEOREM V. *The discriminant of the index-form is equal to the discriminant of the ring corresponding to the index-form.*

In fact, the discriminant of the basis $1, \omega_1, \omega_2$ is equal to

$$|1, \omega_1, \omega_2|^2 = \left|1, \omega_1, \frac{\omega_1^2 + b\omega_1 + ac}{a}\right|^2 = \frac{1}{a^2}|1, \omega_1, \omega_1^2|^2,$$

but $|1, \omega_1, \omega_1^2|^2$ is the discriminant of the number ω_1, or what is the same thing of the equation (4′). Calculating this discriminant and dividing by a^2, we obtain the discriminant of f as follows:

$$D_f = b^2c^2 + 18abcd - 4ac^3 - 4b^3d - 27a^2d^2.$$

§ 16. THE SOLUTION OF THE PROBLEM OF EQUIVALENCE FOR TWO IRREDUCIBLE BINARY CUBIC FORMS WITH INTEGER COEFFICIENTS

Given two binary cubic forms (a, b, c, d) and $(\bar{a}, \bar{b}, \bar{c}, \bar{d})$ with rational integer coefficients, having the same discriminant, then the problem arises of detertermining whether these forms are equivalent, that is whether there exists a substitution $x = \alpha\bar{x} + \beta\bar{y}$, $y = \gamma\bar{x} + \delta\bar{y}$ with rational integer coefficients $\alpha, \beta, \gamma, \delta$ and determinant $\alpha\delta - \beta\gamma = \pm 1$ such that $ax^3 + bx^2y + cxy^2 + dy^3 = \bar{a}\bar{x}^3 + \bar{b}\bar{x}^2\bar{y} + \bar{c}\bar{x}\bar{y}^2 + \bar{d}\bar{y}^3$. To do this, we note that if

$$f = (a, b, c, d) = a(x - \xi y)(x - \xi' y)(x - \xi'' y),$$

where ξ, ξ', ξ'' are roots of the equation $f(x, 1) = 0$, then

$$\bar{f}(\bar{x}, \bar{y}) = a(\alpha\bar{x} + \beta\bar{y} - \xi(\gamma\bar{x} + \delta\bar{y}))\cdot(\alpha\bar{x} + \beta\bar{y} - \xi'(\gamma\bar{x} + \delta\bar{y}))\cdot \cdot(\alpha\bar{x} + \beta\bar{y} - \xi''(\gamma\bar{x} + \delta\bar{y})),$$

that is, the roots of the equation $\bar{f}(\bar{x}, 1) = 0$ are $\bar{\xi} = (\delta\xi - \beta)/(-\gamma\xi + \alpha)$. Hence $\bar{\xi}$ is rationally expressible in terms of ξ. Let $\bar{\xi} = u\xi^2 + v\xi + w$. Then if we let $-b/a = s$, $-c/a = q$, $-d/a = n$, the numbers $\alpha, \beta, \gamma, \delta$ are proportional to the numbers

$$\alpha'' = us + v;\quad \beta'' = u^2n - vw - uws;\quad \gamma'' = u;\quad \delta'' = v^2 - uw - u^2q + uvs. \qquad (1)$$

Bringing these rational numbers to a common denominator we consider the numerators. Taking out their greatest common divisor we obtain the least integers $\alpha', \beta', \gamma', \delta'$ proportional to $\alpha, \beta, \gamma, \delta$ and having the corresponding signs. We shall also assume that $a > 0$ and $\bar{a} > 0$ (since if this were not the case we could arrange it by a preliminary substitution $\begin{pmatrix} -1 & 0 \\ 0 & -1 \end{pmatrix}$). Then the following theorem holds.

THEOREM. *The forms f and $\bar{f}$ are equivalent if and only if $\alpha'\delta' - \beta'\gamma' = \pm 1$, where the transformation $\begin{pmatrix} \alpha & \beta \\ \gamma & \delta \end{pmatrix}$ is $\begin{pmatrix} \alpha' & \beta' \\ \gamma' & \delta' \end{pmatrix}$, in case $\alpha'\delta' - \beta'\gamma' = 1$, and is $\begin{pmatrix} -\alpha' & -\beta' \\ -\gamma' & -\delta' \end{pmatrix}$, if $\alpha'\delta' - \beta'\gamma' = -1$.*

PROOF. In fact $\alpha''\delta'' - \beta''\gamma'' = -u^3(sq + n) + u^2v(s^2 - q) + 2uv^2s + v^3 = f(-\gamma'', \alpha'') = N(-u\xi + v + us) = N((\bar{\xi}' - \bar{\xi}'')/(\xi' - \xi'')) = \pm a/\bar{a}^2$. The last equality holds because $D_f = D_{\bar{f}}$ (here we denote by N the norm in the cubic field Ω_ξ).

Let $\alpha'' = \lambda\alpha'$; $\beta'' = \lambda\beta'$; $\gamma'' = \lambda\gamma'$; $\delta'' = \lambda\delta'$, where $\lambda > 0$. In this case if $\alpha'\delta' - \beta'\gamma' = \pm 1$, then $\alpha''\delta'' - \beta''\gamma'' = \pm\lambda^2$, and therefore $\lambda = |a/\bar{a}|$ and we get $N(-\gamma'\xi + \alpha') = \pm|\bar{a}/a|$. But we have $\bar{f}(\bar{x}, 1) = \bar{a}\cdot N(\bar{x} - (\delta'\xi - \beta')/(-\gamma'\xi + \alpha'))$, and therefore $\bar{f}(\bar{x}, \bar{y}) = (\bar{a}/N(-\gamma'\xi + \alpha'))\cdot N(\alpha'\bar{x} + \beta'\bar{y} - \xi(\gamma'\bar{x} + \delta'\bar{y}))$, from which, taking into consideration the value of $N(-\gamma'\xi + \alpha')$ obtained earlier, we now have

$$\bar{f}(\bar{x}, \bar{y}) = \pm a\cdot N(\alpha'\bar{x} + \beta'\bar{y} - \xi(\gamma'\bar{x} + \delta'\bar{y})) = \pm f(x, y)_{\begin{pmatrix}\alpha' & \beta'\\ \gamma' & \delta'\end{pmatrix}}.$$

EXAMPLE. Given the two forms $(a, b, c, d) = (1, 0, 3, 2)$ and $(\bar{a}, \bar{b}, \bar{c}, \bar{d}) = (116, 219, 138, 29)$; $f(z, 1) = z^3 + 3z + 2$; $\bar{f}(z, 1) = 116z^3 + 219z^2 + 138z + 29$; $D_f = D_{\bar{f}} = -216$; ξ is a root of the equation $z^3 = -3z - 2$ (I); $\bar{\xi}$ is a root of the equation $z^3 = -(219/116)z^2 - (138/116)z - (29/116)$; $\zeta = 116\bar{\xi} + 73$ is a root of the equation $z^3 = -21z + 326$ (II). In the example in §13 we found the transformation function ϕ of equation (I) into (II) to be $\zeta = 3\xi^2 + 2\xi + 6$ and therefore $\bar{\xi} = (3/116)\xi^2 + (2/116)\xi - (67/116)$, from which formula (1) gives

$$\alpha' = 2;\ \beta' = 1;\ \gamma' = 3;\ \delta' = 2;\ \alpha'\delta' - \beta'\gamma' = 1.$$

Hence $(116, 219, 138, 29) = (1, 0, 3, 2)_{\begin{pmatrix}2, & 1\\ 3, & 2\end{pmatrix}}$, and the forms are equivalent.

Hence the solution of the problem of equivalence of two binary cubic forms with integer coefficients is achieved by a combination of the theorem given in this section with the solution of the problem inverse to the Tchirnhausen problem given in §13 without using the theory of the reduction of forms.

§17. CALCULATION OF A BASIS FOR A CUBIC FIELD ACCORDING TO VORONOÏ

We shall next consider the calculation of a basis for any ring containing a given primitive number ρ of a cubic field and the calculation of a basis for the ring of all integers in the cubic field according to Voronoï. Let ρ be any given primitive integer in the cubic field Ω and let $\rho^3 = s\rho^2 + q\rho + n$ be the equation which it satisfies; let O be a ring of integers in the field Ω, containing 1 and the integer ρ.

DEFINITION. We shall call a basis of the ring O "unitary", as it was already done in §15, if it is of the form

$$1,\ \omega_1,\ \omega_2;$$

we shall call it "normal" if it is unitary and if the product $\omega_1 \cdot \omega_2$ is rational and we shall call it "canonical in ρ" if it is of the form

$$1, \quad \frac{u\rho + v}{\Delta}, \quad \frac{\lambda\rho^2 + \mu\rho + \nu}{\Delta},$$

where u, v, λ, μ, ν, Δ are rational integers.

LEMMA. *Every ring O of the above type has a unitary canonical normal basis.*

This is obvious, because we can normalize by transforming a basis to a parallel basis (see §15); this in turn can be transformed into a canonical basis which exists for every such ring (see §§14 and 15).

The method of Voronoĭ seeks a basis of the ring O which is at the same time unitary, normal and canonical in ρ.

Let 1, ϕ, ψ be one of the normal, canonical in ρ bases of a given ring O. From $\phi = (u\rho + v)/\Delta$ we obtain $\rho = (\Delta/u)\,\phi - v/u$.

Since ρ is by assumption a number of the ring O, it must be representable linearly in terms of the basis elements of the ring with integer coefficients. Therefore $\Delta = u \cdot \delta$, $v = -u \cdot t$, where δ and t are rational integers. Hence

$$\phi = \frac{\rho - t}{\delta}. \tag{1}$$

From $\rho = \delta \cdot \phi + t$ we see that $D_\rho = \delta^6 \cdot D_\phi$, that is δ appears to the 6th power in D_ρ. Since O is a ring and 1, ϕ, ψ is a unitary normal basis of O we have

$$\phi^2 = -ac - b\phi + a\psi, \tag{2}$$

$$\psi^2 = -bd - d\phi + c\psi, \tag{3}$$

$$\phi\psi = -ad. \tag{4}$$

We now write the equation satisfied by ϕ in two different forms and equate them. In the first place, eliminating ψ from (2) and (4) we obtain

$$\phi^3 + b\phi^2 + ac\phi + a^2 d = 0; \tag{5}$$

on the other hand, we have

$$F(\rho) = F(t + \delta\phi) = F(t) + F'(t) \cdot \delta\phi + \frac{F''(t)}{1 \cdot 2}\,\delta^2\phi^2 + \delta^3\phi^3 = 0,$$

where

$$F(z) = z^3 - sz^2 - qz - n = 0$$

is the equation satisfied by ρ, that is,

$$\phi^3 + \frac{F''(t)}{2\delta}\cdot\phi^2 + \frac{F'(t)}{\delta^2}\cdot\phi + \frac{F(t)}{\delta^3} = 0. \tag{6}$$

Equating the coefficients of (5) and (6) we obtain

$$b = \frac{F''(t)}{2\delta};\quad c = \frac{F'(t)}{\delta^2 a};\quad d = \frac{F(t)}{\delta^3 a^2}, \tag{7}$$

or writing these as congruences, we have

$$\frac{1}{2}F''(t) \equiv 0 \pmod{\delta};\quad F'(t) \equiv 0 \pmod{\delta^2 a};\quad F(t) \equiv 0 \pmod{\delta^3 a^2}. \tag{7'}$$

The discriminant of O is

$$D_O = |1,\ \varphi,\ \psi|^2 = \left|1,\ \varphi,\ \frac{\varphi^2 + b\varphi + ac}{a}\right|^2 = \frac{1}{a^2}|1,\ \varphi,\ \varphi^2|^2 = \frac{1}{a^2}\cdot D_\varphi,$$

so that a^2 divides D_ϕ; therefore

$$D_\rho = \delta^6\cdot a^2\cdot D_O. \tag{8}$$

From (4) and (7) we obtain

$$\psi = -\frac{ad}{\varphi} = -\frac{F(t)}{\delta^3 a\varphi} = \frac{F(\rho) - F(t)}{\delta^2 a(\rho - t)},$$

from which

$$\psi = \frac{1}{\delta^2 a}[\rho^2 + F_1(t)\rho + F_2(t)], \tag{9}$$

where

$$F_1(t) = t - s,$$
$$F_2(t) = t^2 - st - q.$$

In any ring O of integers in a cubic field Ω_ρ, containing 1 and ρ, the elements of its normal, canonical in ρ basis are of the forms (1) and (9). Conversely, if the rational integers δ, a, D_O, t, satisfy equations (7') and (8), then 1, ϕ, ψ is a normal, canonical basis of such a ring.

In fact, it follows from (9) that $\phi\cdot\psi = -ad$; moreover from (6) $\phi^2 = -ac - b\phi + a\psi$, and from this, multiplying by ψ and remembering that $\phi\psi = -ad$, we obtain $\psi^2 = -bd - d\phi + c\psi$. Finally, eliminating ϕ and ψ from these two equations we have

$$\phi^3 + b\phi^2 + ac\phi + a^2 d = 0$$

and

$$\psi^3 - c\psi^2 + bd\psi - ad^2 = 0.$$

Therefore the numbers ϕ, ψ are integers in the same cubic field and 1, ϕ, ψ is a normal basis of the ring O of integers in this field containing 1. Hence we have proved the following theorem.

THEOREM I. *If* ρ *is a primitive integer in a cubic field satisfying the equation*

$$F(\rho) = \rho^3 - s\rho^2 - q\rho - n = 0,$$

whose discriminant is D_ρ *and if the numbers* δ, a, D_O, *and* t *are rational integers satisfying the condition* $D_\rho = \delta^6 a^2 D_O$ *and the congruences*

$$\frac{1}{2} F''(t) \equiv 0 \pmod{\delta}; \quad F'(t) \equiv 0 \pmod{\delta^2 a}; \quad F(t) \equiv 0 \pmod{\delta^3 a^2},$$

then the numbers

$$1, \quad \frac{\rho - t}{\delta}, \quad \frac{\rho^2 + (t-s)\rho + (t^2 - st - q)}{\delta^2 a}$$

form a normal, canonical in ρ *basis of the ring* O *of integers in the field* Ω_ρ *containing* 1 *and* ρ, *whose discriminant is* D_O. *In this way all normal, canonical in* ρ *bases of all such rings can be obtained. Here we can suppose that* $-a\delta/2 < t \leq a\delta/2$.

The last assertion follows from the fact that if t is a solution of the above congruences for given δ and a, then $t + \delta a \cdot j$, where j is any rational integer, is also a solution of these congruences, as can be easily checked by direct calculations. Theorem I shows that all rings of integers in a cubic field containing 1 and a given primitive integer in the field ρ can be readily found.

REMARK. The index-form (a, b, c, d) of this basis is of the form

$$a = a; \quad b = \frac{F''(t)}{2\delta}; \quad c = \frac{F'(t)}{\delta^2 a}; \quad d = \frac{F(t)}{\delta^3 a^2}.$$

If it is required to calculate a basis for the totality of all integers of the field Ω_ρ, then it will be necessary to find those δ and a for which the above congruences have a solution with $-a\delta/2 < t \leq a\delta/2$ and for which the number $\delta^6 a^2$ has the greatest possible value. This is not difficult since $\delta^6 a^2 D_O = D_\rho$, and therefore in any special case one would have to try in general only a small number of relatively small divisors of D_ρ.

However, the calculation of a basis of the field Ω_ρ can be further simplified. In fact we can take the equation satisfied by ρ in the form not containing the term in ρ^2, i.e.: $\rho^3 = q\rho + n$, and we can also assume that there exists no rational integer τ whose square divides q and whose cube divides n; for if there were such a τ we could replace ρ by $\tau\rho$ and divide out such a common factor. Under the above assumptions

$$\frac{1}{2} F''(t) = 3t = b\delta, \tag{10}$$

where δ and t can have no common factor τ different from unity, since from $F'(t) = 3t^2 - q \equiv 0 \pmod{\delta^2 a}$ it follows that q is divisible by τ^2, and taking this into consideration it follows from $F(t) = t^3 - qt - n \equiv 0 \pmod{\delta^3 a^2}$ that n is divisible by τ^3. But we have assumed that this is not the case. Therefore it follows from (10) that $\delta = 1$ or 3. If the number $(\rho \pm 1)/3$ is not an algebraic integer, then $\delta = 1$; if it is an algebraic integer, then $\delta = 3$. This follows immediately from the properties of a canonical basis. This number can be easily seen to be an integer or not according as the following congruences are satisfied or not.

$$\begin{aligned} 3 - q &\equiv 0 \pmod 9, \\ n \pm (q-1) &\equiv 0 \pmod{27}. \end{aligned} \tag{$*$}$$

This gives us the following theorem of Voronoĭ.

THEOREM II. *If ρ is a primitive integer in a cubic field satisfying the equation $F(\rho) = \rho^3 - q\rho - n = 0$, and if there is no integer τ whose square divides q and whose cube divides n, then a basis of the field Ω_ρ can be found as follows:*

1. *If the congruences (*) are not satisfied, one must find the greatest square factor a of the discriminant D_ρ of the equation $F(\rho) = 0$ for which the congruences*

$$F'(t) \equiv 0 \pmod a,$$
$$F(t) \equiv 0 \pmod{a^2}$$

have a solution with $-a/2 < t \le a/2$. Then

$$1, \quad \rho, \quad \frac{\rho^2 - t\rho + (t^2 - q)}{a}$$

is a basis.

2. *If the congruences (*) are satisfied, then it is necessary to find the largest square factor of the number $D_\rho/729$ (which is an integer in this case) for which the system of congruences*

$$F'(t) \equiv 0 \pmod{9a},$$
$$F(t) \equiv 0 \pmod{27a^2}$$

has a solution with $-3a/2 < t \le 3a/2$. In this case

$$1, \quad \frac{\rho - t}{3}, \quad \frac{\rho^2 + t\rho + (t^2 - q)}{9a}$$

is a basis.

§ 18. THE DECOMPOSITION OF RATIONAL PRIMES INTO PRIME IDEALS IN A CUBIC FIELD

It is a curious fact that the decomposition of a rational prime p into prime ideal factors in any algebraic field of the nth degree coincides essentially with the decomposition, easily carried out in practice, into prime factors modulo p of a primary polynomial $f(x)$ of degree n whose root ρ is one of the algebraic integers generating this field, as long as p does not divide the index of ρ.

We note that in what follows we shall be concerned only with the decomposition of a primary polynomial into primary factors modulo p. We shall say that a primary polynomial $f(x)$ is decomposable into primary factors $U_i(x)$ modulo p if the following identity holds:

$$f(x) = U_1(x) \cdot U_2(x) \cdot \ \ldots \ \cdot U_k(x) + p \cdot G(x), \tag{1}$$

where $G(x)$ is a polynomial with integer coefficients, which as a rule need not be primary. We shall say that the primary polynomials $U_i(x)$ are prime modulo p if they cannot be represented in the same way as a product of primary polynomials of lower degrees modulo p.

The fundamental theorems due to Zolotarev are as follows. If $U_1(x)$, $U_2(x)$, $\ldots$, $U_k(x)$ are prime primary factors of $f(x)$ modulo p and if p does not divide the index of ρ, then

$$p = (p, U_1(\rho)) \cdot (p, U_2(\rho)) \cdot \ \ldots \ \cdot (p, U_k(\rho)), \tag{2}$$

where $(p, U_i(\rho)) = p \cdot \lambda + U_i(\rho) \cdot \mu$ (λ and μ run over all possible integers of the field Ω_ρ) are the prime ideal factors of p. The degrees e_i of the polynomials U_i are the exponents of the powers of p which are the norms of the corresponding ideals, i.e., the so-called degrees of the ideals. If a prime p divides the index of ρ but is not a common divisor of all the indices of all the integers in Ω_ρ, then one can find another generator $\bar{\rho}$ in Ω_ρ whose index is not divisible by p. In this case the decomposition of p into prime ideals can be achieved in an analogous way in terms of the equation satisfied by $\bar{\rho}$. If p is a common divisor of all the indices of all the integers generating Ω_ρ, then p is decomposable in a different but analogous way into prime ideals.

There are fields the indices of all of whose integers have no common factor. If such common factors exist there are very few of them, since they have to divide every conceivable index, and Hensel and Žilinsky have shown that they must all be less than n.

In particular for cubic fields the common divisor of all the indices can therefore be only 2, as we shall show later. We shall give a decomposition of the number 2 into prime ideals in a cubic field in this case. Since the proof of Zolotarev's theorem is the same for general n as for $n = 3$ we shall prove it for any n, and then consider the decomposition of primes p into prime ideal factors specially in the cubic case.

1. The decomposition of a rational prime p not dividing the index of ρ for any n.

THEOREM I. *If the primary polynomials A and B are relatively prime, i.e., if they have no common primary factor modulo* p, *then there exist primary polynomials M and N such that $AM - BN \equiv c \pmod{p}$, where c is a rational integer not divisible by* p.

In fact, we can carry out Euclid's algorithm with polynomials A and B, omitting all the terms whose coefficients are divisible by p. Since the quotient Q_1 of two primary polynomials A and B is also primary, the remainder on division of A by B (we assume that the degree of A is not lower than that of B) cannot be zero modulo p, for if it were zero, then A and B would have a primary factor in common, namely B, contrary to assumption. The remainder R_1^* will not in general be a primary polynomial. We shall multiply it by a rational integer r_1^* such that $r_1 r_1^* \equiv 1 \pmod{p}$, where r_1 is its highest coefficient. Then $r_1^* R_1^* \equiv R_1$ will be a primary polynomial and

$$R_1^* \equiv r_1 R_1 \pmod{p}.$$

Hence we can write the first step of the algorithm as:

$$A = BQ_1 + r_1 R_1 \pmod{p},$$

where the polynomials A, B, Q_1, R_1 are all primary and the rational integer r_1 is not divisible by p. Continuing this, we obtain

$$\begin{aligned} B &\equiv R_1 Q_2 + r_2 R_2, \\ R_1 &\equiv R_2 Q_3 + r_3 R_3, \\ &\dots\dots\dots\dots \\ R_{n-2} &\equiv R_{n-1} Q_n + r_n, \end{aligned}$$

where all the capital letters A, B, Q_i, R_i are primary polynomials, and the r_i are rational integers not divisible by p. The last statement follows from the fact that if one of the remainders were divisible by p, then by going backwards we would find that $A \equiv R_i K$, $B \equiv R_i L$, where R_i is a primary factor of the last remainder, different from zero, and the polynomials K and L are primary, so that A and B would not be relatively prime to each other.

From the above equations we have the sequence $r_1 R_1 \equiv A - BQ_1$, $r_1 r_2 R_2 = -AQ_2 + B(r_1 + Q_1 Q_2)$ and so on, and finally $r_1 r_2 \cdots r_n \equiv AM - BN \pmod{p}$, where the polynomials M and N are primary, which proves the theorem.

THEOREM II. *Every primary polynomial is uniquely decomposable into primary prime factors modulo* p.

Suppose that the product $\phi \cdot \theta$ of two primary polynomials is divisible by a primary polynomial ψ modulo p and that ϕ is not divisible by ψ; then θ must be divisible by ψ.

In fact, in this case the polynomials ϕ and ψ are relatively prime modulo p, since the only divisor of a primary prime polynomial is ψ itself by the definition of primality, and therefore if ϕ and ψ had a common factor, then ϕ would be divisible by ψ contrary to assumption. By Theorem I there exist primary polynomials M and N such that $\phi \cdot M - \psi N \equiv c \pmod{p}$, where c is not divisible by p. Multiplying both sides of this equality by θ we obtain $\phi\theta M - \psi\theta N \equiv c\theta \pmod{p}$ and therefore if $\phi\theta$ is divisible by ψ, then $c\theta \equiv \psi\theta N \pmod{p}$, where $\theta \cdot N$ is a primary polynomial. Therefore first of all $c \equiv 1 \pmod{p}$, and secondly θ is divisible by ψ.

We now suppose that $f = U_1 U_2 \cdots U_k \equiv V_1 V_2 \cdots V_l \pmod{p}$, where U_i and V_i are prime primary polynomials modulo p. In this case, by what we have just seen, at least one of the factors V_j, say V_1, is divisible by $U_1 \pmod{p}$, and since they are both prime they must coincide modulo p. We can therefore cancel these factors since from $U_1 K \equiv U_1 L \pmod{p}$, where U_1, K, L are primary polynomials, it follows that $K \equiv L \pmod{p}$, which is easily established by identifying coefficients. We continue in the same way with the congruence $U_2 \cdots U_k \equiv V_2 \cdots V_l \pmod{p}$ and arrive at the following useful theorem.

THEOREM III. *If* p *does not divide the index of* ρ, *then every integer in the field* Ω_ρ *is congruent modulo* p *to an integer of the field which is expressible as a linear combination with integer coefficients of the "power" basis* $1, \rho, \rho^2, \cdots, \rho^{n-1}$.

In fact every integer of the field Ω_ρ is of the form

$$\omega = \frac{a_1\rho^{n-1} + a_2\rho^{n-2} + \cdots + a_n}{\Delta},$$

where $a_1, a_2, \cdots, a_n$ are rational integers, and Δ is the index of ρ (see § 15).

If Δ is not divisible by p, then two rational integers α and β can be found such that $\alpha\Delta - \beta \cdot p = 1$. From this it follows that

$$\omega + p\beta\omega = \alpha\Delta\omega = \alpha(a_1\rho^{n-1} + a_2\rho^{n+2} + \cdots + a_n),$$

that is, since Δ is not divisible by p, every number ω of the field Ω_ρ is congruent to an integer in the field expressible linearly in terms of the power basis 1, $\rho, \rho^2, \cdots, \rho^{n-1}$ with integer coefficients.

THEOREM IV. *If* p *does not divide the index of* ρ, *then* $(p, U(\rho))$ *is a prime ideal.*

Suppose that an integer ω of the field Ω_ρ is not contained in the ideal $(p, U_i(\rho))$. Consider the integer $\bar{\omega}$ congruent to ω modulo p, which is linearly expressible in terms of the power basis 1, $\rho, \rho^2, \cdots, \rho^{n-1}$ with integer coefficients. The integer $\bar{\omega}$ is of the form $\psi(\rho)$, where ψ is a polynomial in ρ with integer coefficients. Divide $\psi(x)$ by $U_i(x)$. This division is not exact, for if it were we would have $\psi(\rho) = U_i(\rho)\,\lambda(\rho)$, where λ would be the polynomial obtained as the quotient and would also have rational integer coefficients, since the leading coefficient of U_i is unity. Therefore $\lambda(\rho)$ would be an integer in Ω_ρ as well as $\psi(\rho)$ and therefore ω and $\bar{\omega}$ would belong to the ideal $(p, U_i(\rho))$ contrary to assumption. We replace $\psi(x)$ by the remainder $r(x)$ obtained on division by $U_i(x)$. This remainder is of lower degree than $U_i(x)$ and therefore is not divisible by $U_i(x)$ modulo p, and since $U_i(x)$ is prime modulo p it is relatively prime to $U_i(x)$ modulo p. By Theorem I, therefore, there exist two polynomials with integer coefficients $r_1(x)$ and $U_{i_1}(x)$ such that $U_i(x)r_1(x) - r(x)U_{i_1}(x) \equiv c \pmod{p}$, where c is not divisible by p. From this we see (see §5) that $r(\rho)$ and therefore $\psi(\rho)$ and ω are relatively prime to $(p, U_i(\rho))$. But if every integer ω of the field Ω_ρ which is not contained in the ideal $(p, U_i(\rho))$ is relatively prime to this ideal, then the ideal must be a prime ideal. For if it were not a prime ideal and if $\mathfrak{p}$ were one of its prime factors then every number contained in $\mathfrak{p}$ but not contained in $(p, U_i(\rho))$ would not be prime to $(p, U_i(\rho))$.

THEOREM V. *The degree of the prime ideal* $(p, U_i(\rho))$ *is equal to the degree* f_i *of the polynomial* $U_i(x)$.

Consider the incongruent classes of integers in the field Ω_ρ with respect to the ideal $(p, U_i(\rho))$. The number of these classes is, as is well known (see §5), the norm of the ideal $(p, U_i(\rho))$. Since by Theorem III every integer of the field Ω_ρ is congruent modulo p to a number in the ring $[1, \rho, \rho^2, \cdots, \rho^{n-1}]$, it is sufficient to consider the question only for numbers in this ring.

It is obvious that if we write all the polynomials $u_i(x)$ of the $(n-1)$st degree with integer coefficients which are incongruent modulo p, then every number in this ring will be congruent with respect to the ideal $(p, U_i(\rho))$ to one of these polynomials in which ρ has been substituted, since every number in the ring can be reduced to such a number by division by p and $U_i(\rho)$. On the other hand, two such incongruent polynomials give two numbers $u_1(\rho)$ and $u_2(\rho)$ whose difference $u_1(\rho)-u_2(\rho)$ is not contained in the ideal $(p, U_i(\rho))$ and therefore they are incongruent with respect to this ideal as a modulus. We see in this way that the norm of this ideal is equal to p^{f_i}, where f_i is the degree of $U_i(x)$, and hence the degree of the ideal $(p, U_i(\rho))$ is equal to f_i.

THEOREM VI. $p=(p, U_1(\rho))\cdot(p, U_2(\rho))\cdot \;\cdots\; \cdot(p, U_k(\rho))$.

In fact if we multiply the ideals

$$p\lambda_1+U_1(\rho)\,\mu_1,\ p\lambda_2+U_2(\rho)\,\mu_2,\ \cdots,\ p\lambda_k(\rho)\,\mu_k,$$

we will obtain the ideal

$$p^k\nu_1+p^{k-1}U_1(\rho)\,\nu_2+p^{k-1}U_2(\rho)\,\nu_3+\ldots+pU_1(\rho)\,U_2(\rho)\cdot\ldots\cdot U_{k-1}(\rho)\,\nu_{2k-1}+ \\ +U_1(\rho)\cdot\ldots\cdot U_k(\rho)\,\nu_{2k},$$

where λ, μ, ν are arbitrary integers in the field Ω_ρ. But $U_1(\rho)\,U_2(\rho)\cdots U_k(\rho)=p\cdot G(\rho)$ is divisible by p and therefore all the numbers contained in the ideal are divisible by p, or the ideal itself is divisible by p. But it follows from the theorem about the norm of the product of ideals that the degree of the product of the ideal factors of p is the product of the degrees of these ideals and therefore the product under consideration is equal to p.

REMARK I. In order to find for a general n an integer $\bar{\mu}$ whose index is not divisible by p or to show that p is a common factor of all the indices it is sufficient to consider in Ω_ρ only the p^n numbers $\omega=u_1\omega_1+u_2\omega_2+\cdots+u_n\omega_n$, where $\omega_1, \omega_2, \cdots, \omega_n$ is a basis of all the integers in Ω_ρ and $u_1, u_2, \cdots, u_n$ are all possible rational integer coefficients less than p, and then to calculate the indices Δ_ω of these p^n numbers using the relation

$$D_\omega=D_\Omega\Delta_\omega^2.$$

REMARK II. In order to decompose p for an arbitrary n into prime ideals in the field Ω_ρ in the case when p is a common factor of all the indices we note the following. Let $1, \omega_2, \cdots, \omega_n$ be a basis in Ω_ρ. In this case the ideal $\mathfrak{p}$ contains numbers of all n types with respect to this basis. In other words it consists of numbers which are expressed linearly with integer coefficients in terms of only the first element of the basis, or in terms of only the first two (including the second), or the first three (including the third) and so on. For example the numbers $p, p\omega_2, \cdots, p\omega_n$ are such. If we proceed as in §14, we obtain a canonical basis for the ideal in which all the diagonal coefficients are divisors of p (this follows from the existence in the ideal of the numbers $p, p\omega_2, \cdots, p\omega_n$ and because these coefficients are minimal) and hence must be either p or 1. If we renumber the elements of the basis of the field Ω_p we can assume that those basis elements whose diagonal coefficients are p occupy the first f numbers of the basis of the ideal, where f is the degree of the ideal. Then the basis is of the form

$$\begin{aligned}
\theta_1 &= p, \\
\theta_2 &= a_{21} + p\omega_2, \\
&\cdots\cdots\cdots \\
\theta_f &= a_{f1} + a_{f2}\omega_2 + \dots + a_{ff-1}\omega_{f-1} + p\omega_f, \\
\theta_{f+1} &= a_{f+11} + a_{f+12}\omega_2 + \dots \qquad + a_{f+1f}\omega_f + \omega_{f+1}, \\
&\cdots\cdots\cdots\cdots\cdots\cdots \\
\theta_n &= a_{n1} + a_{n2}\omega_2 + \dots \qquad + a_{nf}\omega_f + \omega_n,
\end{aligned}$$

where it can also be assumed that all the a_{ik} are non-negative and less than the diagonal coefficient which heads the column containing a_{ik} (that is, it is less than p when the diagonal element is p, and is zero when the diagonal element is 1). Finally we can suppose that $a_{21} = 0$ if $f \geq 2$, since in this case θ_2 is of the form $a_{21} + p\omega_2$ and must be divisible by the ideal $\mathfrak{p}$, which by assumption consists only of divisors of p and hence a_{21} must be divisible by p. Subtracting from θ_2 an appropriate multiple of θ_1 we obtain a new θ_2 with $a_{21} = 0$.

From this it follows in particular that the bases of prime ideals of the 1st and 2nd degree in a cubic field are of the form:

$$\begin{aligned}
\theta_1 &= p & \qquad \theta_1 &= p \\
\theta_2 &= y + \omega_1 & \text{and} \qquad \theta_2 &= \qquad p\omega_1 \\
\theta_3 &= z + \omega_2 & \qquad \theta_3 &= y + z\omega_1 + \omega_2,
\end{aligned}$$

where $1, \omega_1, \omega_2$ is a basis of integers in this field, and where y and z are non-negative rational integers less than p.

Such a form for a basis of an ideal factor of p may be called normal. However, not all such bases lead to an ideal. In order to obtain an ideal factor of p it is necessary and sufficient that in the first place the lattice $[\theta_1, \theta_2, \cdots, \theta_n]$ be a ring, i.e., that all the products of pairs of numbers in its basis should lie in the lattice. This can be ascertained with the help of a table of multiplication coefficients for the basis $1, \omega_2, \cdots, \omega_n$. With their help one can express the products of numbers in terms of the same basis and then ascertain whether or not they are expressible in terms of the basis $\theta_1, \theta_2, \cdots, \theta_n$ by subtracting successively the appropriate multiples of θ_n, θ_{n-1}, etc. If $[\theta_1, \theta_2, \cdots, \theta_n]$ is a ring, then we must still check whether or not it is an ideal (does the product of any of the numbers $\theta_1, \theta_2, \cdots$ $\cdots, \theta_n$ by any number ω of the field Ω_ρ belong to it). In doing this, it is sufficient, in view of the fact that this lattice is a ring, to choose only the numbers ω inside the parallelepiped based on $\theta_1, \theta_2, \cdots, \theta_n$, i.e., ω is of the same type as $\theta_1, \theta_2, \cdots, \theta_n$.

In this way we can write down a finite number of ideals consisting of the divisors of p which will contain all the prime and composite divisors of p. It is easily ascertained whether one of these ideals divides another or not. To do this it is sufficient to check whether every number in one basis is expressible linearly with integer coefficients in terms of a basis of the other, which can be done by successive subtractions as was pointed out above.

Those of the ideals so obtained that are of the lowest degree are obviously prime ideals and we will be able to select the distinct ones by the method described above. Then we can select the distinct ideals of the next degree and verify whether any of them are divisible by any of the ideals of the least degree and save only those which are not divisible by any of them and so on. In this way we will obtain finally all the prime ideal factors of p.

If p does not divide the discriminant D_Ω of the field, then we have discovered the decomposition of p into prime ideals, since in this case (see the following section) all the prime ideal factors of p appear to the first degree only. If however, p is a divisor of D_Ω, then at least one of these prime ideal factors enters into p to a degree higher than the first. In order to find the power of $\mathfrak{p}$ which is contained in p it is sufficient to see which of the prime ideals considered above, of the highest degree that is a multiple of the degree of $\mathfrak{p}$, is not divisible by the other prime factors of p, a question whose solution is already included in the above calculations.

2. The transition in the case of $n = 3$ to another ρ, whose index is not divisible by p. Given the cubic equation $\rho^3 = s\rho^2 + q\rho + n$ with integer coefficients satisfied by ρ we can find a basis of the field Ω_ρ by Voronoĭ's method (see §17). Then the index-form of the basis (a, b, c, d) is such that

$$a = a;\quad b = \frac{F''(t)}{2\delta};\quad c = \frac{F'(t)}{\delta^2 a};\quad d = \frac{F(t)}{\delta^3 a^2}.$$

If (a, b, c, d) is the index-form of the field, i.e., the index-form of the ring of all integers in the field, then a, b, c, d have no common factor, since the roots of the forms (a, b, c, d) and $k\cdot(a, b, c, d)$, where k is a rational integer, are expressible rationally in terms of each other, i.e., both forms correspond to rings in the same cubic field, while the discriminant of the second is larger than the discriminant of the first form.

THEOREM. *In the case of a cubic field the prime 2 can be the only common factor of all the indices and this is the case if and only if the two end coefficients of the index-form (a, b, c, d) are even, while the two middle coefficients are odd.*

In fact, for every prime $p > 2$ we can find two rational integers u and v such that the index of the number $u\omega_1 + v\omega_2$, i.e., the index-form $f(u, v) = (a, b, c, d) = au^3 + bu^2v + cuv^2 + dv^3$, is not divisible by p. Such will be at least one of the pairs $(1, 0)$, $(0, 1)$, $(1, 1)$ or $(1, -1)$, since the values of f corresponding to them are a, d, $a + b + c + d$, and $a - b + c - d$, respectively, and if all these numbers were divisible by p then so would also be the numbers a, d, $b + c$, $b - c$, $2b$, and $2c$ and therefore a, b, c, d would have a common factor p, which we have shown not to be the case. When $p = 2$, the consideration of the above six numbers leads to the same conclusion except when a and d are both even while b and c are odd. In this case $au^3 + bu^2v + cuv^2 + dv^3$ is always even for any choice of parity for the rational integers u and v.

Hence we see that if $p > 2$, or if $p = 2$ and the exceptional case does not arise, then if p divides the index of ρ we can find rational integers u and v such that $f(u, v)$ is not divisible by p. In this case the number $\bar{\rho} = u\omega_1 + v\omega_2$, where ω_1 and ω_2 are elements of the Voronoĭ basis, will be an integer in the field Ω_ρ, whose index $\bar{\Delta}$ is not divisible by p. Decomposing the left-hand side of the equation $x^3 - \bar{s}x^2 - \bar{q}x - \bar{n} = 0$, which is satisfied by $\bar{\rho}$, into prime factors modulo p we obtain a decomposition of p into prime ideals.

3. The decomposition of the prime 2 into prime ideals in a cubic field in the case when 2 is a common factor of the indices of all the integers in the field. Let a and d be even and b and c be odd, so that 2 is the common factor of all the indices. We prove the following theorem:

THEOREM. *If a and d are even and b and c are odd, then $2 = \mathfrak{p}_1\mathfrak{p}_2\mathfrak{p}_3$, where $\mathfrak{p}_1 = (2, \omega_1 + 1)$, $\mathfrak{p}_2 = (2, \omega_2 + 1)$, $\mathfrak{p}_3 = (2, \omega_1 + \omega_2)$ are three distinct prime ideals of the first degree, where*

$$\omega_1^3 + b\omega_1^2 + ac\omega_1 + a^2d = 0, \quad \omega_2^3 + c\omega_2^2 + bd\omega_2 + ad^2 = 0.$$

In fact, all these three ideals are not unit ideals, since their norms $N(\omega_1 + 1) = 1 - b + ac - a^2d$, $N(\omega_2 + 1) = 1 - c + bd - ad^2$, $N(\omega_1 + \omega_2) = a^2d + ad^2 + ac^2 - b^2d + 2acd$ are all even. Moreover, the ideals $\mathfrak{p}_1, \mathfrak{p}_2, \mathfrak{p}_3$ are relatively prime in pairs, since the ideal $(\mathfrak{p}_1, \mathfrak{p}_2)$, the greatest common divisor of the ideals $\mathfrak{p}_1$ and $\mathfrak{p}_2$, contains the number $2 \cdot \phi + (\omega_1 + 1)\psi + (\omega_2 + 1)\kappa$, where ϕ, ψ, κ are any integers in the field. In particular, it contains the number $-2(ad/2) + \omega_2 + 1 - \omega_2(\omega_1 + 1) = 1$. Similarly the ideals $(\mathfrak{p}_1, \mathfrak{p}_3)$ and $(\mathfrak{p}_2, \mathfrak{p}_3)$ each contain the numbers $(\omega_1 + 1)(\omega_2 + 1) + 2(ad/2) - (\omega_1 + \omega_2) = 1$. But the ideals $\mathfrak{p}_1, \mathfrak{p}_2$ and $\mathfrak{p}_3$ are all divisors of 2 and therefore they must all be of the first degree and $2 = \mathfrak{p}_1\mathfrak{p}_2\mathfrak{p}_3$.

The converse can also be proved, namely that if we have in a cubic field $2 = \mathfrak{p}_1\mathfrak{p}_2\mathfrak{p}_3$, where $\mathfrak{p}_1, \mathfrak{p}_2$ and $\mathfrak{p}_3$ are three distinct prime ideals of the first degree, then 2 is the greatest common divisor of the indices of all the integers in the field.

4. The calculation of a basis for a prime ideal. We shall suppose that p does not divide the index Δ of the number ρ.

CASE 1. $\mathfrak{p} = (p, \rho + \kappa)$, where $\rho + \kappa = U(\rho)$ is a prime ideal factor of p in the first degree. Let $\omega_1 = (\rho + A)/\delta$, $\omega_2 = (\rho^2 + B\rho + C)/\delta^2 a$ be the second and third members in the Voronoĭ basis of the field under consideration. We have shown in subsection 1 that a basis of an ideal $\mathfrak{p}$ is of the form $[p, y + \omega_1, z + \omega_2]$, where y and z are some rational integers, so that the second and third numbers θ_1 and θ_2 of a basis of a prime ideal are of the form

$$\theta_1 = \frac{\rho + A + \delta y}{\delta}; \quad \theta_2 = \frac{\rho^2 + B\rho + C + \delta^2 az}{\delta^2 a}.$$

In order that the numbers θ_1 and θ_2 be divisible by $\mathfrak{p}$ it is necessary and sufficient that their numerators be divisible by $\mathfrak{p}$, since their denominators are divisors of the index Δ of ρ and are therefore not divisible by p, and hence relatively prime to $\mathfrak{p}$. Dividing each of the numerators by $\rho + \kappa$ we will obtain remainders $A + \delta y - \kappa$ and $C - Bk + \delta^2 az + \kappa^2$. In order that the numerators be divisible by p it is sufficient that the remainders be divisible by p, i.e., that y and z satisfy the following congurences, $A + \delta y \equiv \kappa \pmod p$ and $C + \delta^2 az \equiv -\kappa^2 + B\kappa \pmod p$. In view of the fact that δ and a are not divisible by p these congruences always have solutions in rational integers y and z. If such y and z are chosen then θ_1 and θ_2 are numbers of the basis of $\mathfrak{p}$. In fact in this case the lattice $[p, \theta_1, \theta_2]$ is contained in the lattice of $\mathfrak{p}$, and on the other hand the volume of the fundamental parallelepiped of this lattice is the same as that of $\mathfrak{p}$, namely p times as large as the volume of the fundamental parallelepiped of $[1, \omega_1, \omega_2]$, since the determinant of the transformation is

$$\begin{vmatrix} p & 0 & 0 \\ y & 1 & 0 \\ z & 0 & 1 \end{vmatrix} = p.$$

CASE 2. Now let $\mathfrak{q}$ be a prime ideal divisor of p of the second degree, i.e., $\mathfrak{q} = (p, \rho^2 + l\rho + m)$, where $\rho^2 + l\rho + m$ is $U(\rho)$. In view of what was said in subsection 1, the basis of the ideal $\mathfrak{q}$ can be sought in this case in the form $[p, p\omega, y + z\omega_1 + \omega_2]$, where y and z are some non-negative rational integers less than p.

In this way, the second and third members in the basis of $\mathfrak{q}$ are of the form

$$\theta_1 = p\omega_1; \quad \theta_2 = \frac{y\delta^2 a + z\delta a\rho + z\delta a A + \rho^2 + B\rho + C}{\delta^2 a}.$$

Considerations similar to those discussed in Case 1 show that in order that these numbers form a basis for $\mathfrak{q}$ it is sufficient that y and z be such that the numerator of θ_2 is divisible by $\mathfrak{q}$ (since θ_1 is divisible by $\mathfrak{q}$). Dividing this numerator by $\rho^2 + l\rho + m$, we get a remainder $(z\delta a + B - l)\,\rho + (y\delta^2 a + z\delta a A + C - m)$. It is obvious that if we find z and y satisfying the congruences

$$z\delta a + B - l \equiv 0 \pmod p,$$

$$y\delta^2 a + z\delta a A + C - m - \equiv 0 \pmod p,$$

then the numerator of θ_2 will be divisible by $\mathfrak{q}$ and θ_1 and θ_2 form a basis for $\mathfrak{q}$.

It remains to find a basis for prime ideal factors of the number 2 when 2 is a common divisor of all the indices. By analogous considerations we find the following bases: $[2, \omega_1 + 1, \omega_2]$, $[2, \omega_1, \omega_2 + 1]$ and $[2, \omega_1, \omega_2]$.

§19. THE DECOMPOSITION OF RATIONAL PRIMES INTO PRIME IDEALS IN ANY MAXIMAL THREE-DIMENSIONAL LATTICE

Since the set of all integers in a cubic field is equivalent to the set of corresponding coordinates of points in an irreducible maximal three-dimensional multiplicative lattice, and conversely, the results of the previous section give in reality a method for decomposing rational primes p into prime ideals in any three-dimensional lattice if it is irreducible. Since in what follows in the classification of domains of the 4th order we shall have to decompose into prime ideals also reducible three-dimensional maximal lattices, we now consider how this can be accomplished.

We have shown (see §5) that every ideal in a reducible maximal lattice is the direct sum of some ideals in its irreducible parts, where the prime ideal is again the direct sum of prime ideals. If the maximal lattice is $O_3 = O_1 \oplus O_2$, then the decomposition of p into prime ideals in O_3 is determined by the decomposition in the lattice of all the integers in the quadratic field O_2. In fact if $p = \mathfrak{p}'_1 \mathfrak{p}'_2$ in O_2, then $p = \mathfrak{p}_1 \mathfrak{p}_2 \mathfrak{p}_3$ in O_3, where

$$\mathfrak{p}_1 = (p) \oplus (1),$$
$$\mathfrak{p}_2 = (1) \oplus (\mathfrak{p}'_1),$$
$$\mathfrak{p}_3 = (1) \oplus (\mathfrak{p}'_2).$$

If p is not decomposable in O_2, then in O_3 we have $p = \mathfrak{p}\pi$, where

$$\mathfrak{p} = (p) \oplus (1),$$
$$\pi = (1) \oplus (p).$$

If O_3 is the direct sum of three rings of the first degree, then O_3 is simply a real lattice of all the points with rational integer coefficients. It is obvious that every prime p is decomposable in this case into three prime ideals of the first degree, namely, $p = \mathfrak{p}_1 \mathfrak{p}_2 \mathfrak{p}_3$, where

$$\mathfrak{p}_1 = (p) \oplus (1) \oplus (1),$$
$$\mathfrak{p}_2 = (1) \oplus (p) \oplus (1),$$
$$\mathfrak{p}_3 = (1) \oplus (1) \oplus (p).$$

§20. A THEOREM ON THE DISCRIMINANT OF A FIELD

There is a famous theorem of Dedekind that in general a prime p does not contain prime ideal factors to a degree higher than the first. More precisely, a prime p contains a prime ideal factor to a degree greater than the first if and only if it divides the discriminant D_Ω of the field. We shall prove this theorem for a field of degree n for all primes which are not common factors of all the indices, while for the cubic field we shall prove it completely by considering the prime 2, which is the only common factor of all the indices in the case of a cubic field.

THEOREM. *A prime p which is not a common factor of the indices of all the integers in the field* Ω_p *(of any degree n) contains prime ideal factors of this field to a degree greater than the first if and only if it is a divisor of the discriminant* D_Ω *of the field.*

We suppose that p does not divide the index of ρ and that $f(\rho) = 0$ is an irreducible equation of the nth degree satisfied by ρ; then in the relation

$$f(x) = U_1(x)\, U_2(x) \cdots U_k(x) + p \cdot G(x) \tag{1}$$

the polynomials $U_i(x)$ are not distinct modulo p if and only if p is a divisor of the discriminant D_f. In fact if we differentiate (1) with respect to x and substitute $x = \rho$ we obtain

$$f'(\rho) = U_1'(\rho)\, U_2(\rho) \cdots U_k(\rho) + U_1(\rho)\, U_2'(\rho) \cdots U_k(\rho) + \cdots$$
$$\cdots + U_1(\rho)\, U_2(\rho) \cdots U_k'(\rho) + p\, G'(\rho). \tag{2}$$

Suppose now that all the factors $U_1(x), U_2(x), \ldots, U_k(x)$ are distinct modulo p. Then all the terms of the right-hand side of (2) are divisible by the prime ideal $(p, U_1(\rho))$ except for the first term. This follows from the fact that the product $U_2(x), \ldots, U_k(x)$ is relatively prime to $U_1(x)$ modulo p by our assumption that all the $U_i(x)$ are prime and distinct modulo p, while the factor $U_1'(x)$ is of lower degree than $U_1(x)$ and therefore is relatively prime to $U_1(x) \pmod p$. ($U_1'(x)$ is not a primary polynomial, but its rational multiple which is primary modulo p is relatively prime to $U_1(x)$, which is sufficient for our purposes.) By Theorem I, §18 all the factors $U_1'(\rho), U_2(\rho), \ldots, U_k(\rho)$ of the first term of the right-hand side of (2) are not divisible by $(p, U_1(\rho))$ and therefore the first term itself is not divisible by $(p, U_1(\rho))$.

Therefore, if all the factors $U_1(x), U_2(x), \ldots, U_k(x)$ are distinct modulo p then $f'(\rho)$ is not divisible by $(p, U_1(\rho))$.

Analogously we can show that $f'(\rho)$ is not divisible by $(p, U_2(\rho))$, and so on, that is, that $f'(\rho)$ is relatively prime to p. But in this case $N(f'(\rho)) = D_f$ is relatively prime to p, i.e., p does not divide D_f and therefore it does not divide the discriminant D_Ω of the field Ω_ρ.

Now suppose on the contrary that among the factors $U_1(x), \ldots, U_k(x)$ there are some congruent ones modulo p, for example $U_1(x)$ and $U_2(x)$. In this case, obviously, all the terms of the right-hand side of (2) are divisible by $(p, U_1(\rho))$. Then the left-hand side is divisible by $(p, U_1(\rho))$ and therefore $D_f = N(f'(\rho))$ is divisible by p. But since by assumption p does not divide the index Δ_ρ of ρ and since $D_f = D_\Omega \cdot \Delta_\rho^2$, then p must divide the discriminant D_Ω of Ω_ρ.

Dedekind's theorem is therefore proved for all primes p which are not common divisors of all the indices.

In the case of a cubic field, that is when $n = 3$, the only possible common divisor of all the indices is the prime 2. But we have seen that if 2 is a common divisor of all the indices, then the index-form (a, b, c, d) of the field has two end coefficients even and two middle coefficients odd and that 2 is decomposable into three prime ideals of the first degree and that in this case 2 is not a divisor of the discriminant of the field D_Ω, since $D_\Omega = D_{(a,b,c,d)} = b^2c^2 + 18\, abcd - 4\, ac^3 - 4\, b^3d - 27\, a^2d^2$ is in this case odd. This proves Dedekind's theorem in its completeness for the cubic field.

REMARK. Dedekind's theorem is true for any reducible maximal three-dimensional lattice, because from the decompositions given in §19 the prime p can contain a prime ideal of degree greater than the first if and only if $O_3 = O_1 \oplus O_2$ and $p = \mathfrak{p}_1 \mathfrak{p}_2 \mathfrak{p}_3$, where $\mathfrak{p}_2 = (1) \oplus (\mathfrak{p}_1')$, $\mathfrak{p}_3 = (1) \oplus (\mathfrak{p}_2')$, the ideals $\mathfrak{p}_1'$ and $\mathfrak{p}_2'$ of the quadratic field O_2 being equal, i.e., if p contains a prime ideal factor of the quadratic field O_2 to a degree greater than the first. But this will take place if and only if p divides the discriminant D_{O_2} of this quadratic field since, as can be easily seen, there is no common divisor of all the indices in a quadratic field. But $D_{O_3} = D_{O_2} \cdot D_{O_1}$ (here D_{O_1} is even equal to 1) and therefore p has a multiple prime ideal factor in O_3 if and only if p is a divisor of D_{O_3}.

It can be shown analogously that Dedekind's theorem is true for any reducible maximal lattice of any number of dimensions.

§21. FURTHER THEOREMS ON THE DECOMPOSITION OF RATIONAL PRIMES INTO PRIME IDEALS IN A CUBIC FIELD

We denote by $\mathfrak{p}$ the prime ideals of the first degree, by $\mathfrak{q}$ the prime ideals of the second degree and by π those of the third degree. If a prime p is not a divisor of the discriminant of the cubic field, then three cases are possible, namely

$$p = \mathfrak{p}_1 \mathfrak{p}_2 \mathfrak{p}_3,$$
$$p = \mathfrak{p}\mathfrak{q},$$
$$p = \pi,$$

where $\mathfrak{p}_1$, $\mathfrak{p}_2$, $\mathfrak{p}_3$ are distinct prime ideals of the first degree. It can be shown that if the cubic field Ω_ρ is not cyclic, then there are infinitely many primes having decompositions of the first, second and third kind. In fact the density of primes of the three kinds is 1/6, 3/6 and 2/6, respectively. If the cubic field is cyclic, then all the primes have decompositions of the first and third kinds only with the corresponding densities 1/3 and 2/3. Finally if O_3 is a reducible maximal lattice of the type $O_1 \oplus O_2$, then there exist decompositions only of the first and second kind with the corresponding densities 1/2 and 1/2, but if it is of the type $O_1 \oplus O_1 \oplus O_1$, then all the primes are of the first kind. The theorem about lattices of the type $O_1 \oplus O_1 \oplus O_1$ is obvious from §19; the theorem about lattices of the type $O_1 \oplus O_2$ follows easily from theorems about the decomposition of p in a quadratic field. Theorems about the irreducible lattice O_3, that is, about the proper decomposition of p in a cubic field, follow from the following profound theorem of Dedekind-Frobenius, whose proof depends on methods of the analytic theory of numbers (analogous to the proof of the existence of infinitely many primes in arithmetical progressions) and will not be given here.

THEOREM. *If in a given field Ω of the nth degree the degrees of the prime ideal factors of the prime p, that is, the degrees of the polynomials $U_i(x)$ in the decomposition of $f(x)$ modulo p are $f_1, f_2, \cdots, f_k$ (it is sufficient to consider only the primes p which do not divide the discriminant of f), then in the Galois group Γ of this field, considered as a substitution group of its n coordinates, there exists a substitution, the orders of whose irreducible cycles are exactly these degrees.* (This first part of the theorem was proved by Dedekind and can be proved, as for example, in Čebotarev, *Galois theory*, in an elementary way using the theory of finite fields.) *Conversely, if the Galois group Γ has a substitution whose irreducible cycles are of orders $f_1, f_2, \cdots, f_k$, then there exist infinitely many primes p in whose decomposition the prime ideals (or the irreducible polynomials $U_i(x)$) have these same degrees, the densities of such primes being l/N, where l is the number of substitutions of such a cyclic type in the group Γ and N is the order of the group Γ.* (The converse part of the theorem was proved in 1896 by Frobenius and also requires methods of analytic number theory for its proof.)

There exists a simple criterion for discovering whether a given prime p has a decomposition of the first or third kind or one of the second kind. This criterion was given in the dissertation of Voronoĭ as follows. The first case will arise if and only if D_Ω is a quadratic residue and the second if and only if D_Ω is a quadratic nonresidue of p. This criterion is a special case of a more general criterion for fields of the nth degree, which was first discovered by Schtikelberger in 1897. Both these criteria can be proved readily by means of the theory of finite fields. However we shall not give the proofs here.

Finally, the most complete solution of the problem as to which primes admit a decomposition of the first kind, the second kind or the third kind in a cubic field is given by a theorem of Takagi-Hasse, whose proof requires not only methods of the analytical theory of numbers but theorems in class field theory as well (see Hasse [1]). It consists in the following.

THEOREM. *Let* D_Ω *be the discriminant of the cubic field* Ω. *Then all the binary quadratic forms with integer coefficients of discriminant* D_Ω *can be divided into* h *classes, where* h *is a multiple of* 3. *A well defined third of these classes of quadratic forms represents only primes* p *which have a decomposition of the first kind, and the remaining two thirds represent only those* p *which have a decomposition of the third kind. If* D_Ω *is not a perfect square, that is, if the field* Ω *is not cyclic, then all the remaining primes, that is, the primes for which* D_Ω *is a quadratic nonresidue and which therefore are not represented by any of the classes of forms under consideration, have decompositions of the second kind.*

We shall not reproduce the proof of this theorem here.

It should be noted that this theorem was given without proof by Voronoĭ back in 1898 in a report to the Congress of Science and Medicine in Tbilisi and therefore it might be called Voronoĭ's theorem.

§ 22. THE DETERMINATION OF THE GROUP OF CLASSES OF IDEALS IN A CUBIC FIELD

In order to determine the number of classes of ideals in an irreducible maximal ring one must use the fact that every class contains an ideal whose norm does not exceed a certain bound, which can be determined as soon as the discriminant of the ring is known. In Chapter I such a bound was found in § 5, for irreducible maximal rings of any order, to be

$$\left(\frac{4}{\pi}\right)^{\tau}\frac{n!}{n^n}\sqrt{|D|},$$

where n is the degree of the ring, D is the discriminant, and τ is the number of pairs of complex coordinates. From this, in the case of $n = 3$ under consideration, we obtain the following bounds:

$$\frac{2}{9}\sqrt{D} \quad \text{if} \quad D>0,$$
$$\frac{8}{9\pi}\sqrt{|D|} \quad \text{if} \quad D<0.$$

However these estimates can be slightly improved by making use of the estimate for the minimum of binary cubic forms which will be made in the next chapter in §34. This method gives the limits

$$\frac{4}{27}\sqrt{D} \qquad \text{for} \quad D>0,$$

$$\left(\frac{8}{7.53\sqrt{3}}\right)^3\sqrt{|D|} \quad \text{for} \quad D<0.$$

These estimates are slightly better than those obtained from the general estimates with $n = 3$. From this it follows that for $D < 182$, $D > 0$, and for $|D| < 83$, $D < 0$, the number of classes of ideals is equal to 1, for in order that these inequalities hold, each class must have an ideal whose norm is less than 2.

In order to determine the number of classes in general the following procedure is suggested.

1. Determine a limit L for the norm of a representative of each of the classes of ideals.

2. Select in the ring a number ρ with the least possible index.

3. Decompose into prime factors the norms of the numbers $\rho + \kappa$ for

$$-\frac{L}{2} \leq \kappa < \frac{L}{2}$$

in order to find prime factors of the first degree of these norms.

4. Form a basis for prime and composite ideals having norms not exceeding L.

5. By means of a method which will be discussed in Chapter III, test each pair of lattices corresponding to these ideals to see whether they are congruent.

Then the incongruent lattices provide representatives of all classes of ideals. In this way the number of classes of ideals can be found in a finite number of steps.

In the actual determination of the number of classes the number of trials can be considerably reduced because the process of decomposing the numbers $\rho + \kappa$ into prime ideals established a great many equivalence relations between various prime ideals. Sometimes one can avoid altogether testing for congruent lattices.

We illustrate the above by the following example.

EXAMPLE. To determine the number of classes of ideals in $\Omega\sqrt[3]{7}$.

In this case $D_\Omega = -27 \cdot 7^2$ and therefore

$$L = \left(\frac{8}{7.53\sqrt{3}}\right)^3 7\sqrt{27} = 8.5\ldots.$$

We take $\rho = \sqrt[3]{7}$. The index of ρ equals 1.

To solve the problem we must decompose into prime ideals the numbers 2, 3, 5, and 7.

We have

$$\begin{aligned} N(\rho-3) &= -20 = -2^2\cdot 5, \\ N(\rho-2) &= -\ 1, \\ N(\rho-1) &= \ 6 = 2\cdot 3, \\ N(\rho) &= \ 7, \\ N(\rho+1) &= \ 8 = 2^3, \\ N(\rho+2) &= 15 = 3\cdot 5, \\ N(\rho+3) &= 34 = 2\cdot 17. \end{aligned}$$

From these decompositions we conclude that

$$2 = \mathfrak{p}_2\mathfrak{q}_2,\quad 3 = \mathfrak{p}_3^3,\quad 5 = \mathfrak{p}_5\mathfrak{q}_5,\quad 7 = \mathfrak{p}_7^3,$$

where $\rho - 1 = \mathfrak{p}_2\mathfrak{p}_3$, $\rho + 2 = \mathfrak{p}_3\mathfrak{p}_5$, $\rho = \mathfrak{p}_7$.

From $\mathfrak{p}_3^3 = 3$ it follows that the class to which $\mathfrak{p}_3$ belongs gives, on tripling, the principle class. We denote this class by K. From the equation

$$\rho - 1 = \mathfrak{p}_2\mathfrak{p}_3$$

it follows that $\mathfrak{p}_2$ belongs to class K^2 and $\mathfrak{q}$ to class K. From the equation $\rho + 2 = \mathfrak{p}_3\mathfrak{p}_5$ it follows that $\mathfrak{p}_5 \in K^2$, $\mathfrak{q}_5 \in K$.

Therefore the number of classes of ideals is 1 or 3, depending on whether the class K to which $\mathfrak{p}_3$ belongs is the principal class or not.

This question can be settled without recourse to the algorithm in Chapter IV. In fact for our ring we know a unit $\epsilon = 2 - \rho$, which, as can be easily seen by extracting the cube root, is the principal unit. If $\mathfrak{p}_3$ were a principal ideal generated by some number α we would have

$$3 = \alpha^3\epsilon^n.$$

From this it would follow that either 3 or 3ϵ or $3\epsilon^2$ would be a cube of some number in the ring. It can be easily seen by extracting the cube root that this is not the case.

Hence $h = 3$ and the representatives of the classes are 1, $\mathfrak{p}_3$ and $\mathfrak{p}_3^2$.

§ 23. VARIOUS FORMS CONNECTED WITH CUBIC FIELDS

It has been shown in the introductory chapter that certain forms in n variables are connected with multiplicative lattices as well as with lattices which are rationally oriented with respect to these lattices. These forms are the Dirichlet form and the Cayley form.

We will derive formulas which enable us actually to write down these forms for $n = 3$ in the case of a given lattice. We shall agree for brevity to write a ternary cubic form as a triangular table of coefficients. Thus, the form

$$F(x_1, x_2, x_3) = Ax_1^3 + Bx_1^2x_2 + Cx_1^2x_3 + Ex_1x_2^2 + Fx_1x_2x_3 + \\ + Gx_1x_3^2 + Hx_2^3 + Kx_2^2x_3 + Lx_2x_3^2 + Mx_3^3$$

will be written as

$$\begin{matrix} H, & K, & L, & M \\ & E, & F, & G \\ & & B, & C \\ & & & A. \end{matrix}$$

Let the lattice represent the ring given by the index-form

$$f(x, y) = ax^3 + bx^2y + cxy^2 + dy^3.$$

Its Hermitian is the form

$$D_0(x_1, x_2, x_3) = 3x_1^2 + 2bx_1x_2 + 2cx_1x_3 + (b^2 - 2ac)\,x_2^2 + \\ + 6adx_2x_3 + (c^2 - 2bd)\,x_3^2.$$

The Dirichlet form is

$$N(x_1, x_2, x_3) = \begin{matrix} -a^2d, & a(c^2 - 2bd), & d(b^2 - 2ac), & ad^2 \\ ac, & bc - 3ad, & bd & \\ b, & c & & \\ 1. & & & \end{matrix}$$

The Cayley form is

$$N^*(x_1, x_2, x_3) = \begin{matrix} d, & c, & b, & a \\ -2bd, & -bc - 3ad, & -2ac & \\ d(b^2 + ac), & a(c^2 + bd) & & \\ ad(ad - bc). & & & \end{matrix}$$

Finally we derive some facts in the theory of decomposition of ternary cubic forms.

In the first place we shall show that a necessary and sufficient condition for a form to be decomposable is that the Hessian of the form is equal, up to a constant factor, to the form itself.

We shall not give a proof of this proposition. The proof can be found in any course on higher algebra or analytic geometry which covers the elements of the theory of invariants.

The Hessian (more precisely, half the Hessian)

$$\begin{matrix} H', & K', & L', & M' \\ & E', & F', & G' \\ & & B', & C' \\ & & & A' \end{matrix}$$

of the form

$$\begin{matrix} H, & K, & L, & M \\ & E, & F, & G \\ & & B, & C \\ & & & A \end{matrix}$$

may be calculated from the formulas

$$A' = 12AEG - 3AF^2 + 4BCF - 4C^2E - 4B^2G,$$
$$B' = 12AEL + 8BCK + BF^2 - 12AKF - 4B^2L + 36AHG - 12C^2H - 4BEG,$$
$$F' = F^3 - 4F(CK + BL + EG) + 12(BKG + CEL - CHG - AKL - BEM) + \\ + 108AHM.$$

The expressions for the other coefficients are analogous to the above if the triangular scheme of the given form is appropriately rotated.

The multiplier which distinguishes the Hessian of the form from the form itself is nothing else but the discriminant of the form, which can therefore be expressed as a rational function in terms of the coefficients of the form. The discriminant cannot be represented as a rational integer function of the coefficients of the form; however, the square of the discriminant can thus be rationally expressed because of certain relations between the coefficients of the form. In fact

$$D^2 = F^4 - 8F^2(EG + BL + CK) + 24F(BGK + ECL + AKL + HCG + MBE) - \\ - 216FAHM + 16(B^2L^2 + C^2K^2 + E^2G^2 - BLEG - CKEG - BLCK) - \\ - 48(AEL^2 + AGK^2 + HBG^2 + HLC^2 + MKB^2 + MCE^2) + \\ + 144(AHGL + AMEK + HMBC).$$

The square of the discriminant of the decomposed form coincides with one of the invariants of a general cubic ternary form.

Finally, the coefficients of the Cayley form when multiplied by the discriminant can be represented in terms of the coefficients of the original form by the formulas

$$A^* = F(9HM - KL) - 2E(3KM - L^2) - 2G(3HL - K^2),$$
$$B^* = 12BKM - 4BL^2 - 18CMH + 2CKL + F^2L + 6G^2H - 3EFM + 2EGL - \\ - 3FKG,$$
$$F^* = -F^3 + 54AHM + 4F(KC + LB + EG) - 6(AKL + BEM + CGH + \\ + KGB + LEC).$$

The remaining coefficients are analogously expressed when the triangular scheme is suitably rotated. The form whose coefficients are obtained from these formulas is a contravariant of the form $N(x_1, x_2, x_3)$, even in the case when the latter form is indecomposable.

§24. THE CYCLIC CUBIC FIELD

By a cyclic cubic field we mean a cubic field which coincides with its conjugates. If ρ is a generator of such a field, then the conjugates ρ' and ρ'' are rationally expressible in terms of ρ.

We shall show that in order that the field Ω_ρ be cyclic it is necessary and sufficient that the discriminant of the irreducible cubic equation satisfied by ρ be a perfect square of a rational number.

In fact let the field Ω_ρ be cyclic. Then ρ' is rationally expressible in terms of ρ. We represent ρ' in terms of ρ by the canonical form

$$\rho' = a\rho^2 + b\rho + c.$$

Consider now the numbers $\omega_1 = a\rho'^2 + b\rho' + c$ and $\omega_2 = a\rho''^2 + b\rho'' + c$. These numbers together with $\rho' = a\rho^2 + b\rho + c$ are roots of a cubic equation with rational coefficients. Since this equation has the root ρ' in common with the irreducible equation satisfied by ρ and is of the same degree, it must coincide with that equation. Therefore either $\omega_1 = \rho$, $\omega_2 = \rho''$ or $\omega_1 = \rho''$, $\omega_2 = \rho$. The first possibility cannot hold because ρ'' cannot be a root of a quadratic equation with rational coefficients. The second possibility remains, namely

$$\rho'' = \omega_1 = a\rho'^2 + b\rho' + c,$$
$$\rho = \omega_2 = a\rho''^2 + b\rho'' + c.$$

Hence ρ'' is expressible in terms of ρ', and ρ is expressible in terms of ρ'' in exactly the same way as ρ' is expressible in terms of ρ.

We consider the number $\lambda = \rho' - \rho''$. This number belongs to the field Ω_ρ. From the above its conjugates are $\lambda' = \rho'' - \rho$ and $\lambda'' = \rho - \rho'$. The norm of λ, namely $N(\lambda) = (\rho' - \rho'')(\rho'' - \rho)(\rho - \rho')$ is a rational number. But the number

$$(N(\lambda))^2 = [(\rho' - \rho'')(\rho'' - \rho)(\rho - \rho')]^2$$

is the discriminant of ρ. Therefore we have shown that if a field Ω_ρ is cyclic then the discriminant of its generator ρ is the square of a rational number.

Conversely, let ρ be a root of the irreducible equation $\rho^3 = s\rho^2 + q\rho + n$, whose discriminant is a perfect square of a rational number l, namely

$$(\rho - \rho')^2 (\rho' - \rho'')^2 (\rho'' - \rho)^2 = l^2.$$

Then

$$(\rho - \rho') (\rho' - \rho'') (\rho'' - \rho) = l.$$

But $(\rho - \rho') (\rho - \rho'') = \delta(\rho) = 3\rho^2 - 2s\rho + q$. Therefore

$$\rho' - \rho'' = - \frac{l}{3\rho^2 - 2s\rho + q}.$$

On the other hand $\rho' + \rho'' = s - \rho$. Hence $\rho' - \rho''$ and $\rho' + \rho''$ and therefore also ρ' and ρ'' themselves are expressible rationally in ρ, that is, the field Ω_ρ is cyclic, which remained to be proved.

Irreducible cubic equations whose roots belong to a cyclic field are called cyclic cubic equations. It is easy to give a parametric representation for cyclic cubic equations by expressing their coefficients in terms of two parameters α and β in such a way that for rational values of these parameters the equation is cyclic or reducible and conversely every cyclic equation corresponds to rational values of these parameters.

We show that for equations in which the coefficient of ρ^2 is zero such a representation is given by

$$\rho^3 = 3(\alpha^2 + \alpha\beta + \beta^2) \cdot \rho + (\alpha - \beta)(\alpha^2 + \alpha\beta + \beta^2). \tag{1}$$

In fact the discriminant D of such an equation

$$D = 4 \cdot 27 (\alpha^2 + \alpha\beta + \beta^2)^3 - 27 (\alpha - \beta)^2 \cdot (\alpha^2 + \alpha\beta + \beta^2)^2 =$$
$$= 81 (\alpha + \beta)^2 (\alpha^2 + \alpha\beta + \beta^2)^2$$

is a perfect square of a rational number for rational values of α and β. Conversely, if the discriminant of the equation $\rho^3 = q\rho + n$ is a perfect square, then the corresponding rational values of the parameters α and β can be easily found. It is sufficient to let

$$\alpha - \beta = \frac{3n}{q},$$

$$\alpha + \beta = -\frac{\sqrt{D}}{3q}$$

and to solve this system for α and β.

We have therefore shown that equation (1) gives a parametric representation of cyclic cubic equations for which $s = 0$.

We shall say a few words about the units in a cyclic domain. In cyclic domains as well as in all cubic domains with positive discriminant all the units can be represented in terms of products of powers of two fundamental units. If ϵ_1 and ϵ_2 are two fundamental units, then every pair η_1, η_2, where $\eta_1 = \epsilon_1^a \epsilon_2^b$, $\eta_2 = \epsilon_1^c \epsilon_2^d$, is also a pair of fundamental units, provided $ad - bc = \pm 1$. We shall show that every cyclic ring contains a pair of conjugate fundamental units, and if ϵ_0, ϵ_0' is one of these pairs, then all the other possible pairs are given by $\epsilon_0', \epsilon_0''$; ϵ_0'', ϵ_0; $1/\epsilon, 1/\epsilon'$; $1/\epsilon', 1/\epsilon''$; $1/\epsilon'', 1/\epsilon$.

To prove this, consider any pair of fundamental units ϵ_1 and ϵ_2 and introduce their conjugates ϵ_1' and ϵ_2'. They will also be units in the ring under consideration and therefore we can write

$$\epsilon_1' = \epsilon_1^{m_1} \epsilon_2^{n_1},$$
$$\epsilon_2' = \epsilon_1^{m_2} \epsilon_2^{n_2}.$$

The exponents m_1, n_1, m_2, n_2 are of course related. In order to find this relation we consider next the units ϵ_1'' and ϵ_2''. Then

$$\varepsilon_1'' = (\varepsilon_1')^{m_1} (\varepsilon_2')^{n_1} = \varepsilon_1^{m_1^2 + n_1 m_2} \cdot \varepsilon_2^{n_1 m_1 + n_1 n_2},$$
$$\varepsilon_2'' = (\varepsilon_1')^{m_2} (\varepsilon_2')^{n_2} = \varepsilon_1^{m_1 m_2 + m_2 n_2} \cdot \varepsilon_2^{n_1 m_2 + n_2^2}.$$

Since $\epsilon_1 \epsilon_1' \epsilon_1'' = \epsilon_2 \epsilon_2' \epsilon_2'' = 1$, the exponents m_1, n_1, m_2, n_2 satisfy the following equations:

$$\begin{aligned} 1 + m_1 + m_1^2 + n_1 m_2 &= 0, \\ n_1 + n_1 m_1 + n_1 n_2 &= 0, \\ m_2 + m_1 m_2 + n_2 m_2 &= 0, \\ 1 + n_2 + n_2^2 + n_1 m_2 &= 0. \end{aligned}$$

If $1 + m_1 + n_2 \neq 0$, then $n_1 = m_2 = 0$ and the first equation becomes $1 + m_1 + m_1^2 = 0$, which is impossible.

Therefore $1 + m_1 + n_2 = 0$.

This satisfies the second and third equations, while the first and fourth become

$$m_1 n_2 - m_2 n_1 = 1,$$

since

$$1 + m_1 + m_1^2 + n_1 m_2 = 1 - (m_1 n_2 - m_2 n_1) + m_1 (1 + m_1 + n_2),$$
$$1 + n_2 + n_2^2 + n_1 m_2 = 1 - (m_1 n_2 - m_2 n_1) + n_2 (1 + m_1 + n_2).$$

Therefore the exponents satisfy the pair of equations

$$1 + m_1 + n_2 = 0,$$
$$m_1 n_2 - m_2 n_1 = 1.$$

Let $\epsilon_0 = \epsilon_1^x \epsilon_2^y$ be a unit. Then the conjugate unit ϵ_0' can be written in the form

$$\epsilon_0' = \epsilon_1^{m_1 x + m_2 y} \cdot \epsilon_2^{n_1 x + n_2 y}.$$

In order that ϵ_0 and ϵ_0' be a pair of fundamental units it is necessary and sufficient that either

$$x(n_1 x + n_2 y) - y(m_1 x + m_2 y) = \pm 1,$$

or that

$$n_1 x^2 + (n_2 - m_1)\, xy - m_2 y^2 = \pm 1.$$

The discriminant of the quadratic form in the left-hand side of the last equation is

$$(n_2 - m_1)^2 + 4n_1 m_2 = (n_2 + m_1)^2 - 4(m_1 n_2 - n_1 m_2) = -3.$$

It is well known that every quadratic form with rational integer coefficients and with discriminant -3 is equivalent to one of the forms $\pm(x^2 + xy + y^2)$ and represents $+1$ (or -1) in six different ways. These six representations determine the six possible pairs of conjugate fundamental units. If ϵ_0, ϵ_0' is one of these pairs, then the other five are given by

$$\varepsilon_0', \varepsilon_0''; \quad \varepsilon_0'', \varepsilon_0; \quad \frac{1}{\varepsilon_0}, \frac{1}{\varepsilon_0'}; \quad \frac{1}{\varepsilon_0'}, \frac{1}{\varepsilon_0''}; \quad \frac{1}{\varepsilon_0''}, \frac{1}{\varepsilon_0}.$$

This completes the proof.

In conclusion we note some special features in the decomposition of primes into prime ideals in the case of cyclic cubic maximal rings. Since the discriminants of these rings are perfect squares, it is easily seen from Theorem V that a prime p can have only the following decompositions into prime ideals:

$p = \mathfrak{p}^3$ if p divides the discriminant and p is not 2, or

$$p = \mathfrak{p}_1 \mathfrak{p}_2 \mathfrak{p}_3$$

and (p) is a prime ideal.

Cyclic rings contain no prime ideals of the second degree.

It is easily seen that if $p = \mathfrak{p}_1 \mathfrak{p}_2 \mathfrak{p}_3$, then the prime ideals $\mathfrak{p}_1, \mathfrak{p}_2, \mathfrak{p}_3$ are conjugate ideals, i.e., $\mathfrak{p}_2$ and $\mathfrak{p}_3$ can be obtained from $\mathfrak{p}_1$ by a cyclic substitution of coordinates or, in the geometric representation, the lattices corresponding to $\mathfrak{p}_2$ and $\mathfrak{p}_3$ can be obtained from the lattice of the ideal $\mathfrak{p}_1$ by rotation around a rational line by angles of $2\pi/3$ and $4\pi/3$.

In fact, if $\mathfrak{p}_1$ is a prime ideal of the first degree, then the lattices $\mathfrak{p}_1'$ and $\mathfrak{p}_1''$ obtained by rotating the lattice for $\mathfrak{p}_1$ by $2\pi/3$ and $4\pi/3$ around a rational line will also be prime ideals of the first degree dividing the same prime p. If $\mathfrak{p}_1$, $\mathfrak{p}_1'$ and $\mathfrak{p}_1''$ are distinct, then the prime p, being divisible by each of them, must be divisible by their product. Therefore in this case

$$p = \mathfrak{p}_1 \mathfrak{p}_2 \mathfrak{p}_3.$$

It remains to show that if $\mathfrak{p}_1 = \mathfrak{p}_1' = \mathfrak{p}_1''$, then $p = \mathfrak{p}_1^3$. In order to do this, consider the number ρ which is divisible by $\mathfrak{p}_1$ but not by $\mathfrak{p}_1^2$ or by any other ideal dividing p, if such a number exists. This number will be a root of some cubic equation

$$\rho^3 = s\rho^2 + q\rho + n.$$

Since $\mathfrak{p} = \mathfrak{p}' = \mathfrak{p}''$, the numbers ρ' and ρ'' as well as ρ will be divisible by $\mathfrak{p}$. Therefore the coefficients

$$s = \rho + \rho' + \rho'', \quad -q = \rho\rho' + \rho'\rho'' + \rho''\rho \quad \text{and} \quad n = \rho\rho'\rho''$$

will also be divisible by $\mathfrak{p}$ and therefore, being rational integers, by p. Therefore ρ^3 is divisible by p, which is possible only if $p = \mathfrak{p}^3$, since ρ is not divisible by any of the ideals contained in p except $\mathfrak{p}$.

Finally we point out that primes p for which $p = \mathfrak{p}_1 \mathfrak{p}_2 \mathfrak{p}_3$ belong to certain arithmetical progressions with difference $\sqrt{D}$, while the primes which remain prime in a cyclic field belong to the remaining arithmetical progressions with difference $\sqrt{D}$.

We shall not prove this assertion. It is a special case of a more general theorem of Kronecker about abelian fields.

§25. PURELY CUBIC FIELDS

A purely cubic field is a field whose generator is a cube root of a rational number. Such fields play an important part in the theory of cubic numbers, being the simplest cubic fields with a negative discriminant. They have been considered in papers by Markov [29] and Dedekind [10].

The problem of finding a basis for integers in a field is very simple for purely cubic fields. Let $\rho = \sqrt[3]{A}$ be a generator of such a field. Without loss of generality we may assume that A is a positive rational integer having no cubic factors. Let $A = fg^2$, where f and g are integers having no square factors. We introduce the notation $\bar{A} = f^2 g$, $\bar{\rho} = \sqrt[3]{\bar{A}}$. Every number in the field Ω_ρ

$$\omega = \alpha + \beta\rho + \gamma'\rho^2$$

can be represented in the form $\alpha + \beta\rho + \gamma\bar{\rho}$, since $\rho^2 = \sqrt[3]{f^2 g^4} = g\bar{\rho}$.

Let $\omega = \alpha + \beta\rho + \gamma\bar{\rho}$ be an integer in the field Ω_ρ and let $\omega^3 = s\omega^2 + q\omega + n$ be the equation satisfied by ω. The coefficients s, q, and n of this equation are rational integers. It can be easily derived that

$$s = 3\alpha,$$
$$q = -3\alpha^2 + 3\beta\gamma fg,$$
$$n = \alpha^3 + \beta^3 A + \gamma^3\bar{A} - 3\alpha\beta\gamma fg$$

and that the discriminant $D(\omega) = -27(\beta^3 A - \gamma^3 \bar{A})^2$.

From these equations we derive first of all that the numbers

$$3\alpha = s, \quad 9\beta\gamma fg = (3\alpha)^2 + 3q \quad \text{and} \quad 27\beta^3 A + 27\gamma^3\bar{A} = 27n - (3\alpha)^3 + 3\cdot(3\alpha)\cdot(9\beta\gamma fg)$$

are integers. Therefore $27\beta^3 A$ and $27\gamma^3\bar{A}$ are also integers since their sum as well as their product, which is equal to $(9\beta\gamma fg)^3$, are integers. From this it finally follows that 3β and 3γ are integers, since a and $\bar{A}$ contain no cubic factors. Hence if ω is an integer in the field Ω_ρ it can be represented in the form $\omega = (a + b\rho + c\bar{\rho})/3$ with rational integer coefficients a, b, c. These coefficients must satisfy the congruences

$$a^2 - bcfg \equiv 0 \pmod{3}, \tag{1}$$
$$a^3 + b^3 A + c^3\bar{A} - 3abcfg \equiv 0 \pmod{27}. \tag{2}$$

We will show that if one of these numbers a, b, c is divisible by 3 then they are all divisible by 3. It is sufficient to consider the case when a is divisible by 3. Then $b^3 A + c^3\bar{A}$ is divisible by 9, and $bcfg$ by 3. The numbers $b^3 A$ and $c^3\bar{A}$ are both divisible by 9, since their sum is divisible by 9 and their product by 27. Since one of the numbers A or $\bar{A}$ is not divisible by 9, it follows that one of the numbers b or c is divisible by 3, but then by (2) the other number must also be divisible by 3.

We next consider under what conditions the number $\omega = (a + b\rho + c\bar{\rho})/3$ can be an integer when a is not divisible by 3. The numbers a, b, c can be replaced by their absolutely least residues modulo 3, so that a can be taken as 1 Let $b \equiv \sigma_1 = \pm 1$; $c \equiv \sigma_2 = \pm 1$. Congruences (1) and (2) can be written in the form

$$\sigma_1\sigma_2 fg \equiv 1 \pmod 3,$$
$$1 + \sigma_1 fg^2 + \sigma_2 f^2 g - 3\sigma_1\sigma_2 fg \equiv 0 \pmod{27}.$$

From the first of these congruences we conclude that f and g are not divisible by 3 and $\sigma_1 f \equiv \sigma_2 g \pmod 3$. Let $\sigma_1 f = 3k + \lambda$, $\sigma_2 g = 3l + \lambda$, $\lambda = \pm 1$. Substituting into the second congruence we get

$$1 + 2\lambda^3 - 2\lambda^2 + 9(k + l)(\lambda - \lambda^2) + 9(k - l)^2\lambda \equiv 0 \pmod{27},$$

from which it follows that $\lambda = +1$ and $k \equiv l \pmod 3$.

Hence the number $\omega = (1 + \sigma_1\rho + \sigma_2\bar{\rho})/3$ will be an integer for $\sigma_1 = \pm 1$, $\sigma_2 = \pm 1$ if and only if $\sigma_1 f \equiv \sigma_2 g \pmod 9$, $\sigma_1 \equiv f \pmod 3$ and $\sigma_2 \equiv g \pmod 3$. These conditions will be satisfied only if $A \equiv \pm 1 \pmod 9$.

In fact if $\sigma_1 f \equiv \sigma_2 g \pmod 9$, then $A = fg^2 \equiv f^3 \equiv \pm 1 \pmod 9$. Conversely if $A = fg^2 \equiv \pm 1 \pmod 9$, then $fg^3 \equiv \pm g \pmod 9$, but $g^3 \equiv \pm 1 \pmod 9$. Therefore $f \equiv \pm g \pmod 9$ and we can find numbers σ_1 and σ_2 satisfying all the conditions.

Finally the numbers $1, \rho, \bar{\rho}$ can be taken as a basis of a purely cubic field if $A \not\equiv 1 \pmod 9$, while the numbers $1, \rho, (1 + f\rho + g\bar{\rho})/3$ form a basis if $A \equiv 1 \pmod 9$.

We can now give a parametric representation of the equations whose roots are numbers in purely cubic fields. To do this, we show first of all that a necessary and sufficient condition for a cubic number to be a purely cubic number is

$$D(\omega) = -3d^2$$

with d rational. The necessity of this condition follows from our calculations of the discriminant of a purely cubic number.

We now show the sufficiency. Let $\omega^3 = s\omega^2 + q\omega + n$ be an equation whose discriminant is $-3d^2$. Without loss of generality we can let $s = 0$. By Cardan's solution, $\omega = \alpha + \beta$, where α and β satisfy the system of equations

$$\alpha^3 + \beta^3 = n, \quad \alpha\beta = \frac{q}{3}.$$

It is obvious that $(\alpha^3 - \beta^3)^2 = n^2 - 4q^3/27 = -D/27 = \left(\frac{d}{3}\right)^2$. Therefore

$\alpha^3 - \beta^3$ is a rational number and the numbers α and β are purely cubic numbers. Since $\beta = q/3\alpha$, it belongs to the same purely cubic field as α, to which also belongs $\omega = \alpha + \beta$. This proves the condition stated above.

It can now be easily checked that the equation

$$\omega^3 = 3\alpha\beta\omega + \alpha\beta(\alpha - \beta)$$

gives a parametric representation of all the equations with $s = 0$ which are satisfied by numbers in purely cubic fields.

In fact the discriminant of this equation $D = -27\alpha^2\beta^2(\alpha + \beta)^2$ satisfies the necessary and sufficient condition with rational parameters α and β. Conversely, if the discriminant D of the equation $\omega^3 = q\omega + n$ satisfies the condition $D = -3d^2$, then one can find suitable rational values of the parameters from the equations

$$\alpha + \beta = -\frac{d}{q},$$

$$\alpha - \beta = \frac{3n}{q}.$$

We calculate also the discriminant of the cubic field $\Omega\sqrt[3]{A}$. It is

$$D_\Omega = \begin{vmatrix} 1, & \rho, & \bar{\rho} \\ 1, & \rho', & \bar{\rho}' \\ 1, & \rho'', & \bar{\rho}'' \end{vmatrix}^2 = -27f^2g^2,$$

if $A \not\equiv 1 \pmod 9$. It is equal to

$$D_\Omega = \begin{vmatrix} 1, & \rho, & \frac{1 + f\rho + g\bar{\rho}}{3} \\ 1, & \rho', & \frac{1 + f\rho' + g\bar{\rho}'}{3} \\ 1, & \rho'', & \frac{1 + f\rho'' + g\bar{\rho}''}{3} \end{vmatrix}^2 =$$

$$= \frac{1}{9}\begin{vmatrix} 1, & \rho, & \bar{\rho} \\ 1, & \rho', & \bar{\rho}' \\ 1, & \rho'', & \bar{\rho}'' \end{vmatrix}^2 = -3f^2g^2,$$

if $A \equiv 1 \pmod 9$.

In 1928 Artin conjectured that it is possible to show, using class field theory, that there cannot exist two distinct cubic fields with the same discriminant. This can be easily seen to be false. In fact, take any fixed finite set of distinct primes containing the prime 3 and divide it up in various ways into two parts, denoting the product of the numbers in the first part by f and the product of the rest of the numbers by g, and consider all purely cubic fields $\Omega\sqrt[3]{f^2g}$, where f and g are such a pair of numbers. From the fact that either f or g is divisible by 3, since 3 belongs to our finite set, it follows that $A = f^2g \not\equiv 1 \pmod 9$ and therefore the discriminants of all the fields under consideration $D = -27f^2g^2$ are the same. Moreover, it is easily seen that the fields are all distinct.

In fact, let A_1 and A_2 be two of the A's under consideration, and let $p_1, p_2, \cdots, p_k$ be all the primes from our set which appear to the first power in both the A's while $q_1, q_2, \cdots, q_l$ are all the primes which appear to the second power in both the A's. Let $r_1, r_2, \cdots, r_m$ be those of the remaining numbers which appear to the first power in A_1 and to the second power in A_2 and finally let $s_1, s_2, \cdots, s_n$ be the remaining primes which appear to the second power in A_1 and the first power in A_2. If $\rho_1 = \sqrt[3]{A_1}$ and $\rho_2 = \sqrt[3]{A_2}$ generate the same field, then the numbers

$$\theta_1 = r_1 r_2 \ldots r_m \frac{\rho_1}{\rho_2} = \sqrt[3]{s_1 s_2 \ldots s_n r_1^2 r_2^2 \ldots r_m^2}$$

and

$$\theta_2 = \frac{\rho^2_2}{r_1 r_2 \ldots r_m \rho_1} = \sqrt[3]{p_1 p_2 \ldots p_k q_1^2 q_2^2 \ldots q_l^2}$$

will also generate the same field. But the discriminants of the fields Ω_{θ_1} and Ω_{θ_2} are, respectively, $D_1 = -27f_1^2g_1^2$ or $-3f_1^2g_1^2$ and $D_2 = -27f_2^2g_2^2$ or $-3f_2^2g_2^2$, with f_1g_1 relatively prime to f_2g_2. Therefore we cannot have $-27f_1^2g_1^2 = -27f_2^2g_2^2$ or $-3f_1^2g_1^2 = -3f_2^2g_2^2$. Neither can we have $-27f_1^2g_1^2 = -3f_2^2g_2^2$, since this implies $9f_1^2g_1^2 = f_2^2g_2^2$, whereas $f_2^2g_2^2$ is not divisible by any prime factor of $f_1^2g_1^2$.

Therefore we see that there can exist discriminants which correspond to arbitrarily many distinct cubic fields and even purely cubic fields provided we take a sufficiently large number of primes as shown above. (This remark is due to Nagell.)

TABLE of equations $x^3 + bx + c = 0$ for all rational integers b and $c < 0$ less than 10 in absolute value. DISCRIMINANTS of the corresponding fields, BASES if they are not power bases, some UNITS and the NUMBER OF IDEAL CLASSES

(Table computed by Reid [45].)

$x^3 + bx + c$

bc	D_Ω	Basis	ε	h_Ω
01	red			
11	-31		$\alpha,\ \alpha+1$	1
-11	-23		$\alpha,\ \alpha-1,\ \alpha+1$	1
02	-108		$\alpha+1;\ \alpha^2-\alpha+1$	1
12	red			
-12	-104		$\alpha^2+\alpha-1$	1
22	-140		$\alpha+1$	1
-22	-76		$\alpha-1;\ \alpha^2+\alpha-1$	1
21	-59		α	1
-21	red			
03	-243		α^2-2	1
13	-247		$\alpha+1$	1
-13	-239		$\alpha^2+\alpha-1$	1
23	red			
-23	-211		$\alpha^2-2\alpha+2$	1
33	-351		$\alpha+1$	1
-33	-135		$\alpha-1,\ \alpha+2$	1
31	-135		$\alpha,\ 3\alpha+1,\ \alpha^2+3$	1
-31	$+81$		$\alpha,\ \alpha-1,\ \alpha+2$	1
32	-216		$-\alpha^2+\alpha+1$	
-32	red			
04	-108	$\frac{\alpha^2}{2};\ \alpha;\ 1$	$\frac{\alpha^2-2}{2}$	1
14	-436		$21\alpha^2-29\alpha+61$	1
-14	-107	$\frac{\alpha^2+\alpha}{2};\ \alpha;\ 1$	$5\alpha^2-9\alpha+11,\ \alpha^2-\alpha-5;\ \frac{\alpha^2-\alpha+2}{2}$	1
24	-116	$\frac{\alpha^2}{2};\ \alpha;\ 1$	$\alpha+1$	1
-24	red			
34	red			
-34	-324		$\alpha^2-\alpha-7$	1
44	-172	$\frac{\alpha^2}{2};\ \alpha;\ 1$	$\alpha+1;\ \alpha^2-\alpha+5$	1
-44	-44	$\frac{\alpha^2}{2};\ \alpha;\ 1$	$\alpha-1$	1
41	-283		$\alpha;\ 4\alpha+1$	2
-41	$+229$		$\alpha,\ \alpha+2,\ \alpha-2$	1
42	-364		$2\alpha+1$	1
-42	$+148$		$\alpha-1,\ -2\alpha+1$	1
43	-499		$3\alpha+2$	1
-43	red			

bc	D_Ω	Basis	ε	h_Ω
05	-675		$2\alpha^2+4\alpha+1$	1
15	-679		$-4\alpha^2+6\alpha-13$	1
-15	-671		$\alpha+2$	1
25	-707		$3\alpha+4$	1
-25	-643		$\alpha+2$	2
35	-87	$\frac{\alpha^2+\alpha+1}{3}$; α; 1	$\alpha+1,\ \frac{\alpha^2+\alpha+1}{3}$	1
-35	-567		$\alpha^2-2\alpha+2$	1
45	red			
-45	-419		$2\alpha^2-5\alpha+4$	1
55	-1175		$\alpha+1$	1
-55	-175		$\alpha-1$	1
51	-527		α	1
-51	$+473$		α	1
52	-152	$\frac{\alpha^2+\alpha}{2}$; α; 1		1
-52	red			
53	-743			1
-53	$+257$		$\alpha-1$	1
54	-932			1
-54	red			
06	-972		$3\alpha^2+6\alpha+1$	1
16	-244	$\frac{\alpha^2+\alpha}{2}$; α; 1		1
-16	red			
26	-1004		$7\alpha^2+15\alpha+7$	1
-26	-940		$3\alpha^2+7\alpha+1$	1
36	-1080			1
-36	-216	$\frac{\alpha^2+\alpha}{2}$; α; 1	$\frac{-\alpha^2+\alpha+8}{2}$	1
46	-1228		$\alpha+1$	3
-46	-716		$40\alpha^2-101\alpha+95$	1
56	red			
-56	-472			1
66	-1836		$\alpha+1$	3
-66	-108			1
61	-891		α; $6\alpha+1$	3
-61	$+837$		α	1
62	-108	$\frac{\alpha^2+\alpha+1}{3}$; α; 1		1
-62	$+756$		$3\alpha-1$	1
63	-1107		$2\alpha+1$	2
-63	$+621$		$\alpha-2$	1
64	-324	$\frac{\alpha^2}{2}$; α; 1	$\alpha^2-\alpha-1$	1
-64	red			
65	-1539		$2\alpha^2-34\alpha-27$	1
-65	red			
07	-1323		$\alpha+2$	3

bc	D_{Ω}	Basis	ε	d_{Ω}
17	−1327			1
−17	−1319		$\alpha+2$	1
27	−1355			1
−27	−1291			1
37	−1431		$-\alpha^2+2$	1
−37	− 135	$\frac{\alpha^2-\alpha+1}{3}$; α; 1	$\frac{\alpha^2-\alpha+1}{3}$	1
47	−1579			1
−47	−1067			1
57	−1823		$\alpha+1$	2
−57	− 823			1
67	red			
−67	− 459		$2\alpha^2+2\alpha-11$	1
77	−2695		$\alpha+1$	3
−77	+ 49			1
71	−1399		α	2
−71	+1345		α	1
72	−1480			1
−72	+ 316	$\frac{\alpha^2+\alpha}{2}$; α; 1	$\frac{\alpha^2-\alpha}{2}$; $3\alpha^2+\alpha-2$	1
73	−1615			1
−73	+1129		α^2-8	1
74	− 451	$\frac{\alpha^2+\alpha}{2}$; α; 1		1
−74	+ 940		$-2\alpha^2+6\alpha-3$	1
75	−2047			1
−75	+ 697		$\alpha-2$	1
76	−2344			1
−76	red			
08	red			
18	−1732		$6\alpha+11$	2
−18	− 431	$\frac{\alpha^2+\alpha}{2}$; α; 1	$6\alpha-11$	1
28	− 440	$\frac{\alpha^2}{2}$; α; 1		1
−28	− 424	$\frac{\alpha^2}{2}$; α; 1		1
38	− 459	$\frac{\alpha^2+\alpha}{2}$; α; 1	$2\alpha+3$	1
−38	−1620		$2\alpha+5$	3
48	− 31	$\frac{\alpha^2}{4}$; $\frac{\alpha}{2}$; 1		1
−48	− 23	$\frac{\alpha^2}{4}$; $\frac{\alpha}{2}$; 1		1
58	−2228			1
−58	− 307	$\frac{\alpha^2-\alpha}{2}$; α; 1		1
68	− 648	$\frac{\alpha^2}{2}$; α; 1	$\alpha+1$	3
−68	− 216	$\frac{\alpha^2}{2}$; α; 1	$\alpha+3$	1
78	red			
−78	− 356			1

bc	D_Ω	Basis	ε	d_Ω
88	-59	$\frac{\alpha^2}{4};\ \frac{\alpha}{2};\ 1$		1
-88	red			
81	-83	$\frac{\alpha^2+2\alpha+2}{5};\ \alpha;\ 1$	α	1
-81	$+2021$		α	
82	-44	$\frac{\alpha^2-3\alpha+3}{7};\ \alpha;\ 1$		1
-82	$+1940$		$\alpha^2+3\alpha+1$	
83	-2291			1
-83	red			
84	-610	$\frac{\alpha^2}{2};\ \alpha;\ 1$	$2\alpha+1$	1
-84	$+404$	$\frac{\alpha^2}{2};\ \alpha;\ 1$	$2\alpha-1$	1
85	-2723			1
-85	$+1373$			1
86	-3020			3
-86	$+1076$		$3\alpha^2-10\alpha+7$	1
87	red			
09	-243			1
19	-2191		$\alpha-2$	2
-19	-2183		α^2-5	2
29	-2219			2
-29	-2155		$16\alpha^2-25\alpha-152$	1
39	-255	$\frac{\alpha^2}{3};\ \alpha;\ 1$		1
-39	-231	$\frac{\alpha^2}{3};\ \alpha;\ 1$		1
49	-2443		$\alpha^2-4\alpha-8$	2
-49	-1931			2
59	-2687		$3\alpha+4$	2
-59	-1687		$7\alpha^2-20\alpha+22$	1
69	-339	$\frac{\alpha^2}{3};\ \alpha;\ 1$		1
-69	red			
79	-3559		$\alpha+1$	2
-79	-815			1
89	red			
-89	-139		$\alpha-2$	1
99	-567	$\frac{\alpha^2}{3};\ \alpha;\ 1$	$\alpha+1$	1
-99	$+81$			1
91	-327	$\frac{\alpha^2-\alpha+1}{3};\ \alpha;\ 1$	$\alpha;\ 9\alpha+1$	1
-91	$+321$	$\frac{\alpha^2-\alpha+1}{3};\ \alpha;\ 1$	$\alpha;\ \alpha+3;\ \alpha-3$	1
92	-756	$\frac{\alpha^2+\alpha}{2};\ \alpha;\ 1$	$\frac{5\alpha^2-17\alpha-4}{2}$	1

bc	$D_{\mathfrak{Q}}$	Basis	ϵ	$h_{\mathfrak{Q}}$
−92	+2808			1
93	−3159			1
−93	+2673		$3\alpha - 1$	1
94	−3348			1
−94	+ 621	$\frac{\alpha^2+\alpha}{2}$; α; 1	$-4\alpha^2 + 26\alpha - 3$	1
95	−3591		$-4\alpha^2 + 22\alpha + 13$	1
−95	+1241		$-\alpha^2 - 4\alpha - 2$	1
96	− 243			1
−96	+1944			1
97	−4239		$\alpha^2 - 2\alpha - 2$	1
−97	+1593		$\alpha - 1$	1
98	− 516	$\frac{\alpha^2+\alpha+1}{3}$; α; 1		1
010	− 300		$-3\alpha^2 - 6\alpha + 1$	1

TABLE analogous to the preceding for some equations of the form $x^3 + ax^2 + bx + c = 0$

(Table computed by Reid [45].)

abc	$D_{\mathfrak{Q}}$	Basis	ε	h	abc	$D_{\mathfrak{Q}}$	Basis	ε	h
−1 1 1	− 44		α	1	−2 1 2	−116			1
1 1 2	− 83		$\alpha + 1$	1	−1 1 2	−503	$\frac{\alpha^2+\alpha}{2}$; α; 1		1
−1 1 2	−139		$\alpha + 1$	1	−1 2 8	−503			1
−1 −2 1	− 59		$\alpha - 1$; $\alpha + 1$	1	−2 2 2	−204		$-\alpha^2 - 5\alpha + 7$	1
1 2 1	− 23		α	1	2 −2 2	−268		$\alpha + 3$	1
−1 2 1	− 87		α	1	−2 −2 2	+148		$\alpha + 1$, $\alpha - 1$	1
1 −2 1	− 31		α	1	1 4 8	−356	$\frac{\alpha^2+\alpha}{2}$; α; 1		1
−1 −2 1	+ 49		α	1	−1 4 8	−628	$\frac{\alpha^2+\alpha}{2}$; α; 1		1
−1 2 2	−200			1	1 −4 8	−516	$\frac{\alpha^2+\alpha}{2}$; α; 1		1
1 − 2 2	−152		$\alpha^2 - \alpha + 1$	1	−1 −4 8	−212	$\frac{\alpha^2+\alpha}{2}$; α; 1	$\alpha^2 + \alpha - 3$	1

TABLE of the number of classes of purely cubic fields $\Omega_{\sqrt[3]{A}}$

(Table computed by Dedekind [10].)

$D_{\Omega} = -3k^2$ $A = f \cdot g^2$

A=	2	3	5	6	12	7	10	20	11	13	14	28	15	45	17	19	21	63	22	44	23
k=	6	9	15	18	18	21	10	30	33	39	42	14	45	45	17	19	63	63	66	22	69
h=	1	1	1	1	1	3	1	3	2	3	3	3	2	1	1	3	3	6	3	1	1

CHAPTER III

GEOMETRY, TABULATION AND CLASSIFICATION OF ALGEBRAIC FIELDS OF THE THIRD AND FOURTH DEGREE

PART A. TABULATION OF FIELDS OF THE THIRD DEGREE

§26. THE LATTICE W AND ITS NETS $\bar{W}_0$, $\bar{W}_1$ FOR $n = 3$, $r = 0$ AND 1.

In §1 we considered the lattice $W_{n,r}$ consisting of all the points of all the multiplicative lattices of a given dimension n for a given number r of complex conjugate pairs of coordinates. In the cubic case, $n = 3$ and $r = 0$ or 1. We shall consider these two cases separately.

The case $r = 0$, i.e., $D > 0$. Every point ω of the lattice W has in this case coordinates which are roots of a cubic equation

$$\rho^3 - s\rho^2 + q\rho - n = 0, \tag{1}$$

with rational integer coefficients s, q, n (in this chapter we denote by $-q$ the coefficient which was denoted by q in Chapter II), all of whose roots are real (since the number of pairs of complex conjugate roots is assumed to be zero) and whose discriminant is therefore positive. We shall denote by x, y, z the coordinates of the points in the corresponding real signature space $R_{3,0}$. Then the lattice W is determined by the system of equations

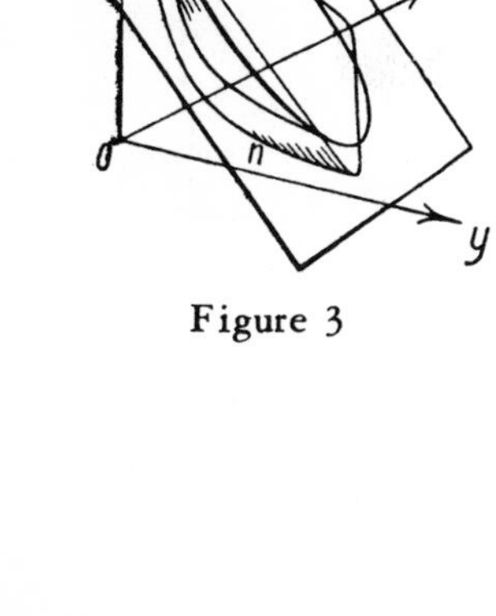

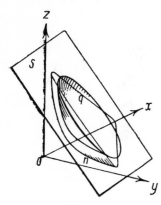

Figure 3

$$\begin{aligned} x + y + z &= s, \\ xy + xz + yz &= q, \\ xyz &= n, \end{aligned} \tag{2}$$

where s, q, n run through all possible rational numbers satisfying the condition that all three roots of (1) are real. The last statement is equivalent to the condition that the surfaces (2) should intersect, i.e., that they should have at least one point in common. To every point of W corresponds a unique definite equation (1), and to each equation (1) correspond six points of W, depending on the numbering of its roots.

The lattice W is therefore the set of all points of intersection of the family of all planes s cutting equal segments of the axes of the coasymptotic hyperboloids of revolution q around the rational line (of one sheet if $q < 0$, and of two sheets if $q > 0$), with the surfaces of the 3rd degree n, which approach asymptotically the coordinate planes for integer s, q, n.

The norm $N(x, y, z) = xyz$ is the volume of the coordinate parallelepiped of the point (x, y, z) and is positive if the point lies in one of the four odd octants and is negative if the point lies in one of the four even coordinate octants. The trace $S(x, y, z) = x + y + z$ is equal to the distance from the origin to the surface n taken with the proper sign and multiplied by $\sqrt{3}$. The different $\delta(x, y, z) = (x - y)(x - z) = (y - x)(z - x)$ is equal to the area of the coordinate rectangle in the YZ-plane of that point $(\bar{y}, \bar{z})$ of this plane which is the projection on this plane of the point (x, y, z) parallel to the so-called "rational direction," that is to the line $x = y = z$. In this way the different is equal to the hyperbolic distance from the origin to the point $(\bar{y}, \bar{z})$, if the axes Y and Z are taken as asymptotes. The discriminant of the point (x, y, z)

$$\begin{aligned} D(x, y, z) &= [(x - y)(x - z)(y - z)]^2 \\ &= s^2q^2 + 18sqn - 4q^3 - 4s^3n - 27n^2 \end{aligned}$$

is equal by §1 to the square of the volume of the parallelepiped constructed on the points $(0, 0, 0)$, $(1, 1, 1)$, (x, y, z), $(x, y, z)^2$.

All the points (x, y, z) having the same discriminant D lie on a cylinder of the sixth degree

$$(x - y)(x - z)(y - z) = \pm\sqrt{D},$$

whose linear generators are parallel to the rational line which, for example, intersects the XY-plane in the curve $(x - y) \cdot x \cdot y = \pm\sqrt{D}$. We shall call two points of W *parallel* if they are connected by the following relation: if (x, y, z) is one point, then $(x + k, y + k, z + k)$ is the other point, where k is a rational integer. Since all the coefficients of the equation corresponding to the first point are rational integers it follows that the coefficients of the equation corresponding to the second point are also rational integers. Therefore every point parallel to a point in W is also a point in W. The lattice W is composed of rows of parallel points, each of these rows lying on a line parallel to the rational line at a distance $\sqrt{3}$ from one another. For any point (x, y, z) of W it is possible to select a rational integer k in such a way that the point $(x + k, y + k, z + k)$ will have $s = -1$, 0 or 1, since in going from the first point to the second, the rational integer s (the trace) changes by $3k$. But the neighboring s planes are at a distance $\sqrt{3}/3$ apart, and therefore every parallel of points in W has one and only one of its points, which could be called its origin, either in the plane $s = -1$, or in the plane $s = 0$, or in the plane $s = 1$. We can visualize the lattice W better if we note that it is sufficient to know the two-dimensional nets of its points $\overline{W}_{-1}$, $\overline{W}_0$, $\overline{W}_1$ which lie in the planes $s = -1$, $s = 0$, $s = 1$, since the remaining points of W can be exhausted by a periodic parallel shift of these nets into the planes $s = \cdots \underbrace{2, 3, 4}, \underbrace{5, 6, 7} \cdots$. In reality it is sufficient to know only the nets $\overline{W}_0$ and $\overline{W}_1$, since the net $\overline{W}_{-1}$ is symmetric to the net $\overline{W}_1$ with respect to the origin. The hyperboloids q intersect the plane $s = 0$ in a system of concentric circles with centers at the origin. The coordinate planes intersect this plane $s = 0$ in three lines going through the origin and forming six equal 60° angles between them. The third-degree curves in which the plane $s = 0$ intersects the surfaces n have these lines for asymptotes. An analogous situation takes place for the plane $s = 1$, except that the point of intersection of this plane with the rational line $x = y = z$, which is the center of the circles q, is not the point of intersection of the lines in the coordinate planes, but is the center of gravity of the equilateral triangle formed by these lines, while the third-degree curves n still approach these lines as asymptotes.

We also note that the discriminant cylinders intersect the plane of trace $s = 0$, and the plane $s = 1$ in similar curves, closely analogous to the curves n, but rotated at an angle of 30° with respect to the origin.

All the systems of curves obtained in the plane $s = 0$ have a six-fold axial symmetry, while those in the plane $s = 1$ have a three-fold axial symmetry.

Carefully drawn charts of the nets $\overline{W}_0$ and $\overline{W}_1$ for $R_{3,0}$ will be found at the end of the book.

The case $r = 1$, i.e., $D < 0$. In this case we shall assume that z is the real root ρ of the equation

$$\rho^3 - s\rho^2 + q\rho - n = 0,$$

while $x + iy$, $x - iy$ are the two complex conjugate roots ρ' and ρ''. Then we have the system

$$\begin{aligned} 2x + z &= s, \\ x^2 + y^2 + 2xz &= q, \\ (x^2 + y^2)\, z &= n, \end{aligned} \tag{3}$$

where s, q, and n are all possible rational integers satisfying the condition $D < 0$, which is again equivalent to the condition that the surfaces s, q, and n intersect. The lattice W is in this case the totality of all the points of intersection of planes s parallel to the Y-axis and cutting off on the Z-axis segments twice as large as those on the X-axis with the coasymptotic hyperboloids q (of one sheet if $q > 0$, and of two sheets if $q < 0$) for which the Z-axis is one of the generators of the asymptotic cone common to all of them, and with the surfaces of revolution n of the third degree around the Z-axis, which approach asymptotically the Z-axis ($+z$ for $n > 0$, and $-z$ for $n < 0$) and the XY-plane, with integer s, q, n.

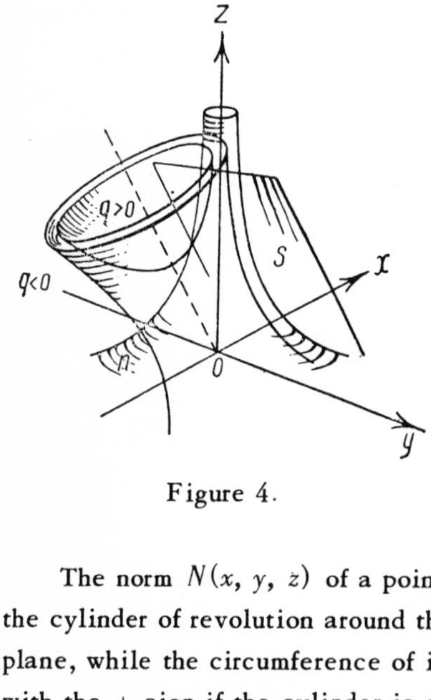

Figure 4.

The norm $N(x, y, z)$ of a point when divided by π is equal to the volume of the cylinder of revolution around the Z-axis, one of whose bases is in the XY-plane, while the circumference of its other base goes through this point, taken with the + sign if the cylinder is above the XY-plane, and with the minus sign if it is below. The trace $S(x, y, z)$ is equal to s. The discriminant $d(x, y, z) = [(\rho - \rho')(\rho - \rho'')(\rho' - \rho'')]^2 = s^2q^2 + 18sqn - 4q^3 - 4s^3n - 27n^2$ is equal to four times the square of the volume of the parallelepiped constructed on the points $(0, 0, 0)$, $(1, 0, 1)$, (x, y, z), $(x^2 - y^2, 2xy, z^2)$. All the points having the same discriminant d lie on the cylinder of the sixth degree

$$4(x^2 + y^2 + z^2 - 2xz)\, y = \pm\sqrt{|d|},$$

that intersects the XY-plane in the curve $4(x^2 + y^2)\, y = \pm\sqrt{|d|}$, which is symmetric with respect to the X-axis and approaches it asymptotically. The generators of this cylinder are parallel to the so-called rational line $z = x + iy = x - iy$, i.e., the line $x = z$, $y = 0$, which in this case contains the point $\rho = \rho' = \rho''$ having the coordinates $(1, 0, 1)$.

Two points are called parallel in this case if they are (ρ, ρ', ρ'') and $(\rho + k, \rho' + k, \rho'' + k)$, i.e., they are (x, y, z) and $(x + k, y + k, z + k)$, where k is a rational integer. In other words they are obtained from each other by a shift parallel to the rational line $x = z$, $y = 0$ by a distance $k\sqrt{2}$. As in the previous case it follows that every point parallel to a point of W is also a point of W. The lattice W consists of rows of parallel points, each of which is a regular row of points lying on a line parallel to the rational line at a distance of $\sqrt{2}$ from one another. As in the previous case the lattice W decomposes into nets $\overline{W}_{-1}, \overline{W}_0, \overline{W}_1$ lying in the planes s, which repeat periodically in the planes $s = \cdots \underbrace{2, 3, 4, 5, 6, 7} \cdots$.

Here the nets $\overline{W}_{-1}$ and $\overline{W}_1$ are again symmetric with respect to the origin, since the system s, as well as the systems q and n, are symmetric with respect to the origin, and therefore again it is sufficient to consider only the nets $\overline{W}_0$ and $\overline{W}_1$. The net $\overline{W}_0$ is composed of a system of coasymptotic hyperbolas q and a system of curves n of the third degree, which approach asymptotically the line of intersection of the plane $s = 0$ with the XY-plane, which is at the same time one of the axes of symmetry of the hyperbolas. This net has the axes of symmetry of the hyperbolas for its axes of symmetry. The net $\overline{W}_1$ is less symmetrical, since in it the asymptotes of the curves n of the third degree are only parallel to the corresponding axis of symmetry of the coasymptotic hyperbolas, but do not coincide with it. The curves of intersection of the cylinders with equal discriminants are quite analogous to the curves n in the net $\overline{W}_0$, but are rotated by 90°. The whole system of curves introduced in the plane $s = 0$ has two axes of symmetry, which are the axes of symmetry of the hyperbolas, while the system of curves in the plane $s = 1$ has only one axis of symmetry, which is one of the axes of symmetry of the hyperbolas.

At the end of the book will be found carefully drawn charts of the projections $\overline{\overline{W}}_0, \overline{\overline{W}}_1$ parallel to the rational direction of the nets $\overline{W}_0$ and $\overline{W}_1$ on the XY-plane.

§27. THE ELIMINATION OF THE REDUCIBLE POINTS IN BOTH CASES

If we wish to eliminate those points of the nets $\overline{W}_0$ and $\overline{W}_1$ which correspond to reducible equations $x^3 - sx^2 + qx - n = 0$, it is sufficient to note that in accordance with the general theory of §2, any such point is the sum of a point of a lattice W_1 (a row of rational integer points) lying on one of the axes, and of a point of a lattice W_2 lying in the plane formed by the other two axes.

In the case $D > 0$, the lattice W_2 lying in the XY-plane is defined by the equations

$$x + y = s,\qquad xy = q. \tag{1}$$

In this case W_2 is a lattice in the two-dimensional space with $\tau = 0$. All these points lie on parallel lines $x + y = s$, at a distance $\sqrt{2}/2$ from each other. Moreover, the rows of points lying on the lines $s = 0$ and $s = 1$, when moved in parallel along a perpendicular to these lines, repeat periodically in the lines $s = \cdots \underbrace{2, 3}, \underbrace{4, 5}, \cdots$. It is easily seen that equation (1) for points of W which lie in the planes $s = 0$ and $s = 1$ respectively is given by

$$\begin{aligned} x + y &= -3r, \\ xy &= 3r^2 + q \end{aligned} \quad \text{and} \quad \begin{aligned} x + y &= 1 - 3r, \\ xy &= 3r^2 - 2r + q, \end{aligned}$$

where r is a rational integer, i.e., in order to exclude the reducible points in $\overline{W}_0$ one must take only those lines s for which s is divisible by 3, while in $\overline{W}_{-1}$ one must take only lines s for which $s \equiv 1 \pmod 3$. One must consider the lattices W_2 lying in the XY-, XZ-, and YZ-planes. If we project the lattices in the XY-, XZ-, and YZ-planes respectively onto the planes $s = 0$ and $s = 1$, parallel to the rational direction, we will obtain in each of these planes three systems of parallel rows of points, lying on equally spaces lines, parallel to the asymptotes of the curves n of the third degree. Moreover, in each of these lattices the rows, when translated in parallel along a perpendicular to these lines, repeat periodically every other one. One of these rows is a row of all the points of $\overline{W}_0$ or $\overline{W}_1$, lying on the corresponding asymptote (i.e., the points of intersection of the asymptote with the circumferences q), while the other row is the result of the intersection of a line parallel to this asymptote. If we exclude in this way the reducible points of $\overline{W}_0$ and $\overline{W}_1$ we obtain in the planes $s = 0$ and $s = 1$ lattices consisting only of irreducible points.

These three rows of parallel lines are drawn in the charts at the end of the book.

If $D < 0$ we obtain the corresponding equations

$$2x = s,\qquad x^2 + y^2 = q. \tag{2}$$

which give the lattice W_2 for $\tau = 1$ in the XY-plane. The lattice W_2 cannot lie in the XZ- or YZ-plane, since in the lattice W_2 either both coordinates correspond to real roots or both to complex roots. All the points of the lattice W_2 lie in parallel lines $2x = s$, at a distance of ½ from each other. Moreover, the rows of points lying on the lines $s = 0$ and $s = 1$, when moved in parallel along a perpendicular to these lines, repeat on the lines $s = \cdots \underbrace{2, 3}, \underbrace{4, 5} \cdots$. The equations (2) for points lying respectively in the plane $s = 0$ and $s = 1$ are given by

$$\begin{aligned} 2x &= -3r \\ x^2 + y^2 &= 3r^2 + q \end{aligned} \quad \text{and} \quad \begin{aligned} 2x &= 1 - 3r \\ x^2 + y^2 &= 3r^2 - 2r + q \end{aligned},$$

where r is a rational integer. In other words, in order to exclude reducible points in $\overline{W}_0$ one should take only lines s where s is a multiple of 3, while for $\overline{W}_1$ we must have $s \equiv 1 \pmod 3$. In the planes $s = 0$ and $s = 1$ themselves we see as before that it is necessary to exclude all the points of W which lie on the asymptotes of the curves n of the third degree, as well as on lines parallel to them, and also every other lattice (which is moved in parallel along the perpendicular to these lines) lying on lines parallel to them and equally spaced from each other.

These lines are indicated in the charts at the end of the book.

In order to ascertain that in $\overline{W}_0$ for $D < 0$ there exist as many irreducible points as you wish we take the neighborhood of a point on the asymptote of the curves n far away from the origin. The net $\overline{W}_0$ in such a neighborhood, as is clear from its geometrical form, is a dense, almost orthogonal net, since the hyperbolas q and the curves n are approximately orthogonal to each other, and both the hyperbolas and the curves are very close together. In this way, in a strip between the asymptote and a parallel line of reducible points neighboring it there are arbitrarily many points of $\overline{W}_0$ but this strip has no reducible points, so that all these points are irreducible. The same thing holds in the other cases, but in the case $D > 0$, the three systems of lines on which the reducible points may lie form a net of equal equilateral triangles. One of these triangles, if located sufficiently far along an asymptote, will contain as many points as we please. In case $D > 0$ in $\overline{W}_1$ one of the triangles of this net of triangles will be, for example, the triangle formed by the asymptotes of the curves n.

§28. LIMITS ON THE COEFFICIENTS q AND n FOR A GIVEN s FOR POINTS CLOSE TO THE ORIGIN IN RINGS OF CUBIC INTEGERS, CONTAINING 1 WHOSE DISCRIMINANT DOES NOT EXCEED L IN ABSOLUTE VALUE

The case $D > 0$. The area $\overline{V}_o$ of the fundamental parallelogram of that lattice $\overline{O}$ which is obtained by the orthogonal projection of some ring O of cubic integer points of positive discriminant containing the point 1, parallel to the rational direction on the plane $s = 0$, is equal to $V_o/\sqrt{3}$ where V_o is the volume of the fundamental parallelepiped of O. This follows from the fact that such a parallelogram is obtained from the projection parallel to 01 of some fundamental parallelepiped, one of whose edges is 01, the plane s being perpendicular to 01, while the length of 01 is $\sqrt{3}$.

But $D_o = V_o^2$ and therefore $\bar{V}_o = \sqrt{D}/\sqrt{3}$. If $D \leq L$, then $\bar{V}_o \leq \sqrt{L}/\sqrt{3}$. All the reducible points of O, if O is an irreducible lattice, lie on a single bisectrix $x = y = z$, i.e., on the rational line, and therefore they project into the origin on the plane $s = 0$, where this plane is intersected by the rational line in the center of the circles q. All the remaining points of $\bar{O}$ are therefore projections of irreducible points of O. We describe in the plane $s = 0$ a circle around the origin such that in it or on its boundary there is at least one point of any $\bar{O}$ such that $\bar{V}_o \leq \sqrt{L}/\sqrt{3}$. It follows from well-known closest parallelogramic packing of circles (by equilateral triangles) that the least distance between two points of a plane lattice, the area of whose fundamental parallelogram is σ, does not exceed $\sqrt{2\sigma/\sqrt{3}}$. Therefore the radius of such a circle is $r = \sqrt{2/3}\,\sqrt[4]{L}$. In order to be sure to capture at least one irreducible point of each lattice O, with $0 < D_o \leq L$, it is necessary to study $\bar{W}_0$ and $\bar{W}_1$ for $0 < D$ and to find all points for which the circle q has a radius less than r. The radius of the circle can easily be calculated to be $\sqrt{-2q}$ for $s = 0$, and $\sqrt{-(2/3)2q}$ for $s = 1$ and therefore we obtain for $s = 0$, and correspondingly for $s = 1$, the following inequalities for the coefficient q, namely

$$-q \leqslant \frac{\sqrt{L}}{3}, \tag{1}$$

$$-q \leqslant \frac{\sqrt{L}-1}{3}. \tag{1'}$$

Now it remains to find for $s = 0$ and $s = 1$ for any given q a bound for n for which the last curve n still intersects the circle q. This inequality for n can be obtained from the condition

$$27D_p = 4(s^2 - 3q)^3 - (27n - 9sq + 2s^3)^2 > 0,$$

from which

$$-2\sqrt{(s^2-3q)^3} + 9sq - 2s^3 < 27n < 2\sqrt{(s^2-3q)^3} + 9sq - 2s^3.$$

In this way we finally obtain the following inequalities for n for $s = 0$ and $s = 1$, respectively:

$$-6q\sqrt{-3q} < 27n < 6q\sqrt{-3q}, \tag{2}$$

$$-2\sqrt{(1-3q)^3} + 9q - 2 < 27n < 2\sqrt{(1-3q)^3} + 9q - 2. \tag{2'}$$

The case $D < 0$. The area $\bar{V}$ of the fundamental parallelogram of that lattice $\bar{O}$ which is obtained by the projection of the ring O of cubic integer points of negative discriminant which contains the point 1, parallel to the rational direction into the XY-plane is equal to V_o. This follows from the fact that if we take for one of the edges of the fundamental parallelepiped the segment 01 on the rational line, and then translate the ends of two other edges from the origin parallel to the rational line into the XY-plane, we obtain an equilateral parallelepiped, the area of whose base is $\bar{V}_o$ and whose height is 1. But in case $S < 0$

$$|D_o| = 4V_o^2,$$

and therefore we have

$$\bar{V}_o = \frac{\sqrt{|D_o|}}{2}.$$

Making use of the same inequality for the least distance between two points of a plane lattice whose fundamental parallelogram has area σ, we obtain at least one point in the circle of radius $r = \sqrt[4]{L/3}$ around the origin in the XY-plane. This point is a projection parallel to the rational direction of a point of the ring O of negative discriminant D_o which does not exceed L in absolute value. Consider now the inequalities for the coefficients q and n, which for $s = 0$ and $s = 1$ give points of W whose projections parallel to the rational direction lie in a given circle.

We denote by $\bar{\bar{W}}_0$ and $\bar{\bar{W}}_1$ the projections parallel to the rational direction of the nets $\bar{W}_0$ and $\bar{W}_1$ lying in the planes $s = 0$ and $s = 1$ into the XY-plane. We next find the equations of the nets $\bar{\bar{W}}_0$ and $\bar{\bar{W}}_1$. In order to do this we denote by v and w the x and y coordinates of the points in the XY-plane. We note that if we project the point (x, y, z) parallel to the rational direction into the XY-plane, then the coordinates u and v of the projection will be $v = x - z$, $w = y$. Eliminating x, y, and z from these two equations and from equations (3) of §26, we obtain the relations

$$v^2 - 3w^2 = -3q + s^2, \tag{3}$$

$$(v^2 + 2uv + s^2 + 9w^2)(s - 2v) = 27n, \tag{4}$$

which define the nets $\bar{\bar{W}}_0$ and $\bar{\bar{W}}_1$ for $s = 0$ and $s = 1$, when q and n assume all possible rational integer values.

Taking into consideration the value of r and considering the farthest hyperbolas which still intersect the circumference of r, we obtain respectively for $s = 0$ and $s = 1$ the following inequalities for q:

$$-\frac{1}{3}\sqrt{\frac{L}{3}} \leqslant q \leqslant \sqrt{\frac{L}{3}}, \tag{5}$$

$$-\frac{1}{3}\sqrt{\frac{L}{3}} + \frac{1}{3} \leqslant q \leqslant \sqrt{\frac{L}{3}} + \frac{1}{3}. \tag{5'}$$

Now we must find bounds for n, i.e., the boundary curves n which still intersect every hyperbola q inside the circle L. To do this we note that

$$r^2 = v^2 + w^2 = (x - z)^2 + y^2,$$

from which

$$r^2 = 3z^2 - 2sz + q = F'(z),$$

where F is the left-hand side of the equation whose roots are $\rho = z$, $\rho' = x + iy$, $\rho'' = x - iy$, i.e., r^2 is the different of ρ. The different $\delta = F'(\rho)$ is a root of the equation

$$\delta^3 - \delta^2(s^2 - 3q) + (-4q^3 - 27n^2 + s^2q^2 + 18sqn - 4s^3n) = 0.$$

If we increase n for given s and q, then for some $n = n'$ we have that δ becomes r^2, i.e., we will have

$$r^6 - r^4(s^2 - 3q) + D_\rho = 0.$$

For smaller values of n, we will have a larger r, which will give a value greater than zero (since for $r = 0$ we get $D_\rho < 0$, i.e., a value less than zero). Hence in each of the cases $s = 0$ and $s = 1$ we must take for every q satisfying the inequalities (5) and (5′) a value of n for which

$$r^6 - r^4(s^2 - 3q) + D_\rho < 0.$$

§29. THE DETERMINATION OF THE THIRD NUMBER IN THE BASIS OF EACH OF THE CAPTURED POINTS

We consider all the irreducible rings O, either of positive or negative discriminant, whose discriminants D_o are less than L in absolute value. In view of the limits obtained in the preceding section for q and n for $s = 0$ and $s = 1$, we are sure that there exists at least one and possibly several equations $\rho^3 - s\rho^2 + q\rho - n = 0$ with rational integer coefficients that correspond to irreducible points of any such ring. Obviously, however, not every equation with rational integer coefficients which are bounded by these limits necessarily corresponds to a point in one of these rings. In the first place the equation may be reducible, in which case it does not correspond to any point of any such ring, with the exception of the the equation $x^3 = 0$, which corresponds to the origin, and belongs to all the rings, but does not interest us. Then it is possible that the discriminant of such an equation

$$D_\rho = s^2q^2 + 18sqn - 4q^3 - 4s^3n - 27n^2,$$

after division by its greatest square factor gives a quotient that exceeds L in absolute value. Such an equation also cannot correspond to any point of any such ring, since the discriminant of any point in the ring is obviously equal to the discriminant of the ring multiplied by the square of a rational integer, namely the index of this point. Such equations must be discarded along with the reducible ones. However, if the discriminant D_o contains a square factor such that the quotient on division by this square factor gives a number which does not exceed L in absolute value, then this does not yet imply that there exists a ring O having a point ρ whose discriminant D_o does not exceed L in absolute value. It is possible that all such points belong to rings whose discriminants are greater than L in absolute value. In order to find out if there exist rings whose discriminants do not exceed L in absolute value, and to find such rings if they exist, it is sufficient to use the method of calculating the bases of all the rings containing the point ρ which was given in §17. Moreover, the situation is somewhat simplified here since we must find only the rings O which have ρ for the second number of the basis. As in §17, we will consider here only those rings which contain the point 1, and therefore since for the first point of the basis we can always take the point 1, it remains only to find the third point of the basis, for which we can use the method of §17.

§30. THE PLAN OF ACTION FOR THE DISCOVERY OF ALL IRREDUCIBLE RINGS, COMPOSED OF CUBIC INTEGER POINTS AND CONTAINING THE POINT 1, WHOSE DISCRIMINANTS DO NOT EXCEED A GIVEN NUMBER IN ABSOLUTE VALUE

The sequence of necessary steps is as follows:

1) For $s = 0$ and $s = 1$ find the bounds for q for a given L, using formulas (1) and (1′) of §28 for $D > 0$, and formulas (5) and (5′) of §28 for $D < 0$.

2) Find the bounds on n for each such q using formulas (2) and (2′) of §28 if $D > 0$, and the method described at the end of §28, if $D < 0$. In this way we obtain in either of the two cases, whether $D > 0$ or $D < 0$, two tables of equations, the projections of whose points lie inside the circle r. These tables may be obtained directly by a careful drawing of the nets $\overline{W}_0$ and $\overline{W}_1$ for $D > 0$, or the corresponding nets $\overline{\overline{W}}_0$ and $\overline{\overline{W}}_1$ for $D < 0$, as is done at the end of the book.

3) Exclude all reducible equations.

4) Calculate all the D_ρ of the remaining equations (this operation takes up most of the time).

5) Factor all these D_ρ and exclude all the equations whose discriminants when divided by the largest square factor contained in them produce a quotient which exceeds L in absolute value.

6) Find for each of the remaining equations, using the rules given in §17, the third number ψ of the basis, and retain only those equations for which $|D_o| = |D_\rho/\Delta^2|$ does not exceed L in absolute value. In this way we obtain all the rings O whose discriminants do not exceed L in absolute value, but we may obtain some of them several times. Therefore it remains to carry out the following step:

7) By the method inverse to the Tschirnhausen transformation (see §13) find out whether the rings so obtained, having the same discriminants, are actually equal or not. Finally, if we wish to find all distinct cubic fields whose discriminants do not exceel L in absolute value we must take the final step:

8) Test whether the rings, whose discriminants are equal to the discriminants of other rings multiplied by a square factor of a rational integer, correspond to unrelated cubic fields or whether they are simply extensions of the corresponding rings. This can be done again by the method inverse to the Tschirnhausen transformation, as explained in §13.

Conclusion. After such a table of cubic rings O is computed by this method, so that for every $|D| \leq L$ all the distinct rings O are calculated, i.e., the coefficients s, q, n of the equation $\rho^3 - s\rho^2 + q\rho - n = 0$ satisfied by ρ are given, as well as the numbers Δ, μ, ν in the expression $\psi = (\rho^2 + \mu\rho + \nu)/\Delta$, where $1, \rho, \psi$ is a basis of the corresponding ring O, we can if we wish rewrite this table as a table of representatives of all classes of binary cubic forms with integer coefficients with $|D| \leq L$ (the index-forms of these rings). In fact, the index-form (a, b, c, d) corresponding to the ring $[1, \rho, \psi]$ has the coefficients (see §17)

$$a = \Delta,\ b = \frac{1}{2}F''(t),\ c = \frac{1}{\Delta}F'(t),\ d = \frac{1}{\Delta^2}F(t),$$

where $F(z) = z^3 - sz^2 + qz - n,\ ut = s + \mu$.

TABLE OF CUBIC FIELDS OF POSITIVE DISCRIMINANT AND OF THE DISCRETE RINGS CONTAINED IN THEM FOR ALL $D \leq 1296$

Calculated by D. K. Faddeev

№	D	Index-form	Remarks	№	D	Index-form	Remarks
1	49	(1,—1,—2, 1)	Maximal	21	761	(1,—1,—6,—1)	Maximal
2	81	(1, 0,—3,—1)	"	22	784	(2,—2,—4, 2)	Contained in 1
3	148	(1,—1,—3, 1)	"	23	785	(1,—1,—6, 5)	Maximal
4	169	(1,—1,—4,—1)	"	24	788	(1,—1,—7,—3)	"
5	229	(1, 0,—4,—1)	"	25	837	(1, 0,—6,—1)	"
6	257	(1,—1,—4, 3)	"	26	892	(1,—1,—8, 10)	
7	316	(1,—1,—4, 2)	"	27	916	(1,—1,—6, 4)	Contained in 5
8	321	(1,—1,—4, 1)	"	28	940	(1, 0,—7,—4)	Maximal
9	361	(1,—1,—6, 7)	"	29	961	(2,—1,—5, 2)	"
10	404	(1,—1,—5,—1)	"	30	985	(1,—1,—6, 1)	"
11	469	(1,—1,—5, 4)	"	31	993	(1,—1,—6, 3)	"
12	473	(1,0,—5,—1)	"	32	1016	(1,—1,—6, 2)	"
13	564	(1,—1,—5, 3)	"	33	1076	(1, 0,—8,—6)	"
14	568	(1,—1,—6,—2)		34	1101	(1,—1,—9, 12)	"
15	592	(1,—1,—5, 1)	Contained in 3	35	1129	(1, 0,—7,—3)	"
16	621	(1, 0,—6,—3)	Maximal	36	1229	(1,—1,—7, 6)	"
17	697	(1, 0,—7,—5)		37	1257	(1,—1,—8, 9)	"
18	729	(1, 0,—9,—9)	Contained in 2	38	1264	(1, 0,—7,—2)	Contained in 7
19	733	(1, —1,—7, 8)	Maximal	39	1264	(1,—1,—7,—1)	" in 7
20	756	(1, 0,—6,—2)	"	40	1296	(2, 0,—6,—2)	" in 2

REMARK. The number of ideal classes for all maximal rings in the table is equal to 1.

§31. AN INDEPENDENT TABULATION OF CUBIC CYCLIC MAXIMAL LATTICES

For cyclic maximal lattices the problem of tabulation can be solved by means of very simple considerations differing from those of the previous section and giving a method of tabulation which requires a small number of calculations.

We shall call a multiplicative lattice formed by numbers in a cubic cyclic region *symmetric* if it goes into itself under a cyclic transformation of the roots of the generating equation. Such a lattice goes into itself on rotation around a rational line by angles of 120° and 240°.

The method of tabulation which will be explained in this section enables us to construct all such lattices in order of increasing discriminants. It is not hard to show by examples that not all rings formed by numbers in a cyclic region are symmetric; however, the maximal rings which interest us most (see §3) are obviously symmetric.

We shall prove two lemmas which will be necessary in what follows.

LEMMA 1. *Every ring contains a "symmetric" basis of the form* $[1, \rho, \rho']$, *where* ρ' *is a number conjugate to* ρ. *All such bases are located along six "parallels". In fact if* $[1, \rho, \rho']$ *is one of the symmetric bases, then all the others are of the form:*

$$[1, \rho+k, \rho'+k]; \quad [1, \rho'+k, \rho''+k]; \quad [1, \rho''+k, \rho+k];$$
$$[1, -\rho+k, -\rho'+k]; \quad [1, -\rho'+k, -\rho''+k]; \quad [1, -\rho''+k, -\rho+k],$$

where k *is a rational integer.*

TABLE OF ALL CUBIC FIELDS OF NEGATIVE DISCRIMINANT D FOR ALL $|D| < 1000$

(Calculated by Berwick and Mathews and recalculated by Delone)

№	$-D$	Index-form	№	$-D$	Index-form
1	23	(1, 1, 2, 1)	34	324	(1, 0,—3,4,)
2	31	(1, 0, 1, 1)	35	327	(1, 4, 3, 3)
3	44	(1,—1, 1, 1)	36	331	(1,—2, 4, 1)
4	59	(1, 0, 2, 1)	37	335	(1,—1, 4, 1)
5	76	(1, 1, 3, 1)	38	339	(1, 2, 0, 3)
6	83	(1,—2, 2, 1)	39	351	(1, 3, 6, 1)
7	87	(1,—1, 2, 1)	40	356	(1, 0—7, 8)
8	104	(1, 0—1, 2)	41	364	(1, 0, 4, 2)
9	107	(1, 2, 4, 1)	42	367	(1, 4, 7, 1)
10	108	(1, 0, 0, 2)	43	379	(1, 1, 1, 4)
11	116	(1, 1, 0, 2)	44	411	(1, 1, 5, 2)
12	135	(1, 0, 3, 1)	45	419	(1, 3—1, 2)
13	139	(1, 4, 6, 1)	46	424	(1,8—7, 2)
14	140	(1, 3, 5, 1)	47	431	(2, 1, 3, 2)
15	152	(1, 1,—2, 2)		aus.	
16	172	(1, 2, 0, 2)	48	432	(1, 0, 0, 4)
17	175	(1,—2, 3, 1)	49	436	(1, 3, 4, 6)
18	199	(1, 1, 4, 1)	50	439	(1, 2,—1, 3)
19	200	(1, 2, 3, 4)	51	440	(1, 7, 6, 2)
20	204	(1; 1, 1, 3)	52	451	(1, 5, 3, 2)
21	211	(1, 6, 10, 1)	53	459	(1, 3,—3, 2)
22	212	(1, 1, 4, 2)	54	460	(1, 1, 5, 3)
23	216	(1, 0, 3, 2)	55	472	(1, 3,—2, 2)
24	231	(1,—4, 5, 1)	56	484	(1, 2, 5, 6)
25	239	(1, 0,—1, 3)	57	491	(1,—4, 6, 1)
26	243	(1, 0, 0, 3)	58	492	(1, 2, 4, 6)
27	244	(1, 5, 4, 2)	59	499	(1, 0, 4, 3)
28	247	(1,—3, 4, 1)	60	503	(2, 5, 5, 4)
29	255	(1, 5, 8, 1,)		aus.	
30	268	(1, 7, 13, 1)	61	515	(1, 4, 4, 5)
31	283	(1, 0, 4, 1)	62	516	(3, 3, 4, 2)
32	300	(1, 4, 2, 2)	63	519	(1, 5, 4, 3)
33	307	(1, 2, 4, 1)	64	524	(1, 1, 3, 5)

№	$-D$	Index-form	№	$-D$	Index-form
65	527	(1, 0, 5, 1)	97	780	(1, 4, 4, 6)
66	543	(1, 1, 2, 5)	98	804	(1, 1, 4, 6)
67	547	(1, 4, 2, 3)	99	808	(1, 0, 2, 6)
68	563	(1, 2, 6, 1)	100	812	(1, 4,—2, 2)
69	567	(1, 3, 0, 3)	101	815	(1, 6, 5, 3)
70	588	(1,—1, 5, 1)	102	823	(1, 3,—2, 3)
71	620	(1, 4, 0, 2)	103	835	(1, 2, 0, 5)
72	628	(2, 5, 6, 5)	104	839	(1, 4, 3, 5)
73	643	(1,—6, 10, 1)	105	843	(3, 3, 5, 2)
74	648	(2, 0, 3, 2)	106	856	(2, 2, 1, 3)
	aus.		107	863	(1, 2, 3, 7)
75	652	(1, 6, 4, 2)	108	867	(1, 7, 5, 2)
76	655	(1, 2, 1, 5)	109	876	(3, 2, 4, 2)
77	671	(1, 3, 2, 5)	110	883	(1, 5,—5, 2)
78	675	(1, 0, 0, 5)	111	888	(2, 2, 5, 3)
79	676	(2, 2, 5, 2)	112	891	(1, 0, 6, 1)
80	679	(1, 3, 4, 7)	113	907	(1, 5, 1, 2)
81	680	(1, 5, 2, 2)	114	908	(2, 6, 4, 3)
82	687	(1, 2, 5, 7)	115	931	(1,—2, 6, 1)
83	695	(1,—5, 8, 1)	116	932	(1, 0, 5, 4)
84	796	(1, 2—1, 4)	117	940	(1, 3, 1, 5)
85	707	(1, 3, 5, 8)	118	948	(1, 2, 1, 6)
86	716	(1, 3,—1, 3)	119	959	(1,—1, 6, 1)
87	728	(1, 1, 6, 2)	120	964	(2, 6, 5, 4)
88	731	(1, 4, 8, 1)	121	971	(2, 3, 1, 3)
89	743	(1, 0, 5, 3)	122	972	(1, 0, 0, 6)
90	744	(1, 4—1, 2)	123	972	(2, 6, 6, 5)
91	748	(1, 2, 2, 6)	124	980	(2, 4, 5, 5)
92	751	(1, 1, 6, 1)	125	983	(1, 1, 6, 5)
93	755	(1, 2, 6, 7)	126	984	(2, 1, 0, 3)
94	756	(2, 3, 6, 3)	127	996	(1, 4, 5, 8)
95	759	(1, 1, 6, 3)	128	999	(2, 3, 3, 4)
96	771	(1, 1, 3, 6)		aus.	

REMARK. We give, if possible, the index-forms which have the first coefficient equal to 1 (i.e., allowing a power basis) and among them, if possible, those having the last coefficient equal to 1. The lattices all of whose indices have a common factor are followed by the letters *aus*. These lattices, and also Nos. 62 and 72 do not have power bases. The lattices 79, 94, 105 and 106 are in doubt in this respect.

TABLE OF ALL DISCRETE RINGS CONTAINING 1 THAT BELONG TO THE FIELDS OF THE PREVIOUS TABLE FOR ALL $|D| < 1000$

$-D$	Index-form	$-D$	Index-form	$-D$	Index-form
176	(1,—1, 3, 1) ⊂ № 3	556	(1, 4, 3, 4) ⊂ № 13	816	(1, 5, 3, 3) ⊂ № 20
236	(1,—2, 1, 2) ⊂ № 4	560	(1, 2, 0, 4) ⊂ № 14	844	(1, 1, 6, 4) ⊂ № 21
279	(1, 2, 5, 1) ⊂ № 2	575	(1,—2, 5, 1) ⊂ № 1	848	(1, 4, 2, 4) ⊂ № 22
304	(1, 5, 7, 1) ⊂ № 5	608	(1, 5, 9, 1) ⊂ № 15	848	(1, 5, 4, 4) ⊂ № 22
332	(1, 1, 2, 4) ⊂ № 6	608	(1, 1, 1, 5) ⊂ № 15	864	(1, 9, 21, 1) ⊂ № 23
368	(2, 2, 4, 2) ⊂ № 1	684	(1, 4—4, 2) ⊂ № 5	864	(1,0,—3,6) ⊂ № 23
416	(1, 1, 5, 1) ⊂ № 8	688	(1, 3, 7, 1) ⊂ № 16	944	(1, 2, 5, 8) ⊂ № 4
416	(1, 2, 1, 4) ⊂ № 8	704	(2, 4, 4, 4) ⊂ № 3	944	(2, 0, 4, 2) ⊂ № 4
428	(1, 3, 2, 4) ⊂ № 9	783	(1, 4, 1, 3) ⊂ № 7	972	(1, 0, 6, 2) ⊂ № 10
432	(1, 0, 0, 4) ⊂ № 10	783	(1, 3, 6, 9) ⊂ № 7	972	(1, 6, 3, 2) ⊂ № 26
464	(1,—3, 5, 1) ⊂ № 11	800	(1, 5, 5, 5) ⊂ № 19	976	(1, 2, 6, 8) ⊂ № 27
464	(1, 3, 5, 7) ⊂ № 11	800	(2, 3, 4, 4) ⊂ № 19	976	(1, 3, 4, 8) ⊂ № 27
496	(2, 0, 2, 2) ⊂ № 2				

PROOF. We project a symmetric ring parallel to the rational direction into the perpendicular plane $x + y + z = 0$. This projection is a plane lattice which coincides with itself on rotation by 120° and 240° around the origin. Consider the point α of the projection which is closest to the origin. Together with this point the projection lattice must contain the point $-\alpha$ and the points obtained by rotating the points α and $-\alpha$ by 120° and 240°. These six points form a regular hexagon with center at the origin. Every parallelogram constructed on the origin and three adjacent points of the hexagon will be empty in the interior and on the boundary and therefore can be taken for the fundamental parallelogram of the lattice. Every other parallelogram constructed on a point of the lattice and on a point obtained from it by rotation of 120° will contain in it or on the boundary at least one vertex of the fundamental hexagon and therefore cannot be taken for the fundamental parallelogram. Therefore only the projections of the fundamental hexagon can be taken for the elements of a symmetric basis of a ring. Every such number, however, can be taken for an element of a symmetric basis, since if a point $(\omega, \omega', \omega'')$ projects into the vertex α, then the conjugate point $(\omega', \omega'', \omega)$ projects into the vertex α'.

This proves the lemma.

LEMMA 2. *Let ρ be a number in a cyclic region and let ρ' be a number conjugate to ρ. The coefficients a, b, c, d of the linear fractional representation $\rho' = (a\rho + b)/(c\rho + d)$ of ρ' in terms of ρ satisfy the relation*

$$ad - bc = (a + d)^2.$$

PROOF. Let

$$\rho' = \frac{a\rho + b}{c\rho + d}.$$

Then

$$\rho'' = \frac{a\rho' + b}{c\rho' + d} \text{ and } \rho = \frac{a\rho'' + b}{c\rho'' + d}.$$

Substituting in the last equation the expression of ρ'' in terms of ρ' we obtain

$$\rho = \frac{a\dfrac{a\rho' + b}{c\rho' + d} + b}{c\dfrac{a\rho' + b}{c\rho' + d} + d} = \frac{(a^2 + bc)\,\rho' + b\,(a + d)}{c\,(a + d)\,\rho' + (d^2 + bc)},$$

from which

$$\rho' = \frac{-(d^2 + bc)\,\rho + b\,(a + d)}{c\,(a + d)\,\rho - (a^2 + bc)}.$$

It follows from the uniqueness of a linear fractional transformation that the following equalities must hold:

$$-(d^2 + bc) = a\lambda, \quad b\,(a + d) = b\lambda, \quad c\,(a + d) = c\lambda, \quad -(a^2 + bc) = d\lambda,$$

from which

$$\lambda = a + d.$$

The first and fourth equalities give

$$a^2 + ad + d^2 + bc = 0,$$

or what is the same thing,

$$(a + d)^2 = ad - bc,$$

which proves the lemma.

We now come to the exposition of the method of tabulation. The idea behind the method consists in the fact that it is possible to determine in every symmetric ring certain "reduced" numbers, which are uniquely defined in the ring and each of which in turn uniquely defines the ring.

Such numbers are the components of a normal basis selected for a parallel of symmetric bases. A symmetric ring contains twelve reduced numbers, since such a ring contains six parallels of symmetric bases, and each parallel leads to the construction of two reduced numbers.

Let ρ be one of the reduced numbers. Another reduced number which forms with it a normal basis must be of the form $\rho' - m$, since it must be in the "parallel" containing the number ρ' conjugate to ρ. From the definition of a normal basis the following relation must hold:

$$\rho(\rho' - m) = k,$$

where k is a rational integer, from which

$$\rho' = \frac{m\rho + k}{\rho}.$$

By the second lemma, the numbers m and k are related by $k = -m^2$ and therefore

$$\rho' = \frac{m\rho - m^2}{\rho}.$$

It is easily seen that $\rho = -m^2/(\rho' - m)$, from which it follows that

$$\rho'' = \frac{-m^2}{\rho - m}.$$

We form an equation whose roots are ρ, ρ', and ρ''. We denote by s the first coefficient of this equation

$$s = \rho + \rho' + \rho''.$$

The other coefficients are easily determined:

$$q = \rho\rho' + \rho'\rho'' + \rho''\rho = m\rho - m^2 + m\rho' - m^2 + m\rho'' - m^2 = ms - 3m^2,$$
$$n = \rho\rho'\rho'' = \rho\frac{m\rho - m^2}{\rho}\cdot\frac{-m^2}{\rho - m} = -m^3.$$

Hence ρ satisfies the equation

$$\rho^3 = s\rho^2 - m(s - 3m)\rho - m^3.$$

It is easily seen that if ρ is one of the reduced numbers, then all the other reduced numbers are

$$\begin{matrix} \rho, & \rho', & \rho'' \\ -\rho, & -\rho', & -\rho'' \\ \rho - m, & \rho' - m, & \rho'' - m \\ m - \rho, & m - \rho', & m - \rho''. \end{matrix}$$

All these numbers are roots of the four equations

$$\begin{aligned} \rho^3 &= s\rho^2 - m(s - 3m)\rho - m^3, \\ \rho_1^3 &= s_1\rho_1^2 - m_1(s_1 - 3m_1)\rho_1 - m_1^3, \\ \rho_2^3 &= s_2\rho_2^2 - m_2(s_2 - 3m_2)\rho_2 - m_2^3, \\ \rho_3^3 &= s_3\rho_3^2 - m_3(s_3 - 3m_3)\rho_3 - m_3^3, \end{aligned}$$

whose parameters s_i and m_i are connected with the parameters s and m of one of them by the relations

$$s_1 = -s, \qquad s_2 = s - 3m, \qquad s_3 = 3m - s,$$
$$m_1 = -m, \qquad m_2 = -m, \qquad m_3 = m.$$

From these four equations we can easily select one by requiring that $m > 0$ and $s \geq 3m/2$.

In this way to every symmetric ring corresponds uniquely an equation of the form

$$\rho^3 = s\rho^2 - m(s - 3m)\rho - m^3,$$

whose parameters s and m satisfy the inequalities $m > 0$, $s \geq 3m/2$.

Any pair of roots of such an equation, together with the number 1, forms a symmetric basis of a ring.

Conversely, every such equation defines uniquely a symmetric ring for any integer values of the parameters s and m. In fact, the discriminant of such an equation

$$\begin{aligned} D(\rho) &= s^2m^2(s-3m)^2 + 4s^3m^3 - 4m^3(s-3m)^3 - 18m^4s(s-3m) - 27m^6 \\ &= m^2(s^2 - 3ms + 9m^2)^2 \end{aligned}$$

is a perfect square, and therefore the roots of this equation are rationally expressible in terms of each other. It is easily seen that one of the roots ρ' is expressible in terms of another root ρ by $(m\rho - m^2)/\rho$.

The numbers ρ and ρ', together with the number 1, can be taken as a symmetric basis of a ring, since the numbers ρ^2, $\rho\rho'$ and ρ'^2 are linearly expressible with integer coefficients in terms of 1, ρ and ρ'. In fact

$$\begin{aligned} \rho^2 &= s\rho - m(s-3m) - \frac{m^3}{\rho} = s\rho + m\rho' - m(s-2m), \\ \rho\rho' &= m\rho - m^2, \\ \rho'^2 &= s\rho' + m\rho'' - m(s-2m) = -m\rho + (s-m)\rho' + 2m^2. \end{aligned}$$

The discriminant of the ring obtained in this way is

$$D = \begin{vmatrix} 1, & \rho, & \rho' \\ 1, & \rho', & \rho'' \\ 1, & \rho'', & \rho \end{vmatrix}^2 = (\rho^2 + \rho'^2 + \rho''^2 - \rho\rho' - \rho'\rho'' - \rho'\rho)^2 = (s^2 - 3ms + 9m^2)^2.$$

Hence, as the numbers s and m assume all possible integer values satisfying the inequalities $m > 0$, $s \geq 3m/2$, we obtain all symmetric rings and each one only once. Since $\sqrt{D} = s^2 - 3ms + 9m^2$ is a positive quadratic form, it is easy to assign the values of m and s in such a way as to get all symmetric rings in increasing order of their discriminants. Among the rings obtained in this way there will be reducible as well as irreducible rings.

After all the rings whose discriminants do not exceed a certain bound have been constructed, the maximal rings can be easily selected.

In this way the above method gives a complete solution of the problem of tabulation of symmetric rings, and in particular of maximal rings of cyclic regions.

TABLE OF GENERATING EQUATIONS OF IRREDUCIBLE MAXIMAL CYCLIC RINGS FOR ALL $\sqrt{D} < 100$

$\sqrt{D}$	$-s$	$-q$	$-n$	$\sqrt{D}$	$-s$	$-q$	$-n$	$\sqrt{D}$	$-s$	$-q$	$-n$	$\sqrt{D}$	$-s$	$-q$	$-n$
7	2	1	−1	31	5	2	−8	63	9	−6	−1	79	10	−7	−1
9	3	0	−1	37	7	−4	−1	63	9	−6	−8	91	11	−10	−8
13	4	−1	−1	43	7	−2	−8	67	7	6	−27	91	10	−3	−27
19	5	−2	−1	61	5	12	−27	73	8	3	−27	97	11	−8	−1

PART B. SOME GEOMETRICAL THEOREMS

§32. GEOMETRY OF A BINARY CUBIC FORM AND ITS COVARIANTS

The interpretation of binary quadratic forms with real coefficients in terms of nets, given in the plane up to ordinary rotation in case $D > 0$, and up to a hyperbolic rotation in case $D < 0$, is well known (see, for example, the Introduction by B. N. Delone to Dirichlet's *Lectures on the theory of numbers*, which has been translated as Supplement I of the present volume). We will show in this section that the binary cubic form f with real coefficients can also be interpreted by a vector pair in a plane, which is completely determined. All the covariants of f, namely H, Q, and D can also be interpreted by the same vector pair as the form f, where the quadratic form H and the discriminant D have the usual meaning.

Let $f(X, Y) = aX^3 + bX^2Y + cXY^2 + dY^3$ be an arbitrary binary cubic form with real or complex coefficients a, b, c, d. As in §15, we call the roots ρ_1, ρ_1', ρ_1'' of the equation $f(X, a) = 0$ the left roots of the form f, while the roots ρ_2, ρ_2', ρ_2'' of $f(d, -Y) = 0$ are called the right roots of the form f. If t_1 is a left root, then it is easily seen that $t_2 = -ad/t_1$ is a right root of f. Two such roots of f will be called corresponding roots and we will assume that ρ_1 and ρ_2, ρ_1' and ρ_2', ρ_1'' and ρ_2'' correspond in pairs.

We shall begin with a lemma which is a paraphrase of the method of Lagrange for solution of cubic equations by means of the resolvent adapted to the case of binary cubic forms.

LEMMA I. *If the coefficients a, b, c, d of the form f are any real or complex numbers, there exists an identity in X, Y, namely*

$$f(X,\ Y)=\frac{1}{3\Delta}(\xi^3-\eta^3),$$

where

$$\xi=\xi_1X+\xi_2Y;\ \eta=\eta_1X+\eta_2Y;\ \xi_1=\rho_1+\varepsilon\rho_1'+\varepsilon^2\rho_1'';\ \eta_1=\rho_1+\varepsilon^2\rho_1'+\varepsilon\rho_1'';$$

$$\xi_2=\rho_2+\varepsilon\rho_2'+\varepsilon^2\rho_2'';\quad \eta_2=\rho_2+\varepsilon^2\rho_2'+\varepsilon\rho_2'',\quad \text{where } \epsilon=e^{\frac{2\pi i}{3}} \text{ and } \Delta=\begin{vmatrix}\xi_1 & \eta_1\\ \xi_2 & \eta_2\end{vmatrix}.$$

In fact, taking into consideration that $\rho_1\rho_2=-ad$, we obtain $a\rho_2=\rho_1^2+b\rho_1+ac$ and $d\rho_1=-\rho_2^2+c\rho_2-bd$. Substituting these into Δ, and then the Δ thus obtained into the coefficients $\bar{a}$, $\bar{b}$, $\bar{c}$, $\bar{d}$ of the expression $(1/3\Delta)/(\xi^3-\eta^3)$, we see by direct calculation that these coefficients are indeed a, b, c, d.

The determination of the covariants, i.e., the Hessian H, the Jacobian Q and the discriminant D of the cubic form f is as follows:

$$H=-\frac{1}{4}\begin{vmatrix}\dfrac{\partial^2 f}{\partial x^2}, & \dfrac{\partial^2 f}{\partial x\,\partial y}\\ \dfrac{\partial^2 f}{\partial x\,\partial y}, & \dfrac{\partial^2 f}{\partial y^2}\end{vmatrix}=(b^2-3ac)X^2+(bc-9ad)XY+(c^2-3bd)Y^2$$
$$=AX^2+BXY+CY^2;$$

$$Q=\begin{vmatrix}\dfrac{\partial f}{\partial x}, & \dfrac{\partial f}{\partial y}\\ \dfrac{\partial H}{\partial x}, & \dfrac{\partial H}{\partial y}\end{vmatrix}=(9abc-2b^3-27a^2d)X^3$$
$$+(18ac^2-3b^2c-27abd)X^2Y$$
$$+(27acd+3bc^2-18b^2d)XY^2$$
$$+(27ad^2+2c^3-9bcd)Y^3$$
$$=a'X^3+b'X^2Y+c'XY^2+d'Y^3;$$

$$D=\frac{1}{3}\begin{vmatrix}\dfrac{\partial^2 H}{\partial x^2}, & \dfrac{\partial^2 H}{\partial x\,dy}\\ \dfrac{\partial^2 H}{\partial y\,\partial x}, & \dfrac{\partial^2 H}{\partial y^2}\end{vmatrix}=b^2c^2-4ac^3-4b^3d+18abcd-27a^2d^2,$$

where the numerical coefficients in front of the determinants are chosen in such a way that if the coefficients a, b, c, d of a given binary cubic form $f(X,\ Y)=aX^3+bX^2Y+cXY^2+dY^3$ are rational integers, then the coefficients of the forms H, Q, and D (i.e., A, B, C; a', b', c', d'; and D) are also rational integers, without identical common factor, and such that if $D>0$, then the form H is also positive.

LEMMA II. *The covariants of a binary cubic form are equal to*

$$H = \xi\eta, \quad Q = \xi^3 + \eta^3, \quad D = -\frac{\Delta^2}{3}.$$

In fact, taking into consideration that $f = (1/3\Delta)(\xi^3 - \eta^3)$, $\xi = \xi_1 X + \xi_2 Y$, $\eta = \eta_1 X + \eta_2 Y$, $\Delta = \begin{vmatrix} \xi_1 & \eta_1 \\ \xi_2 & \eta_2 \end{vmatrix}$, we can calculate and verify these expressions.

These two purely algebraic lemmas give identities which hold for a binary cubic form f with any real or complex coefficients a, b, c, d. From now on we will always assume that the coefficients a, b, c, d are real. Then we have the following further lemmas.

LEMMA III. (A) *If* a, b, c, d *are real and* $D > 0$, *then* $\rho_1, \rho_1', \rho_1''$ *and hence* $\rho_2, \rho_2', \rho_2''$ *are real, while* ξ_1 *and* ξ_2 *are complex. The area* s *of the parallelogram constructed in the complex plane on the vectors terminating in the points* ξ_1 *and* ξ_2 *is then different from zero and the numbers* η_1, η_2 *are complex conjugates of* ξ_1 *and* ξ_2. *Conversely, if* ξ_1 *and* ξ_2 *are complex, and if the area* s *of the parallelogram constructed on them is different from zero, and if* η_1, η_2 *are their complex conjugates, then the coefficients* a, b, c, d *are real and* $D > 0$.
(B) *If* a, b, c, d *are real and* $D < 0$, *then one of the left roots of* f *(we shall denote it by* ρ_1*) is real, and the other two* ρ_1', ρ_1'' *are complex conjugates, the same being true for the corresponding roots* $\rho_2, \rho_2', \rho_2''$. *In this case* $\xi_1, \xi_2, \eta_1, \eta_2$ *are all real and the area* s *of the parallelogram constructed on the vectors* (ξ_1, η_1), (ξ_2, η_2) *is not equal to zero. Conversely, if* $\xi_1, \eta_1, \xi_2, \eta_2$ *are real and the area* s *of the parallelogram is different from zero, then the coefficients* a, b, c, d *are real and* $D < 0$.

This lemma follows from the formulas of Lemma I and from the fact that by Lemma II we have $D = -\Delta^2/3$. By Lemmas I and II the geometric interpretation of a binary cubic form and its covariants can be given as follows.

The case $D > 0$. In this case we associate with a given binary cubic form $f = (1/3\Delta)(\xi^3 - \eta^3)$ the vector-pair which connects the origin in the complex plane $\alpha + \beta i$ with the points $\xi_1 = \alpha_1 + \beta_1 i$ and $\xi_2 = \alpha_2 + \beta_2 i$. The Hessian $H = \xi\eta$ will be in this case a definite binary quadratic form and will be represented by the same vector-pair in the usual way. The Jacobian $Q = \xi^3 + \eta^3$ will also be represented in the same way as the given form f by a vector-pair, symmetric with the vector-pair (α_1, β_1), (α_2, β_2) with respect to the bisectrix of the odd angles in the plane α, β, linearly magnified $\sqrt[3]{6s}$ times, since in case $D > 0$, we have $\Delta = -i \cdot 2s$, and consequently

$$f = \frac{1}{6s}\{[(\beta_1 + \alpha_1 i)X - (\beta_2 + \alpha_2 i)Y]^3$$
$$+ [(\beta_1 - \alpha_1 i)X - (\beta_2 - \alpha_2 i)Y]^3\},$$

while the form $Q = [(\alpha_1 + \beta_1 i)X - (\alpha_2 + \beta_2 i)Y]^3 + [(\alpha_1 - \beta_1 i)X - (\alpha_2 - \beta_2 i)Y]^3$.

Finally,

$$D = \frac{4}{3}s^2.$$

Conversely, every vector-pair in the plane $\alpha + \beta i$ with area s different from zero corresponds in this sense to some binary cubic form with real coefficients and with positive discriminant D and covariants H, Q, D.

The case $D < 0$. In this case we associate with a given binary cubic form $f = (1/3\Delta)(\xi^3 - \eta^3)$ the vector-pair from the origin to the points $(\xi_1, \eta_1), (\xi_2, \eta_2)$ in the ξ, η plane.

The Hessian $H = \xi\eta$ will be in this case an indefinite binary quadratic form and will be represented by the same vector-pair with respect to the asymptotes ξ, η.

The Jacobian $Q = \xi^3 + \eta^3$ will be represented in the same way as the given form f by a vector-pair, symmetric to the vector-pair $(\xi_1, \eta_1), (\xi_2, \eta_2)$ with respect to the ξ-axis and linearly magnified $\sqrt[3]{3s}$ times, since $\Delta = s$ in case $D < 0$, and we find

$$f = \frac{1}{3s}[(\xi_1 X + \xi_2 Y)^3 - (\eta_1 X + \eta_2 Y)^3],$$
$$Q = (\xi_1 X + \xi_2 Y)^3 + (\eta_1 X + \eta_2 Y)^3.$$

Finally the discriminant $D = -s^2/3$.

If we make a real linear homogeneous transformation with determinant $\delta = \pm 1$ of the variables X, Y, then the form f and its covariants H, Q, D transform into another form $\bar{f}$ with covariants $\bar{H}, \bar{Q}, \bar{D}$. These new forms will correspond in the above described sense to a new vector-pair, which is obtained from the old vector-pair by this transformation. If the determinant $\delta \neq \pm 1$, then this will still be the case for H and Q. However, the form $\bar{\bar{f}}$ corresponding to the new vector-pair will not be the transformed form $\bar{f}$, but $\delta/\bar{f}$, since the multiplier $1/\Delta$ entering into the expression of the form in terms of its vector-pair remains invariant under transformation, while if $\delta \neq \pm 1$ the coefficients of X and Y in ξ and η, namely

$\xi_1, \xi_2, \eta_1, \eta_2$ vary, so that the corresponding Δ must be δ times as large. Also $\overline{\overline{D}}$ corresponding to the transformed vector-pair is $\delta^2 D$ while $\overline{D}$ of the transformed form is $\delta^4 D$.

We will now go deeper into the geometric interpretation of a binary cubic form with real coefficients whose discriminant is different from zero, and of its covariants. We will consider the plane α, β in case $D > 0$ and the plane ξ, η in case $D < 0$, in which we represent the form f and its covariants by a vector-pair lying in the space $R_{3,0}$ and $R_{3,1}$ respectively, and if necessary we make an affine transformation of this plane. This enables us to establish a connection between the geometrical theory which we have just expounded and the theory developed in §15.

First of all we prove two lemmas connected with the multiplication of a pair of points in the space $R_{3,0}$ or $R_{3,1}$. As before, the line $x = y = z$ will be called the rational line in $R_{3,0}$, while the line $x = z$, $y = 0$ is the rational line in $R_{3,1}$. We shall call a point *parallel* to the point A if it can be obtained from the point A by a translation parallel to the rational line. Finally we shall call the pair of points B_1, B_2 *normal* if their product (either in $R_{3,0}$ or in $R_{3,1}$) is a point on the rational line.

LEMMA IV. *If A_1, A_2 is any pair of points in $R_{3,0}$ or $R_{3,1}$ noncoplanar with the rational line, then there exists a unique normal pair of points B_1, B_2 parallel to it.*

Let the coordinates of the points A_1 and A_2 be (x_1, y_1, z_1) and (x_2, y_2, z_2) in $R_{3,0}$. In this case the parallel points are given by $(x_1 + r_1, y_1 + r_1, z_1 + r_1)$ and $(x_2 + r_2, y_2 + r_2, z_2 + r_2)$. Their product lies on the rational line if and only if the products of the corresponding coordinates are equal. We obtain a system of two linear equations in r_1 and r_2 whose determinant is $\neq 0$ if the points A_1 and A_2 are noncoplanar with the rational line. In the case of $R_{3,1}$, if $x \pm iy$ are the complex coordinates of the points and if z is real, then the points parallel to A_1 and A_2 are $(x_1 + r_1, y_1, z_1 + r_1)$ and $(x_2 + r_2, y_2, z_2 + r_2)$ and we obtain the same result.

LEMMA V. *The left and right roots of any binary cubic form with real coefficients and $D \neq 0$ determine a normal pair of points (in $R_{3,0}$ in case $D > 0$, and in $R_{3,1}$ in case $D < 0$) and conversely every normal pair of points determines in this sense a certain such form.*

This follows from the definition of left and right roots and from the fact that the product of the corresponding roots is equal to ad.

Finally, we give a proof of a lemma which connects the above geometric interpretation of binary cubic forms by means of a vector-pair in a plane (the plane α, β if $D > 0$, and the plane ξ, η in case $D < 0$) with the theory of the solution of a cubic equation, and for forms with rational integer coefficients with the theory considered in §15.

LEMMA VI. *If B_1, B_2 is a normal pair of points in the space $R_{3,0}$, noncoplanar with the rational line, which corresponds to the binary cubic form f with $D > 0$ and if A_1, A_2 are the orthogonal (i.e., parallel to the rational line) projections of the points B_1, B_2 on the plane S of the zero trace $s = 0$, i.e., on the plane $x + y + z = 0$ in the space $R_{3,0}$, then the vector-pair from the origin to the points A_1 and A_2 corresponds to the form f in the above sense, if for the α-axis in S is taken the orthogonal projection on S of one of the coordinate axes (say the X-axis) of the space $R_{3,0}$, and for the β-axis, its perpendicular, and if corresponding unit segments are taken on these axes, and conversely.*

In fact, denote the distance measured on the segment e from a point in the space $R_{3,0}$ to the plane S by h. Then every point in the space $R_{3,0}$ will have on the one hand the cartesian coordinates x, y, z and on the other hand, the coordinates α, β, h, where the relation between them can be given by the transformation equations

$$\left.\begin{aligned} x &= \frac{1}{\sqrt{6}}(2\cdot\alpha + 0\cdot\beta + \sqrt{2}\cdot h), \\ y &= \frac{1}{\sqrt{6}}(-\alpha + \sqrt{3}\cdot\beta + \sqrt{2}\cdot h), \\ z &= \frac{1}{\sqrt{6}}(-\alpha - \sqrt{3}\cdot\beta + \sqrt{2}\cdot h). \end{aligned}\right\}$$

A straightforward calculation shows that if the coordinates x, y, z of the points B_1 and B_2 are $\rho_1, \rho_1', \rho_1''$ and $\rho_2, \rho_2', \rho_2''$, then $\xi_1 = \alpha_1 + \beta_1 i$, $\xi_2 = \alpha_2 + \beta_2 i$ are in fact $\xi_1 = \rho_1 + \epsilon\rho_1' + \epsilon^2\rho_1''$; $\xi_2 = \rho_2 + \epsilon\rho'_2 + \epsilon^2\rho''_2$.

LEMMA VI'. *If B_1, B_2 is a normal pair of points in the space $R_{3,1}$ (noncoplanar with the rational line) corresponding to the binary cubic form f with $D<0$ and if A_1 and A_2 are the projections of the points B_1, B_2 parallel to the rational line in the space $R_{3,1}$ on the plane S of the zero trace $s = 0$, i.e., on the plane $2x + z = 0$ in the space $R_{3,1}$, and furthermore if this plane is taken for the ξ, η-plane, where the ξ, η-plane is rotated by an affine transformation so that the ξ, η-axes become symmetric with respect to the $y = 0$ plane, so that they coincide* *with the lines of intersection of the plane* S *with the cone* $q = 0$, *and if the corresponding segments are taken as unit segments on these axes, then the vector-pair formed by* A_1, A_2 *on the* ξ, η-*plane will represent the form* f *in the above sense.*

The proof is the same as that for Lemma VI, namely a direct calculation of ξ_1 and ξ_2.

We must remark, however, that in the case $D < 0$ it is more advantageous to locate the ξ, η-plane on the XY-plane of the space $R_{3,1}$, rather than on the $s = 0$ plane, i.e., to project the points B_1 and B_2 not onto the $s = 0$ plane but onto the $z = 0$ plane and to take for the axes not ξ, η, but $\bar{\xi}$, $\bar{\eta}$, that are rotated by an angle of 45° with respect to ξ, η. With such axes, which simply coincide with the X, Y-axes in the XY-plane and whose units coincide with the old units on X, Y, the form f with $D < 0$ is very simply expressed.

In fact if

$$\rho_1' = \alpha_1 + \beta_1 i, \quad \rho_2' = \alpha_2 + \beta_2 i,$$

then

$$(\xi_1 = \alpha_1 - \rho_1, \ \eta_1 = \beta_1), \quad (\xi_2 = \alpha_2 - \rho_2, \ \eta_2 = \beta_2),$$

and we have

$$\rho_1 \rho_2 = \rho_1' \rho_2' = -ad,$$

i.e.,

$$\begin{aligned} \alpha_1 \alpha_2 - \beta_1 \beta_2 &= -ad, \\ \alpha_1 \beta_2 + \alpha_2 \beta_1 &= 0, \end{aligned}$$

or

$$\begin{aligned} (\xi_1 + \rho_1)(\xi_2 + \rho_2) - \eta_1 \eta_2 &= ad, \\ (\xi_1 + \rho_1)\eta_2 + (\xi_2 + \rho_2)\eta_1 &= 0. \end{aligned}$$

From this, by considering the positive quadratic form

$$Ax^2 + 2Bxy + Cy^2,$$

corresponding to the vector-pair $(\xi_1, \eta_1)(\xi_2, \eta_2)$, i.e., by letting

$$\xi_1^2 + \eta_1^2 = A; \quad \xi_1 \xi_2 + \eta_1 \eta_2 = B; \quad \xi_2^2 + \eta_2^2 = C,$$

we obtain

$$\rho_1 = -\frac{A\eta_2}{\Delta}; \quad \rho_2 = \frac{C\eta_1}{\Delta},$$

where

$$\Delta = \begin{vmatrix} \xi_1 & \eta_1 \\ \xi_2 & \eta_2 \end{vmatrix}.$$

Substituting these expressions into ρ_1 and ρ_2 and expressing the coefficients a, b, c, d of the cubic form in terms of $\rho_1, \rho_1', \rho_1'', \rho_2, \rho_2', \rho_2''$, namely:

$$a = \frac{\rho_1\rho_1' + \rho_1\rho_1'' + \rho_1'\rho_1''}{\rho_2 + \rho_2' + \rho_2''}; \quad -b = \rho_1 + \rho_1' + \rho_1'';$$

$$c = \rho_2 + \rho_2' + \rho_2''; \quad -d = \frac{\rho_2\rho_2' + \rho_2\rho_2'' + \rho_2'\rho_2''}{\rho_1 + \rho_1' + \rho_1''},$$

we obtain the following expressions in terms of $\xi_1, \eta_1, \xi_2, \eta_2$:

$$a = \frac{A\eta_1}{\Delta}; \quad b = \frac{A\eta_2 + 2B\eta_1}{\Delta}; \quad c = \frac{C\eta_1 + 2B\eta_2}{\Delta}; \quad d = \frac{C\eta_2}{\Delta}. \tag{*}$$

But the form $\eta(\xi^2 + \eta^2) = a'X^3 + b'X^2Y + c'XY^2 + d'Y^3$, where as before $\xi = \xi_1 X + \xi_2 Y$; $\eta = \eta_1 X + \eta_2 Y$ has coefficients

$$a' = A\eta_1; \quad b' = A\eta_2 + 2B\eta_1; \quad c' = C\eta_1 + 2B\eta_2; \quad d' = C\eta_2. \tag{**}$$

Comparing (*) and (**) we obtain the lemma:

LEMMA VII. *If $\xi = \xi_1 X + \xi_2 Y$, $\eta = \eta_1 X + \eta_2 Y$ and if (ξ_1, η_1) and (ξ_2, η_2) are the x, y coordinates of the projection into the XY-plane parallel to the rational direction of the points of $R_{3,1}$ corresponding to the roots of some form $f(X, Y)$ with $D < 0$, then the form $\eta(\xi^2 + \eta^2)$ differs only by the multiplier Δ from the form $f(X, Y)$.*

§33. REDUCTION THEORY FOR BINARY CUBIC FORMS

We define as *reduced* forms those six forms out of all the binary cubic forms equivalent to a given binary cubic form $f(X, Y)$ with real coefficients (i.e., obtained from it by linear transformations with integer coefficients and determinant equal to 1) for which the corresponding vector-pair is reduced in the sense of Gauss (see Supplement I). This vector-pair is considered in the plane of zero trace in the space $R_{3,0}$ if $D > 0$, and in the XY-plane of the space $R_{3,1}$ if $D < 0$.

In the case $D > 0$ therefore, in order to reduce $f(X, Y)$ it is necessary to calculate the covariant $H(X, Y)$ and reduce it by the method described in sections 19, 49, 50 of Supplement I. If f is a form with integer coefficients, so is H and therefore the reduction of H presents no difficulties. If $\begin{pmatrix} \alpha & \beta \\ \gamma & \delta \end{pmatrix}$ is the substitution which transforms H into an equivalent reduced form according to Gauss, i.e., $\bar{H} = H_{\left(\begin{smallmatrix} \alpha & \beta \\ \gamma & \delta \end{smallmatrix}\right)}$, then $\bar{f} = f_{\left(\begin{smallmatrix} \alpha & \beta \\ \gamma & \delta \end{smallmatrix}\right)}$ is a reduced binary cubic form equivalent to f.

The other reduced forms can then be obtained from $\bar{f}$ by the substitutions

$$\begin{pmatrix}1 & 0\\ 0 & 1\end{pmatrix},\ \begin{pmatrix}0 & -1\\ 1 & 1\end{pmatrix},\ \begin{pmatrix}-1 & -1\\ 1 & 0\end{pmatrix},\ \begin{pmatrix}-1 & 0\\ 0 & -1\end{pmatrix},\ \begin{pmatrix}0 & 1\\ -1 & -1\end{pmatrix},\ \begin{pmatrix}1 & 1\\ -1 & 0\end{pmatrix}.$$

In case $D < 0$, the same can be accomplished by means of the quadratic form $AX^2 + BXY + CY^2$ considered at the end of the previous section. This form, as is geometrically obvious, is also a covariant of the form f, but an irrational covariant, since its coefficients A, B, C are expressible irrationally in terms of the coefficients a, b, c, d of the form f. The reduction of the form (A, B, C) itself by means of calculations with its coefficients is therefore not convenient.

We note, however, that it follows from the formula (*) of the previous section that the expression for $bc - ad$ has the following form:

$$bc - ad = \frac{2}{\Delta^2}(A\eta_2^2 + 2B\eta_1\eta_2 + C\eta_1^2)\cdot B,$$

and therefore in view of the fact that (A, B, C) is a positive form if η_1 and η_2 are not simultaneously equal to zero (which cannot happen because the points B_1, B_2 are noncoplanar with the rational line) we see that the sign of B coincides with the sign of $bc - ad$. In reducing the form f according to Gauss we require that $bc - ad \geq 0$.

This can be summarized as follows:

1°. If $bc - ad < 0$ to start with, we make the substitution $\begin{pmatrix}1 & 1\\ 0 & 1\end{pmatrix}$ several times until for the first time we obtain $bc - ad \geq 0$.

2°. We perform the substitution $\begin{pmatrix}1 & 0\\ -1 & 1\end{pmatrix}$ the maximum number of times without disturbing the non-negative character of $bc - ad$.

3°. Next we perform the substitution $\begin{pmatrix}1 & -1\\ 0 & 1\end{pmatrix}$ the maximum number of times without disturbing the non-negative character of $bc - ad$. We then alternate the operations 2° and 3° until they cannot be repeated any longer.

The form $\bar{f}$ thus obtained will be a reduced form.

§34. BINARY CUBIC FORMS CONSIDERED AS NORMS

We start with a multiplicative lattice O and with some other lattice having O as its ring of multipliers.

We call a point of a lattice *primary* if there exist no other points of the lattice on the segment connecting this point to the origin. Any primary point may be taken for one of the basis points of the lattice. Therefore if we transform a

Dirichlet form into all its equivalent forms in all possible ways, then the numbers standing in the apex of the triangle defining these forms will be the norms of the primary points of that lattice.

By a rational section of the lattice we will understand the totality of all points of the lattice which lie in a plane passing through the origin and containing at least two of its points, noncolinear with the origin. A rational section of a lattice is a two-dimensional lattice. To every rational section we can associate a class of binary cubic forms in the following way. We select a basis of the section and represent all the points of the section in terms of this basis as a linear form in two integer-valued variables. We then obtain the norms of all the points in the section as binary cubic forms. In this way we establish a connection between a basis of a rational section and a binary cubic form, and more generally between the section as a whole and a class of binary cubic forms. Binary forms which correspond in this way to the rational sections are those and only those binary forms which appear along the edges in the triangle defining the Dirichlet forms of a lattice under all possible transformations of this form into equivalent forms.

To every basis of a rational section corresponds a reciprocal point which, after normalization of the reciprocal lattice, transforms into a completely determined point of the polar lattice. This point obviously does not depend on the choice of the basis of the section and therefore corresponds to the section as a whole. It will obviously be a primary point of the polar lattice.

Conversely, to every primary point of the lattice can be made to correspond in this sense a rational section of the polar lattice. In order to do this one must construct reciprocal points for all pairs formed by the given point and each of the remaining points of the lattice.

We shall show that the binary form, which is the norm of a section of the polar lattice corresponding to some primary point of the given lattice, is in a sense a generalization of the index-form.

In order to do this we generalize the notion of the index to points on any normalized lattice in the following way. By a *mutual index* of two points Ω and T belonging to the same normalized lattice we will understand the square root of the ratio of the discriminant of the form $N(x\Omega + yT)$ to the discriminant of the lattice. We shall now calculate this mutual index.

Let $N(x\Omega + yT) = ax^3 + bx^2y + cxy^2 + dy^3$.

By definition of the discriminant of a binary cubic form it is equal to

$$a^4D\left(-\frac{T}{\Omega}\right)=(\omega\omega'\omega'')^4\cdot\left(\frac{\tau}{\omega}-\frac{\tau'}{\omega'}\right)^2\cdot\left(\frac{\tau'}{\omega'}-\frac{\tau''}{\omega''}\right)^2\cdot\left(\frac{\tau''}{\omega''}-\frac{\tau}{\omega}\right)^2$$

$$=(\tau\omega'-\tau'\omega)^2(\tau'\omega''-\tau''\omega')^2(\tau''\omega-\tau\omega'')^2=N^2(T\times\Omega).$$

Here τ, τ', τ'' and $\omega, \omega', \omega''$ are the coordinates of the points T and Ω, and $T\times\Omega$ is the reciprocal point for the pair T, Ω.

After normalization of the reciprocal lattice, the point $T\times\Omega$ transforms into the point Φ of the polar lattice and $N(T\times\Omega)=\sqrt{D}\cdot N(\Phi)$, where D is the discriminant of the lattice. Therefore the mutual index of the pair T, Ω is equal to the norm of the point of the polar lattice which corresponds to the pair T, Ω.

It follows from the definition of the mutual index that the ordinary index of a number belonging to a ring is the mutual index of the pair formed by the image of this point and of unity under a geometric representation of the ring as a lattice.

If we consider Ω as the fixed primary point and let T run over all the points of the lattice we will obtain the mutual indices of the pairs (T, Ω) as a binary cubic form, which we shall call the index-form of the lattice with respect to the primary point Ω. An ordinary index-form of a ring will then be the index-form of the ring with respect to the point 1. The index-form of the lattice with respect to the point Ω is nothing else but the norm-form of a section of the polar lattice corresponding to the primary point Ω of the original lattice. Conversely every norm-form of the rational section of a given lattice may be regarded as an index-form of the polar lattice with respect to the point, corresponding to the given rational section of the original lattice.

§35. ESTIMATING THE MINIMA OF BINARY CUBIC FORMS

The representation of a binary cubic form as an index-form of some cubic ring enables us to estimate from above the minimum value of this form for integer values of the variables in terms of the discriminant of the form, i.e., to find a limit below which values of this form can always be found.

We shall give this estimate separately for forms of positive and negative discriminants.

We begin with the case of a binary cubic form $f(x, y)$ with rational integer coefficients and positive discriminant D. The ring corresponding to the form is represented as a multiplicative lattice in the real three-dimensional space. We take a point $(\omega', \omega'', \omega''')$ of the ring and represent it in terms of the normal basis of the ring as follows:

$$\omega = x\omega_1 + y\omega_2 + z.$$

The index of the point ω with respect to the ring will be equal to a value of the form $f(x, y)$. It can be written in terms of the coordinates of the point ω as follows:

$$f(x, y) = \frac{1}{\sqrt{D}}(\omega'' - \omega''')(\omega''' - \omega')(\omega' - \omega'').$$

The index-form $f(x, y)$ has the same value for all points lying on the same parallel and therefore it can be expressed in terms of the coordinates of the projection of the point ω on the plane of zero trace $\omega' + \omega'' + \omega''' = 0$. We take for the coordinate axes in the plane $\omega' + \omega'' + \omega''' = 0$ the line $O\xi$, which is the projection of the axis $O\omega'$, and the perpendicular to it, the line $O\eta$. With this choice of axes the projection of the point ω will have the coordinates

$$\xi = \frac{2\omega' - \omega'' - \omega'''}{\sqrt{6}},$$

$$\eta = \frac{\omega'' - \omega'''}{\sqrt{2}}.$$

From these formulas we obtain readily that

$$\begin{aligned} f(x,y) &= \frac{1}{\sqrt{D}}(\omega'' - \omega''')(\omega''' - \omega')(\omega' - \omega'') \\ &= \frac{1}{\sqrt{D}}\cdot\eta\sqrt{2}.(-1).\ \frac{\xi\sqrt{6}+\eta\sqrt{2}}{2}\cdot\frac{\xi\sqrt{6}-\eta\sqrt{2}}{2} \\ &= \frac{\eta(\eta^2 - 3\xi^2)}{\sqrt{2D}} \end{aligned}$$

If the point ω runs over the whole ring, then its projection will go over a parallelogrammatic lattice with area of the fundamental parallelogram equal to $\sqrt{D}/\sqrt{3}$, since this lattice is an orthogonal projection of a space lattice with volume $\sqrt{D}$, parallel to the direction in which the shortest vector of the lattice is of length $\sqrt{3}$.

Hence

$$f(x,y) = \frac{\eta(\eta^2 - 3\xi^2)}{\sqrt{2D}},$$

where to integer values (x, y) correspond points (ξ, η) which form a lattice with area of fundamental parallelogram equal to $\sqrt{D}/\sqrt{3}$.

We consider the curve with equation

$$\eta(\eta^2 - 3\xi^2) = \pm c.$$

This curve consists of six "hyperbolic" branches, which can be obtained from one of them by rotation through angles which are multiples of 60°. We construct a hexagon from the tangents to the curve at points closest to the origin. This hexagon is completely interior to the star-shaped figure bounded by the curve and therefore all the coordinates of its points satisfy the inequality

$$|\eta(\eta^2 - 3\xi^2)| \leq c.$$

If c is selected in such a way that the area of the hexagon is equal to four times the area of the fundamental parallelogram of the lattice, then by the theorem of Minkowski on convex bodies, there will be at least one point (ξ_0, η_0) of the lattice, different from the origin, which is inside or on the boundary of the hexagon. We shall select such a c. Since the area of the hexagon is

$$2\sqrt{3}\, c^{\frac{2}{3}},$$

we must have

$$2\sqrt{3}\, c^{\frac{2}{3}} = 4\sqrt{\frac{D}{3}},$$

from which

$$c = \left(\frac{2}{3}\right)^{\frac{3}{2}} \cdot D^{\frac{3}{4}}.$$

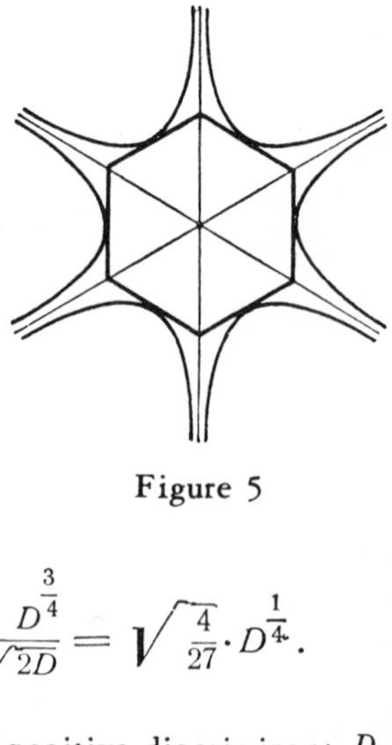

Figure 5

If we denote by (x_0, y_0) the values of the variables (x, y) for those points whose projections (ξ_0, η_0) are inside the hexagon, we obtain

$$|f(x_0, y_0)| = \left| \frac{\eta_0(\eta_0^2 - 3\xi_0^2)}{\sqrt{2D}} \right| \leq \left(\frac{2}{3}\right)^{\frac{3}{2}} \cdot \frac{D^{\frac{3}{4}}}{\sqrt{2D}} = \sqrt{\frac{4}{27}} \cdot D^{\frac{1}{4}}.$$

Therefore for every binary cubic form $f(x, y)$ of positive discriminant D there exist integer values of the arguments (x_0, y_0) such that

$$|f(x_0, y_0)| \leq \sqrt{\frac{4}{27}} \cdot D^{\frac{1}{4}}.$$

For forms of negative discriminant we give next an analogous discussion.

Consider the ring, for which the given form $f(x, y)$ of negative discriminant is an index-form, as a lattice in the space K_3. We then introduce real coordinates, in the signature space which contains the points of the ring, that preserve the metric of the space. In order to do this we must take as the real coordinates of the point $(\omega', \omega'', \omega''') = (\omega', \alpha + \beta i, \alpha - \beta i)$ the numbers $(\alpha\sqrt{2}, \beta\sqrt{2}, \omega')$. With this choice the point 1 will have coordinates $(\sqrt{2}, 0, 1)$, and therefore the length of the shortest rational integer vector will be $\sqrt{3}$, as in the real case. The plane of zero trace will be perpendicular to the rational line, and the volume of the fundamental parallelepiped of the lattice which represents the ring will be equal to $\sqrt{|D|}$. Therefore, the area of the fundamental parallelogram of the projection of the ring on the plane of zero trace will also be equal to $\sqrt{|D|/3}$, as in the real case.

In the plane of zero trace we take for the axis $O\eta$ the "imaginary axis" of the three-dimensional space. For the $O\xi$ axis we take the projection perpendicular to it of the "real axis". The coordinates of the projection of the point $(\omega', \omega'', \omega''')$ with respect to these axes are

$$\eta = \frac{\omega'' - \omega'''}{\sqrt{2}i}; \qquad \xi = \frac{2\omega' - \omega'' - \omega'''}{\sqrt{6}}.$$

By means of these formulas, as in the previous case, it is easy to represent the values of the index-form $f(x, y)$ in terms of the coordinates of the projection of the point ω on the plane of zero trace as follows:

$$f(x, y) = \frac{(\omega'' - \omega''')(\omega''' - \omega')(\omega' - \omega'')}{\sqrt{D}} = \frac{\eta(\eta^2 + 3\xi^2)}{\sqrt{2|D|}}.$$

The curve $\eta(\eta^2 + 3\xi^2) = \pm c$ consists of two branches, which are asymptotic to the $O\xi$ axis. Both these branches have for inflection points the points of intersection with the bisectors of the coordinates angles. The tangents at the points of inflection form angles of 45° with the $O\xi$ axis. Obviously, the figure bounded by the tangents at the points of inflection and by the portions of the curve between the points of inflection is a centrally symmetric convex figure. By the theorem on convex bodies this figure must contain in the interior or on the boundary a point of the lattice, provided that the area of the figure is equal to four times the area of the fundamental parallelogram of the lattice. The area of the figure may be easily calculated to be approximately $7.53\,(c/4)^{2/3}$. Therefore, inside or on the boundary

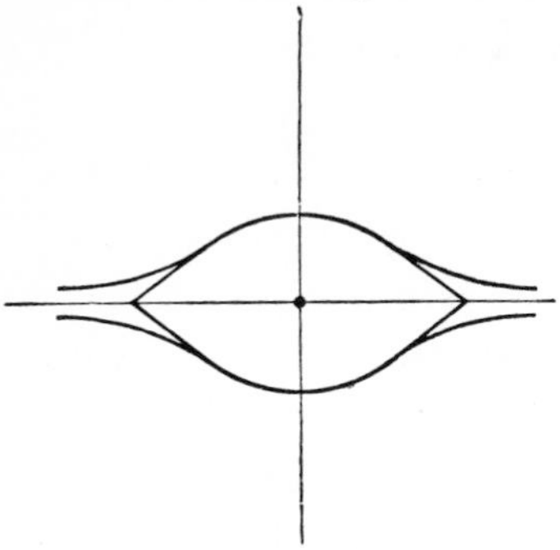

Figure 6

of the figure the projection (ξ_0, η_0) of some point $\omega_0 = x_0\omega_1 + y_0\omega_2 + z$ of the ring will be found, provided

$$c = \frac{32}{(7{,}53)^{\frac{3}{2}}} \left(\frac{|D|}{3}\right)^{\frac{3}{4}}.$$

For points, lying in the interior or on the boundary of the figure we obviously have the inequality $|\eta(\eta^2 + 3\xi^2)| \leq c$. For the index of the point ω_0 it follows that

$$|f(x_0, y_0)| = \frac{1}{\sqrt{2|D|}} |\eta_0(\eta_0^2 + 3\xi_0^2)| \leqslant \left(\frac{8}{7{,}53...\sqrt{3}}\right)^{\frac{3}{2}} D^{\frac{1}{4}}.$$

From the above estimates we draw the following conclusions:

1.
$$D \geqslant \left(\frac{\sqrt{27}}{4}\right)^4 = 44{,}5... \quad \text{for } D > 0,$$

$$|D| \geqslant 27 \cdot \left(\frac{7{,}53...}{8}\right)^6 = 18{,}8... \quad \text{for } D < 0.$$

These estimates from below for the discriminant of a cubic ring are more accurate than those obtained from general estimates given in Chapter 1 for $n = 3$, and, as can be seen from the tables, are very close to the true values.

2. For $0 < D < 729$ and for $0 < -D \leq 300$

all rings have a canonical basis. In fact, for such discriminants one can always find a number in the ring which is less than 2, and is therefore equal to unity. Such a number, together with its square and with unity, forms a canonical basis of the ring.

On the basis of these estimates it is possible to give an estimate from above for the minimal norm for ideals in every class to which we have referred in §22 of Chapter II.

In fact, let $\Gamma_0, \Gamma_1, \Gamma_2 \cdots$ be the principal and nonprincipal lattices of the maximal cubic ring and let L be the least number having the property that in every lattice there exists a point whose norm does not exceed L, or, what is the same thing, such that every class of ideals contains an ideal whose norm does not exceed L. Take in some lattice a point A such that $N(A) \leq L$. The point A can be assumed to be primary, since otherwise there would be another point closer to the origin on the line joining A to the origin with a smaller norm. The polar lattice contains a rational section corresponding to the point A. The norm-form of this section has a discriminant equal to $D \cdot N^2(A)$ and by the theorem about minima of the values of this form there will be a value less than

$$kD^{\frac{1}{4}}[N(A)]^{\frac{1}{2}} \leqslant kD^{\frac{1}{4}}L^{\frac{1}{2}},$$

where $k = \sqrt{4/27}$ for $D > 0$ and $k = (8/7.53\sqrt{3})^{3/2}$ for $D < 0$. But the values of the norm-form are norms of the points of the section. Therefore every lattice contains a point whose norm does not exceed $kD^{1/4}L^{1/2}$, since every lattice is polar with respect to some other lattice. Since L is the least number for which there exists a point with norm not exceeding this number in each lattice, we must have

$$L \leqslant L^{\frac{1}{2}}k|D|^{\frac{1}{4}},$$

from which

$$L \leqslant k^2|D|^{\frac{1}{2}} \begin{cases} = \frac{4}{27}\sqrt{D} & \text{for } D > 0, \\ = \left(\frac{8}{7{,}53\sqrt{3}}\right)^3\sqrt{|D|} & \text{for } D < 0. \end{cases}$$

Subsequently, H. Davenport gave exact values for these minima. [*The minimum of a binary cubic form*, J. London Math. Soc. 18 (1943), 168–176]. This was also done by B. Delone [Izv. Akad. Nauk SSSR, 1946, p. 133].

§36. A THEOREM OF TARTAKOVSKIĬ

We consider those integer cubic numbers whose norms and discriminants are bounded in absolute value; for example

$$|n| < N, \quad |D| < L,$$

where N and L are given positive constants. Can there be infinitely many such numbers, or is there only a finite number of them? It turns out that there is only a finite number of such numbers and that they can all be found.

We shall prove this theorem only for numbers whose norm is ± 1, i.e., only for cubic units. The more general theorem is proved in an analogous manner.

THEOREM. *There exists only a finite number of cubic units whose discriminants are less than a given bound L in absolute value, and all these units can be found.*

We first prove the theorem in the case $D<0$, i.e., for $W_{3,1}$. It is obvious in the first place that we need only consider the units ϵ with positive norm, i.e., for which $z>0$ in $R_{3,1}$, since if ϵ has a negative norm, then $-\epsilon$ has a positive norm and $D_{\epsilon}=D_{-\epsilon}$. We note also that $D_{\epsilon}=D_{\epsilon}^{-1}$, since

$$\begin{aligned} D_{\varepsilon^{-1}} &= [(\varepsilon^{-1}-\varepsilon'^{-1})(\varepsilon^{-1}-\varepsilon''^{-1})(\varepsilon'^{-1}-\varepsilon''^{-1})]^2 \\ &= [(\varepsilon-\varepsilon')(\varepsilon-\varepsilon'')(\varepsilon'-\varepsilon'')]^2.(\varepsilon^{-1}\varepsilon'^{-1})^2.(\varepsilon^{-1}\varepsilon''^{-1})^2.(\varepsilon'^{-1}\varepsilon''^{-1})^2 \\ &= D_{\varepsilon}\cdot((\varepsilon\varepsilon'\varepsilon'')^{-1})^2 = D_{\varepsilon}, \end{aligned}$$

and therefore out of the two reciprocal units ϵ and ϵ^{-1} with positive norm it is sufficient to consider that one for which $z<1$. We shall call such units *canonical* units and will consider only such units. They all lie in $R_{3,1}$ in the "lower" (below $z=1$) part of the surface of revolution $(x^2+y^2)z=1$ which asymptotically approaches the x, y-plane. All these units lie in this portion of the surface on lines of intersection with the planes $2x+z=s$, where s runs through all possible rational integer values. Every such line, in view of the fact that the lower part of the surface $(x^2+y^2)z=1$ approaches the x, y-plane, is almost "parallel" to the y-axis.

We shall call these lines the s-lines. The points of $W_{3,1}$ lying on a given s-line have smaller discriminants the closer the line is to the $y=0$ plane. On each s-line we consider a point of $W_{3,1}$ that is closest to the $y=0$ plane (the only points of $W_{3,1}$ that lie in the $y=0$ plane are points on the rational line, i.e., the only unit is the point 1). To prove the theorem for $D<0$, it is obviously sufficient to show that even among these points there is only a finite number of points with discriminant $<L$ in absolute value.

We have

$$s=2x+z;\quad q=x^2+y^2+2xz;\quad n=(x^2+y^2)z,$$

from which

$$x=\frac{s-z}{2};\quad q=\frac{(s-z)^2}{4}+y^2+(s-z)z,$$

or

$$s^2+2sz-3z^2-4q=-4y^2,$$

and we obtain

$$-2\sqrt{q+z^2}<s-z<2\sqrt{q+z^2}.$$

We note that for all integer points on an s-line we have $q>0$, and that the integer point closest to the $y=0$ plane is the point of intersection of this line with the surface q, where q is the least q for which such a point of intersection exists. We have $sz = z^2 + 2xz$. But $(x^2 + y^2)z = 1$ for points on an s-line and therefore $x^2 z < 1$, i.e., $|xz|$ decreases as x increases. Hence (and this will be of importance later) (*) *as x increases z and xz decrease.*

Let $s > 0$. In this case the least q which for a given s gives a surface q which intersects the line s is the least q for which the inequality $s + z < 2\sqrt{q + z^2}$ holds.

α) Let $s = 2\sigma - 1$ (where $\sigma > 0$), i.e., let s be odd. Then the required q is $q = \sigma^2 - \sigma + 1$, since $2\sqrt{\sigma^2 - \sigma + 1 - 1 + z^2} < 2\sigma - 1 + z < 2\sqrt{\sigma^2 - \sigma + 1 + z^2}$. These inequalities are equivalent to $0 < 4\sigma z - 2z - 3z^2 < 4$. The right-hand side for large x follows from (*), while the left-hand side, namely $0 < 4\sigma - 2 - 3z$ also follows from (*).

β) Let $s = 2\sigma$ (where $\sigma > 0$), i.e., let s be even. Then the required q is $q = \sigma^2 + 1$, since $2\sqrt{\sigma^2 + z^2} < 2\sigma + z < 2\sqrt{\sigma^2 + 1 + z^2}$. These inequalities are equivalent to $0 < 4\sigma z - 3z^2 < 4$. The right-hand side follows from (*) for large x, while the left-hand side, namely $0 < 4\sigma - 3z$, also follows from (*).

Now let $s < 0$. In this case the least q for a given s for which the surface q intersects the line s is the least q which satisfies the inequality $-2\sqrt{q + z^2} < s + z$.

γ) Let $s = -2\sigma + 1$ (where $\sigma > 0$), i.e., let s be odd. Then the desired q is $q = \sigma^2 - \sigma$, since $2\sqrt{\sigma^2 - \sigma + z^2} < 2\sigma - 1 - z < 2\sqrt{\sigma^2 - \sigma + 1 + z^2}$. These inequalities are equivalent to $0 < 1 - 4\sigma z + 2z - 3z^2 < 4 + 4z^2$, and both follow from (*).

δ) Let $s = -2\sigma$ (where $\sigma > 0$), i.e., let s be even. Then the desired q is $q = \sigma^2 - 1$, since $2\sqrt{\sigma^2 - 1 + z^2} < 2\sigma - z < 2\sqrt{\sigma^2 + z^2}$. These inequalities are equivalent to $0 < 4\sigma z - 3z^2 < 4$; the right-hand side follows from (*), while the left-hand side is equivalent to $0 < 4\sigma - 3z$ and also follows from (*).

We can tabulate the above results as follows. The point with least discriminant D on a given curve s is given by one of four completely determined polynomials in σ of the fourth degree, since

if	$s = -2\sigma$;	$s = -2\sigma + 1$;	$s = 2\sigma + 1$;	$s = 2\sigma$	$(\sigma > 0)$
then	$q = \sigma^2 - 1$;	$q = \sigma^2 - \sigma$;	$q = \sigma^2 - \sigma + 1$;	$q = \sigma^2 + 1$.	

As σ increases these polynomials increase without bound (like any polynomials). Therefore there is only a finite number of values of σ, and thus also of s, which have points with $|D| < L$.

From the proof of the theorem for $D < 0$, we can immediately prove the corresponding theorem for $D > 0$, since it can be easily seen that

$$q = \sigma^2 - 2; \quad q = \sigma^2 - \sigma - 1; \quad q = \sigma^2 - \sigma; \quad q = \sigma^2,$$

i.e., the values of q diminished by 1 give units in $W_{3,0}$ with least discriminants for the corresponding values of s and again we obtain four (of course different) polynomials of the fourth degree in σ for these discriminants.

PART C. TABULATION OF FIELDS OF THE FOURTH DEGREE

In this and the following sections we will consider the problem of tabulating all the irreducible rings O consisting of all the integer points of the fourth degree, containing the point 1, and in this way tabulating all the fields of the fourth degree. Besides the purely trivial complications which arise as the number of dimensions increases, there is another essential difficulty. Points other than the origin can be the projections, parallel to the rational direction, of nonprimitive points of the ring, for they could be projections of quadratic points of the ring. In order to avoid this difficulty we also project two-dimensional rays parallel to the bisectrices in which the quadratic points lie. In the following sections we give the tabulation of the rings (and fields) of the fourth degree. In the last part of the chapter we give the classification of the cubic fields in terms of the quadratic, and of quartic fields in terms of the cubic fields. These two classifications are closely connected.

§37. THE LATTICE W AND ITS NETS $\overline{W}_0$, $\overline{W}_1$, $\overline{W}_2$ FOR $n = 4$, $r = 0$

We shall write the quartic equation in the form

$$x^4 - sx^3 + px^2 - qx + n = 0. \tag{1}$$

As is well known, the conditions for such an equation to have real roots are given by

$$p - \frac{3}{8}s^2 < 0, \tag{2}$$

$$p^2 - s^2p + \frac{3}{16}s^4 + sq - 4n < 0, \tag{3}$$

and the discriminant is positive, i.e.,

$$27D = 4(p^2 - 3sq + 12n)^3 - (2p^3 - 72pn + 27s^2n - 9spq + 27q^2)^2 > 0. \tag{4}$$

These are the conditions for the number r of pairs of conjugate complex roots to be equal to zero.

We shall denote the coordinates of the points corresponding to this case in a real four-dimensional signature space $R_{4,0}$ by x, y, z, t. The lattice W is then defined by the system of equations

$$\left.\begin{array}{c} x+y+z+t=s, \\ xy+xz+xt+yz+yt+zt=p, \\ xyz+xyt+xzt+yzt=q, \\ xyzt=n, \end{array}\right\} \quad (5)$$

where s, p, q, and n are all the possible rational integers satisfying conditions (2), (3) and (4). The conditions that the four roots of (1) be real are therefore equivalent to saying that the rational integers s, p, q, and n are such that the surfaces (5) intersect, i.e., have at least one common point.

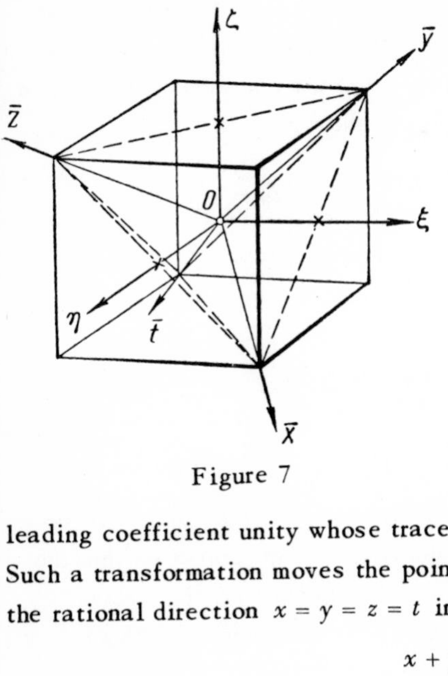

Figure 7

To every point of W corresponds a definite equation (1) and to every equation (1) correspond 24 points of W depending on the various ways of numbering its roots.

The surfaces s are three-dimensional "planes" cutting equal segments on all the coordinate axes. The substitution $x = x_1 + k$, where k is a rational integer can transform (1) into another equation with rational integer coefficients and leading coefficient unity whose trace, i.e., coefficient s, is equal to 0, 1, 2, or 3. Such a transformation moves the point corresponding to this equation parallel to the rational direction $x = y = z = t$ into the "plane"

$$x + y + z + t = s,$$

(where $s = 0, 1, 2$, or 3).

We now denote by $\overline{W}_0$, $\overline{W}_1$, $\overline{W}_2$ and $\overline{W}_3$ the three-dimensional nets of W, lying in the "planes" $s = 0, 1, 2$, and 3. It is clear from what has been said above that the lattice W consists of periodically repeating nets obtained from $\overline{W}_0$, $\overline{W}_1$, $\overline{W}_2$ and $\overline{W}_3$ by means of parallel translations of these nets parallel to the rational direction into the vectors (1, 1, 1, 1), (2, 2, 2, 2), ... We note that the net $\overline{W}_3$ can be obtained from the net $\overline{W}_{-1}$, which is symmetric to the net $\overline{W}_1$ with respect to the origin, by translating it into the vector (1, 1, 1, 1). Since every ring O is symmetric with respect to the origin we need not consider the net $\overline{W}_3$, and we accordingly confine our discussions to the nets $\overline{W}_0$, $\overline{W}_1$, and $\overline{W}_2$.

It is obvious that the coordinate axes X, Y, Z, T, when projected parallel to the rational direction into the "plane" $s = 0$ of zero trace, will give lines X, Y, Z, T lying in this "plane" (three-dimensional space) which, because of the symmetry of this direction with respect to the coordinate axes, go through the origin and form equal angles with each other. We mark equal segments from the origin on these lines. Then these points will form a regular tetrahedron. We now construct a cube, four of whose vertices are the vertices of this tetrahedron, and select as the coordinate axes in the "plane" $s = 0$ the lines ξ, η, ζ starting at the origin, i.e., at the center of this cube, and parallel to the edges of this cube. It is not hard to see that the following relations exist between the coordinates x, y, z, t of a point in our four-dimensional space and the coordinates ξ, η, ζ of its projection parallel to the rational direction into the "plane" $s = 0$:

$$\begin{aligned} x+y+z+t&=s; & x&=\frac{2\xi+2\eta-2\zeta+s}{4};\\ x+y-z-t&=2\xi; & y&=\frac{2\xi-2\eta+2\zeta+s}{4};\\ x-y+z-t&=2\eta; & z&=\frac{-2\xi+2\eta+2\zeta+s}{4};\\ -x+y-z+t&=2\zeta; & t&=\frac{-2\xi-2\eta-2\zeta+s}{4}. \end{aligned} \tag{6}$$

If we now replace in equations (5) the variables x, y, z, t by their expressions in terms of ξ, η, ζ in (6) we will obtain the equations of the projection into the "plane" $x = 0$ of the intersection of each of these surfaces with the "plane" s. The equations of the intersections formed by the surfaces p with the "plane" x are of the form

$$\xi^2+\eta^2+\zeta^2=\frac{3s^2}{4}-2p, \tag{7}$$

i.e., they are spheres. Each such sphere is divided up by the coordinated planes $XYZT$ into 14 spherical polygons, 8 of which are quadrilaterals and 6 of which are triangles (see Figure 8). The projections of the intersections of the surfaces q with the "plane" s give analogously the equations

$$\xi\eta\zeta = -\frac{s^3 + 4sp}{8} + q. \tag{8}$$

These surfaces intersect each of the spheres p inside each octant of the axes ξ, η, ζ, as is shown in Figure 8. Finally the intersections of the surfaces $n = xyzt$ with the "planes" s, as can be seen directly in the x, y, z, t coordinates, give as projections surfaces which intersect the same spheres inside each of the above mentioned 14 spherical polygons, as is shown in Figure 8. In the case of purely real fields in four dimensions each of the figures given by us at the end of the book for $s = 0$ and $s = 1$ for the three-dimensional case is replaced by a sequence of such spheres which can be thought of as concentric (but if we tried to draw them inside of each other, the picture would become extremely complicated).

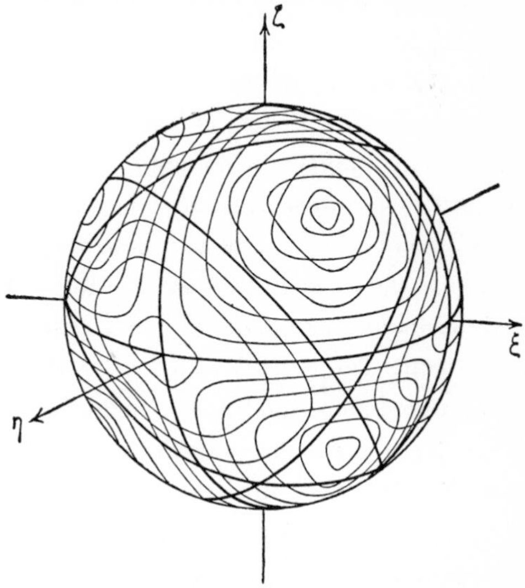

Figure 8

§38. THE EXCLUSION OF REDUCIBLE POINTS

In four dimensions a point of W_4 can be reducible either because it is the sum of a point of W_1 that lies on one of the axes and a point of W_3 that lies in the three-dimensional space defined by the remaining three axes, or because it is the sum of two points of W_2 that lie in the plane of two of the axes and another point of W_2 that lies in the plane of the other two axes. If W_4 has $\tau = 0$ then W_1, in case of reducible points of the form $W_1 + W_3$ can lie on either one of the axes of W_2, while in case of reducible points of the form $W_2 + W_2$, points of each W_2 can lie in a plane defined by any pair of axes and both lattices W_2 have $\tau = 0$. If the lattice W_4 has $\tau = 1$, however, then the points of W_1 can lie only on one of the two axes corresponding to real roots, while in the two lattices W_2 and W_2', the first W_2 has $\tau = 0$ and lies in the plane corresponding to real roots, while the other W_2' has $\tau = 1$ and lies in a plane corresponding to the pair of complex conjugate roots. Finally, if W_4 has $\tau = 2$, then there are no reducible points of the form $W_1 + W_3$, and all the reducible points are of the form $W_2' + W_2'$, where each lattice W_2' has $\tau = 1$ and lies in a plane corresponding to a pair of complex conjugate roots.

The case $\tau = 0$. The reduced points of $W_{4,0}$ of the form $W_{1,0} + W_{3,0}$ lie in four systems of planes, parallel to the asymptotic planes of the surfaces n of the fourth degree, where one of the planes in each system is the asymptotic plane itself. The totality of these four systems represents the division of the three-dimensional space of the "plane" $s = 0$ (and analogously for $s = 1$ and $s = 2$) into regular tetrahedra. In each of these systems there is a periodic repetition of nets (after every three planes) which differ only affinely from the nets $\overline{W}_3$. The reduced points of $W_{4,0}$ of the form $W_{2,0} + W_{2,0}$ lie in four systems of planes parallel to the asymptotic planes of the surfaces q of the third degree, where one of the surfaces in each of the three systems is the corresponding asymptotic plane itself. The totality of all these three systems of planes produces a division of the three-dimensional space of the "plane" $s = 0$ (and analogously of $s = 1$ and $s = 2$) into cubes. In each of these systems periodically (after every 2 planes) the nets differ only affinely from the nets $\overline{W}_3$.

In practice the reduced points are excluded by testing the equation $x^4 - sx^3 + px^2 - qx + n = 0$ for reducibility, which occurs (in the form $W_1 + W_3$) in case the equation has a rational root, i.e., if one of the rational integer divisors of n is a root, or (in the form $W_2 + W_2$) in case

$$x^4 - sx^3 + px^2 - qx + n = (x^2 + \alpha x + \beta)(x^2 + \gamma x + \delta),$$

where $\alpha, \beta, \gamma, \delta$ are rational integers. But then $\beta\delta = n$, from which β and δ have only a finite number of values. Moreover $\alpha\gamma + (\beta + \delta) = p$, from which for every α and γ there is only a finite number of pairs β and δ, and finally $\alpha + \gamma = -s$.

§39. LIMITING THE COEFFICIENTS p, q, n

Given a number L we shall find all maximal irreducible rings of integer points of degree 4 whose discriminants do not exceed L in absolute value.

The case $\tau = 0$. We have already given above conditions for all four roots $\rho, \rho', \rho'', \rho'''$ of the equation $x^4 - sx^3 + px^2 - qx + n = 0$ to be real. The condition $D_o \leq L$ implies geometrically that the volume of the fundamental parallelepipeds in $R_{4,0}$ is $V_o \leq \sqrt{L}$.

Since the volume $\bar{V}_o$ of the fundamental parallelepiped of the lattice $\bar{O}$ which is obtained by the projection of O parallel to the rational direction, i.e., to the vector $\overrightarrow{01}$ into the "plane" s, is equal to $V_o/2$, where V_o is the volume of the fundamental parallelepiped of O, we see that $\bar{V}_o \leq \sqrt{L}/2$. It is necessary to capture in the projection at least one irreducible point of every such O for which $V_o \leq \sqrt{L}$. In order to do this we describe in the "plane" $s = 0$ such a three-dimensional sphere from the origin that in it or on its surface there is at least one point that is a projection of an irrational point of each such O. In order to do this it is necessary and sufficient that the radius of the sphere be not less than the least of the vectors in $\bar{O}$.

Therefore the problem reduces to the determination of the maximum length of the smallest vector of the lattice for a given volume $\bar{V}$ of its fundamental parallelepiped. From the closest packing of equal spheres in a regular tetrahedron it follows that the maximum length of such a vector

$$l \leq \sqrt[6]{2\bar{V}^2}$$

(see the articles of Korkin and Zolotarev, or, for example B. Delone, Trudy Mat. Inst. Steklov 4 (1933), 63–69). In our case $\bar{V} \leq \sqrt{L}/2$, and therefore the radius of such a sphere is

$$r \leqslant \sqrt[6]{\frac{L}{2}}. \tag{1}$$

Hence in every O whose discriminant is $\leq L$ there are points, different from rational points, which lie in the "planes" $s = 0, 1, 2$, whose projections parallel to the rational direction into the plane $s = 0$ lie inside or on the surface of a sphere of this radius. It remains to discover how the coefficients p, q, n of the equations of these points are bounded and then it will be possible to tabulate the equations which represent these rings O. From (7) we obtain directly a bound for p, namely

$$\left|\frac{3s^2}{4} - 2p\right| \leqslant \sqrt[3]{\frac{L}{2}} \quad (s = 0,\ 1,\ 2). \tag{2}$$

Hence we have found a finite number of spheres p for each $s = 0, 1, 2$ on which the points lie that can serve as representatives of the rings O with discriminants $\leq L$. We must now see what net of lines (network) is formed by q and n on each of these spheres (s, p) in order to obtain a bound for q depending on s and p, and then to find a bound for each n depending on s, p and q. In order to find a bound for q we must find the last surface $\xi\eta\zeta = -(s^3 + 4sp)/8 + q$ which still has points in common with the sphere (s, p), i.e., whose intersection with the line $\xi = \eta = \zeta$ is still not outside of the sphere. We obtain

$$|q| \leqslant \left| \frac{r\sqrt[3]{3}}{27} - \frac{s^3 + 4sp}{8} \right| \quad (s = 0,\ 1,\ 2). \tag{3}$$

Analogously, examining the network (Figure 8) we see that in order to find a bound for n it will become necessary to examine the planes n which intersect either one of the axes ξ, η, ζ or the line $\xi = \eta = \zeta$ not outside the sphere. In the first place we obtain

$$|n| \leqslant \left| \frac{3sq - p^2}{12} \right| \quad (s = 0,\ 1,\ 2) \tag{4}$$

and in the second place

$$|n| \leqslant \left(\frac{s^2 - 4r^2}{16} \right)^2 \quad (s = 0,\ 1,\ 2). \tag{4'}$$

In this way we obtain a sequence of equations among which there is at least one equation corresponding to each of the rings O whose discriminant is $\leq L$ for $\tau = 0$.

This method, using the sphere, has the advantage in the case $\tau = 0$ over the method based on the parallelepiped which was used in the proof of Hermite's theorem (Theorem 2, Chapter 1) in that the surfaces (s, p) are themselves spheres and hence we can make use of all the symmetries which are enjoyed by the net W in this case.

We note in passing that if it were possible to draw the spheres very carefully, as was done in Figure 8, then it would be possible to read the whole table from the drawing without making any calculations.

All the O which were thus obtained by means of their irreducible points are known in the sense that starting from any point ρ it is possible to obtain a ring with the power basis $[1, \rho, \rho^2, \rho^3]$, and then using the method similar to the one used in the calculation of a basis according to Voronoĭ, it is possible to obtain all the rings O which center this ring and in particular the maximal ring which centers this ring. One would have to discard this value of ρ if the discriminant of even this maximal ring is greater than L.

If a reducible point of an irreducible ring O is captured, then this point must be of the form $W_2 + W_2$, since the equation corresponding to an irreducible ring O is either irreducible or is a square of an irreducible quadratic equation, or else a fourth power of a linear equation. But in the latter case the projection of the corresponding point on the "plane" $s = 0$ would lie at the origin, and hence there are only the first two possibilities. Hence, if a captured point of an irreducible ring is reducible, then it is of type $W_2 + W_2$. We see therefore that we can simply disregard all the points on the spheres (s, p) whose equations are reducible and are not the squares of irreducible quadratics. If the captured point of the ring is of the type $W_2 + W_2$, then the ring itself is not yet discovered because it remains to discover the quadratic equation with coefficients in a quadratic field which is irreducible and gives a point of the lattice W_4 contained in the irreducible ring O with discriminant $\leq L$. But this is not easily done.

In order to find all the irreducible rings O, without exception, whose discriminants are $\leq L$, and in particular the maximal irreducible rings which we need, it is necessary to project these rings not parallel to the rational direction, but by two-dimensional rays parallel to their quadratic subrings, which we shall do next.

§40. THE PARALLEL PROJECTION OF A QUADRATIC SUBFIELD; LIMITING THE COEFFICIENTS α_1 AND α_2

From what has been shown in Chapter I, §3, it is clear that a quartic field can have only quadratic subfields (other than rational ones) and that any given quartic field can have at most three quadratic subfields, since there are only three two-dimensional "bisectrices" of the four-dimensional axes.

We will show that if there are two subfields then there will be a completely determined third one. Let us assume, for example, that two "bisectrices", 1 and 2, are quadratic subfields of a given quartic field. As a consequence of the symmetry of a system of integer points of a real quadratic field with respect to the rational line, it follows that there are integer points in the field whose coordinates are equal in absolute value and are of opposite sign. Thus the first "bisectrix" has an integer point of the form $(a, a, -a, -a)$ and the second "bisectrix" has an integer point of the form $(b, -b, b, -b)$. The product $(ab, -ab, -ab, ab)$ is also an integer point of the system of integer points of the given quartic field; it lies in the third "bisectrix" but does not lie on the rational lines. Hence the third "bisectrix" contains a quadratic subfield.

The following examples show that all three possibilities are realized; namely, there exists purely real quartic fields with no quadratic subfields, with only one quadratic subfield, and with three quadratic subfields.

1. The quartic field with discriminant 1957 does not have a quadratic subfield.

2. The quartic field with discriminant 725 has one quadratic subfield (whose discriminant is 5).

3. The quartic field with discriminant 1600 has three quadratic subfields (with discriminants 5, 8, and 40).

We first consider a bound for all quadratic subrings $\underline{O}$ containing 1, which, under projection of the corresponding quartic subring O parallel to the rational direction on the "plane" $s = 0$, gives points either inside or on the boundary of the sphere of radius $r = \sqrt[6]{L/2}$. Since the projection is parallel to the rational direction, i.e., to the vector $\overrightarrow{01}$ which may be taken as one of the sides of the basic parallelogram of the sublattice $\underline{O}$, the length of the projection of the second side of this parallelogram is equal to the area of this parallelogram divided by the length of the vector $\overrightarrow{01}$, which is equal to 2. This parallelogram is linearly $\sqrt{2}$ times larger than the basic parallelogram of the quadratic ring $\underline{O}$ considered in its own two-dimensional space. Let the area of this parallelogram be S. Then $S = \sqrt{d}$, where d is the discriminant of the quadratic ring, and thus the area of the basic parallelogram of the subring $\underline{O}$ is equal to $2\sqrt{d}$, i.e., the projection of the second side of the parallelogram is equal to $2\sqrt{d}/2 = \sqrt{d}$. But this projector must be $\leq \sqrt[6]{L/2}$ from which we see that the discriminants of the quadratic rings that interest us here do not exceed $\sqrt[6]{L/2}$.

We now consider the projection of the quartic ring O parallel to the quadratic "bisectrices". In order to find those quartic rings O that have as subrings the quadratic rings now under consideration, it is necessary, for each of these subrings, that all the quartic superrings O constructed on a given subring be projected onto the plane Q orthogonal to P by two-dimensional rays parallel to P, where P is the plane of the "bisectrix" in which the subring lies.

Without loss of generality, we may assume that this "bisectrix" is

$$x = y,$$
$$z = t.$$

Then the plane orthogonal to it will be

$$x + y = 0,$$
$$z + t = 0.$$

We consider the quadratic equations satisfied by the points of those quartic rings O for which the quadratic ring O, considered in the four-dimensional space

$R_{4,0}$, is a subring with coefficients belonging to the quadratic field corresponding to $\underline{O}$, namely:

$$\omega^2 + \alpha_1\omega + \alpha_2 = 0 \text{ with roots } \omega \text{ and } \omega',$$

and

$$\omega^2 + \alpha_1'\omega + \alpha_2' = 0, \text{ with roots } \omega'' \text{ and } \omega''',$$

where ω, ω', ω'', and ω''' are the coordinates of a point of such a ring O. In such a case α_1' is the quadratic conjugate of α_1, and α_2' is the quadratic conjugate of α_2.

We consider first the net (Q_α) formed by the (two-dimensional) plane

$$x + y = -\alpha_1, \quad z + t = -\alpha_1',$$

perpendicular to the two-dimensional "bisectrix" P which contains $\underline{O}$ in the intersection with the two-dimensional surface α_2.

This net gives the systems of equations

$$x + y = -\alpha_1, \quad xy = \alpha_2,$$

$$z + t = -\alpha_1', \quad zt = \alpha_2'.$$

Grouping the systems differently,

$$x + y = -\alpha_1, \quad z + t = -\alpha_1',$$

$$xy = \alpha_2, \qquad zt = \alpha_2'.$$

The set of these systems is equivalent to the previous one. They may be written differently:

$$x = -\frac{\alpha_1}{2} + \sqrt{\frac{\alpha_1^2}{4} - \alpha_2}; \quad y = -\frac{\alpha_1}{2} - \sqrt{\frac{\alpha_1^2}{4} - \alpha_2};$$

$$z = -\frac{\alpha_1'}{2} + \sqrt{\frac{\alpha_1'^2}{4} - \alpha_2'}; \quad t = -\frac{\alpha_1'}{2} - \sqrt{\frac{\alpha_1'^2}{4} - \alpha_2'}.$$

Let $\xi = (x - y)/2$, $\eta = (z - t)/2$ and for coordinate axes in the plane Q take ξ, η:

$$(\xi) \left.\begin{aligned} x + y &= -\alpha_1, \\ z + t &= -\alpha_1, \\ z - t &= 0, \end{aligned}\right\} \qquad (\eta) \left.\begin{aligned} x + y &= -\alpha_1, \\ z + t &= -\alpha_1, \\ x - y &= 0. \end{aligned}\right\}$$

It is not difficult to see that these axes are orthogonal.

Then $\xi^2 = \alpha_1^2/4 - \alpha_2$, $\eta^2 = \alpha_1'^2/4 - \alpha_2'$ and hence, for a given α_1 there will correspond to any point α_2 of the ring O a completely determined point ξ, η, and the net (Q_α) will be determined by the system

$$\xi^2 + \eta^2 = \frac{\alpha_1^2 + \alpha_1'^2}{4} - (\alpha_2 + \alpha_2'),$$

$$\xi^2 - \eta^2 = \frac{\alpha_1^2 - \alpha_1'^2}{4} - (\alpha_2 - \alpha_2').$$

It is sufficient to find the nets (Q_α) for $\alpha_1 = 0, 1, \omega_1$, and $1 + \omega_1$, where 1, ω_1 is a basis for the ring $\underline{O}$. In fact, the substitution $\omega = \overline{\omega} - \alpha$ transforms the equation

$$\overline{\omega}^2 - (\alpha_1 - 2\alpha)\overline{\omega} + (\alpha^2 - \alpha\alpha_1 - \alpha_2) = 0$$

into

$$\omega^2 + \alpha_1\omega + \alpha_2 = 0,$$

or, setting

$$\alpha = a + b\omega_1; \quad \alpha_1 = a_1 + b_1\omega_1,$$

we obtain

$$\overline{\omega}^2 + (a_1 + b_1\omega_1 - 2a - 2b\omega_1)\,\overline{\omega} + (a + b\omega_1)^2 - (a + b\omega_1)\,(a_1 + b_1\omega_1) - \alpha_2 = 0.$$

Obviously we may choose integers a and b so that the coefficient of $\overline{\omega}$ will be either $0, 1, \omega_1$, or $1 + \omega_1$. Setting

$$a_1 + b_1\omega_1 - 2a - 2b\omega_1 = \overline{\alpha}_1 = \overline{a} + \overline{b}\omega_1,$$
$$(a + b\omega_1)^2 - (a + b\omega_1)(a_1 + b_1\omega_1) - \alpha_2 = \overline{\alpha}_2 = u + v\omega_1.$$

we obtain

$$\omega^2 + (\overline{a} + \overline{b}\omega_1)\omega + (u + vw_1) = 0$$

and the system

$$\xi^2 + \eta^2 = \frac{\overline{\alpha}_1^2 + \overline{\alpha}_1'^2}{4} - (\overline{\alpha}_2 + \overline{\alpha}_2'),$$

$$\xi^2 - \eta^2 = \frac{\overline{\alpha}_1^2 - \overline{\alpha}_1'^2}{4} - (\overline{\alpha}_2 - \overline{\alpha}_1'),$$

for the net (Q_α). In the projection on the plane Q we must capture at least one integer point from all the real purely quartic rings O whose discriminants are less than or equal to L and which have the given quadratic ring $\underline{O}$ as subring. To do this, we describe in the plane Q a circle around the origin of such a radius that there is at least one point either inside it or on its boundary that is the projection parallel to P of a primitive point of each of the rings O that have been determined. For this it is sufficient for the radius of such a circle to be not less than the shortest vector in the two-dimensional lattices obtained from such a projection of each of the O on the plane Q. The basic parallelogram of each of these lattices has an area $S \leq \sqrt{L}/2\sqrt{d}$, since the volume of the four-dimensional parallelepiped O (which is $\leq \sqrt{L}$) is clearly equal to the product of the area of the projection S by the area $2\sqrt{d}$ of the lattice $\underline{O}$. As a matter of fact, it is generally true that when we project an n-dimensional real lattice parallel to one of its m-dimensional sublattices onto a linear $(n-m)$-dimensional space complementary and orthogonal to its own m-dimensional subspace, the volume of the basic parallelogram of the n-dimensional lattice is equal to the product of the volumes of the basic parallelograms of the given m-dimensional sublattice and its $(n-m)$-dimensional projection. The problem thus reduces to the determination of the maximum length l of the shortest vector of a two-dimensional lattice for a given area S of its basic parallelogram. From the closest packing of circles in equilateral triangles, we obtain $l^2\sqrt{3}/4 \leq S/2 \leq \sqrt{L}/4\sqrt{d}$ and hence $l^4 \leq L/3d$.

Let $\bar{\alpha}_1, \bar{\alpha}_2$ denote the point M of the net (P_α) whose projection $\bar{M}$ onto the plane Q is the closest point to the origin obtained from the projection of P. Then $O\bar{M}^2 = \frac{1}{2}(\bar{\alpha}_1^2 + \bar{\alpha}'^2_1) - 2(\bar{\alpha}_2 + \bar{\alpha}'_2)$ and thus, in order to obtain in the projection into the plane at least one integer point from the regions of interest to us, it is sufficient to consider those α_1, α_2 for which

$$\frac{\bar{\alpha}_1^2 + \bar{\alpha}_1'^2}{2} - 2(\bar{\alpha}_2 + \bar{\alpha}_2') \leqslant \sqrt{\frac{L}{3d}},$$

so that in the net (Q_α) it is sufficient to construct circles ξ and η, whose radii do not exceed $\frac{1}{2}\sqrt{L/3d}$, and hyperbolas whose real half-axes do not exceed the radius of the largest circle of the net.

Thus we have

$$0 < \frac{\bar{\alpha}_1^2 + \bar{\alpha}_1'^2}{4} - (\bar{\alpha}_2 + \bar{\alpha}_2') \leqslant \frac{1}{2}\sqrt{\frac{L}{3d}},$$

$$\left| \frac{\alpha_1^2 - \bar{\alpha}_1'^2}{4} - (\bar{\alpha}_2 - \bar{\alpha}_2') \right| \leqslant \frac{1}{2}\sqrt{\frac{L}{3d}},$$

or

$$0 < \frac{2\bar{a}^2 + 2\bar{a}\bar{b}(\omega_1 + \omega_1') + \bar{b}^2(\omega_1^2 + \omega_1'^2)}{4} - 2u - v(\omega_1 + \omega_1') \leqslant \frac{1}{2}\sqrt{\frac{L}{3d}},$$

$$\left|\frac{2\bar{a}\bar{b}(\omega_1 - \omega_1') + \bar{b}^2(\omega_1^2 - \omega_1'^2)}{4} - v(\omega_1 - \omega_1')\right| \leqslant \frac{1}{2}\sqrt{\frac{L}{3d}}.$$

We consider two cases separately:

1. The discriminant of the quadratic field $d \equiv 0 \pmod 4$.

In this case $\omega_1 = \sqrt{d}/2$; $\omega_1' = -\sqrt{d}/2$ and the system (Q_α) has the form:

$$\xi^2 + \eta^2 = \frac{4\bar{a}^2 + \bar{b}^2 d}{8} - 2u,$$

$$\xi^2 - \eta^2 = \frac{\bar{a}\bar{b}\sqrt{d}}{2} - v\sqrt{d}.$$

Hence, for given $\bar{a}$, $\bar{b}$, $\bar{d}$, it is sufficient to take u and v such that

$$0 < \frac{4\bar{a}^2 + \bar{b}^2 d}{4} - 4u \leqslant \sqrt{\frac{L}{3d}}, \tag{1}$$

$$|\bar{a}\bar{b} - 2v| \leqslant \sqrt{\frac{L}{3d}} \tag{2}$$

2. The discriminant of the quadratic field $d \equiv 1 \pmod 4$. In this case $\omega_1 = (1+\sqrt{d})/2$; $\omega_1' = (1-\sqrt{d})/2$ and the system (Q_α) has the form

$$\xi^2 + \eta^2 = \frac{2\bar{a}^2 + 2\bar{a}\bar{b} + \bar{b}^2(1+d)}{4} - 2u - v,$$

$$\xi^2 - \eta^2 = \left(\frac{2\bar{a}\bar{b} + \bar{b}^2}{4} - v\right)\sqrt{d}.$$

Thus we find the following inequalities for u and v

$$0 < \frac{2\bar{a}^2 + 2\bar{a}\bar{b} + \bar{b}^2(1+d)}{2} - 4u - 2v \leqslant \sqrt{\frac{L}{3d}}, \tag{1'}$$

$$\left|\frac{2\bar{a}\bar{b} + \bar{b}^2}{2} - 2v\right| \leqslant \sqrt{\frac{L}{3d}}. \tag{2'}$$

As was already shown, it is sufficient to take only one of the pairs of values 0, 0; 0, 1; 1, 0; or 1, 1 for the coefficients $\bar{a}$, $\bar{b}$. For any given pair and a given d, the formulas above give bounds for u and v.

It is easy to see that when all maximal rings O with quadratic subrings are projected parallel to the quadratic bisectrix and onto the plane Q orthogonal to the bisectrix, we construct on the least vector obtained in the projection not only the maximal quartic rings with one quadratic subfield that interest us, but also those that have three such subrings. In fact, when we project onto the plane Q

parallel to the plane P of the corresponding bisectrix, we obtain either the projection of an irreducible point of a quartic ring O or the projection of a primitive point ω_2 belonging to some quadratic subring. If the first is true, we construct O on its irreducible point ρ, as before. If the latter situation holds, then from ω_1 ω_2 we form (as was described above) a primitive point ω_3 of the third quadratic subring. Then 1, ω_1, ω_2, and ω_3 are noncoplanar with the origin (linearly independent) and thus we may either find from them an irreducible point ρ of the ring O or directly find a basis for O.

§41. THE PLAN OF ACTION FOR OBTAINING ALL PURELY REAL QUARTIC FIELDS WHOSE DISCRIMINANTS ARE LESS THAN L

The sequence of steps in the calculation of a table of such fields (arranged by their discriminants) follows:

1) Find a bound for p depending on the choice of L by formula (2) in §39. (It is convenient to take L in the form $2 \cdot \gamma^6$ so that r will be a rational integer.)

2) Find a bound for q and n for each p by the formulas (3), (4), and (4′) in §39. It is necessary to make this calculation for $s = 0$, 1, and 2. We thus obtain three tables of equations lying in the sphere r.

3) Exclude from these tables all reducible equations.

4) Calculate all the discriminants of all the remaining equations.

5) Factor all the discriminants and delete all those that give a quotient larger than L when divided by their largest square factor.

6) Find bases for the fields determined by the remaining equations.

Let $\omega_0, \omega_1, \omega_2, \omega_3$ be a basis for all the integers of the quartic field formed by a root ρ of the equation $x^4 - sx^3 + px^2 - qx + n = 0$ (1). As we know (see §14), we may take 1 for ω_0 and find ω_1, ω_2, and ω_3 in the forms

$$\frac{\rho + c_2}{\Delta_1}, \quad \frac{\rho^2 + b_1\rho + c_1}{\Delta_2}, \quad \frac{\rho^3 + a\rho^2 + b\rho + c}{\Delta_3},$$

where $a, b, b_1, c, c_1, c_2, \Delta_1, \Delta_2, \Delta_3$ are the coefficients and denominators of the elements of the basis. To calculate these coefficients and denominators we transform equation (1) in §37 according to Tschirnhausen, taking

$$y = \frac{u\rho^3 + v\rho^2 + w\rho + t}{\Delta},$$

$$y^4 + F_1 y^3 + F_2 y^2 + F_3 y + F_4 = 0,$$

where

$$\Delta^4 \cdot F_4 = t^4 + At^3 + Bt^2 + Ct + D = \Phi(t),$$
$$\Delta^3 \cdot F_3 = \Phi'(t), \quad \Delta^2 \cdot F_2 = \frac{1}{2!}\Phi''(t), \quad \Delta \cdot F_1 = \frac{1}{3!}\Phi'''(t),$$

if we set

$$A = w \cdot s + v \cdot (s^2 - 2p) + u \cdot (s^3 - 3sp + 3q);$$
$$B = w^2 \cdot p + vw \cdot (sp - 3q) + uw \cdot (s^2 - 2p^2 - sq + 4n) + v^2 \cdot (p^2 - 2sq + 2n) + uv \cdot (sp^2 - 2s^2q - pq - 5sn) + u^2 \cdot (p^3 - 3spq + 3s^2n + 3q^2 - 3pn);$$
$$C = w^3 \cdot q + vw^2 \cdot (sq - 4n) + v^2w \cdot (pq - 3sn) + uw^2 \cdot (s^2q - 2pq - sn) + v^3 \cdot (q^2 - 2pn) + uvw \cdot (spq - 3s^2n - 3q^2 + 4pn) + uv^2 \cdot (sq^2 - 2spn - qn) + u^2w \cdot (p^2q - 2sq^2 + spq + 5qn) + u^2v \cdot (pq^2 - 2p^2n - sqn + 4n^2) + u^3 \cdot (q^3 - 3pqn + 3sn^2);$$
$$D = w^4 \cdot n + vw^2sn + uw^3 \cdot (s^2n - 2pn) + v^2w^2 \cdot pn + uvw^2(spn - 3qn) + v^3wqn + uv^2w \cdot (sqn - 4n^2) + u^2w^2 \cdot (p^2n - 2sqn + 2n^2) + u^2vw \cdot (pqn - 3sn^2) + u^3w \cdot (q^2n - 2pn^2) + v^4 \cdot n^2 + uv^3 \cdot sn^2 + u^2v^2pn^2 + u^3v \cdot qn^2 + u^4.$$

Giving the numbers u, v, w, t, Δ values corresponding to the elements of the basis, while keeping in mind that the coefficients of the equation with respect to y must be rational integers, we easily obtain all the congruences necessary to determine the coefficients of the basis. When the basis of the field corresponding to the given ρ (i.e., to the equation under consideration) is calculated, we obtain the result that the discriminant D of this field is equal to $D_\rho/\Delta_1\Delta_2\Delta_3$.

We eliminate all equations for which $D > L$.

7) Perform analogous calculations for fields obtained by means of quadratic subfields as in §40. Namely, write out all quadratic fields whose discriminants are less than $\sqrt[3]{L/2}$; for each of these quadratic fields, use formulas (1), (2) or (1′), (2′) of §40 to find bounds for u and v for $\alpha_1 = 0, 1, \omega_1$ and $1 + \omega_1$; we thus obtain another table of equations with which to proceed through steps 3, 4, 5, and 6.

As a result of the above we obtain all purely real quartic fields whose discriminants are less than L, with each field represented by its basis. If we thus obtain several bases for some discriminant D, it is necessary to find out whether they are not merely different bases for the same field. To do this, it is necessary to solve the problem inverse to the Tschirnhausen problem for the equations defining the corresponding ρ. In solving this problem inverse to the Tschirnhausen problem for two quartic equations one may use the method of Čebotarev [66], which is a generalization of the method of solution of this problem for two cubic equations given in §13, but this method leads to a great deal of calculation. When all four roots of the quartic equations are real, it is convenient to use the method suggested in the work of Delone [18], based on the introduction of the Bezoutian. However, it is best to use (in all cases) the method suggested by Faddeev in §49.

After the solution of the question whether the quartic fields are identical or distinct, the table is ready.

I. Sominskiĭ and K. Billevič calculated in this way the accompanying table for purely real ($r = 0$) quartic fields (cf. [18]). The table of quartic fields was calculated by C. Poplavskiĭ for $r = 1$ and by D. K. Faddeev for $r = 2$ (for fields having quadratic subfields).

TABLE OF PURELY REAL QUARTIC FIELDS
WHOSE DISCRIMINANTS DO NOT EXCEED 8112

(Table calculated by I. Sominskiĭ and K. Billevič)

Discriminant of the field	Coefficients of $x^4 - sx^3 - px^2 - qx + n = 0$	Basis of the field	Discriminant of subfield	Group
725	$s=1,\ p=-3,\ q=-1,\ n=1$	$[1, \rho, \rho^2, \rho^3]$	5	8th order
1125	1, —4, —4, 1	$[1, \rho, \rho^2, \rho^3]$	5	Cyclic
1600	0, —6, 0, 4	$\left[1, \rho, \frac{\rho^2}{2}, \frac{\rho^3}{2}\right]$	5, 8, 40	Four-group
1957	0, —4, —1, 1	$[1, \rho, \rho^2, \rho^3]$	—	Symmetric
2000	0, —5, 0, 5	$[1, \rho, \rho^2, \rho^3]$	5	Cyclic
2048	0, —4, 0, 2	$[1, \rho, \rho^2, \rho^3]$	8	Cyclic
2225	1, —5, —2, 4	$\left[1, \rho, \rho^2, \frac{\rho^3+\rho^2+\rho^2}{2}\right]$	5	8th order
2304	0, —4, 0, 1	$[1, \rho, \rho^2, \rho^3]$	8, 12, 24	Four-group
2525	2, —4, —5, 5	$[1, \rho, \rho^2, \rho^3]$	5	8th order
2624	2, —3, —2, 1	$[1, \rho, \rho^2, \rho^3]$	8	8th order
2777	1, —4, —1, 2	$[1, \rho, \rho^2, \rho^3]$	—	Symmetric
3600	2, —7, —8, 1	$\left[1, \rho, \rho^2, \frac{\rho^3+2\rho^2+\rho-2}{7}\right]$	5, 12, 60	Four-group
3981	1, —4, —2, 1	$[1, \rho, \rho^2, \rho^3]$	—	Symmetric
4205	1, —5, 1, 1	$[1, \rho, \rho^2, \rho^3]$	29	8th order
4225	0, —9, 0, 4	$\left[1, \rho, \frac{\rho^2+\rho}{2}, \frac{\rho^3+\rho+2}{4}\right]$	5, 13, 65	Four-group
4352	0, —6, —4, 2	$[1, \rho, \rho^2, \rho^3]$	8	8th order
4400	0, —7, 0, 11	$[1, \rho, \rho^2, \rho^3]$	5	8th order
4525	1, —7, —3, 9	$\left[1, \rho, \rho^2, \frac{\rho^3-\rho^2-\rho}{3}\right]$	5	8th order

(Table continued on following page)

Discriminant of the field	Coefficients of $x^4 - sx^3 - px^2 - qx + n = 0$	Basis of the field	Discriminant of subfield	Group
4752	2, —3, —4, 1	$[1, \rho, \rho^2, \rho^3]$	12	8th order
4913	1, —6, —1, 1	$\left[1, \rho, \rho^2, \frac{\rho^3+1}{2}\right]$	17	Cyclic
5125	2, —6, —7, 11	$[1, \rho, \rho^2, \rho^3]$	5	8th order
5225	1, —8, —1, 11	$\left[1, \rho, \rho^2, \frac{\rho^3+1}{2}\right]$	5	8th order
5725	1, —8, —6, 11	$\left[1, \rho, \rho^2, \frac{\rho^3+\rho+1}{3}\right]$	5	8th order
5744	0, —5, —2, 1	$[1, \rho, \rho^2, \rho^3]$	—	Symmetric
6125	1, —9, —9, 11	$[1, \rho, \rho^2, \rho^3]$	5	Cyclic
6224	2, —4, —2, 2	$[1, \rho, \rho^2, \rho^3]$	—	Symmetric
6809	0, —5, —1, 1	$[1, \rho, \rho^2, \rho^3]$	—	Symmetric
7053	2, —4, —3, 3	$[1, \rho, \rho^2, \rho^3]$	—	Symmetric
7056	0, —5, 0, 1	$[1, \rho, \rho^2, \rho^3]$	12, 21, 28	Four-group
7168	0, —6, 0, 7	$[1, \rho, \rho^2, \rho^3]$	8	8th order
7225	0, —11, 0, 9	$\left[1, \rho, \frac{\rho^2+\rho+1}{2}, \frac{\rho^3-2\rho+3}{6}\right]$	5, 17, 85	Four-group
7232	2, —5, —4, 4	$\left[1, \rho, \rho^2, \frac{\rho^3+\rho}{2}\right]$	8	8th order
7260	1, —7, —8. —2	$[1, \rho, \rho^2, \rho^3]$	—	Symmetric
7488	2, —4, —2, 1	$[1, \rho, \rho^2, \rho^3]$	12	8th order
7537	1, —5, —4, 3	$[1, \rho, \rho^2, \rho^3]$	—	Symmetric
7600	0, —9, 0, 19	$[1, \rho, \rho^2, \rho^3]$	5	8th order
7625	1, —9, —4, 1	$\left[1, \rho, \rho^2, \frac{\rho^3-\rho^2-\rho}{4}\right]$	5	8th order
8000	0, —10, 0, 20	$\left[1, \rho, \frac{\rho^2}{2}, \frac{\rho^3}{2}\right]$	5	Cyclic
8069	1, —5, —5, 1	$[1, \rho, \rho^2, \rho^3]$	—	Symmetric
8112	0, —5, 0, 3	$[1, \rho, \rho^2, \rho^3]$	13	8th order

TABLE OF QUARTIC FIELDS OF SIGNATURE $\tau = 1$, for which $|D| \leq 848$

(Table calculated by C. Poplavskiĭ)

Discriminant of the field	Coefficients of $x^4 - sx^3 + px^2 - qx + n = 0$	Basis of the field	Discriminant of subfield	Group
—275	1, 0, —2, —1	$[1, \rho, \rho^2, \rho^3]$	5	8th order
—283	0, 0, 1, —1	$[1, \rho, \rho^2, \rho^3]$	—	Symmetric
—331	0, —2, 3, —1	$[1, \rho, \rho^2, \rho^3]$	—	Symmetric
—430	0, 1, 0, —1	$[1, \rho, \rho^2, \rho^3]$	5	8th order
—448	2, 1, 2, 1	$[1, \rho, \rho^2, \rho^3]$	8	8th order
—475	1, —2, 2, —1	$[1, \rho, \rho^2, \rho^3]$	5	8th order
—491	2, 2, —3, 1	$[1, \rho, \rho^2, \rho^3]$	—	Symmetric
—507	1, —1, 1, 1	$[1, \rho, \rho^2, \rho^3]$	13	8th order
—563	1, 1, 1, —1	$[1, \rho, \rho^2, \rho^3]$	—	Symmetric
—643	1, 0, 2, 1	$[1, \rho, \rho^2, \rho^3]$	—	Symmetric
—688	2, 0, 0, —1	$[1, \rho, \rho^2, \rho^3]$	—	Symmetric
—731	0, —2, 1, —1	$[1, \rho, \rho^2, \rho^3]$	—	Symmetric
—751	0, —3, 1, 2	$[1, \rho, \rho^2, \rho^3]$	—	Symmetric
—775	1,0,3,1	$\left[1, \rho, \rho^2, \frac{\rho^2+\rho^3}{2}\right]$	5	8th order
—848	0, 1, 2, 1	$[1, \rho, \rho^2, \rho^3]$	—	Symmetric

TABLE OF QUARTIC FIELDS OF SIGNATURE $\tau = 2$ HAVING QUADRATIC SUBFIELDS WHOSE DISCRIMINANTS DO NOT EXCEED 1296

(Table calculated by D. K. Faddeev)

Notation: $i = \sqrt{-1}$, $\xi = -\frac{1}{2} + i\frac{\sqrt{3}}{2}$

No.	Generator	D	Group	No.	Generator	D	Group
1	$\sqrt{4+\xi}$	117	$\mathfrak{G}$	11	$i, \sqrt{5}$	400	$\mathfrak{V}$
2	$\sqrt{\frac{-5+\sqrt{5}}{2}}$	125	$\mathfrak{G}$	12	$\sqrt{-1-2\xi}\ (\sqrt[4]{-3})$	432	$\mathfrak{G}$
				13	$\xi, \sqrt{-7}$	441	$\mathfrak{V}$
3	ξ, i	144	$\mathfrak{V}$	14	$\sqrt{1+i}$	512	$\mathfrak{G}$
4	$\sqrt{-5-\xi}$	189	$\mathfrak{G}$	15	$\sqrt{8+\xi}$	513	$\mathfrak{G}$
5	$\xi, \sqrt{5}$	225	$\mathfrak{V}$	16	$\sqrt{9+4\xi}$	549	$\mathfrak{G}$
6	$i, \sqrt{2}$	256	$\mathfrak{V}$	17	$\sqrt{2}, \xi$	576	$\mathfrak{V}$
7	$\sqrt{1+4i}$	272	$\mathfrak{G}$	18	$\sqrt{-2}, \xi$	576	$\mathfrak{V}$
8	$\sqrt{1+2i}$	320	$\mathfrak{G}$				
9	$\sqrt{7+3\xi}$	333	$\mathfrak{G}$	19	$\sqrt{\frac{3+\sqrt{-11}}{2}}$	605	$\mathfrak{G}$
10	$\sqrt{\frac{-1+\sqrt{-7}}{2}}$	392	$\mathfrak{G}$				

(Table continued on following page)

No.	Generator	D	Group	No.	Generator	D	Group
20	$\sqrt{5+4i}$	656	$\mathfrak{G}$	30	$\sqrt{7+4i}$	1040	$\mathfrak{G}$
21	$\sqrt{-9-\xi}$	657	$\mathfrak{G}$	31	$\sqrt{1+8i}$	1040	$\mathfrak{G}$
22	$\sqrt{-7}, i$	784	$\mathfrak{B}$	32	$\sqrt{3+2\sqrt{-2}}$	1088	$\mathfrak{G}$
23	$\sqrt{3+2i}$	832	$\mathfrak{G}$	33	$\sqrt{-5+2\sqrt{2}}$	1088	$\mathfrak{G}$
24	$\sqrt{-11-4\xi}$	837	$\mathfrak{G}$	34	$\xi, \sqrt{-11}$	1089	$\mathfrak{B}$
25	$\sqrt{11+3\xi}$	873	$\mathfrak{G}$	35	$\sqrt{-13-5\xi}$	1141	$\mathfrak{G}$
26	$\sqrt{12+5\xi}$	981	$\mathfrak{G}$	36	$\sqrt{3+8i}$	1168	$\mathfrak{G}$
27	$\sqrt{3+\xi}$	1008	$\mathfrak{G}$	37	$\sqrt{12+\xi}$	1197	$\mathfrak{G}$
28	$\sqrt{-3-\xi}$	1008	$\mathfrak{G}$	38	$\sqrt{13+4\xi}$	1197	$\mathfrak{G}$
29	$\sqrt{\dfrac{-13+\sqrt{5}}{2}}$	1025	$\mathfrak{G}$	39	$\sqrt{-7}, \sqrt{5}$	1225	$\mathfrak{B}$
				40	$\sqrt{2+i}$	1280	$\mathfrak{G}$

PART D. THE CONSTRUCTION OF CUBIC REGIONS ON QUADRATIC REGIONS

§42. BASING CUBIC REGIONS ON QUADRATIC REGIONS

We first set forth the following simple geometric argument.

Let $(\omega, \omega', \omega'')$ be a point in the space $R_{3,0}$. (For simplicity, we will first assume that ω, ω', and ω'' are real. However, this restriction is not essential and we will later remove it.)

We will subject the space $R_{3,0}$ to an axial-superposition, i.e., to a transformation that consists of the same simulataneous permutations of the coordinates of all the points of the space. The axial-superpositions form a transformation group, isomorphic to the symmetric group of permutations of three elements.

All these transformations leave invariant the rational line and take the plane of "zero trace" $u + u' + u'' = 0$ into itself. They induce in this plane transformations consisting of rotations of $2\pi/3$ and $4\pi/3$ degrees about the origin, and of reflections with respect to the projection of the coordinate axes. These may all be constructed from only one rotation and one reflection. It is especially easy to write these transformations algebraically if we take the plane of zero trace for the complex "axis" whose real direction coincides with the projection of one of the coordinate axes of the three-dimensional space; we then find that the axial-superpositions induce a group of transformations with the above-mentioned generators consisting of multiplication by $\epsilon = e^{2\pi i/3}$ (rotation) and conjugation (reflection).

It is easy to see that the projection of the point $(\omega, \omega', \omega'')$ on the plane of zero trace parallel to the rational line will have the coordinates

$$\left\{\frac{2\omega - \omega' - \omega''}{\sqrt{6}}, \frac{\omega' - \omega''}{\sqrt{2}}\right\}$$

if we take for the axes the projection of the Ox-axis and the straight line perpendicular to it, while preserving the scale. The complex coordinate of the projection will be

$$\frac{2\omega - \omega' - \omega''}{\sqrt{6}} + i\frac{\omega' - \omega''}{\sqrt{2}} = \frac{2}{\sqrt{6}}(\omega + \omega'\varepsilon + \omega''\varepsilon^2).$$

Properly changing the scale, we obtain a simpler expression for the complex coordinate of the projection,

$$\eta = \omega + \omega'\epsilon + \omega''\epsilon^2,$$

which is nothing other than the Lagrange resolvent of the point $(\omega, \omega', \omega'')$. If we do not assume the point $(\omega, \omega', \omega'')$ to be in the real section of the space K_3, then we must consider the plane of zero trace as a complex two-dimensional plane. Clearly, if we choose the vectors $(1, \epsilon, \epsilon^2)$, $(1, \epsilon^2, \epsilon)$ for axes and take a corresponding scale, the projection will be given by two complex coordinates η and $\bar{\eta}$, where

$$\eta = \omega + \omega'\epsilon + \omega''\epsilon^2, \quad \bar{\eta} = \omega + \omega'\epsilon^2 + \omega''\epsilon.$$

Such a projection will be a point of the complex space when $\omega, \omega', \omega''$ are all real, and a point of the real space if ω is real and ω' and ω'' are complex conjugates.

Under axial-superposition, the projection $(\eta, \bar{\eta})$ of the point $\omega, \omega', \omega''$ will undergo the transformations

$$\begin{matrix}\eta \to \eta \\ \bar{\eta} \to \bar{\eta}\end{matrix}; \quad \begin{matrix}\eta \to \eta\varepsilon \\ \bar{\eta} \to \bar{\eta}\varepsilon^2\end{matrix}; \quad \begin{matrix}\eta \to \eta\varepsilon^2 \\ \bar{\eta} \to \bar{\eta}\varepsilon\end{matrix}; \quad \begin{matrix}\eta \to \bar{\eta} \\ \bar{\eta} \to \eta\end{matrix}; \quad \begin{matrix}\eta \to \bar{\eta}\varepsilon \\ \bar{\eta} \to \eta\varepsilon\end{matrix}; \quad \begin{matrix}\eta \to \bar{\eta}\varepsilon^2; \\ \bar{\eta} \to \eta\varepsilon.\end{matrix}$$

We consider the cube of the projection, i.e., the point $(\theta, \bar{\theta})$ whose coordinates are $\theta = \eta^3$, $\bar{\theta} = \bar{\eta}^3$.

The point $(\theta, \bar{\theta})$ does not change under the first three axial-superpositions, although its last coordinates are interchanged. If ϵ is exchanged for ϵ^2, then θ and $\bar{\theta}$ also interchange places. Thus, each symmetric function of θ and $\bar{\theta}$ may be rationally expressed in terms of the coefficients of the equation whose roots are ω, ω', and ω''. From this we conclude that the cube of a projection of a cubic number is a point of some quadratic region.

We will now consider this region. We may take $\theta - \bar{\theta}$ for its generator if it is different from zero. But it is easy to see that

$$\begin{aligned} \theta - \bar{\theta} = & \ (\eta - \bar{\eta})(\eta - \bar{\eta}\varepsilon)(\eta - \bar{\eta}\varepsilon^2) \\ = & \ (\omega + \omega'\varepsilon + \omega''\varepsilon^2 - \omega - \omega'\varepsilon^2 - \omega''\varepsilon)\cdot(\omega + \omega'\varepsilon + \omega''\varepsilon^2 - \omega\varepsilon - \omega' - \omega''\varepsilon^2) \\ & \cdot(\omega + \omega'\varepsilon + \omega''\varepsilon^2 - \omega\varepsilon^2 - \omega'\varepsilon - \omega'') \\ = & -(\varepsilon - \varepsilon^2)(1 - \varepsilon)(1 - \varepsilon^2)(\omega - \omega')(\omega' - \omega'')(\omega'' - \omega) \\ = & -3\sqrt{-3D(\omega)}, \end{aligned}$$

where $D(\omega)$ is the discriminant of the number ω.

From this we may conclude that the cubes of the projections of all numbers of the same cubic region will belong to the same quadratic region $R(\sqrt{-3D})$, where D is the discriminant of the maximal ring of the region,, since all the $D(\omega)$ differ from D only by factors that are squares of rational numbers. In the future we will call this region the region on which the cubic region is based. Further, we will denote the cubic region by U, and the quadratic region on which U is based by Q. We will denote their discriminants by D and d respectively. They are obviously connected by the relation

$$D = -3^{\pm 1} d s^2,$$

where s is a rational integer.

§43. SOME THEOREMS ON PROJECTIONS OF CUBIC NUMBERS

THEOREM 1. *In order that the point η, $\bar{\eta}$ be a projection of a number of a cubic region, it is necessary and sufficient for it to satisfy the following conditions:*

a) *η^3 and $\bar{\eta}^3$ are roots of a quadratic equation with rational coefficients,*

b) *$\eta\bar{\eta}$ is a rational number.*

PROOF. The necessity of the first condition was shown earlier. The necessity of the second condition may be verified directly. In fact, if $(\eta, \bar{\eta})$ is the projection of the cubic number ω, then

$$\begin{aligned} \eta\bar{\eta} &= (\omega + \omega'\varepsilon + \omega''\varepsilon^2)(\omega + \omega'\varepsilon^2 + \omega''\varepsilon) \\ &= \omega^2 + \omega'^2 + \omega''^2 - \omega\omega' - \omega'\omega'' - \omega''\omega = s^2 - 3q, \end{aligned}$$

where s and q are coefficients of the equation $\omega^3 = s\omega^2 - q\omega + n$ whose roots are ω, ω', and ω''.

Conversely, let the point $(\eta, \bar{\eta})$ satisfy the conditions a) and b). Clearly, this point will be the projection of a point $(\omega, \omega', \omega'')$ whose coordinates satisfy the equations

$$\omega+\omega'+\omega''=0, \quad \omega+\omega'\varepsilon+\omega''\varepsilon^2=\eta, \quad \omega+\omega'\varepsilon^2+\omega''\varepsilon=\bar{\eta}.$$

Together with the first equation, we may take the equation $\omega+\omega'+\omega''=s$ for any rational value of s. The choice made for s indicates that the point $(\omega, \omega', \omega'')$ that we are looking for is on the plane of zero trace.

Solving the system, we obtain the following values for the coordinates of the point $(\omega, \omega', \omega'')$:

$$\omega=\frac{\eta+\bar{\eta}}{3};$$

$$\omega'=\frac{\eta\varepsilon^2+\bar{\eta}\varepsilon}{3};$$

$$\omega''=\frac{\eta\varepsilon+\bar{\eta}\varepsilon^2}{3}.$$

Forming the elementary symmetric functions of ω, ω', and ω'', we obtain

$$s=\omega+\omega'+\omega''=0,$$

$$q=\omega\omega'+\omega'\omega''+\omega''\omega=-\frac{\eta\bar{\eta}}{3},$$

$$n=\omega\omega'\omega''=\frac{\eta^3+\bar{\eta}^3}{27}.$$

Under the assumptions made with respect to the point $(\eta, \bar{\eta})$, all these numbers are rational and hence ω, ω', and ω'' are roots of an equation with rational coefficients. With this, the proof of the theorem is complete.

THEOREM 2. *In order for the points* $(\eta_1, \bar{\eta}_1)$ *and* $(\eta_2, \bar{\eta}_2)$ *to be projections of numbers* ω_1 *and* ω_2 *of the same cubic region, it is necessary and sufficient for the points to satisfy the conditions of Theorem* 1, *and for the point* $(\eta_2/\eta_1, \bar{\eta}_2/\eta_1)$ *to belong to the quadratic region* Q *defined by the quadratic equation whose roots are* η_1^3 *and* $\bar{\eta}_1^3$.

PROOF. We will first show the necessity. Let the numbers ω_1 and ω_2 belong to the same cubic region. Clearly, the coordinates of the point $(\eta_2/\eta_1, \bar{\eta}_2/\bar{\eta}_1)$, under axial-superposition and under an exchange of ϵ for ϵ^2, will be subjected to the same transformation as the coordinates of the point $(\eta_1^3, \bar{\eta}_1^3)$ that belongs to the region Q. Thus the point $(\eta_2/\eta_1, \bar{\eta}_2/\bar{\eta}_1)$ must belong to the same region Q, in view of the well-known theorem of Galois theory. However, it is easy to obtain this result by direct calculation. Let us make the calculation since it will lead to the proof ot the sufficiency. Let

$$\omega_2 = a\omega_1^2 + b\omega_1 + c;$$
$$\omega_1^3 = s\omega_1^2 - q\omega_1 + n.$$

We calculate η_2/η_1

$$\frac{\eta_2}{\eta_1} = \frac{\omega_2 + \omega_2'\varepsilon + \omega_2''\varepsilon^2}{\omega_1 + \omega_1'\varepsilon + \omega_1''\varepsilon^2} = a\,\frac{\omega_1^2 + \omega_1'^2\varepsilon + \omega_1''^2\varepsilon^2}{\omega_1 + \omega_1'\varepsilon + \omega_1''\varepsilon^2} + b$$

$$= a\,\frac{(\omega_1^2 + \omega_1'^2\varepsilon + \omega_1''^2\varepsilon^2)(\omega_1 + \omega_1'\varepsilon^2 + \omega_1''\varepsilon)}{(\omega_1 + \omega_1'\varepsilon + \omega_1''\varepsilon^2)(\omega_1 + \omega_1'\varepsilon^2 + \omega_1''\varepsilon)} + b$$

$$= a\,\frac{2s^3 - 7sq + 9n + \sqrt{-3D(\omega_1)}}{2(s^2 - 3q)} + b.$$

We see that η_2/η_1 is rationally expressible in terms of $\sqrt{-3D(\omega_1)}$. It is easy to obtain that $\bar{\eta}_2/\bar{\eta}_1$ differs from η_2/η_1 only in the sign of $\sqrt{-3D(\omega_1)}$. By this, the necessity is shown for the theorem. The sufficiency also follows directly from the representation found for η_2/η_1 and $\bar{\eta}_2/\bar{\eta}_1$.

In fact, if the point $(\eta_2/\eta_1, \bar{\eta}_2/\bar{\eta}_1)$ belongs to the region Q, its coefficients must be represented correspondingly in the form

$$\frac{\eta_2}{\eta_1} = u + v\sqrt{-3D(\omega_1)},$$
$$\frac{\bar{\eta}_2}{\bar{\eta}_1} = u - v\sqrt{-3D(\omega_1)}$$

with rational coefficients u and v.

From comparison of these formulas with the formula for the representation of η_2/η_1 in terms of the coefficients a and b, it is easy to find these latter representations. They turn out to be rational. The theorem is thus proven in full.

THEOREM 3. *In order for the cubic region U to be reducible, it is necessary and sufficient that one of the points $(\eta, \bar{\eta})$, $(\eta\epsilon, \bar{\eta}\epsilon^2)$, or $(\eta\epsilon^2, \bar{\eta}\epsilon)$ belong to the quadratic region Q. Here $(\eta, \bar{\eta})$ denotes the projection of an arbitrary generic point of the region U.*

PROOF. Let the region U be reducible. Then the coordinates of any one of its generic points will be the roots of a reducible cubic equation $\omega^3 - s\omega^2 + q\omega - n = 0$. We denote by ω a rational root of the equation, and by ω' and ω'' the remaining roots. The latter may be represented in the form $u \pm v\sqrt{D}$, where u and v are rational numbers and D is the discriminant of the maximal ring of the region. In this case the coordinates of the projection will be

$$\eta = \omega + \omega'\varepsilon + \omega''\varepsilon^2 = \omega - u + v\sqrt{-3D},$$
$$\bar{\eta} = \omega + \omega'\varepsilon^2 + \omega''\varepsilon = \omega - u - v\sqrt{-3D},$$

and hence the point $(\eta, \bar{\eta})$ belongs to the region Q.

If the point ω were not a rational root, but either ω or ω' were, then either the point $(\eta\epsilon, \bar{\eta}\epsilon^2)$ or the point $(\eta\epsilon^2, \bar{\eta}\epsilon)$ would belong to the region Q.

Conversely, if one of the points $(\eta, \bar{\eta})$, $(\eta\epsilon, \bar{\eta}\epsilon^2)$, or $(\eta\epsilon^2, \bar{\eta}\epsilon)$ belongs to the quadratic region, then one of the numbers

$$\omega = \frac{\eta + \bar{\eta}}{3}, \quad \omega' = \frac{\eta\varepsilon + \bar{\eta}\varepsilon^2}{3}, \quad \omega'' = \frac{\eta\varepsilon^2 + \bar{\eta}\varepsilon}{3}$$

will be rational, and hence the equation satisfied by the coordinates of the points whose projection is $(\eta, \bar{\eta})$ will be reducible.

THEOREM 4. *In order for the quadratic region Q on which the cubic region U is based to be reducible, it is necessary and sufficient that the region U be purely cubic or produced by the equation $\omega^3 - 1 = 0$.*

The proof follows from the fact that $-3D$ is a perfect square for those and only those cubic regions that satisfy the above conditions.

§44. CHARACTERISTICS OF A PROJECTION OF A MAXIMAL CUBIC LATTICE

In the preceding section we investigated projections of points of a cubic region, i.e., points rationally associated with points of some maximal cubic lattice. On the basis of this investigation we are now able to give a method of constructing a maximal cubic lattice from the quadratic one upon which it is based.

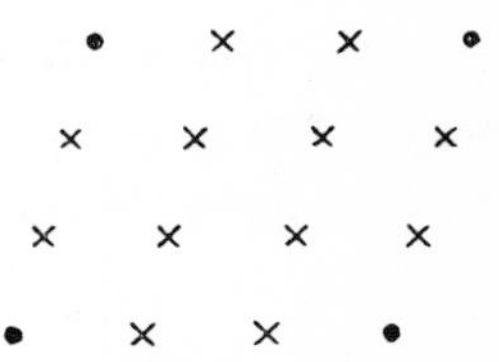

Figure 9

Obviously the projection parallel to the rational direction of a cubic lattice is itself a lattice. All the points of the lattice obtained from the projection satisfy the conditions of Theorem 1 and are related to each other by the conditions of Theorem 2. Moreover, the coordinates of all the points of this lattice are algebraic integers. This follows directly from the formulas

$$\eta = \omega + \omega'\varepsilon + \omega''\varepsilon^2;$$
$$\bar{\eta} = \omega + \omega'\varepsilon^2 + \omega''\varepsilon.$$

However, if the point $(\eta, \bar{\eta})$ satisfies the condition of Theorem 1 and its coordinates are algebraic integers, we cannot thereby conclude that it is the projection of an integer point, i.e., the projection of a point of a maximal lattice. In fact, in the formulas

$$\begin{aligned} \omega &= \frac{s+\eta+\bar{\eta}}{3}, \\ \omega' &= \frac{s+\eta\varepsilon^2+\bar{\eta}\varepsilon}{3}, \\ \omega'' &= \frac{s+\eta\varepsilon+\bar{\eta}\varepsilon^2}{3}, \end{aligned} \tag{*}$$

that express the coordinates of the projected point in terms of the coordinates of the projection and the traces s, the number 3 is in the denominator, so that the coordinates ω, ω', and ω'' may be fractional for any choice of the rational integer s. Nevertheless it is convenient for us to consider the collection L of all points satisfying the conditions of Theorems 1 and 2 and having algebraic integer coordinates. We denote by $3L$ the collection of points obtained by multiplication of the points of the system L by 3. The formulas (*) show that each point of the system $3L$ is a projection of some point with algebraic integer coefficients, i.e., of a point of a corresponding maximal ring. It is sufficient to take $s = 0$ in these formulas [or $s \equiv 0 \pmod 3$]. The system L is obviously additive and subtractive. It is two-dimensional, for it contains a two-dimensional lattice, namely the projection of the maximal ring.

It is discrete, since the system $3L$ that is similar to it is contained in the discrete projection of the maximal ring. Hence, the system L is a two-dimensional lattice. The system $3L$ is also a lattice. The lattice L centers the lattice $3L$ with index 9 (Figure 9).

It is further obvious that the lattice L is multiplicative for any point of a maximal ring of the region Q. Thus it is similar to one of the lattices of the basic figure of the region Q:

$$L = \gamma\Gamma.$$

Here Γ denotes the lattice of the basic figure that is similar to the lattice L and γ is the "coefficient" of similarity. The coefficient of similarity γ has algebraic integer coordinates since all the points of the lattice L have algebraic integer coordinates, while among the points of the lattice Γ there exist points whose coordinates are relatively prime to any previously given rational integer, and hence to any previously given algebraic number of degree as high as is desired.

Further, the norm of the coefficient γ is a rational number since the norms of all the points of the lattices L and Γ are rational integers. Since the coordinates of the coefficient are algebraic *integers*, the norm of γ is a rational *integer*.

We cube the lattice L by the rule for the multiplication of lattices. We obtain a new lattice $\Lambda = L^3$ which will be similar to the lattice that belongs, together with Γ, to the basic figure of the region Q. The coefficient of similarity will clearly be γ^3:

$$\Lambda = \gamma^3\Gamma^3.$$

The lattice Λ is generated by numbers of the region Q, since the cube of each point of the lattice L is a number of the region Q, while the lattice $\Lambda = L^3$ is rationally related to a lattice constructed on any two of its points, which may be taken from cubes of points of the lattice L. Further, all the points of the lattice Λ are integers of the region Q, and hence the lattice Λ is a sublattice of a maximal ring of the region Q. Also, Λ is an ideal of this maximal ring, since Λ and the lattice Γ^3 that is similar to it are multiplicative for all points of the maximal ring. The ideal Λ belongs to the class corresponding to the lattice Γ^{-3}.

The coefficient of similarity γ^3 in the equation $\Lambda = \gamma^3\Gamma^3$ is a point of the lattice Γ^{-3} which corresponds to the ideal Λ and replaces it in questions of divisibility, in accordance with the general theory of auxiliary lattices.

The norm of the ideal Λ is clearly equal to the norm γ^3, and hence is equal to the cube of the rational integer $N(\gamma)$.

It is easy to see that Λ is not divisible by the cube of an ideal that has a norm that is different from unity. In fact, if Λ were divisible by an ideal $\mathfrak{a}^3$, then the factor γ^3 would be divisible by α^3, where α is a point of one of the lattices of the basic figure associated with the ideal $\mathfrak{a}$. From this it follows that γ/α has algebraic integer coordinates. Let α belong to the lattice Γ_1. Then the lattice $L_1 = \gamma(\Gamma_1\Gamma)/\alpha$ will consist of points with algebraic integer coordinates and contain the lattice $L = \gamma\Gamma$ as a proper part, since the lattice Γ_1 contains the point α and $|N(\gamma/\alpha)| < |N(\gamma)|$. This is impossible, since it follows from the definition of the lattice L that one cannot center the lattice L with points with integer coordinates. Thus the ideal L is not divisible by the cube of any ideal that is not a unit ideal. From this it is easy to conclude that the norm of the ideal Λ is not divisible by any of the primes that are nonfactorable primes in the region Q, nor by any of the primes included in the discriminant. In fact, each such prime is divisible only by one prime ideal and, since the norm of Λ is a perfect cube, Λ must be divisible by a cube of a prime ideal, which we saw was impossible. The factorization of the ideal Λ into prime ideals must have the form

$$\Lambda = \mathfrak{p}_1^2\bar{\mathfrak{p}}_1\mathfrak{p}_2^2\bar{\mathfrak{p}}_2\cdots,$$

where $\mathfrak{p}_1, \bar{\mathfrak{p}}_1; \mathfrak{p}_2, \bar{\mathfrak{p}}_2; \cdots$ are *distinct* prime ideals contained in pairs in the primes $p_1, p_2, \cdots$.

In view of the fact that $\mathfrak{p}_1\bar{\mathfrak{p}}_1 = p_1$, $\mathfrak{p}_2\bar{\mathfrak{p}}_2 = p_2, \cdots$, we have

$$\Lambda = p_1p_2\cdots\mathfrak{p}_1\mathfrak{p}_2\cdots = l\mathfrak{l},$$

where $\mathfrak{l} = \mathfrak{p}_1\mathfrak{p}_2\cdots$, $l = p_1p_2\cdots = N(\mathfrak{l})$.

The ideal $\mathfrak{l}$ is equivalent to the ideal Λ and hence similar to the lattice Γ^3:

$$\mathfrak{l} = \lambda\Gamma^3.$$

The coefficient of similarity λ is a point of the lattice Γ^{-3}.

Thus, $\Lambda = l\lambda\Gamma^3$. Consequently, $\gamma^3 = l\lambda$, $\gamma = \sqrt[3]{l\lambda}$ and $L = \sqrt[3]{l\lambda}\cdot\Gamma$.

We note that the extraction of the cube root in the formula $\gamma = \sqrt[3]{l\lambda}$ must be performed using both coordinates of the point $l\lambda$. However, of the nine possible values for γ we need take only those three for which the product of the coordinates is rational.

Thus the lattice L has the following characteristics:

1. L is similar to some lattice Γ of the basic figure of the region Q.

2. The cube of the coefficient of similarity is the product of some point λ of the lattice Γ^{-3} by the norm of this point.

3. The norm l of the point λ decomposes into distinct prime factors and is relatively prime to the discriminant d of the region Q.

The converse is obvious, i.e., if a lattice satisfies the properties 1, 2, and 3, then it may be taken as the lattice L for some cubic maximal ring. In fact, all the points of such a lattice satisfy the conditions 1 and 2 of the foregoing §43 and thus are projections of points of some cubic region. Moreover, *all* the projections with algebraic integer coordinates belong to this lattice and hence form a lattice L.

We have established that the properties 1, 2, and 3 completely characterize the lattice L. This allows the actual construction of the lattice L for a cubic region beginning with a given region Q. For this we must choose all the lattices Γ and all the appropriate factors λ.

We will obtain lattices L corresponding to reducible cubic regions only when $\lambda = 1$ and Γ_0 is the principal lattice. This follows directly from Theorem 3.

The same cubic region may be situated in a three-dimensional space in six different ways. Thus each cubic region corresponds to six different lattices L. If L is one of these, then the remaining ones will clearly be

$$L\epsilon,\ L\epsilon^2,$$
$$\bar{L},\ \bar{L}\epsilon,\ \bar{L}\epsilon^2,$$

where ϵ is a point with coordinates $e^{2\pi i/3}$, $e^{4\pi i/3}$ and $\bar{L}$ is a lattice conjugate to L, i.e., a lattice whose points have coordinates obtained from a transposition of the coordinates of the points of L. Thus, if we wish to construct a lattice L for each *different* cubic region, we must take only one of the values of the cube root in the formula $\gamma = \sqrt[3]{\mathfrak{l}\lambda}$ and only one of the lattices L and $\bar{L}$. Clearly, for this it is necessary to choose one of the two lattices Γ and $\bar{\Gamma}$ corresponding to the conjugate classes of ideals. If $\Gamma \neq \bar{\Gamma}$, it is necessary to take all possible values for the factor λ, including those corresponding to the conjugate ideals $\mathfrak{l}$ and $\bar{\mathfrak{l}}$ if they belong to the same class. If $\Gamma = \bar{\Gamma}$, then it is necessary to take only one of the values of λ corresponding to the conjugate ideals $\mathfrak{l}$ and $\bar{\mathfrak{l}}$.

The point λ in the equation $\mathfrak{l} = \lambda\Gamma^3$ is determined up to a factor that is a unit of the maximal ring of the region Q. Consequently, if we choose the ideal $\mathfrak{l}$ and the lattice Γ, we may obtain several distinct lattices L. However, the factors λ which differ by the cube of a unit of a maximal ring determine the same lattice. We now investigate in more detail the possible different cases that may arise.

1. $d = -3$. In this case there exists in the basic figure only one lattice, namely the principal lattice Γ_0. There are six units: $1, \epsilon, \epsilon^2, -1, -\epsilon, -\epsilon^2$. In view of the fact that $-1 = (-1)^3$, it is not necessary to consider the last three units. If $l \neq 1$, then the factors λ, $\lambda\epsilon$, and $\lambda\epsilon^2$ give distinct lattices L corresponding to distinct cubic regions. For $l = 1$, $\lambda = 1$ determines a lattice L for a cubic region that is reducible into three "direct summands." $\lambda = \epsilon$ and $\lambda = \epsilon^2$ determine distinct lattices L, but they correspond to the same cubic region since $\epsilon^2 = \bar{\epsilon}$.

2. $d = -4$. Four units exist in the maximal rings: 1, i, -1, and $-i$. In view of the fact that $i = (-i)^3$, $-1 = (-1)^3$, and $-i = i^3$ the adjoining of the units to the factor λ does not change the lattice L.

3. $d < -4$. In this case there exists only one unit ± 1. The adjoining of -1 to λ does not change the lattice L.

4. $d = 1$. The region Q is reducible. It contains four units, $(1, 1)$, $(1, -1)$, $(-1, 1)$, and $(-1, -1)$, each of which is a cube. The adjoining of these units to λ does not change the lattice L.

5. $d > 1$. In this case all the units are in the form of powers of a basic unit ϵ_0 and may differ only by cubic factors from 1, ϵ_0 and ϵ_0^{-1}. If $l \neq 1$, the factors λ, $\lambda\epsilon_0$ and $\lambda\epsilon_0^{-1}$ determine lattices L corresponding to distinct cubic regions. If $l = 1$ and $\Gamma \neq \Gamma_0$, the same thing is true. Finally, if $l = 1$ and $\Gamma = \Gamma_0$, then when $\lambda = 1$ we obtain a lattice for a reducible cubic region, and when $\lambda = \epsilon_0$ or $\lambda = \epsilon_0^{-1}$ we obtain lattices L corresponding to the same cubic region, since they are conjugate.

The actual construction of the lattices L may be carried out without going into the construction of all the lattices of the basic figure of the maximal ring of the region Q. In fact, let us choose the ideal $\mathfrak{l}$ and the class of ideals K corresponding to the lattice Γ. The lattice Γ is similar to the lattice of any ideal of the class K^{-1}. Let us take an arbitrary ideal $\mathfrak{a}$ from this class and specify it concretely by means of a basis. The ideal $\mathfrak{l}$ must belong to the class K^{-3} and hence must be equivalent to the ideal $\mathfrak{a}^3$, which we may actually find. The coefficient of similarity μ in the equation $\mathfrak{l} = \mu\,\mathfrak{a}^3$ may also be found in practice. In general, it will be a fraction in the region Q.

Obviously L will then be:

$$L = \sqrt[3]{l\mu} \cdot \mathfrak{a}.$$

Since we know the basis of the ideal $\mathfrak{a}$, we may find from it a basis for the lattice L.

§45. THE CONSTRUCTION OF MAXIMAL CUBIC LATTICES

In the preceding section we gave a method for the construction of lattices L that was closely connected with the projection of a maximal ring. It is now necessary for us to construct the maximal ring itself, assuming the lattice L to be known. We saw that the projection of the maximal ring is contained in the lattice L and contains the lattice $3L$. From this it follows that the projection of the maximal ring either coincides with the lattice $3L$ or centers it with an index of either 3 or 9.

We will denote by $\mathfrak{M}$ the collection of all integer points of U that have as projections points of $3L$. This collection is a lattice formed with points of the system $3L$ that are located in the plane $u + u' + u'' = 0$ of three-dimensional space, and with all the points parallel to those points. It is easy to find a basis for the lattice $\mathfrak{M}$. Let the points $(\beta_1, \bar{\beta}_1)$ and $(\beta_2, \bar{\beta}_2)$ form a basis for the lattice L. The points $(3\beta_1, 3\bar{\beta}_1)$ and $(3\beta_2, 3\bar{\beta}_2)$ will form a basis for the lattice $3L$. The coordinates of these points with respect to the coordinate axes of the space will

will be

$$\omega_1=\beta_1+\overline{\beta}_1;\quad \omega_1'=\beta_1\varepsilon^2+\overline{\beta}_1\varepsilon;\quad \omega_1''=\beta_1\varepsilon+\overline{\beta}_1\varepsilon^2;$$
$$\omega_2=\beta_2+\overline{\beta}_2;\quad \omega_2'=\beta_2\varepsilon^2+\overline{\beta}_2\varepsilon;\quad \omega_2''=\beta_2\varepsilon+\overline{\beta}_2\varepsilon^2.$$

By means of simple calculations which were introduced in the present section it is easy to find equations defining the points ω_1 and ω_2 and to determine the Tschirnhausen transformation corresponding to them. The basis of the lattice $\mathfrak{M}$ will clearly be $[1; \omega_1; \omega_2]$.

The discriminant $D(\mathfrak{M})$ of the lattice $\mathfrak{M}$ will be

$$\begin{vmatrix} 1, & \beta_1+\overline{\beta}_1, & \beta_2+\overline{\beta}_2 \\ 1, & \beta_1\varepsilon^2+\overline{\beta}_1\varepsilon, & \beta_2\varepsilon^2+\overline{\beta}_2\varepsilon \\ 1, & \beta_1\varepsilon+\overline{\beta}_1\varepsilon^2, & \beta_2\varepsilon+\overline{\beta}_2\varepsilon^2 \end{vmatrix}^2 = \begin{vmatrix} 1 & 1 & 1 \\ 1 & \varepsilon^2 & \varepsilon \\ 1 & \varepsilon & \varepsilon^2 \end{vmatrix}^2 \cdot \begin{vmatrix} 1 & 0 & 0 \\ 0 & \beta_1 & \beta_2 \\ 0 & \overline{\beta}_1 & \overline{\beta}_2 \end{vmatrix}^2$$
$$= -27\begin{vmatrix} \beta_1, & \beta_2 \\ \overline{\beta}_1, & \overline{\beta}_2 \end{vmatrix} = -27\,D(L),$$

where $D(L)$ denotes the discriminant of the lattice L. But $D(L)$ is equal to the product of the square of the norm of the factor γ by the discriminant of the lattice Γ, which is the same as the discriminant of the maximal ring of the region Q, in view of the basic property of auxiliary lattices of the region. Thus

$$D(\mathfrak{M})=-27\,dl^2,$$

since

$$N(\gamma)=\sqrt[3]{N(l\lambda)}=l.$$

After finding the lattice $\mathfrak{M}$, we may find the maximal ring with a few more calculations. It is only necessary to decide whether or not there are integers among the numbers

$$\frac{a_1+a_2\omega_1+a_3\omega_2}{3}\quad \text{при } a_1=0,\pm 1;\ a_2=0,\pm 1;\ a_3=0,\pm 1.$$

At most, this will involve $13 = (27-1)/2$ trials.

We now study the lattice $\mathfrak{M}$ in more detail.

THEOREM 5. *The lattice $\mathfrak{M}$ is a ring.*

PROOF. Let ω be one of the numbers in the lattice $\mathfrak{M}$ and let

$$\omega^3 = s\omega^2 - q\omega + n$$

be the equation whose roots are ω, ω', and ω''.

The coordinates $\theta, \overline{\theta}$ of the cube of the projection of the point ω satisfy the equation

$$\theta^2 - (2s^3 - 9sq + 27n)\,\theta + (s^2 - 3q)^3 = 0.$$

In order for the number ω to belong to the lattice $\mathfrak{M}$, it is necessary and sufficient that its projection belong to the lattice $3L$, and hence that the coordinates of the cube of the projection be divisible by 27. For this it is necessary to satisfy the conditions

$$\begin{aligned} 2s^3 - 9sq + 27n &\equiv 0 \pmod{27}, \\ s^2 - 3q &\equiv 0 \pmod{9}, \end{aligned}$$

for which in turn it is necessary and sufficient to satisfy the condition

$$s \equiv q \equiv 0 \pmod 3.$$

Let the number ω belong to the lattice $\mathfrak{M}$. Then ω^2 also belongs to the lattice $\mathfrak{M}$. In fact, the coefficients s_1 and q_1 of the equation whose root is ω^2 are connected by the relations

$$s_1 = s^2 - 2q,\ q_1 = q^2 - 2sn$$

with the coefficients s and q. If $s \equiv q \equiv 0 \pmod 3$, then

$$s_1 \equiv q_1 \equiv 0 \pmod 3.$$

Now let the numbers ω_1 and ω_2 belong to the lattice $\mathfrak{M}$.

Then the number $2\omega_1\omega_2$ belongs to the lattice $\mathfrak{M}$, since

$$2\omega_1\omega_2 = (\omega_1 + \omega_2)^2 - \omega_1^2 - \omega_2^2,$$

and the *lattice* $\mathfrak{M}$ is additive and subtractive.

But the number $\omega_1\omega_2$ also clearly belongs to the lattice $\mathfrak{M}$, since if the coefficients s and q for the number $2\omega_1\omega_2$ are divisible by 3, then the same will be true for the coefficients of the equation satisfied by $\omega_1\omega_2$.

Thus the lattice $\mathfrak{M}$ is multiplicative and the theorem is proved in full.

It is not difficult to give a formula for the index-form of the ring $\mathfrak{M}$.

Let $\omega = x\omega_1 + y\omega_2 + z$ be a general number of the ring $\mathfrak{M}$. Then the index-form of the ring will be equal to

$$f(x, y) = \frac{\sqrt{D(\omega)}}{\sqrt{D(\mathfrak{M})}} = \frac{(\omega' - \omega'')(\omega'' - \omega)(\omega - \omega')}{\sqrt{-27dl^2}}.$$

Substituting for ω_1, ω_2 and their conjugate numbers their expressions in terms of the basis of the lattice L, we obtain after simple calculations

$$f(x, y) = \frac{(x\beta_1 + y\beta_2)^3 - (x\bar{\beta}_1 + y\bar{\beta}_2)^3}{l\sqrt{d}}.$$

This expression may be given an even simpler form if we turn to the representation of the basis of the lattice L in terms of the basis $[\alpha_1, \alpha_2]$ of the similar ideal $\mathfrak{a}$, using the relation

$$L = \sqrt[3]{l\mu} \cdot \mathfrak{a},$$

where μ is a number suitably chosen from the region Q. From this relation we obtain

$$\gamma_1 = \sqrt[3]{l\mu}\,\alpha_1, \qquad \gamma_2 = \sqrt[3]{l\mu}\,\alpha_2,$$
$$\bar{\gamma}_1 = \sqrt[3]{l\bar{\mu}}\,\bar{\alpha}_1, \qquad \bar{\gamma}_2 = \sqrt[3]{l\bar{\mu}}\,\bar{\alpha}_2,$$

from which we have

$$f(x, y) = \frac{\mu(x\alpha_1 + y\alpha_2)^3 - \bar{\mu}(x\bar{\alpha}_1 + y\bar{\alpha}_2)^3}{\sqrt{d}},$$

i.e., $f(x, y)$ is the form multiplying $\sqrt{d}$ in the representation of $\mu(x\alpha_1 + y\alpha_2)^3$ in the form $(F(x, y) + f(x, y)\sqrt{d})/2$.

From the method of choice of the factor μ it follows that the numbers $\mu\alpha_1^3$, $\mu\alpha_1^2\alpha_2$, $\mu\alpha_1\alpha_2^2$, and $\mu\alpha_2^3$ are integers in the region Q, and consequently that $f(x, y)$ actually has integer coefficients such that the middle coefficients are divisible by 3.

Having constructed the index-form of the ring $\mathfrak{M}$ it is easy to discover how the maximal ring centers the ring $\mathfrak{M}$.

Let $f(x, y) = ax^3 + 3bx^2y + 3cxy^2 + ey^3$ be the index-form of the ring $\mathfrak{M}$. Clearly, if the maximal ring centers the ring $\mathfrak{M}$ with index 9, the coefficients a and e must be divisible by 3. If the maximal ring centers the ring $\mathfrak{M}$ with index 3, then there must exist a linear permutation of the variables with a determinant equal to 3 that would take the form $f(x, y)$ into a new form, all of whose coefficients would be divisible by 9. Obviously, this is possible if and only if one of the numbers a, e, $a + 3b + 3c + e$, and $a - 3b + 3c - e$ is divisible by 9 and the remaining ones are not divisible by 3.

In this manner the introduction of the index-form of the ring $\mathfrak{M}$ permits us to determine the maximal ring almost without calculations.

We will now explain how the possibilities of this and other centerings of the the ring $\mathfrak{M}$ are connected with the discriminant of the quadratic region and with the number l.

THEOREM. *If d is divisible by 3, then the maximal ring either coincides with $\mathfrak{M}$ or centers $\mathfrak{M}$ with index 9. If d is not divisible by 3, but l is divisible* *by 3, then $\mathfrak{M}$ coincides with the maximal ring. Finally, if d is not divisible by 3, and l is not divisible by 3, then the maximal ring coincides with $\mathfrak{M}$ or centers $\mathfrak{M}$ with index 3.*

PROOF. The theorem consists of three assertions, each of which we will prove separately. We begin with the first.

Let d be divisible by 3, and let

$$f(x, y) = ax^3 + 3bx^2y + 3cxy^2 + ey^3$$

be the index-form of the ring $\mathfrak{M}$. Namely, let us assume that the maximal ring centers $\mathfrak{M}$ with index 3. Then we may turn from the form $f(x, y)$ to an equivalent one in which the coefficient e will be divisible by 9 and the coefficient a will not be divisible by 3. The discriminant of this form is

$$\begin{aligned} D(f) &= 81b^2c^2 - 4\cdot 27ac^3 - 4\cdot 27eb^3 + 18\cdot 9abce - 27e^2 \\ &\equiv -4\cdot 27ac^3 + 81b^2c^2 \pmod{243}. \end{aligned}$$

The discriminant $D(f)$ is by assumption divisible by 81 but not divisible by 243. The last equation shows that this is impossible. The first assertion is now proven.

The third assertion of the theorem is obvious. It remains to show the second. Let d be not divisible by 3, while e is divisible by 3. Then all points ω which lie in the plane of zero trace and which project into points of the lattice $3L$ have the property that ω^3 is divisible by 3. In fact, the coefficient q of the equation $\omega^3 = -q\omega + n$ (whose root is ω) must be divisible by 3 for every point that projects into a point of the lattice $3L$. The coefficient n (equal to $\bar{\alpha}^3 + \alpha^3$ where $(3\alpha, 3\bar{\alpha})$ is the projection of ω) is also divisible by 3, since $\bar{\alpha}^3$ and α^3 are by assumption both divisible by l, which is divisible by 3. Because of this, the ring $\mathfrak{M}$ may not be centered by points that are not parallel to points of zero trace. In fact, such points may be represented in the form $(\omega + k)/3$ where ω is a point of zero trace projected into a point of the lattice $3L$, and k is not divisible by 3. But it is obvious that $\omega + k$ is relatively prime to 3, and $(\omega + k)/3$ cannot be an integer. It remains to assume that the ring $\mathfrak{M}$ is centered with points that are parallel to points of zero trace. Let ω be one of these centering points and let

$$\omega^3 = s\omega^2 - q\omega + n$$

be the equation of which it is a root. The coefficient s of this equation is divisible by 3, but the coefficient q is not divisible by 3, since otherwise ω would belong to the lattice $\mathfrak{M}$.

The discriminant of the number ω, equal to

$$s^2q^2 - 4q^3 - 4s^3n + 18snq - 27n^2 \equiv - 4q^3 \pmod 3,$$

is not divisible by 3, and hence the discriminant of the maximal ring to which ω belongs is not divisible by 3. But this is possible only for d divisible by 3, which is contrary to assumption. Thus, under our assumptions the ring $\mathfrak{M}$ can not be centered by integer points and consequently coincides with the maximal ring.

The theorem is proved in full.

§46. SOME PROPERTIES OF THE DISCRIMINANTS OF CUBIC FIELDS

From what has been said above it is possible to obtain some interesting consequences concerning discriminants of cubic maximal rings.

In the first place, we find that a discriminant of a cubic region may contain at most the square of a prime number other than 2 or 3, and that it may contain only the square or cube of two and only the first, second, third, fourth, or fifth power of 3.

In fact, $D = - 27dl^2$ if $l \equiv 0$ (3); $D = - 27dl^2$ or $-(1/3)dl^2$ if $d \equiv 0$ (3); $D = - 27dl^2$ or $-3dl^2$ if neither d nor l is divisible by 3. d and l are relatively prime and are not divisible by the square of any prime other than 2, while d may by divisible by 2^2 or 2^3.

Secondly, it is easy to show that the discriminants of cubic fields do not increase faster than numbers in a certain arithmetical progression.

In fact, the discriminants of quadratic regions grow no faster than the numbers of a certain arithmetic progression. If $d > 0$, we may construct a cubic region on each quadratic region, assuming that $\Gamma = \Gamma_0$ and $\lambda = \epsilon_0$ in the construction of the lattice L. The discriminants of the corresponding maximal cubic rings will not exceed $27d$ in absolute value, and hence will grow no faster than the numbers of some arithmetic progression.

It is also easy to construct cubic regions with small discriminants on quadratic regions of negative discriminants. Let us consider only $d \equiv -7$ (8). Such discriminants are distributed no less densely than the numbers of some arithmetic progression. For such regions the number 2 decomposes into two distinct prime factors:

$$2 = \mathfrak{p}_2\bar{\mathfrak{p}}_2.$$

Let $\mathfrak{p}_2$ belong to some class K. If the number of classes is not divisible by 3, then we can find a class K_1 such that $KK_1^3 = K_0$ is the principal class. In this case it is possible to construct the lattice L taking $\mathfrak{l} = \mathfrak{p}_2$ and for the lattice Γ choosing the lattice corresponding to the class K_1.

If the number of classes is divisible by 3, then there exists a class K whose cube is the principal class. The lattice L may be constructed taking $\lambda = 1$ and for the lattice Γ choosing the lattice corresponding to the class K. The discriminant of the maximal ring constructed on the lattice L will not exceed $108d$ in the first case and will not exceed $27d$ in the second, thus growing no more rapidly than the numbers in some arithmetic progression.

From these considerations we could also have obtained the character of the decomposition into prime ideals of primes entering into the discriminant of the region. We will not do this, since we have already obtained results concerning this question by another means.

At the end of the section we introduce some examples of constructions of cubic regions on quadratic regions.

EXAMPLE 1. To construct some cubic regions on $R(\sqrt{-15})$.

The quadratic region $R(\sqrt{-15})$ has two classes of ideals. The representative of the class $K_1 \neq K_0$ is the ideal $\mathfrak{p}_3$.

Let us factor the smallest primes into prime ideals:

$$\begin{aligned}
2 &= \mathfrak{p}_2 \overline{\mathfrak{p}}_2; & \mathfrak{p}_2 &\sim \overline{\mathfrak{p}}_2 \sim \mathfrak{p}_3;\\
3 &= \mathfrak{p}_3^2;\\
5 &= \mathfrak{p}_5^2; & \mathfrak{p}_5 &\sim \mathfrak{p}_3;\\
17 &= \mathfrak{p}_{17}\overline{\mathfrak{p}}_{17}; & \mathfrak{p}_{17} &\sim \overline{\mathfrak{p}}_{17} \sim \mathfrak{p}_3;\\
19 &= \mathfrak{p}_{19}\overline{\mathfrak{p}}_{19}; & \mathfrak{p}_{19} &\sim \overline{\mathfrak{p}}_{19} \sim 1;\\
23 &= \mathfrak{p}_{23}\overline{\mathfrak{p}}_{23}; & \mathfrak{p}_{23} &\sim \overline{\mathfrak{p}}_{23} \sim \mathfrak{p}_3;\\
31 &= \mathfrak{p}_{31}\overline{\mathfrak{p}}_{31}; & \mathfrak{p}_{31} &\sim \overline{\mathfrak{p}}_{31} \sim 1.
\end{aligned}$$

The lattice L may be constructed beginning with either the lattice Γ_0 or the lattice Γ_1. Since $\Gamma^{-3} = \Gamma_0$ and $\Gamma_1^{-3} = \Gamma_1$, it is necessary to choose corresponding factors λ from the lattices Γ_0 and Γ_1.

Let $\rho = (1 + \sqrt{-15})/2$.

When constructing the lattice L from the lattice Γ_0, we obtain for the index-form of the ring $\mathfrak{M}$ the value

$f(x, y) =$ the coefficient of ρ in the expression

$\phi_0(x, y) = \mu(x + y\rho)^3 = \mu[x^3 - 12xy^2 - 4y^3 + \rho(3x^2y + 3xy^2 - 3y^3)]$, where

μ is any number of the principal class whose norm is not divisible by a square of a prime and is not divisible by 3 or 5.

When constructing the lattice L from the lattice Γ_1, we obtain for the index-form a representation in the form of the coefficient of ρ in the expression

$$\phi_1(x, y) = \mu[3x + (1+\rho)y]^3,$$

where μ is the transition factor from the ideal $\mathfrak{l}$ to the ideal $\mathfrak{p}^3$, i.e., $[\mu] = \mathfrak{l}\mathfrak{p}_3/9$.

Changing $\phi_1(x, y)$ somewhat, we obtain

$$\varphi_1(x, y) = \frac{\mathfrak{l}\mathfrak{p}_3}{3}[9x^3 + 9x^2y - 9xy^2 - 5y^3 + \rho(9x^2y + 9xy^2 + y^3)].$$

The factor $\mathfrak{l}\mathfrak{p}_3$ may be any integer whose norm is not divisible by 3, 5, or the square of any prime.

We write out some of the smallest values for μ and $\mathfrak{l}\mathfrak{p}_3$.

$$\mu\colon\ \mathfrak{p}_{19} = 1 + 2\rho;\quad \mathfrak{p}_{31} = 3 + 2\rho;\quad \mathfrak{p}_2\mathfrak{p}_{17} = 5 + \rho;\quad \mathfrak{p}_2\bar{\mathfrak{p}}_{17} = -1 + 3\rho;$$

$$\mathfrak{l}\mathfrak{p}_3\colon\ \mathfrak{p}_2\mathfrak{p}_3 = 1 + \rho;\quad \mathfrak{p}_3\mathfrak{p}_{17} = 5 + 2\rho;\quad \mathfrak{p}_3\mathfrak{p}_{23} = 1 + 4\rho;$$

$$\mathfrak{p}_2\mathfrak{p}_3\mathfrak{p}_{19} = 10 + \rho;\quad \mathfrak{p}_2\mathfrak{p}_3\bar{\mathfrak{p}}_{19} = 2 + 5\rho.$$

Beginning with these factors, we obtain the index-forms of the rings $\mathfrak{M}$: for Γ_0,

$$\begin{aligned} f(x, y) &= 2x^3 + 9x^2y - 15xy^2 - 17y^3; & D &= 5\cdot 3^4\cdot 19^2;\\ f(x, y) &= 2x^3 + 15x^2y - 9xy^2 - 23y^3; & D &= 5\cdot 3^4\cdot 31^2;\\ f(x, y) &= x^3 + 18x^2y + 6xy^2 - 22y^3; & D &= 5\cdot 3^4\cdot 2^2\cdot 17^2;\\ f(x, y) &= 3x^3 + 6x^2y - 30xy^2 - 18y^3; & D &= 5\cdot 3^4\cdot 2^2\cdot 17^2; \end{aligned}$$

for Γ_1,

$$\begin{aligned} f(x, y) &= 3x^3 + 9x^2y + 3xy^2 - y^3; & D &= 5\cdot 3^4\cdot 2^2;\\ f(x, y) &= 6x^3 + 27x^2y + 15xy^2 - y^3; & D &= 5\cdot 3^4\cdot 17^2;\\ f(x, y) &= 12x^3 + 27x^2y + 3xy^2 - 5y^3; & D &= 5\cdot 3^4\cdot 23^4;\\ f(x, y) &= 3x^3 + 36x^2y + 30xy^2 + 2y^3; & D &= 5\cdot 3^4\cdot 2^2\cdot 19^2;\\ f(x, y) &= 15x^3 + 36x^2y + 6xy^2 - 6y^3; & D &= 5\cdot 3^4\cdot 2^2\cdot 19^2. \end{aligned}$$

From the consideration of the nine cases, it is seen that in only two is there a centering. The maximal rings of least discriminant are given by the forms

$$\begin{aligned} 3x^3 + 9x^2y + 3xy^2 - y^3; &\quad D = 5\cdot 3^4\cdot 2^2;\\ x^3 + 2x^2y - 10xy^2 - 6y^3; &\quad D = 5\cdot 2^2\cdot 17^2;\\ 5x^3 + 12x^2y + 2xy^2 - 2y^3; &\quad D = 5\cdot 2^2\cdot 19^2. \end{aligned}$$

EXAMPLE 2. To construct some cubic regions based on $R(\sqrt{5})$.

There exists only one class in the region $R(\sqrt{5})$.

Let us denote by ϵ_0 the basic unit $(1+\sqrt{5})/2$ of the maximal ring. The index-form $f(x, y)$ of the ring $\mathfrak{M}$ based on $R(\sqrt{5})$ will be obtained from the expression

$$\mu (x + y\varepsilon_0)^3 = \frac{I(x, y) + f(x, y)\sqrt{5}}{2},$$

where μ is any number whose norm is not divisible by 5 or the square of any prime.

Let us write down several factors with the smallest norms:

$$\mu = \varepsilon_0; \quad \mu = \pi_{11} = 3 + \varepsilon_0; \quad \mu = \pi_{11}\varepsilon_0 = 1 + 4\varepsilon_0; \quad \mu = \pi_{11}\varepsilon_0^{-1} = -2 + 3\varepsilon_0.$$

The corresponding index-forms of the ring $\mathfrak{M}$ will be

$$\begin{aligned} f(x, y) &= x^3 + 3x^2y + 6xy^2 + 3y^3; & D &= -5\cdot 2^3; \\ f(x, y) &= x^3 + 12x^2y + 15xy^2 + 9y^3; & D &= -5\cdot 3^3\cdot 11^2; \\ f(x, y) &= 4x^3 + 15x^2y + 27xy^2 + 24y^3; & D &= -5\cdot 3^3\cdot 11^2; \\ f(x, y) &= 3x^3 + 3x^2y + 12xy^2 + 5y^3; & D &= -5\cdot 3^3\cdot 11^2. \end{aligned}$$

In these four cases, the maximal ring will center the ring $\mathfrak{M}$ in only the second case. The index-form of the maximal ring in this case will be equal to $3x^3 + 12x^2y + 5xy^2 + y^3$ with a discriminant $-5\cdot 3\cdot 11^2$. In the remaining three cases the maximal ring coincides with the ring $\mathfrak{M}$.

PART E. THE CONSTRUCTION OF A QUARTIC REGION ON A CUBIC REGION

In a manner similar to the one we gave in the preceding section for the construction of cubic regions by classifying them according to the quadratic regions on which they were based, we can also classify quartic regions according to cubic regions, and we can give a method for their construction. For this it is necessary to carry out the converse of the well-known method of Lagrange for the solution of a quartic equation in radicals.

§47. BASING A QUARTIC REGION ON A CUBIC REGION

We consider the four-dimensional space K_4 with coordinate axes Ou, Ou', Ou'', Ou''', which we will at first assume to be real for simplicity in geometrical constructions. Each real quartic region is, by definition, formed by the collection of all points rationally situated with respect to some multiplicative lattice. A given lattice may be situated in the space in 24 different ways. A transformation from one situation to another consists in the same simultaneous transformation of the coordinates of all of the points of the space.

We have called such transformations axial-superpositions. The axial-superpositions obviously form a group that is isomorphic to the symmetric group of transformations on four elements. Under all the axial-superpositions, the points of the "rational line" $u = u' = u'' = u'''$ do not change their positions. The three-dimensional "space of zero trace" $u + u' + u'' + u''' = 0$ orthogonal to the rational line goes into itself under all axial-superpositions.

We project the space K_4 onto the space of zero trace parallel to the rational direction. Obviously the projections of the coordinate axes make up in the space of zero trace a set of four lines which form pairwise equal angles with each other. Such four lines may obviously be taken for the diagonals of some cube, where the positive directions of these lines connect the center of the cube with the vertices of one of the tetrahedra inscribed in the cube (see Figure 7). Let us assume that the axes of symmetry of fourth order of this cube are the axes of coordinates Ov, Ov', Ov'' of the space of zero trace, their direction being chosen according to the figure. The projections of the points (1, 0, 0, 0), (0, 1, 0, 0), (0, 0, 1, 0) and (0, 0, 0, 1) in these axes under conservation of the scale will obviously have the coordinates (1/2, 1/2, 1/2), (1/2, − 1/2, − 1/2), (− 1/2, 1/2, − 1/2) and (− 1/2, − 1/2, 1/2) Thus, the point (u, u', u'', u''') will have as its projection the point (v, v', v'') whose coordinates are obtained by the formulas

$$v = \frac{1}{2}(u + u' - u'' - u'''),$$
$$v' = \frac{1}{2}(u - u' + u'' - u'''),$$
$$v'' = \frac{1}{2}(u - u' - u'' + u''').$$

For convenience in calculating, we reduce by half the scale in the space of zero trace. Then the projection of the point (u, u', u'', u''') will be the point $(u + u' - u'' - u''', u - u' + u'' - u''', u - u' - u'' + u''')$.

We note that the coordinate axes chosen by us in the space of zero trace are projections onto that space of the "bisectrix planes"

$$u = u';\quad u'' = u''';$$
$$u = u'';\quad u' = u''';$$
$$u = u''';\quad u' = u''.$$

Under axial-superposition in the space K_4, the space of zero trace will undergo an orthogonal transformation that will take the tetrahedron $AA'A''A'''$ into itself. Twelve of these transformations will be rotations of the space, while twelve will be rotations with reflections.

Under axial-superposition the coordinates of the projection will undergo all possible permutations and, moreover, will change signs in pairs.

We introduce in the space of zero trace the operation of multiplication of points in the usual manner by the multiplication of coordinates. Obviously, coordinates of squares of points of zero trace, and also of products of two different points, will only be permuted by axial-superpositions that do not change signs.

From this it follows that the squares of the projections of points of a quartic region, and also the products of the projections of two different points, will belong to some completely determined cubic region. We will call this region the cubic region upon which the quartic region is based.

In the future, we will denote quartic regions by T, and the cubic region upon which a quartic region T is based, by U. We will denote their discriminants by Δ and D, respectively.

The assumption as to the real character of the space K_4 is not essential. In the complex space, as in the real case, we will denote the projection of the point (u, u', u'', u''') by $(u + u' - u'' - u''', u - u' + u'' - u''', u - u' - u'' + u''')$. It is easy to see that this actually is the projection for an appropriate choice of axes and scale.

§48. SOME THEOREMS ABOUT PROJECTIONS OF FOURTH ORDER NUMBERS

THEOREM 1. *In order for the point* (η, η', η'') *to be the projection of a point of a quartic region, it is necessary and sufficient for the following conditions to be satisfied:*

1. *The square of the point* (η, η', η'') *belongs to some cubic region.*
2. $N(\eta) = \eta\eta'\eta''$ *is rational.*

PROOF. Let ω be a point of a quartic region. Its coordinates are roots of some equation

$$\omega^4 - f_1\omega^3 + f_2\omega^2 - f_3\omega + f_4 = 0$$

whose coefficients are rational.

The coordinates of the square of the projection of the point

$$\theta = (\omega + \omega' - \omega'' - \omega''')^2, \quad \theta' = (\omega - \omega' + \omega'' - \omega''')^2, \quad \theta'' = (\omega - \omega' - \omega'' + \omega''')^2$$

are roots of a cubic equation whose coefficients, being symmetric functions of ω, ω', ω'', and ω''', rationally expressible in terms of the coefficients f_1, f_2, f_3, and f_4, are therefore rational.

The norm of the projection

$$\eta\eta'\eta'' = (\omega + \omega' - \omega'' - \omega''')(\omega - \omega' + \omega'' - \omega''')(\omega - \omega' - \omega'' + \omega''')$$

is also a symmetric function of ω, ω', ω'', and ω''' and is therefore rational.

Well-known calculations show that θ is a root of the equation

$$\theta^3-(3f_1^2-8f_2)\,\theta^2+(3f_1^4-16f_1^2f_2+16f_2^2+16f_1f_3-64f_4)\,\theta-r^2=0,$$

where

$$r=N(\eta)=f_1^3-4f_1f_2+8f_3.$$

Conversely, let the coordinates of the point (η, η', η'') satisfy the conditions of the theorem. The point (η, η', η'') is the projection of the point $(\omega, \omega', \omega'', \omega''')$ whose coordinates are calculated by the formulas

$$\omega=\frac{\eta+\eta'+\eta''}{4};\quad \omega'=\frac{\eta-\eta'-\eta''}{4};\quad \omega''=\frac{-\eta+\eta'-\eta''}{4};\quad \omega'''=\frac{-\eta-\eta'+\eta''}{4},$$

as is easily shown.

We must show that the coefficients of the equation whose roots are ω, ω', ω'', and ω''' are rational.

We set up the equation

$$\omega^4-f_1\omega^3+f_2\omega^2-f_3\omega+f_4=0.$$

Its coefficients will be the numbers

$$\begin{aligned} f_1&=\omega+\omega'+\omega''+\omega'''=0,\\ f_2&=\omega\omega'+\dots\qquad=-\frac{\theta+\theta'+\theta''}{8},\\ f_3&=\omega\omega'\omega''+\dots\qquad=\frac{\eta\eta'\eta''}{8},\\ f_4&=\omega\omega'\omega''\omega'''\dots\qquad=\frac{(\theta+\theta'+\theta'')^2-4(\theta\theta'+\theta\theta''+\theta'\theta'')}{256}.\end{aligned}$$

They are all rational, since the coordinates of the point (η, η', η'') satisfy the conditions of the theorem.

The theorem is proven in full.

In the proof of the sufficiency of the conditions of the theorem, we took the point ω lying in the plane of zero trace, which geometrically coincides with its projection η, but we considered it in other coordinates. However, we could have taken any point $\omega+s/4$ parallel to it and lying on the plane $\omega+\omega'+\omega''+\omega'''=s$.

For a rational s any such point obviously belongs to the same region as ω.

THEOREM 2. *In order for points $(\eta_1, \eta'_1, \eta''_1)$ and $(\eta_2, \eta'_2, \eta''_2)$ satisfying the conditions of Theorem 1 to be projections of points in the same quartic region, it is necessary that the point $(\eta_1\eta_2, \eta'_1\eta'_2, \eta''_1\eta''_2)$ belong to the cubic region U, to which $(\eta_1^2, \eta_1'^2, \eta_1''^2)$ belongs. This condition is also sufficient if the point $(\eta_1^2, \eta_1'^2, \eta_1''^2)$ is a generic point of the region U.*

PROOF. Let ω_1 and ω_2 be two points of the quartic region, let η_1 and η_2

be their projections, and let θ_1 and θ_2 be the squares of their projections. We first assume that the point ω_1 is a generic point. Then ω_2 may be represented in the form

$$\omega_2 = a\omega_1^3 + b\omega_1^2 + c\omega_1 + d$$

with rational coefficients a, b, c, and d. Moreover, we may assume without loss of generality that the point ω_1 is located in the space of zero trace, so that the equation which has ω as a root is of the form

$$\omega_1^4 + f_2\omega_1^2 - f_3\omega_1 + f_4 = 0.$$

Then the square of the projection of the point ω_1 satisfies the equation

$$\theta^3 + 8f_2\theta^2 + 16(f_2 - 4f_4)\theta - 64f_3^2 = 0,$$

and the norm of the projection $\eta_1\eta_1'\eta_1''$, is equal to $8f_3$.

It is easy to check by direct calculations that

$$\eta_2 = a\left(-\frac{\eta_1^3}{8} - \frac{3}{2}f_2\eta_1\right) + \frac{b}{2}\eta_1'\eta_1'' + c\eta_1,$$

from which it follows that

$$\eta_1\eta_2 = -\frac{a}{8}\theta_1^2 + \left(-\frac{3}{2}af_2 + c\right)\theta_1 + 4bf_3.$$

This means that $\eta_1\eta_2$ belongs to the same region as θ_1.

If ω_1 is not a generic point, then we find in the region T a generic point ω the square of whose projection is also a generic point in its space. Such a point ω obviously exists. Denoting by η and θ the projection and the square of the projection of the point ω, we get that $\eta\eta_1$ and $\eta\eta_2$ belong to the same region as θ. But then $\eta\eta_1\eta\eta_2 = \eta_1\eta_2\theta$ will belong to the same region, and hence also $\eta_1\eta_2$, since θ is not a zero divisor. With this the necessity part of the theorem is shown.

Assuming that $\theta_1 = \eta_1^2$ is a generic point, we will now show the sufficiency of the conditions of the theorem.

Let $\eta_1\eta_2$ belong to the region containing θ_1. Then $\eta_1\eta_2$ may be represented in the form

$$\eta_1\eta_2 = \alpha\theta_1^2 + \beta\theta_1 + \gamma$$

with rational coefficients α, β, and γ.

Let ω_1 be a point whose projection is η_1. Obviously,

$$\omega_2 = -8\alpha\omega_1^3 + \frac{\gamma}{4f_3}\omega_1^2 + (\beta - 12\alpha f_2)\omega_1 + k$$

will have η_2 as its projection for any rational k. This follows directly from the formulas derived in the proof of the necessity.

Under the given assumptions, the expression for ω_2 is meaningful, since $f_3 = \sqrt{\theta\theta'\theta''}/8 \neq 0$, in view of the fact that the point $(\theta_1, \theta'_1, \theta''_1)$ is a generic point. Thus ω_2 is rationally expressible in terms of ω_1, and consequently ω_1 and ω_2 belong to the same region. Theorem 2 is now proved in full.

§49. THE SOLUTION OF THE PROBLEM INVERSE TO THE PROBLEM OF TSCHIRNHAUSEN FOR TWO QUARTIC EQUATIONS

We note that the proven theorems give a simple and convenient method for solution of the problem inverse to the problem of the Tschirnhausen transformation for quartic equations. In fact, let two quartic numbers ω_1 and ω_2 be given with their equations. The problem inverse to the problem of the Tschirnhausen transformation consists in finding whether or not the given numbers belong to the same region, and if they do, to find an expression for ω_2 in terms of ω_1, or conversely. For a solution, it is necessary to construct equations for the squares of the projections of the points ω_1 and ω_2, and solve for them the problem inverse to the Tschirnhausen transformation. Then we construct an equation satisfied by the product $\theta_1\theta_2$ of the squares of the projections. If ω_1 and ω_2 belong to the same region, $\theta_1\theta_2$ must be a perfect square. Extracting the square root of the cubic number by the means presented earlier, we find the product of the projections $\eta_1\eta_2$. The representation of $\eta_1\eta_2$ in terms of θ_1 will give us a substitution connecting ω_2 with ω_1.

EXAMPLE. To solve the problem inverse to the problem of the Tschirnhausen transformation for the equations

$$\omega_1^4 - \omega_1 - 1 = 0, \quad \omega_2^4 + \omega_2^3 + 5\omega_2^2 - 7\omega_2 - 1 = 0.$$

SOLUTION. We set up the equations for the squares of the projections

$$\theta_1^3 + 64\theta_1 - 64 = 0; \qquad N(\eta_1) = +8,$$
$$\theta_2^3 + 37\theta_2^2 + 275\theta_2 - 75^2 = 0; \quad N(\eta_2) = +75.$$

We establish the Tschirnhausen transformation between them:

$$\theta_2 = \frac{1}{2}\theta_1^2 - \theta_1 + 9.$$

We set up the equation whose roots are

$$\mu = \theta_1\theta_2 = -\theta_1^2 - 23\theta_1 + 32,$$

$$\mu^3 - 7\cdot 32\mu^2 + 7\cdot 16^2\cdot 25\mu - 8^2\cdot 75^2 = 0.$$

We look for the square root ν of the number μ:

$$\nu^3 - s\cdot\nu^2 + q\nu - 8\cdot 75 = 0,$$
$$s^2 - 2q = 7\cdot 32,$$
$$q^2 - 2\cdot 8\cdot 75 s = 7\cdot 16^2\cdot 25,$$

from which we obtain through simple calculations that

$$s = 28;\quad q = 280.$$

We express ν in terms of θ_1:

$$\nu = 4 - \theta_1 - \frac{\theta_1^2}{7}.$$

We note that $\eta_1\eta_2 = +\nu$, on the basis of the sign of the norm. Finally, we find a substitution connecting ω_2 with ω_1:

$$\omega_2 = \omega_1^3 + \omega_1^2 - \omega_1 + k.$$

It is easy to see that $k = 1$. The problem is solved.

§50. PROPERTIES OF THE PROJECTION OF A MAXIMAL QUARTIC LATTICE

We turn now to the study of the projection of a maximal quartic lattice. Obviously, such a projection is a three-dimensional lattice whose points satisfy the conditions of Theorems 1 and 2 of §48 and, moreover, have algebraic integer coordinates. We will denote by L the collection of all points rationally related to the projection of some maximal lattice and having algebraic integer coordinates. It is impossible to assert that all the points of the system L are projections of integer points corresponding to a quartic region, but the points of the system $4L$ are all projections of integer points, and hence completely included in the projection of the maximal ring. From this it follows that the system $4L$, and consequently L, are discrete. The latter is obviously three-dimensional, additive, and subtractive, and thus is a lattice. The lattice L centers the lattice $4L$ with an index $4^3 = 64$. The projection of the maximal lattice is contained in the lattice L and contains $4L$, and hence must center the lattice $4L$ with an index 2^α, where $0 \leq \alpha \leq 6$. Thus, if we construct the lattice L, the problem of constructing the projection of the maximal lattice is reduced to a finite number of trials.

We will now study the properties of the lattice L more deeply.

The lattice L is clearly multiplicative in all the integer points of the cubic region on which the quadratic region is based, and hence L is similar to one of the lattices of the basic figure of the maximal ring of this cubic region

$$L = \gamma\Gamma.$$

The square of the lattice L is generated by numbers of the cubic region U and is multiplicative for all integers of the region, i.e., for all points of the maximal ring. Hence,

$$\Lambda = L^2 = \gamma^2\Gamma^2$$

is an ideal of the maximal ring. This ideal belongs to the class K^{-2}, where K is the class corresponding to the lattice Γ. The transition factor $\lambda = \gamma^2$ is a point of the lattice Γ^{-2}. The norm of the ideal Λ is equal to the square of a rational integer, but the ideal Λ is not divisible by any square of an ideal other than unity. In the opposite case, the lattice L could have been centered by points with integer coordinates, which contradicts the definition of the lattice L.

From this it is easy to conclude that the ideal Λ may be decomposed into prime ideals only in the following form:

$$\Lambda = \mathfrak{p}_1\bar{\mathfrak{p}}_1\mathfrak{p}_2\bar{\mathfrak{p}}_2 \ldots \mathfrak{q}_1\mathfrak{q}_2 \ldots \mathfrak{m}_1\bar{\mathfrak{m}}_1\mathfrak{m}_2\bar{\mathfrak{m}}_2 \ldots,$$

where by $\mathfrak{p}$ and $\bar{\mathfrak{p}}$ we denote prime ideals of the first degree entering pairwise into the decomposition of prime ideals decomposing into three distinct prime ideals by $\mathfrak{q}$ we denote ideals of second degree, and finally, by $\mathfrak{M}$ and $\bar{\mathfrak{M}}$ we denote ideals entering into those prime divisors of the discriminant which decompose into prime ideals in the form $\mathfrak{M}^2\bar{\mathfrak{M}}$.

The norm of the ideal Λ may thus be represented in the form

$$N(\Lambda) = l^2 = k^2m^2,$$

where k^2 is the product of the norms of all $\mathfrak{p}$, $\bar{\mathfrak{p}}$, and $\mathfrak{q}$, and m^2 is the product of the norms of all $\mathfrak{M}$ and $\bar{\mathfrak{M}}$. The numbers k and m are relatively prime and divisible by no square of a prime. Moreover, k is relatively prime to the discriminant of the cubic region, and m consists of primes which may be included in the discriminant only to the first degree, with the exception of the number 2, whose cube may be included in the discriminant of the cubic region to the third degree and is nevertheless decomposable into prime ideals of the form $\mathfrak{M}^2\bar{\mathfrak{M}}$.

The factor λ in the equality

$$\Lambda = \lambda\Gamma^2$$

is determined only up to a unit of the maximal ring of the cubic region. However, factors λ differing by a square of a unit clearly determine the same lattice L under an appropriate choice of the square root in the equation $\gamma = \sqrt{\lambda}$. When extracting a root in the equation $\gamma = \sqrt{\lambda}$, we may obtain eight different values for λ corresponding to a given γ, since in the extraction of the square root of each of the coordinates we may take either of two values. However, these eight values determine only four different lattices L, since the factors $(\lambda, \lambda', \lambda'')$ and $(-\lambda, -\lambda', -\lambda'')$ clearly determine the same lattice L. These four lattices L will also be associated with the same quartic region, being only differently situated in four-dimensional space.

We also note that the six lattices L obtained one from the other with axial-superposition in three-dimensional space also correspond to the same quartic region, while being differently situated in space. Thus, if we wish to construct the lattice L for distinct quartic regions, we must stop at each value of the square root in the equation $\gamma = \sqrt{\lambda}$ and not take lattices L that may be obtained from each other by axial-superposition.

The lattice L may be actually constructed without turning to the space of all lattices of the basic figure of the cubic region, in a manner similar to what we did in the construction of the lattice L for cubic regions. In fact, let K be the class of ideals corresponding to the lattice Γ, and let Λ be an ideal of the class K^{-2} that has the desired form of decomposition into prime ideals. We take an ideal $\mathfrak{a}$ from the class K^{-1}. The lattice Γ will be similar to the lattice of the ideal $\mathfrak{a}$. The ideal Λ will be similar to the ideal $\mathfrak{a}^2$:

$$\Lambda = \mu \mathfrak{a}^2.$$

The coefficient of similarity μ is either an integer or a fraction in the cubic region and may actually be found. For this it is necessary to choose a factor μ that has a positive norm; this may always be arranged by multiplying if necessary by -1. The lattice L is found from the equation

$$L = \sqrt{\mu} \cdot \mathfrak{a}.$$

§51. THE CONSTRUCTION OF MAXIMAL QUARTIC LATTICES ON LATTICES L

We denote by $\mathfrak{M}$ the collection of all integer points of the region T whose projections form the lattice $4L$. This collection is a lattice consisting of points of the lattice $4L$ considered in four-dimensional coordinates and of points parallel to those points. A basis of this lattice is formed from the number 1 and the basis of the lattice $4L$ considered relative to the four-dimensional coordinate axes, and hence is easy to find. The maximal ring centers the lattice $\mathfrak{M}$ with an index 2^{α}, where $0 \leq \alpha \leq 6$. However, if we conduct a more careful analysis, we can narrow down the possibilities for the centering, namely by showing that $1 \leq \alpha \leq 4$. We now turn to this question.

We first show that the lattice $\mathfrak{M}$ is a ring. For this purpose we find necessary and sufficient conditions in order that the projection of a point satisfying the given equation $\omega^4 - f_1\omega^3 + f_2\omega^2 - f_3\omega + f_4 = 0$ belong to the lattice $4L$. Such a condition will obviously be the divisibility of all the coordinates of the square of the projection θ by 16.

We recall the equation that has θ as a root,

$$\theta^3 - (3f_1^2 - 8f_2)\theta^2 + (3f_1^4 - 16f_1^2f_2 + 16f_2^2 + 16f_1f_3 - 64f_4)\theta - (f_1^3 - 4f_1f_2 + 8f_3)^2 = 0.$$

Thus a necessary and sufficient condition is the satisfaction of the congruences

$$3f_1^2 - 8f_2 \equiv 0 \pmod{16},$$
$$3f_1^4 - 16f_1^2f_2 + 16f_2^2 + 16f_1f_3 - 64f_4 \equiv 0 \pmod{16^2},$$
$$f_1^3 - 4f_1f_2 + 8f_3 \equiv 0 \pmod{64}.$$

It follows from the first equation that

$$f_1 \equiv 0 \pmod 4; \quad f_2 \equiv 0 \pmod 2).$$

From the third we have

$$f_3 \equiv 0 \pmod 4.$$

Taking all this into consideration, we may rewrite the second and third equations in the form

$$\left(\frac{f_2}{2}\right)^2 \equiv f_4 \pmod 4,$$
$$\frac{f_1}{4} \cdot \frac{f_2}{2} \equiv \frac{f_3}{4} \pmod 2,$$

from which there follow the two possibilities:

A. $f_2 \equiv 0 \pmod 4$; then $f_4 \equiv 0 \pmod 4$; $f_3 \equiv 0 \pmod 8$.
B. $f_2 \equiv 2 \pmod 4$; then $f_4 \equiv 1 \pmod 4$; $f_3 \equiv f_1 \pmod 8$.

Thus a necessary and sufficient condition for ω to belong to the lattice $\mathfrak{M}$ is that one of the following systems of congruences is satisfied:

A)	B)
$f_1 \equiv 0 \pmod 4$,	$f_1 \equiv 0 \pmod 4$,
$f_2 \equiv 0 \pmod 4$,	$f_2 \equiv 2 \pmod 4$,
$f_3 \equiv 0 \pmod 8$,	$f_3 \equiv f_1 \pmod 8$,
$f_4 \equiv 0 \pmod 4$.	$f_4 \equiv 1 \pmod 4$.

Accordingly, all the points of the lattice $\mathfrak{M}$ are divided into two classes A and B, depending on which of the systems of congruences they satisfy.

Obviously, if ω belongs to the class A, then $\omega+1$ belongs to the class B and conversely.

It is easy to show that if ω belongs to the class A, then $\omega^2/2$ belongs to the lattice $\mathfrak{M}$.

In fact, let f_1', f_2', f_3' and f_4' be the coefficients of an equation that has $\omega^2/2$ as a root. They are connected with the coefficients f_1, f_2, f_3, and f_4 by the equations

$$f_1'=\frac{f_1^2-2f_2}{2}\equiv f_2 \quad (\text{mod } 8),$$

$$f_2'=\frac{f_2^2-2f_1f_3+2f_4}{4}\equiv\frac{f_4}{2} \quad (\text{mod } 4),$$

$$f_3'=\frac{f_3^2-2f_2f_4}{8}\equiv\frac{1}{4}f_2f_4 \quad (\text{mod } 8),$$

$$f_4'=\frac{1}{16}f_4^2.$$

It follows directly from this that if $f_4\equiv 4 \pmod 8$, then $\omega_1^2/2$ belongs to the class B, while if $f_4\equiv 0 \pmod 8$, then $\omega_1^2/2$ belongs to the class A, i.e., in both cases $\omega_1^2/2$ belongs to the lattice $\mathfrak{M}$.

It is easy to see that the points of the class A form a lattice.

In fact, let ω_1 and ω_2 be two points of the class A. Their difference must belong to the lattice $\mathfrak{M}$ and hence to one of the classes A or B. But $\omega_1-\omega_2$ can not belong to the class B, since $(\omega_1-\omega_2)^2/2=\omega_1^2/2+\omega_2^2/2-\omega_1\omega_2$ has integer coordinates, while half of a square of a point from the class B can not have integer coordinates.

Hence, the collection of points of the class A is subtractive, and is thus a lattice.

Now it is easy to show that the system $\mathfrak{M}$ is a ring, i.e., is multiplicative. It is sufficient to show that it is multiplicative for points of the class A, since

$$\omega_1\omega_2=(\omega_1+1)\,\omega_2-\omega_2=\omega_1\,(\omega_2+1)-\omega_1=(\omega_1+1)\,(\omega_2+1)-\omega_1-\omega_2-1,$$

while one of the points ω or $\omega+1$ must belong to the class A. But

$$\omega_1\omega_2=\frac{(\omega_1+\omega_2)^2}{2}-\frac{\omega_1^2}{2}-\frac{\omega_2^2}{2}.$$

If ω_1 and ω_2 belong to the class A, then $\omega_1+\omega_2$ also does. We already know that half of a square of any point from the class A belongs to the lattice $\mathfrak{M}$.

Thus $\omega_1\omega_2$ also belongs to the lattice $\mathfrak{M}$.

Thus we have shown that the lattice $\mathfrak{M}$ is a ring. It is easy to see that this ring can not be maximal. In fact, its sublattice A is an ideal of the ring $\mathfrak{M}$. The norm of this ideal is equal to 2, since $\mathfrak{M}$ centers A with an index of 2. On the other hand, the square of each point of the ideal A is divisible by 2. These two properties would be inconsistent if $\mathfrak{M}$ were a maximal ring.

Thus a maximal ring must center the ring $\mathfrak{M}$ with an index that is at least 2.

We consider now the projection of the maximal ring from a different standpoint. All points of the maximal ring are "parallel" to points lying in the "spaces"

$$\omega+\omega'+\omega''+\omega'''=0, \qquad \omega+\omega'+\omega''+\omega'''=1,$$
$$\omega+\omega'+\omega''+\omega'''=2 \quad \text{и} \quad \omega+\omega'+\omega''+\omega'''=3$$

(i.e., differ from these points by rational integer terms). Hence the projection of the maximal ring may be obtained as the result of superposing the projections of the points of these four "spaces." These projections obviously can not coincide with each other. Some of them may be empty, but the projections of nonempty systems of points lying in these spaces will be congruent. Consequently, the projection of the maximal ring may either coincide with the result of the superposition of the projections of the points of the spaces $\omega+\omega'+\omega''+\omega'''=0$ and $\omega+\omega'+\omega''+\omega'''=2$, or center it with an index of 2.

But it is easy to see that all the points of these two systems project into points of the lattice $2L$.

In fact the squares of the projections of such points will be divisible by 4. This may be seen from the expressions for the coefficients of the equation that has θ as a root:

$$\begin{aligned} &3f_1^2-8f_2 &&\equiv 0 \pmod 4,\\ &3f_1^4-16f_1^2f_2+16f_2^2+16f_1f_3-64f_4 &&\equiv 0 \pmod{16},\\ &f_1^3-4f_1f_2+8f_3 &&\equiv 0 \pmod 8,\end{aligned}$$

provided that $f_1 \equiv 0 \pmod 2$, which occurs for all points of the two spaces we are considering.

The lattice $2L$ centers the lattice $4L$ with an index of 8, and hence the projection of the maximal ring centers the lattice $4L$ with an index of at most 16. Accordingly, the maximal ring centers the ring $\mathfrak{M}$ with an index of at most 16.

Consequently, we have shown that the maximal ring centers the ring $\mathfrak{M}$ with an index of 2^α, where $1 \leq \alpha \leq 4$.

It is now easy to calculate the discriminant of the ring $\mathfrak{M}$ and of the maximal ring.

Let $[(\lambda_1, \lambda'_1, \lambda''_1), (\lambda_2, \lambda'_2, \lambda''_2), (\lambda_3, \lambda'_3, \lambda''_3)]$ be a basis of the lattice L. Then, as we have seen, the basis of the ring $\mathfrak{M}$ will be given by the points

$$(1,\ 1,\ 1,\ 1),$$
$$(\lambda_1+\lambda'_1+\lambda''_1,\ \lambda_1-\lambda'_1-\lambda''_1,\ -\lambda_1+\lambda'_1-\lambda''_1,\ -\lambda_1-\lambda'_1+\lambda''_1),$$
$$(\lambda_2+\lambda'_2+\lambda''_2,\ \lambda_2-\lambda'_2-\lambda''_2,\ -\lambda_2+\lambda'_2-\lambda''_2,\ -\lambda_2-\lambda'_2+\lambda''_2),$$
$$(\lambda_3+\lambda'_3+\lambda''_3,\ \lambda_3-\lambda'_3-\lambda''_3,\ -\lambda_3+\lambda'_3-\lambda''_3,\ -\lambda_3-\lambda'_3+\lambda''_3).$$

The discriminant of the ring $\mathfrak{M}$ is equal to

$$\Delta(\mathfrak{M}) = \begin{vmatrix} 1, & \lambda_1+\lambda'_1+\lambda''_1, & \lambda_2+\lambda'_2+\lambda''_2, & \lambda_3+\lambda'_3+\lambda''_3 \\ 1, & \lambda_1-\lambda'_1-\lambda''_1, & \lambda_2-\lambda'_2-\lambda''_2, & \lambda_3-\lambda'_3-\lambda''_3 \\ 1, & -\lambda_1+\lambda'_1-\lambda''_1, & -\lambda_2+\lambda'_2-\lambda''_2, & -\lambda_3+\lambda'_3-\lambda''_3 \\ 1, & -\lambda_1-\lambda'_1+\lambda''_1, & -\lambda_2-\lambda'_2+\lambda''_2, & -\lambda_3-\lambda'_3+\lambda''_3 \end{vmatrix}^2$$

$$= \begin{vmatrix} 1, & 1, & 1, & 1 \\ 1, & 1, & -1, & -1 \\ 1, & -1, & 1, & -1 \\ 1, & -1, & -1, & 1 \end{vmatrix}^2 \cdot \begin{vmatrix} 1 & 0 & 0 & 0 \\ 0 & \lambda_1 & \lambda_2 & \lambda_3 \\ 0 & \lambda'_1 & \lambda'_2 & \lambda'_3 \\ 0 & \lambda''_1 & \lambda''_2 & \lambda''_3 \end{vmatrix}^2$$

$$= 256\, D(L) = 256\, D \cdot (N(\gamma))^2 = 256\, Dk^2m^2,$$

where $[N(\gamma)]^2 = N(\Lambda) = k^2m^2$.

It follows from this that the discriminant of the maximal ring is equal to

$$\Delta = 4^{\alpha}Dk^2m^2 \quad 0 \le \alpha \le 3.$$

We deduce the following corollaries:

1. Δ is divisible by at most a cube of a prime that is not 2 or 3. The highest possible power of 3 in the discriminant Δ is 3^5, while the highest possible power of 2 in Δ is 2^{11}.

2. The discriminants of quartic regions that have a symmetric group as their Galois group grow no faster than the numbers of some arithmetic progression.

In fact, we have already proven the analogous theorem for cubic regions. On every cubic region one may construct a quartic region with a discriminant Δ that does not exceed $64\,|D|$ in absolute value, where D is the discriminant of the cubic region. For this it is sufficient to take a principal lattice for Γ, and a basic unit of the region for λ. In the following section we will see that a quartic region constructed in such a manner will have a symmetric group as its Galois group.

It is necessary to note that quartic regions may be of three signature types. For two of these the discriminant is positive, while for the third it is negative. In the construction of quartic regions on cubic regions of negative discriminants, we obtain quartic regions of negative discriminants, and hence of a definite signature type. In the construction of quartic regions on cubic regions of positive discriminants, we may obtain quartic regions of two signature types, and the method of construction used ensures the "slow" growth of the discriminant for both types connected together. By a simple change in argument, we can show that the discriminants of the quartic regions of each of the signature types also grow no faster than the numbers of some arithmetic progression.

§52. THE STRUCTURE OF A QUARTIC REGION AND OF THE CUBIC REGION UPON WHICH IT IS BASED AS DETERMINED BY THE GALOIS GROUP

Everything that was said in a previous section relates in an equal manner to reducible and irreducible quartic regions, and to the reducible and irreducible cubic regions upon which they are based. We now explain the peculiarities of the structure of the quartic regions and their projections which depend on their particular Galois group.

The Galois group of a quartic region may be any group of permutations on four elements. There may be 11 of these groups in all, if one does not consider as distinct those groups which go into each other under an appropriate change in the enumeration of the permuted elements, which in the given case are the coordinates of the points of the region. We will enumerate all these groups.

1. The symmetric group of permutations on four elements. We will denote this group by $\mathfrak{S}_4$. Its order is 24.

2. The collection of permutations that does not change the element u, while permuting in all possible ways the elements u', u'', and u'''. This group will be denoted by $\mathfrak{S}_3$. Its order is 6.

3. The alternating group of permutations on four elements. This group will be denoted by $\mathfrak{A}_4$. Its order is 12.

4. The group of permutations that does not change the element u, while *cyclicly* permuting u', u'', and u'''. This group will be denoted by $\mathfrak{A}_3$. Its order is 3.

5. The eighth order group of permutations formed by the permutations E (identity), (uu'), $(u''u''')$, $(uu')(u''u''')$, $(uu'')(u'u''')$, $(uu''')(u'u'')$, $(uu''u'u''')$, and $(uu'''u'u'')$. This group will be denoted by $\mathfrak{G}$.

6. The fourth order group formed by the permutations E, (uu'), $(u''u''')$, $(uu')(u''u''')$. We denote this by $\overline{\mathfrak{B}}$.

7. The second order group: E, (uu'). It is denoted by $\overline{Q}$.

8. The cyclic group formed by the permutations E, $(uu''u'u''')$, $(uu')(u''u''')$, and $(uu'''u'u'')$. We denote this by $\mathfrak{C}$.

9. The four-group $\overline{\mathfrak{B}}$, formed by the elements E, $(uu')(u''u''')$, $(uu'')(u'u''')$, and $(uu''')(u'u'')$.

10. The second order group Q of E and $(uu')(u''u''')$.

11. The identity group E, consisting of the identity permutation alone. Five of these groups $\mathfrak{S}_4$, $\mathfrak{A}$, $\mathfrak{G}$, $\mathfrak{C}$, and $\mathfrak{B}$, are transitive and correspond to an irreducible quartic region, while the remaining six, $\mathfrak{S}_3$, $\mathfrak{A}_3$, $\overline{\mathfrak{B}}$, $\overline{Q}$, and E, are intransitive and correspond to a reducible region.

We give a similar description of the regions corresponding to all these groups and we explain the properties of their projections.

1. $\mathfrak{S}_4$. The quartic region is irreducible and does not have subregions. The square of the projection belongs to a cubic region with a symmetric group, but the projection itself does not belong to a cubic region.

2. $\mathfrak{S}_3$. The quartic region is reducible and is the direct sum of a linear region and a cubic region with a symmetric group. The cubic region upon which the quartic region is based is the same as the cubic region that enters into the quartic region as a direct summand. Not only the square of the projection, but also the projection itself, belongs to this cubic region.

3. $\mathfrak{A}_4$. The quartic region is irreducible and does not have subregions. The square of its projection belongs to the cyclic cubic region, while the projection itself does not belong to the region.

4. $\mathfrak{A}_3$. The quartic region is reducible and is the direct sum of a linear region and a cyclic cubic region. The cubic region upon which it is based is identical with its "direct summand." Not only the square of the projection, but also the projection itself, belongs to this region.

5. $\mathfrak{G}$. The quartic region is irreducible and has a subregion that lies in the bisectrix $u = u'$; $u'' = u'''$. The cubic region upon which it is based is reducible

and is the direct sum of a linear region and an irreducible quadratic region. Accordingly, the projection is the direct sum of some linear form and a plane set of points. The linear form is a projection of the subregion parallel to the rational direction onto the line which is the linear intersection of the space of zero trace and the bisectrix on which the subregion lies. Therefore, it is representable in the form of the product of a generating square root of the subregion with the collection of all integer points. The plane collection included in the projection as a "direct summand" is the projection of the quartic region parallel to the subregion. The square of this projection is the quadratic region included as a direct summand in the cubic region upon which the quartic region is based. In this case this quadratic region is distinct from the subregion.

6. $\overline{\mathfrak{B}}$. The quartic region is reducible and decomposes into the direct sum of two different irreducible quadratic regions. It has a reducible quadratic "subregion" on the bisectrix $u = u'$; $u'' = u'''$.

The cubic region upon which the quartic region is based is reducible and is the direct sum of a linear region and an irreducible quadratic region. The projection is a direct sum of a linear set of rationals and the projection of the region parallel to the "subregion." The square of this projection belongs to the quadratic region included in the cubic region as a direct summand, but the projection itself parallel to the subregion does not belong to the above-mentioned quadratic region.

7. $\overline{Q}$. The quartic region is reducible and decomposes into the direct sum of two linear regions and one quadratic region. It contains the reducible quadratic "subregion" on the bisectrix $u = u'$; $u'' = u'''$. We may say the same thing about the projection as was said in the preceding case, with the single difference that the projection of the region parallel to the subregion belongs itself to the quadratic region included as a direct summand in the cubic region upon which the quadratic region is based.

8. $\mathfrak{C}$. The situation here is the same as for $\mathfrak{G}$ with the single difference that the quadratic region included as a direct summand in the cubic region upon which the quartic region is based is identical with the subregion of the latter.

9. $\mathfrak{B}$. The quartic region is irreducible and contains three quadratic subregions on the bisectrices $u = u'$, $u'' = u'''$; $u = u''$, $u' = u'''$; $u = u'''$, $u' = u''$.

The cubic region upon which the quartic region is based is reducible into three direct summands, so that the coordinates of all of the points of the square of the projection are rational. The coordinates of all the points of the projection itself are all irrational (if they are different from 0).

10. Q. The quartic region is reducible and decomposes into the direct sum of two identical quadratic regions. The cubic region upon which it is based decomposes into the direct sum of three linear regions. One coordinate of all of the points of the projection is rational, while the remaining two are irrational.

11. E. The region is reducible and decomposes into the direct sum of four linear regions. All the coordinates of all the points of the regions are rational.

The proofs of all these assertions are based on direct applications of the most elementary considerations of Galois theory to the individual cases.

We are most interested in the constructions of the irreducible regions (groups $\mathfrak{S}_4$, $\mathfrak{A}_4$, $\mathfrak{G}$, $\mathfrak{C}$, and $\mathfrak{B}$). We consider in more detail the construction of the lattice L for each of these cases.

1. $\mathfrak{S}_4$. For the construction of the lattice L for each case we must start from the cubic region with the symmetric group.

We choose in such a region some class of ideals K corresponding to the lattice Γ of the basic figure. We take an ideal $\mathfrak{a}$ in the class K^{-1}. Its lattice will be similar to the lattice Γ. We square the ideal $\mathfrak{a}$. We take an ideal Λ in the class K^{-2} that has the required form of decomposition into prime ideals, and we find the coefficient of similarity of the ideals $\mathfrak{a}^2$ and Λ:

$$\Lambda = \mu \mathfrak{a}^2.$$

For this, we choose a coefficient having a positive norm. The lattice L is obtained by the formula

$$L = \sqrt{\mu} \cdot \mathfrak{a}.$$

The choice of sign in the extraction of the root is immaterial. For a definite class K and a specific choice for the ideal Λ, we may obtain two different lattices L when $D < 0$ because the coefficient μ may be multiplied by the fundamental unit, and we may obtain four lattices L when $D > 0$ because of the multiplication of μ by the units ϵ_1, ϵ_2, and $\epsilon_1\epsilon_2$, where ϵ_1 and ϵ_2 are fundamental units.

When K is the principal class and $\Lambda = [1]$, and only in this case, one of the lattices L will correspond to an irreducible region with a group γ_3. Namely, in this case it is possible to take $\mathfrak{a} = [1]$ and when $\mu = 1$ we obtain such a lattice L. If we take $\mu = \epsilon$ where ϵ is one of the fundamental units, we obtain a lattice L for an irreducible region.

2. $\mathfrak{A}_4$. We start from the cyclic cubic region. We may construct the lattice L for quartic regions with the group $\mathfrak{A}_4$ by the same means as for $\mathfrak{S}_4$. However,

However, as a result of the fact that the cyclic cubic region goes into itself under cyclic axial-superposition, we will obtain, after looking over all possible classes K and ideals Λ, three lattices L corresponding to the same quartic regions, but differently situated in four-dimensional space. We will analyze in more detail how to avoid this in the particular cases that can arise here.

α) $K \neq K'$ (we denote by K' the class consisting of the ideals conjugate with the ideals of the class K).

In this case we must take only one of the three classes K, K', and K'' in the construction of the lattices L but must, however, take all possible ideals Λ and transition coefficients μ, including also the conjugates (in case such conjugates belong to one class).

β) $K = K' = K''$; $\Lambda \neq [1]$.

It is easy to see that in this case $\Lambda \neq \Lambda'$, but Λ is equivalent to Λ' and Λ''. It is necessary to select only one of the three ideals Λ, Λ', and Λ'', using, however, all four possible transition coefficients μ.

γ) $K = K' = K''$; $\Lambda = [1]$.

This is possible only when $K = K_0$ is the principal class, since, on the one hand, $K^{-2} = K_0$, since to the class K^{-2} belongs the principal ideal Λ, and, on the other hand, $K^3 = KK'K'' = K_0$.

In this case it is possible to take $\mathfrak{a} = [1]$.

The transition coefficients may be $\mu = 1$, $\mu = \epsilon_1$, $\mu = \epsilon_2$, and $\mu = \epsilon_1\epsilon_2$, where ϵ_1 and ϵ_2 are a pair of fundamental units of the region, and $\mu = 1$ defines a reducible region with the group $\mathfrak{A}_3$, and $\mu = \epsilon_1$, ϵ_2 and $\epsilon_1\epsilon_2$ give lattices L that correspond to the same quartic region. This follows from the fact that in a suitable manner we may take for fundamental units of the cyclic region the units ϵ and ϵ' which were chosen to be conjugate. Then also $\epsilon_1\epsilon_2 = \epsilon''(\epsilon'')^{-2}$ differs from the third conjugate number by a factor equal to the square of a unit.

We also note one peculiarity of the decomposition of the ideal Λ into prime ideals. In a cyclic maximal ring we can not have second degree ideals or divisors of the discriminant having a decomposition $\mathfrak{m}^2\overline{\mathfrak{m}}$. First degree prime ideals dividing the same number are conjugate to each other. Hence $\Lambda = \mathfrak{p}_1\mathfrak{p}_1'\mathfrak{p}_2\mathfrak{p}_2'\cdots$.

3. $\mathfrak{G}$ and $\mathfrak{C}$. It is necessary to base both these cases on the reducible cubic region that decomposes into the direct sum of a linear region and a quadratic region,

$$U = U_1 \oplus U_2.$$

We consider in more detail the form of the ideal Λ

$$\Lambda = \mathfrak{p}_1\bar{\mathfrak{p}}_1\mathfrak{p}_2\bar{\mathfrak{p}}_2 \ldots \; \mathfrak{q}_1\mathfrak{q}_2 \ldots \; \mathfrak{m}_1\bar{\mathfrak{m}}_1\mathfrak{m}_2\bar{\mathfrak{m}}_2 \ldots .$$

In the reducible region the second degree ideals are of the form $[1] \oplus [p]$, where p is an irreducible prime in the quadratic region U_2. The first degree ideals, denoted by $\mathfrak{p}$, may be of two kinds,

$$[p] \oplus [1] \text{ and } [1] \oplus [\pi],$$

where π is a first degree prime ideal of the quadratic region U_2. One of the first degree ideals of the first kind and two of the second kind are contained in a prime that decomposes in the cubic region U into three distinct prime ideals. Thus the products $\mathfrak{p}\bar{\mathfrak{p}}$ that are contained in the ideal Λ may be of two kinds. Namely, some of them may have the form $[p] \oplus [\pi]$, while others have the form $[1] \oplus [\pi\pi'] = [1] \oplus [p]$.

The ideals $\mathfrak{m}$ have the form $[q] \oplus [1]$ and $[1] \oplus \mu$, where $[q] = \mu^2$ is a prime divisor of the discriminant of the region U_2. The products $\mathfrak{m}\bar{\mathfrak{m}}$ have the form $[q] \oplus \mu$. Considering all that has been said, we obtain

$$\Lambda = [k_1 m] \oplus k_2 \mathfrak{l},$$

where $\mathfrak{l}$ is an ideal of the quadratic region U_2 that has a norm of $k_1 m$, while k_1 and k_2 are relatively prime to each other and to the discriminant of U_2, and m divides the discriminant. None of the three numbers m, k_1, or k_2 is divisible by any square of a prime.

It is easy to see that the ideal $\mathfrak{l}$ must belong to the class K^{-2}, which is equal to the square of some other class K^{-1}. This is necessary for such a condition to be realized for the ideal Λ.

Let $\mathfrak{l} = \gamma\mathfrak{a}^2$, where $\mathfrak{a}$ is some ideal from the class K^{-1} and γ is the transition coefficient. Then

$$\Lambda = \lambda([1] \oplus \mathfrak{a})^2,$$

where

$$\lambda = \pm k_1 m \oplus k_2 \gamma.$$

In order for the "three-dimensional" norm of the factor γ to be positive, it is necessary to choose the sign in the first component of the factor γ to be the same as the sign of the norm of λ in this calculation. $\sqrt{\pm k_1 m}$ is a generating number of the subregion of the constructed quartic region. It follows from this that in our construction we may obtain reducible regions only when $\mathfrak{l} = [1]$ and $N(\gamma) > 0$, and cyclic regions only when $\mathfrak{l} = [\sqrt{b}\,]$ and $bN(\gamma) > 0$, where b is a generating number of the quadratic region U_2. In the remaining cases we will obtain regions with the group $\mathfrak{G}$.

For a given class K and a given ideal $\mathfrak{l}$, we may still obtain distinct lattices L because of the adjoining of units to the factor γ. If the discriminant of the region U_2 is negative, it is possible to construct two distinct lattices L, using the factors γ and $-\gamma$ (γ and $i\gamma$ for $D = -4$). If the discriminant of the region U_2 is positive, it is possible to construct four distinct lattices L, using the factors $\pm\gamma$ and $\pm\gamma\epsilon_0$, where ϵ_0 is a fundamental unit of the region.

In the majority of cases, for these values, lattices L for distinct quartic regions will be obtained. However, some cases are exceptions, and we list now all those cases that may arise here.

1. $K \neq K'$. In the construction of lattices for distinct quartic regions, it is sufficient to choose one from the two classes K and K', while it is necessary to take all possible ideals $\mathfrak{l}$ and all transition coefficients.

2. $K = K'$, $\mathfrak{l} \neq \mathfrak{l}'$. It is sufficient to choose one of the two ideals $\mathfrak{l}$ and $\mathfrak{l}'$, but it is necessary to take all of the transition factors.

3. $K = K'$, $\mathfrak{l} = \mathfrak{l}'$. This case is the most complicated.

In this case, as in the preceding one, the ideal $\mathfrak{l}$ can only be a principal ideal:

$$\mathfrak{l} = \lambda \cdot [1].$$

Since $\mathfrak{l} = \mathfrak{l}'$, the numbers λ and λ' must be associated. The ideal $\mathfrak{l}$ must be a divisor of the discriminant. The square of the ideal $\mathfrak{l}$ is a principal ideal constructed on a rational integer. If the discriminant of the region U_2 is negative or if the fundamental unit of the region has a negative norm, λ may be either 1 or $\sqrt{b}$. If the discriminant is positive and the norm of the fundamental unit is positive, there are two more possibilities. For these possibilities $\lambda' = \pm\epsilon_0\lambda$ (for one case the plus sign, for the other the minus).

Let $\mathfrak{a}$ be some ideal of the class K^{-1}. Then $\mathfrak{a}^2 = \alpha[1]$, since $\mathfrak{a}^2$ is the principal ideal.

Let us denote the norm of $\mathfrak{a}$ by a. Then $N(\alpha) = \pm a^2$ and $\mathfrak{a}' = (a/\alpha)\,\mathfrak{a}$. From this it follows that

$$\mathfrak{l} = \frac{\lambda}{\alpha}\,\mathfrak{a}^2.$$

We denote by L_1 the lattice $\sqrt{(\lambda/\alpha)}\,\mathfrak{a}$. If L_1 and L_1' are conjugate lattices, then the lattices L corresponding to them are also conjugate. But

$$L_1' = \sqrt{\frac{\lambda'}{a'}}\,\mathfrak{u}' = \sqrt{\frac{\lambda'}{a'}\cdot\frac{a^2}{a^2}}\,\mathfrak{u} = \sqrt{\frac{\lambda'}{\lambda}}\sqrt{\pm\frac{\lambda}{a}}\,\mathfrak{a} = \sqrt{\pm\frac{\lambda'}{\lambda}}\,L_1.$$

The $\pm$ signs under the roots are in accordance with the sign of the norm of α.

If $\lambda = 1$ and $N(\alpha) = +a^2$, then $L_1' = L_1$, but in this case the corresponding quartic region is reducible, and this case does not interest us.

If $\lambda = 1$ and $N(\alpha) = -a^2$, then $L_1' = L_1 \cdot \sqrt{-1}$; this means that the adjoining of the factor -1 to α changes the lattice L, but takes it into a conjugate, and hence into a lattice corresponding to the same quartic region.

If $\lambda = \sqrt{b}$ and $N(\alpha) = +a^2$, then $L_1' = L_1\sqrt{-1}$, and the same statements hold as in the preceding case.

If $\lambda = \sqrt{b}$ and $N(\alpha) = -a^2$, then the quartic region has as its group the group $\mathfrak{C}$.

The lattices L and L' are in this case the same; hence the adjoining of -1 to the factor α changes the lattice L and also the quartic region corresponding to it.

Finally, if $\lambda' = \epsilon_0\lambda$, then, depending on the sign of $N(\alpha)$, the adjoining of the units $+\epsilon_0$ or $-\epsilon_0$ to the factor α does not change the quartic region.

Thus we have given a method for constructing the lattices L and in this case we have completely explored the question of how lattices L are obtained corresponding to distinct quartic regions.

We note that quartic regions with cyclic groups can not be constructed on all reducible cubic regions. We saw that in order to construct a quartic region with a cyclic group on a reducible cubic region, it was necessary and sufficient for the quadratic constituent of the cubic region to contain a number with a negative norm, so that the principal ideal $[\alpha]$ would be equal to the square of another ideal.

Such a number may exist only in quadratic regions of positive discriminant, whose generating number is the sum of two squares.

4. $\mathfrak{B}$. These regions are based on a cubic region that is reducible into three linear regions.

It is easy to see that the ideal Λ is of the form

$$\Lambda = [k_1] \oplus [k_2] \oplus [k_3] = (k_1,\ k_2,\ k_3), \qquad [1]$$

where the integers k_1, k_2 and k_3 are not divisible by a square of any prime, and whose product is a perfect square. On adjoining the four units of positive norm $(1, 1, 1), (1, -1, -1), (-1, 1, -1)$, and $(-1, -1, 1)$ to the transition factor (k_1, k_2, k_3), different quartic regions are defined if none of the numbers k_1, k_2, or k_3 is equal to the identity. If $k_1 = 1$, then $k_2 = k_3$. The factors $(1, k_2, k_2)$ and $(1, -k_2, -k_2)$ define reducible regions, while the factors $(-1, k_2, -k_2)$ and $(-1, -k_2, k_2)$ define the same region with the group but differently situated.

§53. ANOTHER METHOD OF CONSTRUCTION OF QUARTIC REGIONS WITH THE GROUPS 𝔊, ℭ AND 𝔅

Besides the method of construction of quartic region with the groups 𝔊, ℭ and 𝔅 that was described in the end of the preceding section, it is possible to indicate another simpler and more convenient method.

We note that the previous method was based in essence on the projection of the region parallel to the subregion, for all the calculation that we carried out took place in the quadratic component of the reducible cubic region; the first component played no role. The second method, with which we would now like to concern ourselves, is also based on the projection of the region parallel to the subregion.

We first assume for simplicity that the quartic region is purely real. The coordinates of the projection of the point (u, u', u'', u''') parallel to the subregion $u = u'$, $u'' = u'''$ are equal, as we saw earlier, to the numbers $u - u' + u'' - u'''$ and $u - u' - u'' + u'''$ for an appropriate choice of coordinate axes. We rotate the coordinate axes in the projection by an angle of 45° and change the scale by a factor of $\sqrt{2}$. We obtain for the projection of the point (u, u', u'', u''') the coordinates $\eta = u - u'$; $\bar{\eta} = u'' - u'''$.

In this section we will call the point with coordinates $\eta, \bar{\eta}$ the projection of the point (u, u', u'', u''') parallel to the subregion.

Clearly, under permutations of the group 𝔊 the projection undergoes the transformations

$$\begin{matrix} \underline{\eta} \to \eta \\ \eta \to \underline{\eta} \end{matrix}; \quad \begin{matrix} \underline{\eta} \to -\underline{\eta} \\ \eta \to \underline{\eta} \end{matrix}; \quad \begin{matrix} \underline{\eta} \to \eta \\ \eta \to -\underline{\eta} \end{matrix}; \quad \begin{matrix} \underline{\eta} \to -\underline{\eta} \\ \eta \to -\underline{\eta} \end{matrix};$$

$$\begin{matrix} \underline{\eta} \to \eta \\ \eta \to \eta \end{matrix}; \quad \begin{matrix} \underline{\eta} \to \eta \\ \eta \to -\eta \end{matrix}; \quad \begin{matrix} \underline{\eta} \to -\eta \\ \eta \to \eta \end{matrix}; \quad \begin{matrix} \underline{\eta} \to -\eta \\ \eta \to -\eta \end{matrix}.$$

Permutations of the group 𝔅 induce the transformations

$$\begin{matrix} \underline{\eta} \to \underline{\eta} \\ \eta \to \eta \end{matrix}; \quad \begin{matrix} \underline{\eta} \to -\eta \\ \eta \to -\eta \end{matrix}; \quad \begin{matrix} \underline{\bar{\eta}} \to \underline{\bar{\eta}} \\ \eta \to \eta \end{matrix}; \quad \begin{matrix} \underline{\eta} \to -\bar{\eta} \\ \eta \to -\eta \end{matrix}.$$

Permutations of the group $\mathfrak{C}$ induce the transformations

$$\frac{\eta \to \eta}{\bar\eta \to \bar\eta}; \quad \frac{\eta \to \bar\eta}{\bar\eta \to -\eta}; \quad \frac{\eta \to -\eta}{\bar\eta \to -\bar\eta}; \quad \frac{\eta \to -\bar\eta}{\bar\eta \to -\eta}.$$

From this it follows easily that the square of the projection $(\theta, \bar\theta)$ belongs to some quadratic region, namely to a subregion of the quartic region T.

When the Galois group is equal to $\mathfrak{B}$, then $\eta\bar\eta$ is rational.

If the Galois group is equal to $\mathfrak{C}$, then $\eta\bar\eta$, as well as $\eta^2 - \bar\eta^2$, changes signs under permutations of the group, from which it follows that $\eta\bar\eta = \sqrt{b} \cdot r$, where b is a generating number of the quadratic region and r is a rational.

Further, it is obvious that the ratio of the projections of two distinct points of the same region is transposed under permutations of the Galois group in the same way as the coordinates of the squares of the projections, from which it follows that such a ratio belongs to the subregion. Conversely, if η is a projection of a quartic number and α is a number of a subregion, then $\eta\alpha$ is again a projection of a quartic number of the same region.

We will project a quartic maximal ring. In the projection we will obtain a plane lattice of points, each of which has algebraic integer coordinates. We introduce the lattice L, namely the set of all points rationally related to the projection of the maximal ring and having algebraic integer coordinates. The lattice L contains the projection of the maximal ring, which in turn contains the lattice $2L$. In fact, the point $(\eta, \bar\eta)$ has four-dimensional coordinates ω, ω', ω'', and ω''', which are found from the equations

$$\omega - \omega' = \eta, \quad \omega'' - \omega''' = \bar\eta,$$
$$\omega + \omega' = 0, \quad \omega'' + \omega''' = 0,$$

from which we get $\omega = \frac{1}{2}\eta$, $\omega' = -\frac{1}{2}\eta$, $\omega'' = \frac{1}{2}\bar\eta$, and $\omega''' = -\frac{1}{2}\bar\eta$.

If $(\eta, \bar\eta)$ belongs to the lattice $2L$, then with respect to four-dimensional axes it has algebraic integer coordinates ω, ω', ω'', ω''', and hence belongs to the maximal ring. The lattice L is similar to one of the lattices of the basic figure of the maximal ring of the quadratic region, since it is multiplicative for all points of the maximal ring:

$$L = \gamma\Gamma.$$

The lattice $\Lambda = L^2$ is an ideal of the quadratic region that is not divisible by any square of a prime ideal, and which belongs to a class of ideals that is the square of some other class.

The decomposition of the ideal Λ into prime ideals gives

$$\Lambda = \mathfrak{p}_1\mathfrak{p}_2 \cdots \mathfrak{q}_1\mathfrak{q}_2 \cdots \mathfrak{m}_1\mathfrak{m}_2 \cdots = k_1 \mathfrak{l},$$

where k_1 is a rational integer that is relatively prime to the discriminant of the quadratic region, and which is not divisible by the square of any prime; the ideal $\mathfrak{l}$ has a norm that is relatively prime to k_1 and is not divisible by the square of any prime.

In the following, the ideal $\mathfrak{l}$ is completely arbitrary.

Given the ideal Λ and the class K corresponding to the lattice Γ which is similar to the lattice L, it is easy to construct the lattice L. We take an arbitrary ideal $\mathfrak{a}$ belonging to the class K^{-1}. The lattice of the ideal $\mathfrak{a}$ will be similar to the lattice Γ. Then we find the factor μ in the equation

$$\Lambda = \mu\mathfrak{a}^2.$$

Such a factor exists, since the ideal Λ is equivalent to the ideal $\mathfrak{a}^2$. Then the lattice L is defined by the formula

$$L = \sqrt{\mu} \cdot \mathfrak{a}.$$

The choice of the signs in the extractions of roots of μ is immaterial.

The lattice L for a reducible quartic region will be obtainable if and only if $\sqrt{\mu}$ belongs to the quadratic region. This is possible only when K is the principal class and $\Lambda = [1]$. In this case it is possible to take $\mathfrak{a} = [1]$. If we take $\mu = 1$, then we obtain the lattice L for a reducible region. If we take $\mu = -1$ or $\mu = +\epsilon_0$, where ϵ_0 is a fundamental unit of the region, then we obtain a lattice L for an irreducible region.

We will obtain a region with a group $\mathfrak{B}$ if and only if $\Lambda = [k]$ and $N(\mu) > 0$. We will obtain a region with a group $\mathfrak{C}$ if and only if $\Lambda = [k\sqrt{b}]$ and $N(\mu) > 0$. In this method, the effect of adjoining units to the factor μ is completely analogous to that in the preceding method, and therefore we will not enumerate here the various possible cases.

The constructions of the maximal quartic ring on the lattice L are made simpler by this method as a result of the fact that its projection can center the lattice $2L$ only with indices 1, 2, or 4, so that fewer trials are needed in the search for a basis of the maximal ring.

We denote by $\mathfrak{M}$ the collection of all points of a maximal ring projected into the lattice $2L$. It is possible to prove that the lattice $\mathfrak{M}$ is a ring.

The discriminant of the ring $\mathfrak{M}$ is equal to

$$16d^2l,$$

where d is the discriminant of the quadratic region, $l = N(\Lambda)$, and where l is chosen with the sign of the norm of the factor μ in the equation $\Lambda = \mu\alpha^2$.

Hence the discriminant of the maximal ring is equal to $16d^2l$, $4d^2l$ or d^2l.

In conclusion we examine some examples.

EXAMPLE 1. To construct quartic regions over $R(\rho)$, where ρ is given by the equation $\rho^3 + \rho - 1 = 0$.

The given cubic region is a region with a symmetric group; the discriminant of its maximal ring is -31; the number of classes of ideals is 1; the basis of the maximal ring is formed by the numbers $1, \rho, \rho^2$; and the fundamental unit is ρ. The smallest prime numbers have the following decompositions: 2 is a prime, $3 = \mathfrak{p}_3\mathfrak{q}_3 = (\rho + 1)(\rho^2 - \rho + 2)$, 5 is a prime, 7 is a prime.

We construct quartic regions, starting with $\Lambda = [1]$ and $\Lambda = \mathfrak{q}_3 = [\rho^2 - \rho + 2]$. In the first case it is possible to take $\mu = \epsilon_0 = \rho$ in the equation

$$\Lambda = \mu[1]^2.$$

In the second case it is possible, in the equation $\Lambda = \mu[1]^2$, to take

$$\mu = \rho^2 - \rho + 2 \text{ and } \mu = -\rho^2 + \rho + 1.$$

For the first case a basis of the ring $\mathfrak{M}$ will be

$$1, \quad \omega_1, \quad \frac{\omega_1^2}{2}, \quad \frac{\omega_1^3}{2},$$

where ω_1 is a root of the equation

$$\omega_1^4 - 8\omega_1 - 4 = 0.$$

A basis of the maximal ring will be

$$1, \quad \omega_1, \quad \frac{\omega_1^2}{2}, \quad \frac{\omega_1^3}{4} + \frac{\omega_1}{2}.$$

The discriminant of the maximal ring is $-64 \cdot 31$.

For the remaining cases the maximal rings will consist of two rings with bases

$$1, \omega, \frac{\omega^2}{2}, \quad \frac{\omega^3}{4} + \frac{\omega}{2}, \text{where } \omega^4 - 8\omega^2 - 24\omega - 20 = 0,$$

$$1, \omega, \frac{\omega^2}{2}, \quad \frac{\omega^3}{4}, \text{where } \omega^4 + 4\omega^3 - 4\omega^2 - 40\omega - 56 = 0.$$

The discriminant is in both cases equal to $-64 \cdot 9 \cdot 31$.

EXAMPLE 2. To construct cyclic quartic regions over $R(\sqrt{5})$.

We turn to the second method of construction. The ideal Λ must have the form $\Lambda = k[\sqrt{5}]$, where k is any rational integer relatively prime to 5. There exists only one class of ideals in the region $R(\sqrt{5})$, namely the principal class. The basic unit of the region, $\epsilon = (1+\sqrt{5})/2$, has a negative norm. The transition coefficient in the equation

$$\Lambda = \mu[1]$$

may be chosen with positive norm, and hence equal to $\pm k\epsilon\sqrt{5} = k_1\epsilon\sqrt{5}$, where k_1 may be positive or negative.

The maximal ring has a basis

$$1, \ \varepsilon, \ \sqrt{k_1\varepsilon\sqrt{5}}, \qquad \varepsilon\sqrt{k_1\varepsilon\sqrt{5}}, \qquad \text{if } k_1 \not\equiv 3 \pmod 4,$$

and its discriminant is equal to $16\cdot 5^3\cdot k_1^2$.

The maximal ring has a basis

$$1, \ \varepsilon, \ \frac{\sqrt{k_1\varepsilon\sqrt{5}}+1+\varepsilon}{2}, \qquad \frac{\varepsilon\sqrt{\sqrt{5}\,\varepsilon k_1}+1}{2}, \qquad \text{if } k_1 \equiv 3 \pmod 4$$

and its discriminant is equal to $5^3\cdot k_1^2$.

CHAPTER IV

THE ALGORITHM OF VORONOǏ

PART A. THE CASE $D > 0$

§54. CHAINS OF RELATIVE MINIMA

We saw in Chapter I that the location of the so-called relative minima of lattices plays an important role in certain questions related to the theory of multiplicative lattices. By a relative minimum we understand a point whose normed body (constructed on the point) contains no point of the lattice other than the origin of coordinates, neither within the body nor on its boundary. In this chapter we will finish discussing the question of the determination of chains of relative minima for the case $n = 3$, and we will give methods for the practical solution of the problem of similarity of two lattices and of the problem of multiplicative automorphisms of lattices. The methods given here differ only slightly from the way this was done by G. F. Voronoǐ in his doctoral dissertation. Here, of course, it is necessary for us to consider separately the cases of real and complex lattices. We begin with the first, more complicated, case of a real lattice, and limit our considerations to lattices that do not contain zero divisors.

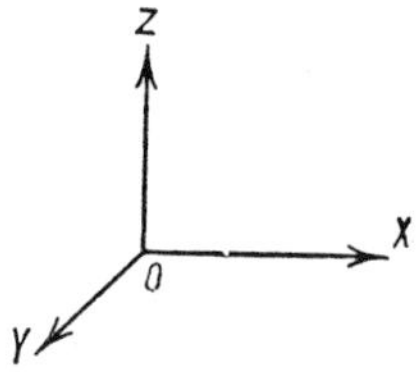

Figure 10

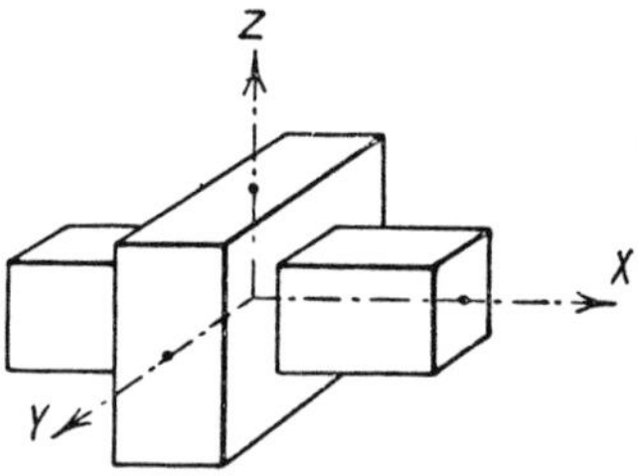

Figure 11

In this case a normed body constructed on a point has the form of a rectangular parallelepiped with center at the origin and with faces parallel to the coordinate planes. The given point is located at one of the vertices of the normed parallelepiped. A relative minimum is in this case a point whose normed body is devoid inside and on its boundary of points of the lattice (other than the point O). By a relative minimum we will often mean not only the point of the lattice, but also the normed parallelepiped constructed on it.

In the future we will often have to compare such parallelepipeds, and to facilitate the presentation we introduce some terminology. We will characterize by the words "longer" and "shorter," "wider" and "narrower," "higher" and "lower," the results of comparison of parallepipeds in the directions corresponding to the axes OX, OY, and OZ, respectively, the arrangement of these axes being as shown in Figure 10.

Two given normed parallelepipeds may be situated with respect to each other in two essentially different ways, namely, their surfaces may or may not intersect. In the first case one parallelepiped is included within the other. In the second case, one of the parallelepipeds will have one dimension greater and two dimensions smaller than in the second parallelepiped. In this case we will say that the first parallelepiped pierces the second, while the second overlaps the first. When necessary we will indicate the direction of the piercing or the overlapping. Thus, in Figure 11, the parallelepiped Ω pierces the parallelepiped T in the direction OX, while the parallelepiped T overlaps the parallelepiped Ω in the direction OX.

The relative minimum adjacent on OX to a given relative minimum Ω we will call the shortest relative minimum piercing the relative minimum Ω on OX. The construction of a relative minimum adjacent on OX to a given relative minimum Ω may be realized in the following way (Figure 12). Having constructed the normed body parallelepiped on Ω, we will translate its right face $AA'\,A''\,A'''$, by moving its center in the positive direction of OX and leaving it parallel to the YOZ-plane. The first point of the lattice that is met by the face in this movement will obviously be a relative minimum, since the normed parallelepiped constructed on it will be contained within the empty parallelepiped $BB'\,B''\,B'''\,\alpha\alpha'\,\alpha''\alpha'''$, and this will be a relative minimum adjacent with Ω on OX.

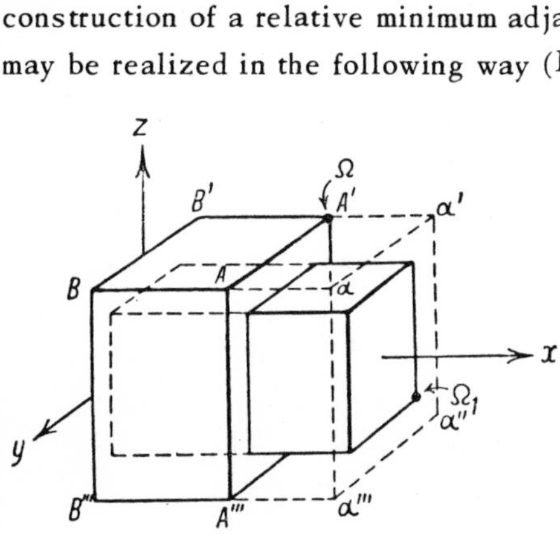

Figure 12

That the face $AA'A''\,A'''$ must meet a point of the lattice, follows directly from the theorem of Minkowski about the volume of an empty, centrally symmetric, convex body. Thus, for a given relative minimum

Ω there exists a relative minimum Ω_1 adjacent to it on OX. For Ω_1 in turn there exists a relative minimum Ω adjacent to it on OX, and so on.

The sequence of relative minima $\Omega, \Omega_1, \Omega_2, \cdots$, in which each successive minimum is adjacent on OX to the preceding one, will be called a chain of relative minima on OX or, more briefly, an x-chain generated by the point Ω. We will denote the x- chain generated by the point Ω by $\{\Omega\}_x$.

Analogously to the concept of a relative minimum adjacent on OX, we introduce the concepts of relative minima adjacent on OY and on OZ. A y-chain may be formed from relative minima adjacent on OY, and a z-chain from those adjacent on OZ. The concepts of relative minima and of chains of relative minima introduced here naturally generalizes these concepts for plane lattices. (Cf., for example, the article on the geometry of quadratic forms in Supplement I of the present volume.) However, in our case there is one essential difference from the case of plane lattices. For a plane lattice each relative minimum is adjacent to some other relative minimum on OX. As a result, a chain of relative minima may be infinitely extended in both directions. In the spatial case, a given relative minimum may be adjacent to a number of distant relative minima on OX, or may be adjacent to none on OX.

We verify this with examples.

Let the coordinate parallelepipeds of the three points A, B, and Γ belonging to some lattice be situated so that the parallelepiped of A pierces the parallelepipeds of B and Γ on OX, which in turn do not pierce each other on OX; also, the coordinate parallelepiped that is bound by the faces of the parallelepipeds A, B, and Γ that are furthest from the coordinate planes contains within itself no points of the lattice (other than the origin). Then A, B, and Γ are obviously relative minima of the lattice, and A is simultaneously adjacent on OX with the relative minima B and Γ (Figure 13). If the parallelepipeds B and Γ pierce the parallelepiped A in the directions OY and OZ and the coordinate parallelepiped bound by the faces of the parallelepipeds A, B, and Γ that are furthest from the coordinate planes contains no points of the lattice, then obviously A, being a relative minimum, cannot be adjacent on OX to either of the relative minima (Figure 14).

In fact, assume that A is adjacent on OX with some relative minimum Ω.

The following three possibilities present themselves.

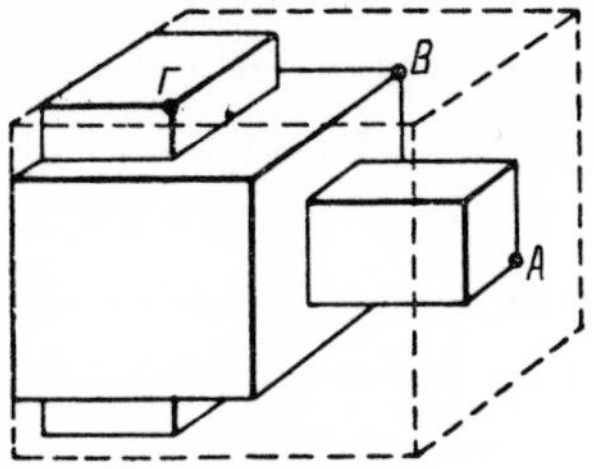

Figure 13

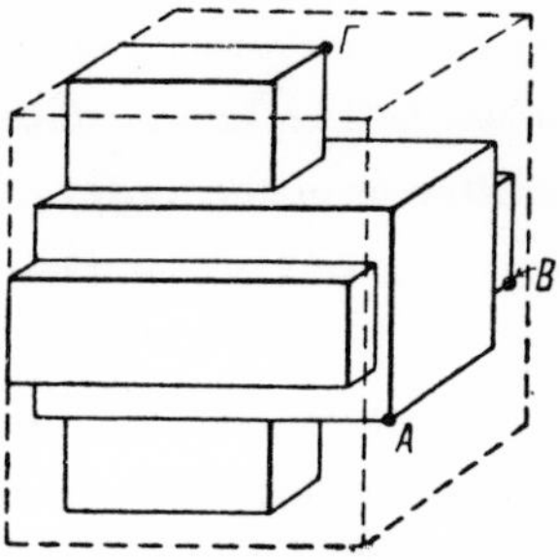

Figure 14

1. Ω is higher than Γ. Moreover, Ω is wider than Γ, since Ω is wider than A and A is wider than Γ. Hence, Ω must be shorter than Γ, for otherwise Ω would not be a relative minimum. But then A could be adjacent with Ω on OX, since the right face of Ω in its movement to the right would meet the point Γ before the point A. Consequently, this possibility is eliminated.

2. Ω is wider than B. This is eliminated, analogously to the preceding possibility.

3. Ω is lower than Γ and narrower than B. This is impossible, since Ω is also shorter than A. In this case the whole parallelepiped would be included within the parallelepiped bounded by the faces of the parallelepipeds A, B, and Γ that are furthest from the coordinate planes, but by assumption this parallelepiped contains no points of the lattice within itself.

We will show that it is in fact possible to choose points satisfying the requirements of both examples.

We take points with coordinates $A(1, \alpha, -\beta)$, $B(-\gamma, 1, \delta)$ and $\Gamma(\epsilon, -\theta, 1)$. Here α, β, γ, δ, ϵ, and θ denote positive numbers less than unity.

We take the points A, B, and Γ for a basis of the lattice and show under what conditions the unit cube, which in the given case will be the parallelepiped bounded by the faces of the parallelepipeds A, B, and Γ that are furthest from the origin, may contain points of the lattice within itself.

The coordinates of any point of the lattice may be obtained from the formulas

$$\begin{aligned} \xi &= u - \gamma v + \varepsilon w, \\ \eta &= \alpha u + v - \theta w, \\ \zeta &= -\beta u + \delta v + w \end{aligned}$$

for integers u, v, and w.

We first note that $u \neq 0$. In fact, if $u = 0$, then either $|\eta| = |v - \theta w|$ or $|\zeta| = |\delta v + w|$ will be greater than unity, depending on whether the signs of v and w are different or the same. For the same reason $v \neq 0$ and $w \neq 0$.

Further, u, v, and w must have the same signs, for otherwise either $|\xi| = |u - \gamma v + \epsilon w|$, $|\eta| = |\alpha u + v - \theta w|$, or $|\zeta| = |-\beta u + \delta v + w|$ will be larger than unity. Without loss of generality we may assume that u, v, and w are positive. Then it follows from the inequality $u - \gamma v + \epsilon w < 1$ that $\gamma v > u - 1$ and hence, $v \geq u$ for $\gamma < 1$.

In the same manner, the inequalities $w \geq v$ and $u \geq w$ must hold. It follows then that $u = v = w$. If for some value of $u = v = w$ a point of the lattice falls within the unit cube, then the point obtained for $u = v = w = 1$ also falls within the unit cube. But this is clearly possible only when

$$\gamma > \epsilon, \quad \theta > \alpha, \quad \beta > \delta.$$

If even one of these inequalities is not satisfied, the unit cube will not contain within itself any point of the lattice constructed on A, B, and Γ other than the origin.

Taking $\delta > \beta$ and $\theta > \alpha$, we obtain points A, B, and Γ satisfying all the requirements of the first example. In fact, the parallelepiped A will pierce the parallelepipeds B and Γ on OX, and the parallelepiped bounded by the furthest sides of the parallelepipeds A, B, and Γ (in our case the unit cube) will contain within itself no points of the lattice.

Taking $\beta > \delta$ and $\theta < \alpha$, we obtain points A, B, and Γ satisfying all the requirements of the second example.

§55. A THEOREM ON PARALLEL CHAINS

Suppose that we are given an x-chain of relative minima

$$\{\Omega\}_x = \Omega, \Omega_1, \Omega_2, \cdots,$$

and a relative minimum T.

We will say that the relative minimum T is situated higher than the chain $\{\Omega\}_x$ if there is an element in the chain that is lower and wider than T. Similarly, if the chain $\{\Omega\}_x$ contains an element that is higher and narrower than T, we will say that T is situated lower than the chain $\{\Omega\}_x$ (Figures 15 and 16).

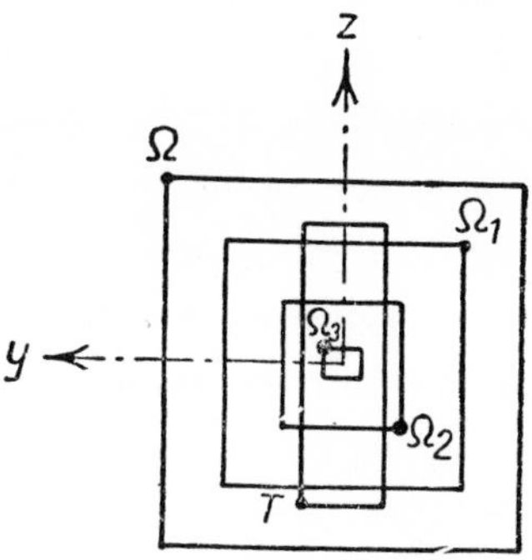

Figure 15

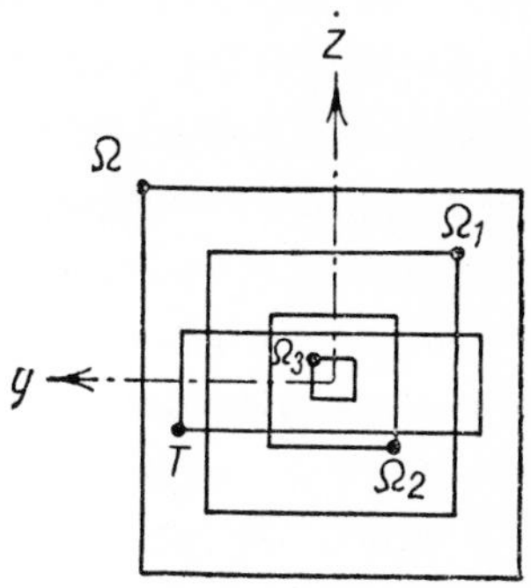

Figure 16

It is easy to see that the given relative minimum T cannot be simultaneously higher and lower than the given chain $\{\Omega\}_x$. Otherwise this chain would contain elements Ω_i and Ω_k not overlapping each other in the OX direction, which is impossible (Figure 17).

THEOREM 1. *If the relative minimum T does not overlap the relative minimum Ω on OX, then T either belongs to an x-chain generated by Ω, or is situated either higher or lower than it. No fourth possibility exists.*

PROOF. The following possibilities exist:

1. T coincides with Ω. Then T belongs to $\{\Omega\}_x$.
2. T is higher and narrower than Ω. Then T is higher than $\{\Omega\}_x$.
3. T is wider and higher than Ω. Then T is lower than $\{\Omega\}_x$.
4. T is lower and narrower than Ω or, in our terminology, T pierces Ω on OX (Figure 18).

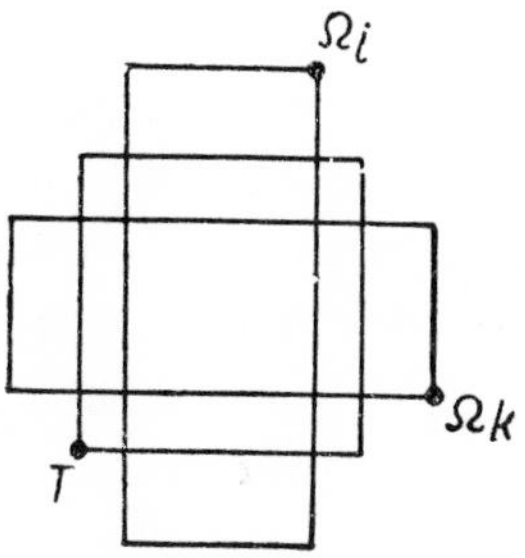

Figure 17

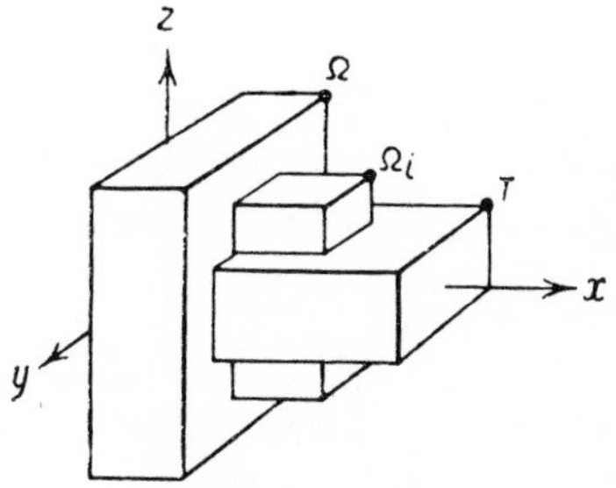

Figure 18

We consider the longest element Ω_i of the chain $\{\Omega\}_x$ which is still shorter than T. One of the following three cases must hold.

5. Ω_i is higher and narrower than T (Figure 18). Then T is lower than $\{\Omega\}_x$.

6. Ω_i is lower and wider than T. Then T is higher than $\{\Omega\}_x$.

7. Ω_i is higher and wider than T (Figure 19), i.e., Ω_i overlaps T on OX. The right face of the parallelepiped Ω_i meets for the first time the point T under movement to the right, since otherwise the chain $\{\Omega\}_x$ would contain an element Ω_{i+1} which would be shorter than T, in contradiction to the choice of Ω_i. Hence in this case T will be the relative minimum adjacent to Ω_i and will thus belong to the chain $\{\Omega\}_x$.

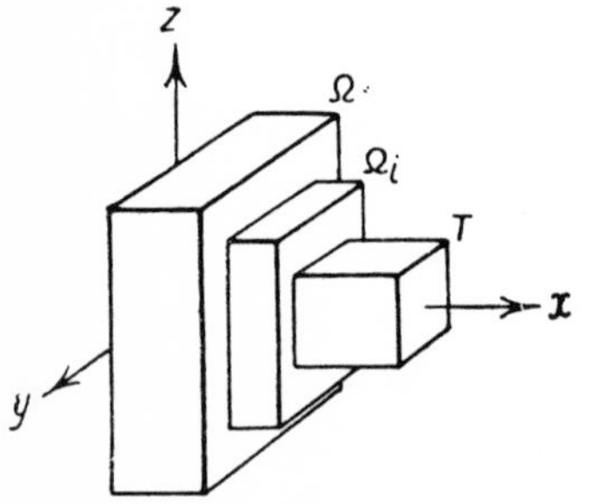

Figure 19

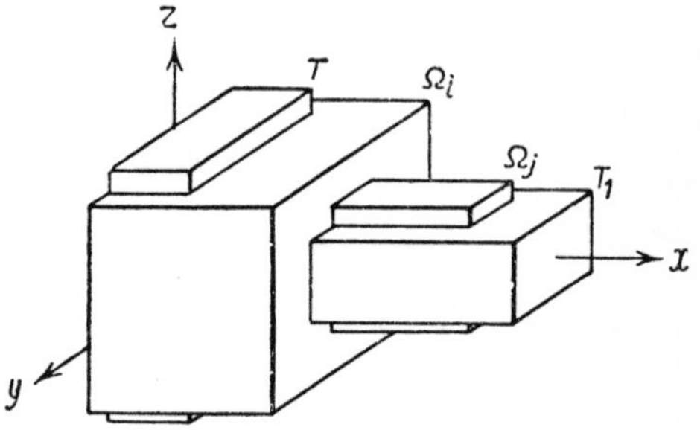

Figure 20

With this the theorem is proved.

THEOREM 2. *If a relative minimum T is situated higher than the x-chain generated by the relative minimum Ω, then the relative minimum T_1 adjacent to T on OX will either be situated higher than the chain $\{\Omega\}_x$ or will be one of its elements.*

PROOF. Let the relative minimum T be situated higher than the chain $\{\Omega\}_x$. This means that the chain contains an element Ω_i which will be lower and wider than T. Compairng Ω_i with T_1, we see that Ω_i is wider than T_1, since it is wider than T, and T is wider than T_1. If Ω_i is here lower than T_1, then T_1 is by definition situated higher than the chain $\{\Omega\}_x$. If Ω_i is higher than T_1, then Ω_i is shorter than T_1, for otherwise Ω_i would not be a relative minimum. Now consider Ω_j, namely the longest element of the chain $\{\Omega\}_x$ that is still shorter than T_1. If Ω_j is higher and wider than T_1, then $\Omega_{j+1} = T_1$, and the element T_1 belongs to the chain $\{\Omega\}_x$. If Ω_j is lower and wider than T_1, then T_1 is situated higher than the chain $\{\Omega\}_x$. There remains the case when Ω_j is higher and narrower than T_1. However, this case is impossible (Figure 20). In fact Ω_j is lower than Ω_i, and thus lower than T. On the other hand Ω_j is narrower than T_1 and hence narrower than T. Thus Ω_j pierces T on OX and therefore T_1, being longer than Ω_j, cannot be a relative minimum adjacent to T on OX.

With this the theorem is proved.

It follows directly from Theorem 2 that if a relative minimum T is situated higher than the chain $\{\Omega\}_x$, then any element of the chain $\{T\}_x$ is either situated higher than the chain $\{\Omega\}_x$ or is in it.

It is shown in exactly the same way that if T is situated lower than $\{\Omega\}_x$, then the relative minimum T_1 adjacent to it on OX is either situated lower than the chain $\{\Omega\}_x$ or is an element of it.

As a result of all this, the concept of a relative minimum T situated either higher or lower than a chain $\{\Omega\}_x$ can be generalized to the case when T overlaps the first element Ω of the chain $\{\Omega\}_x$ on OX. Namely, we may say that T is situated higher than the chain $\{\Omega\}_x$ if at least one element of the chain $\{T\}_x$ is situated higher than $\{\Omega\}_x$, and that T is situated lower than the chain $\{\Omega\}_x$ if at least one element of the chain $\{T\}_x$ is situated lower than the chain $\{\Omega\}_x$, and finally that T belongs to the chain $\{\Omega\}_x$ if Ω belongs to the chain $\{T\}_x$ and hence the whole chain $\{\Omega\}_x$ is included in $\{T\}_x$.

The following propositions are obvious:

If T is higher than $\{\Omega\}_x$, then Ω is lower than $\{T\}_x$.

If Φ is higher than $\{T\}_x$ and T is higher than $\{\Omega\}_x$, then Φ is higher than $\{\Omega\}_x$.

Thus each x-chain of relative minima divides all the relative minima into three classes, namely the class of those situated higher than the chain, the class of those situated lower than the chain, and the class of those belonging to the chain. The properties given above for this decomposition permit an analogy between a chain of relative minima and a linear sequence of points on a plane. The different x-chains play the role of parallel lines in this analogy.

Obviously y-chains and z-chains produce the same decomposition of relative minima with respect to these chains, we introduce the corresponding terminology: relative minimum situated higher or lower than a y-chain, relative minimum situaated to the right or to the left of a z-chain. It is obvious that a theorem analogous to Theorem 2 is valid for these relations.

§56. THEOREMS ON CHAINS OF DIFFERENT DIRECTIONS

THEOREM 3. *If the relative minimum* T *is situated to the right of* $\{\Omega\}_z$ *and lower than* $\{\Omega\}_x$, *then the chains* $\{\Omega\}_x$ *and* $\{T\}_x$ *have a common element.*

PROOF. Two relative minima Ω and T may be situated with respect to each other in six different ways: Ω overlaps T on OX, Ω pierces T on OX, Ω overlaps T on OY, Ω pierces T on OY, Ω overlaps T on OZ, and finally, Ω pierces T on OZ. Only two of these six situations satisfy the conditions of the theorem: Ω overlaps T on OX, and Ω pierces T on OZ.

For definiteness we settle on the first possibility.

Thus, let Ω overlap T on OX (Figure 21). By assumption, T lies lower than $\{\Omega\}_x$. Hence, the chain $\{\Omega\}_x$ contains an element which is shorter, higher, and narrower than T; for if there were no such element, and all the elements of the chain $\{\Omega\}_x$ that were shorter than T were higher and wider than T, then T would belong to $\{\Omega\}_x$, contrary to assumption. Let Ω_i be the first such element of the chain $\{\Omega\}_x$, i.e., such that the preceding element Ω_{i-1} overlaps T on OX.

The relative minimum T overlaps Ω_i on OZ. We will show that Ω_i either belongs to the chain $\{T\}_z$ or lies to the left of it. In fact, we consider elements of the chain $\{T\}_z$ which are lower than Ω_i. If they all overlap Ω_i on OZ, then Ω_i belongs to the chain $\{T\}_z$, and the theorem is proved. If the chain $\{T\}_z$ contains an element T_s that does not overlap Ω_i on OZ, then it may be either shorter and wider than Ω_i or longer and narrower than it. But the first possibility may be eliminated, since then the vertex T_s would fall in the space between the adjacent relative minima Ω_{i-1} and Ω_i, which is impossible. There remains the second possibility, that T_s is longer and narrower than Ω_i. But this means that Ω_i lies to the left of the chain $\{T\}_z$.

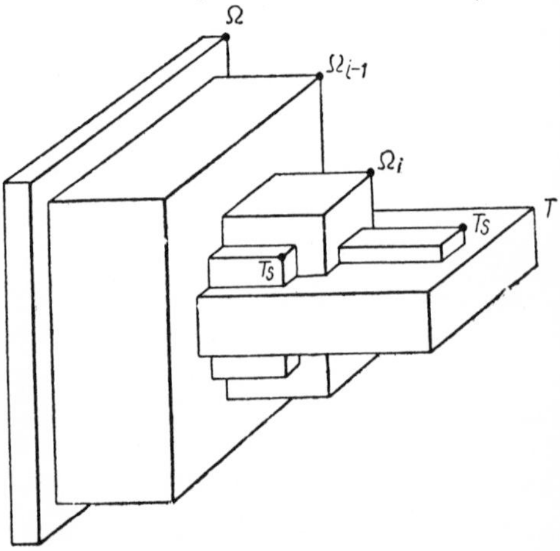

Figure 21

Thus, T and Ω_i again satisfy the conditions of the theorem, but this time T overlaps Ω on OZ. We repeat the same argument. We find the first element T_k of the chain $\{T\}_z$ which does not overlap Ω_i on OZ, and we show as before that T_k either belongs to the chain $\{\Omega_i\}_x$ which is a continuation of the chain $\{\Omega\}_x$, or lies lower than it. In the latter case we again repeat the same argument, and so on. All the relative minima that we introduce in this manner are shorter than T, lower than Ω, and narrower than both of them. There can be only a finite number of such minima, and consequently our process must end after a finite number of steps. But it can end only when some element of the chain $\{\Omega\}_x$ coincides with some element of the chain $\{T\}_z$. With this the theorem is proved.

Similar theorems may be proved also for other chains of different directions. Namely, the chains $\{\Omega\}_y$ and $\{T\}_x$ have a common element if T is situated lower than $\{\Omega\}_x$ and lower than $\{\Omega\}_y$, and finally, the chains $\{\Omega\}_y$ and $\{T\}_z$ have a common element if T is situated lower than $\{\Omega\}_x$ and to the left of $\{\Omega\}_z$.

Theorem 4. *Let two relative minima Ω and T be given. One of the chains $\{\Omega\}_x$, $\{\Omega\}_y$, or $\{\Omega\}_z$ will have an element in common with one of the chains $\{T\}_x$, $\{T\}_y$, or $\{T\}_z$.*

Proof. Let Ω overlap T on the OX-axis so that T is situated to the right of the chain $\{\Omega\}_z$ and lower than the chain $\{\Omega\}_y$. We consider the longest element Ω_i of the chain $\{\Omega\}_x$ which is still shorter than T. If it is wider and higher than T, then T belongs to the chain $\{\Omega\}_x$, and hence $\{\Omega\}_x$ has the common element T with the chains $\{T\}_y$ and $\{T\}_z$. If Ω_i is higher and narrower than T, then T is situated lower than the chain $\{\Omega\}_x$ and by Theorem 3 $\{\Omega\}_x$ and $\{T\}_y$ have a point in common. If Ω_i is lower and wider than T, then T is situated higher than the chain $\{\Omega\}_x$, and by one of the theorems analogous to Theorem 3, the chains $\{\Omega\}_x$ and $\{T\}_y$ have a common element. We may consider similarly all the other cases of the situations of Ω and T.

Theorem 5. *Let the relative minimum Φ be given. Let the relative minimum Ω belong to $\{\Phi\}_z$, and let T belong to $\{\Phi\}_x$. Then the chains $\{\Omega\}_x$ and $\{T\}_z$ will have a common element.*

Proof. Ω and T obviously satisfy the conditions of Theorem 3, from which the present theorem follows directly.

Theorem 3 again affirms the existence of an analogy between the location of relative minima and points in a plane forming linear sequences. Theorem 3 is similar to the statement that two straight lines of different directions have a point in common.

In conclusion we note that Theorems 1–5 are true not only for lattices, but also for any discrete set of points for which it is possible to construct an unbounded chain of relative minima.

§57. THE SOLUTION OF THE PROBLEM OF SIMILARITY OF TWO LATTICES THAT ARE RATIONALLY ASSOCIATED WITH AN IRREDUCIBLE MAXIMAL MULTIPLICATIVE LATTICE IN $R_{3,0}$, OR OF LATTICES THAT ARE SIMILAR TO SUCH LATTICES

We recall some definitions and results given in Chapter I.

If a lattice is multiplied by some point in space that is not a zero divisor, the result is a new lattice that is said to be similar to the original lattice. Under simi larity transformations relative minima go into relative minima, adjacent ones into adjacent ones, and, in general, the relative situation of coordinate parallelepipeds does not change. Among all the lattices similar to a certain given lattice, an especially important role is played by those that are obtained by division of the given lattice by its relative minima. All of these contain the point (1, 1, 1), and 1 is a relative minimum for each of these. In order for a lattice to contain only a finite number of distinct points, it is necessary and sufficient for the lattice to be similar to a lattice that is rationally associated with an irreducible multiplicative lattice.

In the remainder of this section we will be concerned only with the investigation of such lattices, and we will understand by the word "lattice" a lattice of this type.

The solution of the problem of similarity of two lattices. Let the lattice S be similar to a lattice that is rationally associated with an irreducible multiplicative lattice. We find in it some relative minimum Ω and construct a chain of relative minima starting from it:

$$\Omega, \Omega_1, \Omega_2, \cdots, \Omega_m, \cdots.$$

We divide S successively by $\Omega, \Omega_1, \Omega_2, \cdots, \Omega_m, \cdots$. We obtain a sequence of lattices

$$S_0 = \frac{1}{\Omega} S,\ S_1 = \frac{1}{\Omega_1} S, \ldots, S_m = \frac{1}{\Omega_m} S, \ldots.$$

Some of these lattices are equal. Let S_k be the first lattice for which there exists a lattice equal to it, and let S_{k+n} be the first lattice equal to S_k. Then the point $\epsilon_1 = \Omega_{k+n}/\Omega_k$ will give a multiplicative automorphism for the lattice S and for all the lattices similar to it. The point ϵ_1 will belong to the lattice S_k and will be the nth relative minimum in the chain generated by the element 1.

We consider this chain in more detail. Let its elements be

$$\Phi_0 = 1,\ \Phi_1,\ \Phi_2,\ \cdots,\ \Phi_{n-1},\ \Phi_n = \epsilon_1,\ \Phi_{n+1},\ \cdots$$

In view of the fact that the lattice S_k goes into itself under multiplication by ϵ_1, while the point $1 = \Phi_0$ goes into $\epsilon_1 = \Phi_n$, it follows that the point Φ_1 goes into Φ_{n+1}, Φ_2 into Φ_{n+2}, and so on. Consequently,

$$\Phi_{n+s} = \epsilon_1 \Phi_s$$

for any s, and the chain has the form

$$\Phi_0 = 1,\ \Phi_1,\ \Phi_2,\ \cdots,\ \Phi_{n-1},\ \Phi_n = \epsilon_1,\ \epsilon_1\Phi_1,\ \epsilon_1\Phi_2,\ \cdots,\ \epsilon_1^2,\ \cdots.$$

We will call such a chain of relative minima a *purely periodic chain.*

The argument mentioned above shows that each chain of relative minima in the lattices under consideration is, starting at some point, purely periodic.

Purely periodic chains have the remarkable property that they may be continued infinitely in both directions. In fact, let us consider the lattice S_k. The point $\Phi_{-1} = \Phi_{n-1}\epsilon_1^{-1}$ will clearly belong to it, and will be a relative minimum in it. The minimum adjacent to Φ_{-1} will be Φ_0. In the same way, $\Phi_{-2} = \Phi_{n-2}\epsilon_1^{-1}$ will be a relative minimum whose adjacent minimum will be Φ_{-1}, and so on.

The chain

$$\cdots,\ \Phi_{-3},\ \Phi_{-2},\ \Phi_{-1},\ \Phi_0,\ \Phi_1,\ \Phi_2,\ \Phi_3,\ \cdots$$

will be called a *two-sided chain of relative minima.*

Conversely, each chain of relative minima that may be infinitely extended in the opposite direction must be purely periodic. In fact, let there exist $n + 1$ relative minima

$$\Phi_{-n-1},\ \Phi_{-n},\Phi_{-n+1},\ \cdots,\ \Phi_1,$$

preceding the relative minimum Φ_0. Here n denotes the number of such relative minima, division by which of the original lattice gives distinct results. Then there will exist among these relative minima a pair differing by a multiplicative automorphism, and beginning with this pair, the chain will become purely periodic.

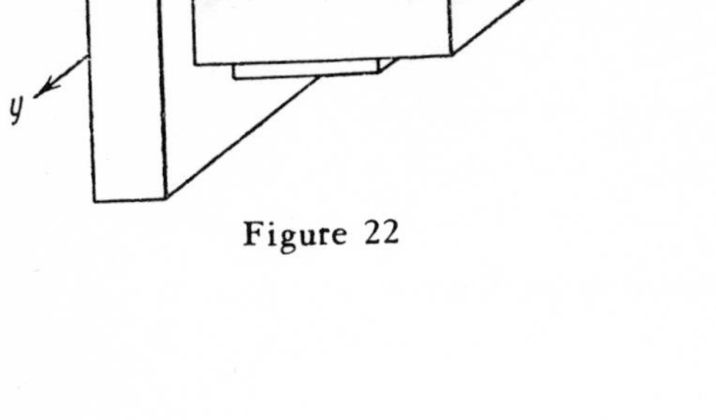

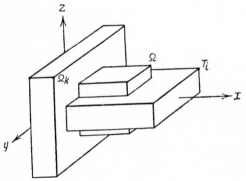

Figure 22

Consequently, the chain

$$\Phi_0, \Phi_1 \dots$$

will also be purely periodic.

Theorem 6. *Two two-sided chains of relative minima of different directions have a common element.*

Proof. We consider for definiteness an x-chain $\{\Phi\}_x$ and a z-chain $\{T\}_z$.

We find in the chain $\{T\}_z$ the relative minimum T_i (possibly with a negative subscript i) that overlaps Ω on OZ. Such a minimum necessarily exists, since in a two-sided chain there exist arbitrarily large elements in the direction perpendicular to the direction of the chain. There there exists in the chain $\{\Omega\}_x$ an element Ω_k overlapping T_i on OX (Figure 22). The conditions of Theorem 3 are satisfied for the chains $\{\Omega\}_x$ and $\{T_i\}_z$, and hence they will have a common element which will also be a common element of the two-sided chains $\{\Omega\}_x$ and $\{T\}_z$.

Now we are able to prove a theorem, by means of which the problem of the similarity of two lattices is solved in a finite number of steps, and, in particular, the problem of the equivalence of two lattices is also solved.

Theorem 7. *In order for the two lattices S and R to be similar, it is necessary and sufficient that one of the lattices obtained by division of S by elements of an x-chain in S coincide with one of the lattices obtained from R by division by elements of a z-chain in R.*

Proof. The sufficiency of the above conditions is obvious, for two lattices similar to a third lattice are similar to each other.

We will now show the necessity of the conditions.

Let $R = \lambda S$, where λ, the "coefficient" of similarity, is a point of the space. We take a relative minimum Ω in S and construct from it a two-sided x-chain $\{\Omega\}_x$ (which may fail to contain Ω). Then we choose in R some relative minimum T and construct from it a two-sided chain $\{T\}_z$. Under division by λ this chain goes into some two-sided z-chain of the lattice S. In view of Theorem 6, this chain will have an element Φ in common with the chain $\{\Omega\}_x$. Then $\Phi' = \lambda\Phi$ will be an element of the chain $\{T\}_z$ in R. But

$$\frac{1}{\Phi} S = \frac{1}{\Phi'} R.$$

With this the theorem is proved.

This theorem actually solves the problem of the similairty of lattices in a finite number of steps; for if we wish to obtain distinct lattices S/Φ, where Φ belongs to a two-sided x-chain, in S, it is sufficient to divide by Φ within the bounds of one period, that is, by a finite number of relative minima Φ. The same is true for the division of R by elements of a z-chain.

§58. THE DETERMINATION OF THE BASIC MULTIPLICATIVE AUTOMORPHISMS FOR A LATTICE RATIONALLY ASSOCIATED WITH AN IRREDUCIBLE MULTIPLICATIVE LATTICE IN $R_{3,0}$, OR FOR A LATTICE SIMILAR TO SUCH A LATTICE

In Chapter I we established the existence of $\sigma + \tau - 1$ independent multiplicative automorphisms for an irreducible mulitplicative lattice, where σ was the number of real coordinates and τ was the number of pairs of complex conjugate coordinates. Then, turning to the logarithmic space and using the discreteness and subtractivity of the system of points formed by the logarithms of the automorphisms, we saw that all automorphisms could be represented in the form

$$\varepsilon = E \cdot \varepsilon_1^{a_1} \varepsilon_2^{a_2}, \ldots, \varepsilon_{\sigma+\tau-1}^{a_{\sigma+\tau-1}},$$

where E is one of the "special automorphisms," i.e., a root of unity, and ϵ_1, $\epsilon_2, \cdots, \epsilon_{\sigma+\tau-1}$ are the so-called basic automorphisms, while $a_1, a_2, \cdots, a_{\sigma+\tau-1}$ are numbers that assume independently of one another all rational integer values. This proof, however, did not provide a convenient solution of the problem of the determination of the basic automorphisms of the lattice. Now, on the basis of the theorems about the location of chains of relative minima, we can give an algorithm for the actual determination of the basic automorphisms for a three-dimensional real lattice.

Thus, let it be required to find the basic automorphisms for a three-dimensional real multiplicative lattice S. To simplify the argument, we will assume that the lattice contains the point $1 = (1, 1, 1)$ and that 1 is a relative minimum having a purely periodic x-chain. One may always obtain such a lattice by dividing the original lattice by a point of any purely periodic x-chain.

We denote by ϵ_1 the first automorphism of the x-chain of the lattice S constructed by starting from the element 1. All the remaining automorphisms included in this chain (which we assume is two-sided) will have the form ϵ_1^n for all integer n, positive or negative.

We denote the elements of the x-chain $\{1\}_x$ by

$$\cdots, 1 = \Phi_0, \Phi_1, \Phi_2, \cdots, \Phi_n = \epsilon_1, \cdots.$$

We now consider other automorphisms of the lattice S. They will all be relative minima of the lattice. We will construct an x-chain starting from each of these. These x-chains will obviously all be purely periodic and thus extended in both directions, and their elements will be associated with elements of the chain $\{1\}_x$ (i.e., they will differ only by factors that are automorphisms of S). The converse is also obvious: if we construct an x-chain starting with a point of the lattice that is associated with some point of the chain $\{1\}_x$, then we obtain a purely periodic chain including automorphisms. The automorphisms included in each of these chains have the form $\epsilon\epsilon_1^n$, where ϵ is one of the automorphisms included in the chain and ϵ_1 is the first automorphism in the chain $\{1\}_x$. All these chains may be arranged by "height," since for any two x-chains we can say which is higher and which is lower than the other, and this relationship is transitive.

We now construct a z-chain of relative minima starting from each element of the chain $\{1\}_x$. By the theorem about the intersection of chains, each such chain will have a point in common with each of the chains $\{\epsilon\}_x$ lying higher than the chain $\{1\}_x$. These common elements will be situated in a z-chain in order of "increasing height" of the chains $\{\epsilon\}_x$. Thus there is a first chain in the $\{\epsilon\}_x$ situated higher than $\{1\}_x$, above it a second, a third, and so on. Each succeeding chain will be situated higher than the preceding one, and all the chains $\{\epsilon\}_x$ constructed on automorphisms lying higher than $\{1\}_x$ will fall into this sequence.

Let ϵ_2 be an automorphism contained in the first chain of the sequence under consideration. Division by ϵ_2 will obviously take the first chain following $\{1\}_x$ directly into $\{1\}_x$, the second into the first, the third into the second, and so on.

Thus the second chain contains the automorphism ϵ_2^2, the third, ϵ_2^3, and the mth, ϵ_2^m for any positive integer m.

Let ϵ be any automorphism. There are three possible situations of this automorphism with respect to the chain $\{1\}_x$.

1. ϵ lies in $\{1\}_x$.

Then $\epsilon = \epsilon_2^n$, where n is some positive or negative integer.

2. ϵ lies higher than $\{1\}_x$.

Then ϵ falls into one of the x-chains of the sequence considered above. Let it be the mth. This latter contains the automorphism ϵ_2^m among its elements, and all the other automorphisms that it contains are of the form $\epsilon_2^m \epsilon_1^n$.

Hence in this case

$$\epsilon = \epsilon_2^m \epsilon_1^n,$$

where m is a *positive* integer.

3. ϵ lies lower than $\{1\}_x$.

Then 1 lies higher than $\{\epsilon\}_x$. Division by ϵ takes 1 into $1/\epsilon$ and ϵ into 1. Thus $1/\epsilon$ lies higher than $\{1\}_x$, and by the above remarks,

$$\frac{1}{\varepsilon}=\varepsilon_2^m\,\varepsilon_1^n,$$

from which it follows that

$$\varepsilon=\varepsilon_2^{-m}\,\varepsilon_1^{-n}.$$

All this shows that the automorphisms ϵ_1 and ϵ_2 may be taken for basic automorphisms of the lattice S.

We will now find operations by means of which it is possible actually to find ϵ_1 and ϵ_2 for any lattice, even for one for which the chain $\{1\}_x$ does not satisfy the condition of pure periodicity. We already know how to find ϵ_1. Starting from any relative minimum, we must construct an x-chain and divide the lattice each time by elements of the chain. Let some lattice S repeat for the first time. The ratio of corresponding relative minima (preceding and succeeding) is equal to the automorphism ϵ_1. For the lattice S the element 1 will have a purely periodic chain $1, \Phi_1, \Phi_2, \cdots, \Phi_n = \epsilon_1$. During the computations we obtain all the lattices $1/\Phi_i\, S$, $i = 1, 2, \cdots, n-1$.

It is necessary to perform further calculations with the lattice S.

Starting with the element 1, we construct the z-chain

$$1,\ \psi_1,\ \psi_2,\ \cdots.$$

We divide the lattice S successively by $\psi_1, \psi_2, \cdots$ and observe when we first obtain one of the lattices S/Φ_i, $i = 0, 1, \cdots, n-1$. Suppose that for the first time

$$\frac{1}{\psi_k}\,S=\frac{1}{\Phi_i}\,S.$$

Then ψ_k/Φ_i will be an automorphism of the lattice S, and moreover it will be the same automorphism as we perviously denoted by ϵ_2. In fact, the chain $\{\psi_k\}_x$ will be formed of elements that are associated with elements of the chain $\{1\}_x$ and will contain ψ_k/Φ_i as the ith element preceding ψ_k, since 1 is the ith element preceding Φ_i in the lattice $\{1\}_x$. From the choice of ψ_k it follows that the chain $\{\psi_k\}_x$ will be the lowest x-chain that contains automorphisms situated higher than $\{1\}_x$. Thus any automorphism contained in $\{\psi_k\}_x$, in particular ψ_k/Φ_i, may be taken for ϵ_2.

Thus we have established a rule for the determination of the basic automorphisms of a lattice by means of the formation of chains of relative minima.

§59. AN ALGORITHM FOR THE DETERMINATION OF THE RELATIVE MINIMUM ADJACENT TO A GIVEN ONE FOR A LATTICE THAT IS RATIONALLY ASSOCIATED WITH AN IRREDUCIBLE LATTICE IN $R_{3,0}$, OR FOR ONE THAT IS SIMILAR TO SUCH A LATTICE

In this section we undertake to solve the following problem. Given a basis (χ_1, χ_2, χ_3) determining a lattice, we wish to find out whether or not the point χ_1 is a relative minimum. If it is, we wish to find the minimum adjacent to it on Ox, and if it is not, we wish to find a point within the coordinate parallelepiped constructed on χ_1.

Without loss of generality we may assume that $\chi_1 = 1$.

We make the following construction for the solution of the problem.

We separate all the points of the lattice into parallels. By this name we mean a collection of points of the lattice lying on a straight line parallel to the "rational line" $x = y = z$. The collection of points of the lattice lying on each nonempty parallel forms a linear sequence. The projection of a segment connecting two neighboring points of this sequence onto each of the coordinate axes is equal to 1. Each plane that is not parallel to the rational line intersects the set of nonempty parallels in a plane lattice that is the projection of the original lattice on the given plane parallel to the rational line.

As the projection plane we take the plane $y + z = 0$,[1] which is a diagonal plane of the unit cube. For convenience in calculations we go to the new system of coordinates (ξ, η, ζ), taking for the axes $O\eta$ and $O\zeta$ of the bisectrices the fourth and first coordinate anlges in the plane YZ, and taking as the scalar unit for these axes the interval equal to $\sqrt{2}$ times the scalar unit for the previous axes (Figure 23).

The formulas for the transformation to the new coordinates are

$$\xi = x, \quad \eta = \frac{y - z}{2}, \quad \zeta = \frac{y + z}{2}.$$

In particular, the new coordinates of the point 1 (1, 1, 1) will be (1, 0, 1).

1) G. F. Voronoĭ took $z = 0$ as the projection plane.

The projection plane $y + z = 0$ in the new coordinates will be the coordinate plane $x\eta$. The prism formed by the faces of the unit cube that are parallel to the Ox-axis are situated with respect to the new coordinate axes in accordance with Figure 24. The length of edges of this prism up to the Ox-axis will be 1.

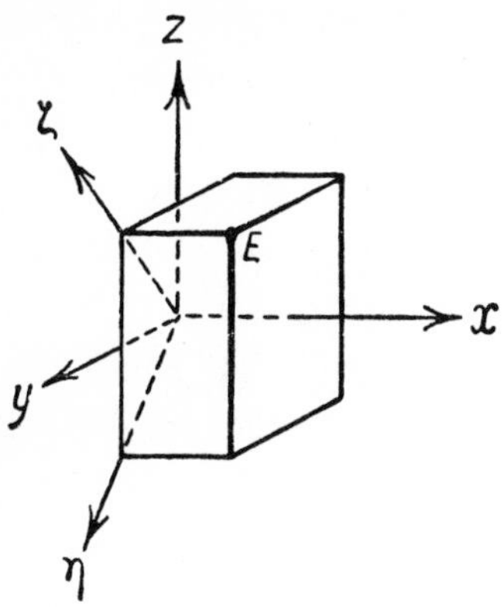

Figure 23

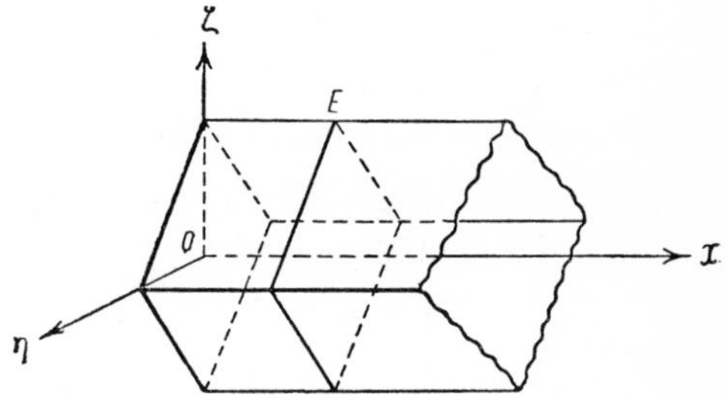

Figure 24

The points of intersection of the parallels with the plane $x\eta$ will be called "punctures." Because of the symmetry of the lattice with respect to the origin it is necessary to consider only points whose punctures lie to the right of the $O\eta$-axis.

The basic vector pair for the plane lattice of the punctures will obviously be formed by the vectors connecting the origin with the punctures of the ends of the second and third vectors of the basis $(1, \chi_2, \chi_3)$ of the lattice.

The coordinates of the puncture of the point (x, y, z) will be

$$\xi = \frac{2x - y - z}{2}; \quad \eta = \frac{y - z}{2}; \quad \zeta = 0.$$

Here ξ is the x of the puncture.

The problem which we wish to solve may be formulated as follows: to find a point within the unit prism whose distance from the plane $\eta\zeta$ is less than 1 or, if there is no such point, to find a point within the prism closest to the $\eta\zeta$-plane.

Obviously, only those points whose punctures lie between the edges of the prism, i.e., in the band $|\eta| < 1$, can lie within the prism; moreover, out of all the points having a given puncture, there can appear within the prism only the points of the parallel (on both sides of the plane) that are closest to the puncture. These points will be called the upper and lower points of the given puncture.

Punctures located within the band $|\eta| < 1$ may be divided into two categories, namely, a first category containing punctures lying in the band $|\eta| < 1/2$ and a second category containing those outside this band.

Punctures of the first category have the property that one of the points belonging to them must lie within the prism, while it is possible for both points to lie there. This follows from the fact that the segment of the parallel cut off by the prism passing through such a puncture has a projection on the Ox-axis that is greater than unity, and consequently at least one point of the lattice lies on this segment, and there may be two points on it.

On the other hand, there can lie within the prism only one of the points belonging to a puncture of the second category, and it is possible that there may be no point within the prism.

Before going further, we place a further restriction on the lattice; namely, we assume that the coordinates of the puncture, i.e., the numbers

$$\xi = \frac{2x - y - z}{2} \quad \text{and} \quad \eta = \frac{y - z}{2}$$

are irrational for all points other than points of the rational line. This is obviously satisfied in the case of interest to us here, namely an irreducible multiplicative lattice. This limitation is not essential, but it simplifies the

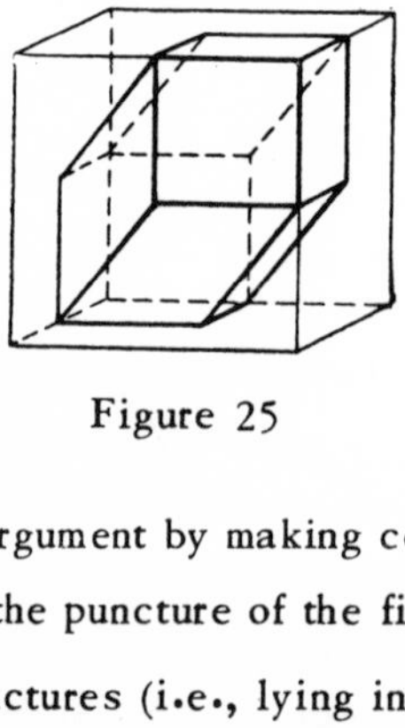

Figure 25

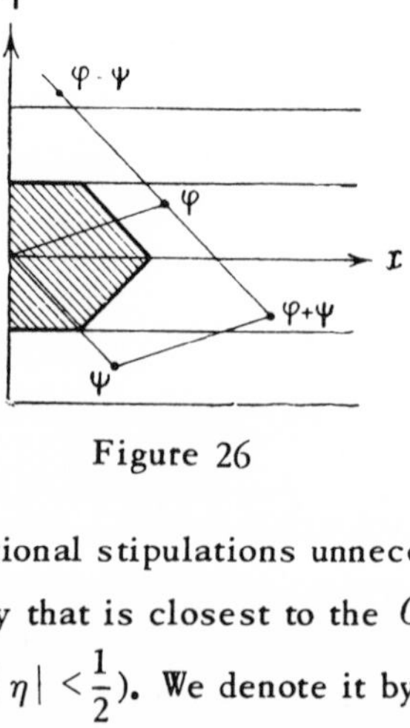

Figure 26

subsequent argument by making certain additional stipulations unnecessary.

We find the puncture of the first category that is closest to the $O\eta$-axis in the lattice of punctures (i.e., lying in the band $|\eta| < \frac{1}{2}$). We denote it by ϕ.

We find the puncture ψ closest to the axis Ox that lies in the band between the axis $O\eta$ and the straight line parallel to $O\eta$ and passing through the puncture ϕ. It is known that the punctures ϕ and ψ chosen in such a manner lie on different sides of the axis Ox and that the two punctures form a basis for the system of punctures. In this system they form adjacent relative minima in the same sense as was established for plane lattices. As we know, they can be found by means of the algorithm of continued fractions.

THEOREM. *The desired point, i.e., an interior point for the unit cube or the relative minimum adjacent to* 1 *on* Ox, *belongs to one of the punctures* ϕ, ψ, $\phi+\psi$, $\phi-\psi$, *or* $2\phi+\psi$; *moreover, it may belong to the last puncture only when both points belonging to the puncture* $\phi+\psi$ *lie outside the prism and if the puncture* ψ, *and hence also* $\phi-\psi$, *lie beyond the limits of the band* $|\eta|<1$.

Before we prove the theorem, we establish some useful propositions.

LEMMA 1. *The desired point belongs to one of the punctures* $m\phi+n\psi$ *for* $0\le m\le 4$, $1\le n\le m+1$.

PROOF. We consider the collection of points of the unit cube with the property that the segments of the parallel within the cube passing through any point of the collection has a projection on Ox greater than 1. This collection fills out a six-faced prism as depicted in Figure 25. The projection of this prism onto the plane $O\eta$ is a hexagon, half of which is shown in Figure 26.

We consider the lattice of punctures. There are two cases: either there is a point within the unit cube belonging to the puncture ϕ, or there is none. In the first case the lemma is proved.

In the second case $\xi_\phi>\frac{1}{2}$. This is true, for if ξ_ϕ were less than $\frac{1}{2}$, then ϕ would fall within the shaded region (of Figure 26), and there would be a point within the unit cube belonging to the puncture ϕ. We denote by Φ the lowest point belonging to the puncture ϕ if the point lies within the prism, or the highest point if the lowest point is located outside the prism. Obviously,

$$-1<\zeta_\Phi<\frac{1}{2}.$$

In fact, we project the prism orthogonally onto the plane $\eta\zeta$. The projection Φ must be within the parallelogram $OQQ'P$ (Figure 27).

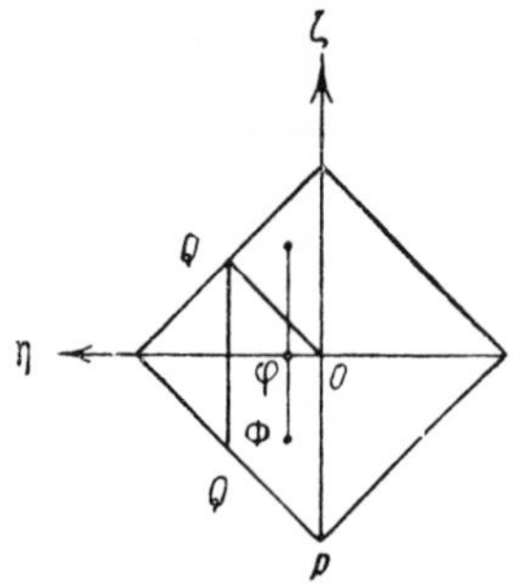

Figure 27

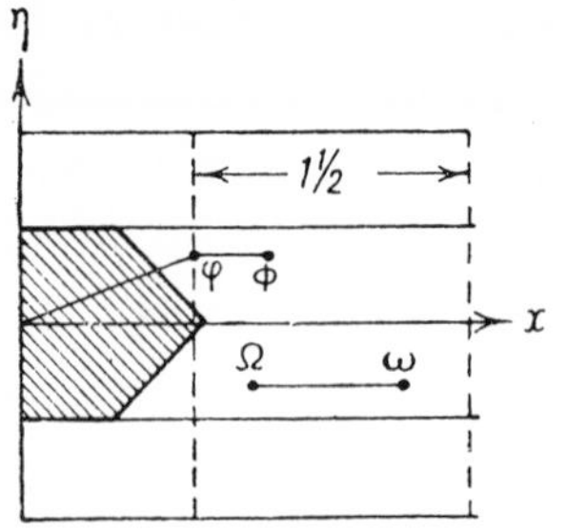

Figure 28

It follows directly from this that the puncture ω, to which belongs the point Ω that is closer to the yz-plane than the point Φ, can be no more than $1\frac{1}{2}$ units further from $O\eta$ than ϕ (Figure 28), since the projections of the segments of the parallel onto Ox and $O\zeta$ are identical.

Thus all the punctures that interest us lie within the rectangle

$$|\eta| < 1, \quad |\xi| < \xi_\phi + 1\frac{1}{2}.$$

It is sufficient to consider the puncture $m\phi + n\psi$ for $m \geq 0$. For $m = 0$ it is only possible that $n = 1$, since the point 2ψ already lies beyond the limits of the band $|\eta| < 1$.

For $m > 1$, it is obvious that $n \geq -1$; for if $n \leq -2$, then the point $m\phi + n\psi$ would also certainly lie beyond the limits of the band $|\eta| < 1$, since η_ϕ and η_ψ have different signs and $|\eta_\psi| > \frac{1}{2}$.

Consequently, $\xi_{m\phi+n\psi} \geq \xi_{m\phi-\psi} > \xi_{(m-1)\phi} = (m-1)\xi_\phi$.

However, it must be true that

$$\xi_{m\phi+n\psi} < \xi_\phi + \frac{3}{2}.$$

Hence, $(m-1)\xi_\phi < \xi_\phi + 3/2$, from which it follows that $m < 2 + 3/2\xi_\phi < 5$, since $\xi_\phi > 1/2$.

Moreover, the punctures $\phi + \psi$ and ψ lie on the same side of the axis Ox. Consequently, the punctures $m(\phi + \psi) + k\psi$ for $k \geq 2$ lie beyond the limits of the band $|\eta| \leq 1$. Hence $m \leq 4$, and $-1 \leq n \leq m + 1$, which is what we wished to prove.

LEMMA 2. *Let ω be a puncture of the first category, and let τ be a puncture* *lying on the same side of the axis Ox as ω and further from $O\eta$ than ω. If there belongs to the puncture a point T within the prism closer to $O\eta\zeta$ than the point Ω belonging to the puncture ω, then there is a point within the unit cube belonging to the puncture $\tau - \omega$.*

PROOF. We consider the orthogonal projection of the prism onto the plane $O\eta\zeta$ (Figure 29). In this projection the point Ω may be located either in region II or III, and the point T in one of the regions I, II, and III. Since τ lies further from $O\eta$ than ω, the point Ω must be higher in Figure 29 than the point T.

We construct the square equal and parallel to the cross-section of the basic prism with center at the point Ω. If Ω belongs to the region III (Figure 29), this square will cover all the points of the cross-section of the basic prisms that lie lower than the point Ω and hence will cover the point T.

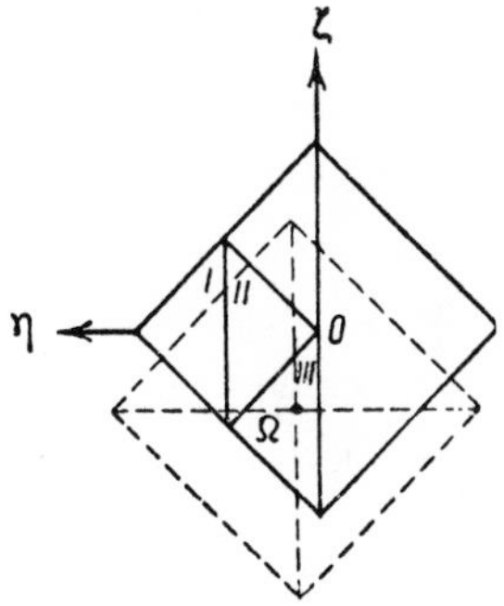

Figure 29

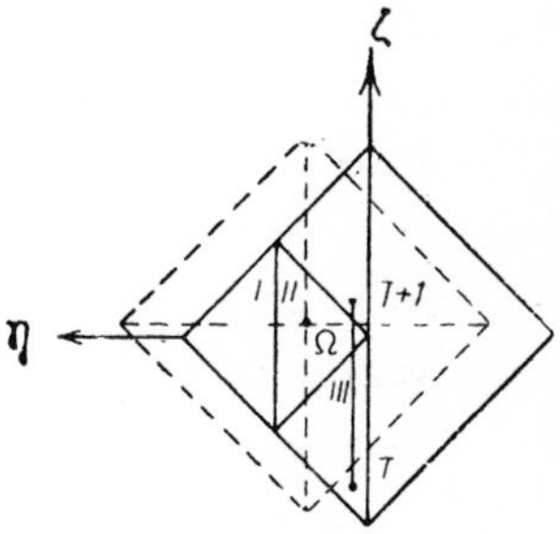

Figure 30

If the point Ω lies in the region II of Figure 30, then this square will cover regions I and II completely and will cover a part of region III. If the point T is located in the part of region II which is not covered by the constructed square, the point $T + 1$ nevertheless will fall inside it. This means that either $T - \Omega$ or $T - \Omega + 1$ is located within the prism. Both these points have as their puncture $\tau - \omega$, which has a positive abscissa because of the stipulation that the puncture τ is further from $O\eta$ than ω. Consequently the point $T - \Omega$ has an abscissa greater than -1 if it lies within the prism, and greater than $-1\frac{1}{2}$ in the contrary case. But as we have seen, in the contrary case the point $T - \Omega + 1$ lies within the prism and its abscissa will be larger than $-\frac{1}{2}$ and less than 1, since the abscissa of the point $T - \Omega$ is negative. Thus either the point $T - \Omega$ or the point $T - \Omega + 1$ lies within the unit cube, which is what we wanted to show.

Lemma 2 allows us to exclude from our consideration a whole sequence of points mentioned in Lemma 1.

Namely, all the points $\tau = m\phi + n\psi$ for $n = 0$ and $n = -1$, other than the point $\phi - \psi$, satisfy the stipulations of the lemma for $\omega = \phi$, so that out of all those points only the point $\phi - \psi$ is needed. Further, the points $\tau = m\phi + n\psi$ for $n \geq m$, other than the point $\phi + \psi$, will be within the band $|\eta| < 1$ only when $\phi + \psi$ lies in the band $|\eta| < \frac{1}{2}$, and they will satisfy the conditions of Lemma 2 for $\omega = \phi + \psi$. Consequently, they may also be excluded from consideration.

Hence, other than the points ϕ, ψ, $\phi - \psi$, and $\phi + \psi$, there remain only the points $m\phi + n\psi$ for $2 \leq m \leq 4$, $1 \leq n \leq m - 1$.

LEMMA 3. *If the distance between the puncture τ and the closest puncture ω to $O\eta$ is greater than* 1, *while the point T lies within the prism and is closer to the plane $\zeta O\eta$ than the point Ω, which also lies within the prism, then the point $T - \Omega + 1$ lies within the unit cube.*

PROOF. In the given case, the projection of the point Ω onto the cross-section of the prism can be located only within the triangle OAC (Figure 31), while the projection of the point T is lower than the projection of the point $\Omega - 1$. Constructing the square equal to the cross-section of the prism with center in the projection of the point $\Omega - 1$, we see that it covers that region of the cross-section of the prism in which the projection of the point T can be found. Consequently the point $T - \Omega + 1$ lies within the prism. Its abscissa

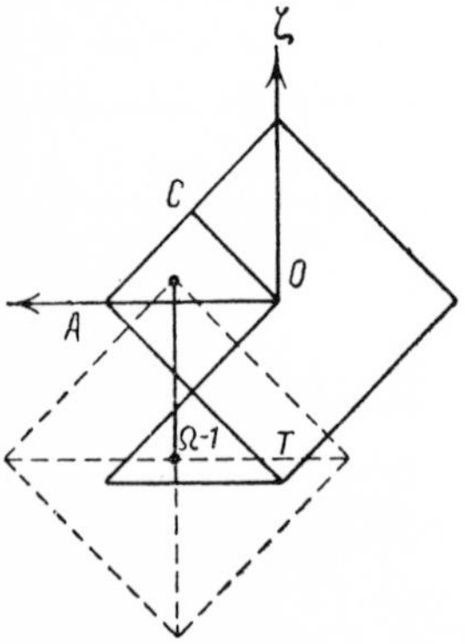

Figure 31

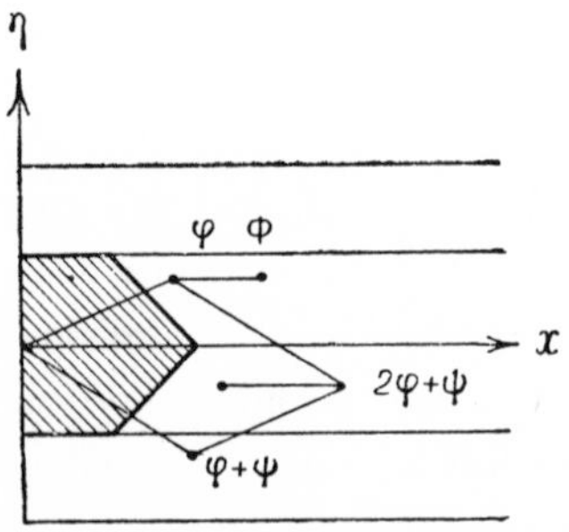

Figure 32

is obviously positive and greater than 1, since the abscissa of the point $T - \Omega$ is negative and greater than $-\frac{1}{2}$. Hence, the point $T - \Omega + 1$ lies within the unit cube, which is what we wanted to show.

Lemma 3 excludes from consideration the points $m\phi + n\psi$ for $m \geq 3$. Thus there remain only the points ϕ, ψ, $\phi - \psi$, $\phi + \psi$, and $2\phi + \psi$.

We investigate the puncture $2\phi + \psi$ in more detail.

First, it is clear that if the abscissa of the puncture $\phi + \psi$ is greater than 1, then the puncture $\tau = 2\phi + \psi$ satisfies the stipulations of Lemma 3 for $\omega = \phi$ and thus need not be considered. Thus it is necessary to consider only the case when the abscissa of $\phi + \psi$, and hence the abscissa of ϕ, is less than 1 (Figure 32).

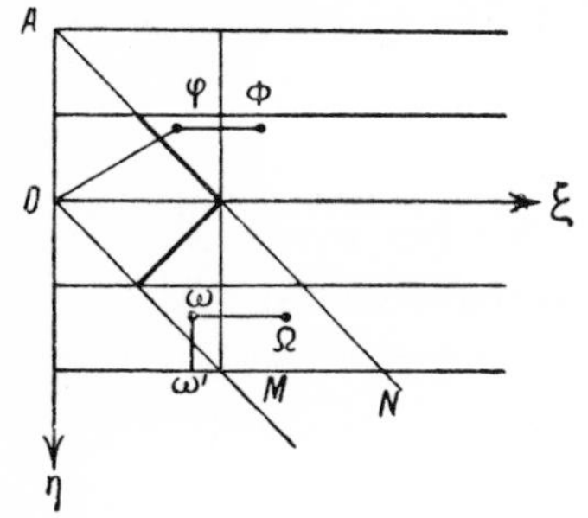

Figure 33

In this case, if the lower point belonging to the puncture ϕ or to $\phi + \psi$ is within the prism, then it will be within the unit cube, and the point $2\phi + \psi$ may also be excluded from consideration.

We now assume that the lower points of the punctures ϕ and $\phi + \psi$ lie outside the prism. We denote their higher points respectively by Φ and Ω. Their coordinates ζ_Φ and ζ_Ω will be respectively less than $|\eta_\Phi|$ and $|\eta_\Omega|$. Hence,

$$\zeta_{\Phi+\Omega} < |\eta_\Phi| + |\eta_\Omega| = |\eta_\phi - \eta_{\phi+\psi}| = |\eta_\psi|.$$

We now show that the point $2\phi + \psi$ need be considered only when $|\eta_\psi| > 1$. In fact, let $|\eta_\psi| < 1$. Then $\zeta_{\Phi+\Omega} < 1$, and hence to the puncture $2\phi + \psi$ will belong the points $\Phi + \Omega$ and $\Phi + \Omega - 1$.

If the abscissa of the point Ω is greater than 1, then the point $\Phi + \Omega - 1$ can be no closer than the point Φ to the plane $O\eta\zeta$ and must be eliminated from consideration. It remains to consider the case when the abscissa of Ω is less than 1. If the point Ω is within the prism it is also within the unit cube, and the point $2\phi + \psi$ need not be considered.

There remains the case when the abscissa of Ω is less than 1 and Ω lies within the prism, However, this is impossible if $|\eta_\psi| < 1$.

In fact, the point Ω, being located outside the prism, must have a projection onto the plane $x\eta$ that is further than $\omega\omega'$ from its puncture $\omega = \phi + \psi$ (Figure 33). Thus, in order for the abscissa to be less than unity, it is necessary for ω to lie lower than the line OM. But the point ϕ lies higher than the parallel line AN. Hence the point $\psi = \omega - \phi$ must lie lower than the line FK, i.e., beyond the limits of the band $|\eta| < 1$.

The theorem is now proved in full.

It is easy to show in the same manner that the point $\phi + \psi$ need be considered only when there exists a point within the prism belonging to the puncture ψ.

Thus we have established that, in order to find a point of the lattice constructed on the basis $(1, \chi_2, \chi_3)$ within the unit cube, or to show that the unit cube is empty, and to find the point that is the relative minimum adjacent on Ox to the relative minimum 1, it is necessary to carry out the following steps:

1. Determine the coordinates of the "punctures" for the points χ_2 and χ_3 by the formulas

$$\xi = \frac{2x - y - z}{2}; \quad \eta = \frac{y - z}{2}.$$

2. By means of the algorithm of continued fractions find points ϕ and ψ that are adjacent relative minima in the lattice of punctures so that

$$\xi_\phi > 0; \quad \xi_\psi > 0; \quad |\eta_\phi| < \frac{1}{2}; \quad |\eta_\psi| > \frac{1}{2}.$$

Express these points in terms of the points $\bar{\chi}_2$ and $\bar{\chi}_3$ of the basis of the lattice of punctures

$$\varphi = m_1\bar{\chi}_2 + n_1\bar{\chi}_3, \quad \psi = m_2\bar{\chi}_2 + n_2\bar{\chi}_3.$$

3. Calculate the coordinates of the points $\Phi = m_1\chi_2 + n_1\chi_3$ and $\Psi = m_2\chi_2 + n_2\chi_3$.

4. Choose an integer t_1 so that the coordinates y and z of the point $\Phi_0 = \Phi + t1$ (1 is the unit point (1, 1, 1)) are less than unity in absolute value. It is certainly possible to do this in at least one way, and if it is possible in two ways, then take that value for t_1 which gives the least value for the x coordinate of the point $\Phi + t1$.

5. Choose in the same way numbers t_2 and t_3 for the points Ψ and $\Phi - \Psi$. If this can be done at all, it is possible in only one way.

6. If there is a suitable number t_2 for the point Ψ, compare the abscissae of the points Φ_0, Ψ_0, and $\Phi - \Psi + t_3 1$. That point whose abscissa is least will lie within the unit cube or will be the relative minimum adjacent to 1 on Ox.

7. If there does not exist a suitable number t_2 for Ψ, then try to find in the same way a number t_4 for the point $\Phi + \Psi$, and if such a t_4 exists, compare the abscissae of the points Φ_0, $\Phi - \Psi + t_3 1$, and $\Phi + \Psi + t_4 1$.

8. If there does not exist a suitable number t_4 for the point $\Phi + \Psi$, and if, moreover, $|\eta_\psi| > 1$ and $\xi_{\phi+\psi} < 1$, then choose a number t_5 in the same way for the point $2\Phi + \Psi$ and compare the abscissae of the points Φ_0 and $2\Phi + \Psi + t_5 1$.

EXAMPLE. To find the fundamental units of the field $\Omega(\rho)$, where ρ is given by the equation $\rho^3 = 6\rho + 2$.

SOLUTION. The fundamental units are represented geometrically in the form of basic multiplicative automorphisms for the lattice formed by the collection of all algebraic integers of the field $\Omega(\rho)$. This lattice will have a power basis $1, \rho, \rho^2$, as can easily be seen by using the methods of determining a basis described in Chapter II.

For the construction of the chains of the relative minima, it is necessray to know the approximate value for the coordinates of the points of the basis, i.e., for the roots and the squares of the roots of the equation $\rho^3 = 6\rho + 2$.

These values are as follows:

$$\rho \approx 2.6017; \quad \rho' \approx -2.2618; \quad \rho'' \approx 0.3399;$$
$$\rho^2 \approx 6.7688; \quad \rho'^2 \approx 5.1157; \quad \rho''^2 \approx 0.1155.$$

Let us agree to place the coordinate ρ on the axis OX, ρ' on OY, and ρ'' on OZ.

We will now construct an x-chain starting from the point $(1, 1, 1)$, which is obviously a relative minimum. First we must project the basis of the lattice parallel to the rational direction onto the plane $y + z = 0$. The coordinates of the projections or, as we have called them, of the punctures, are found by the formulas

$$\xi = \frac{2x - y - z}{2}; \quad \eta = \frac{y - z}{2}.$$

This gives us the following coordinates for the punctures ρ and ρ^2:

$$\rho \ldots (3.90, \quad -0.96);$$
$$\rho^2 \ldots (4.15, \quad 2.50).$$

We now make a reduction of the basis for the lattice of punctures by means of the algorithm of continued fractions, which it is necessary to apply to the ordinates of the punctures ρ and ρ^2.

$$\rho^2 + 2\rho \ldots (11.96, \quad 0.58);$$
$$\rho^2 + 3\rho \ldots (15.86, \quad -0.38).$$

We must take the puncture $\rho^2 + 3\rho$ for the point ϕ and the puncture $\rho^2 + 2\rho$ for the point ψ. The relative minimum adjacent to $(1, 1, 1)$ can be only a point belonging to the punctures $\phi - \psi$, ϕ, and ψ, since the puncture $\phi + \psi$ is at a distance greater than one unit away from ϕ in the OX direction.

The parallel corersponding to the puncture $\phi - \psi$ includes the point ρ whose space coordinates are $(2.60, -2.26, -0.34)$. This parallel does not contain points within the prism $|y| \leq 1$, $|z| \leq 1$.

The parallel corresponding to the puncture ψ contains the point $\rho^2 + 2\rho$, whose space coordinates are (11.97, 0.59, −0.56). This will be the only point of the parallel lying within the prism $|y| \leq 1$, $|z| \leq 1$.

Points corresponding to the puncture ϕ need not be investigated, since their abscissae will certainly be greater than the abscissa of the point $\rho^2 + 2\rho$.

Hence the point $\rho^2 + 2\rho$ is a relative minimum adjacent to (1, 1, 1) on OX.

In order to find the next relative minimum, we divide the original lattice by $\rho^2 + 2\rho$. We obtain a new lattice whose canonical basis will be

$$\left(1, \ \frac{\rho}{2}, \ \frac{\rho^2}{2}\right).$$

Then we repeat the same process with this lattice.

The punctures of the basis will be

$$\frac{\rho}{2} \dots (1.95, \quad -0.48),$$
$$\frac{\rho^2}{2} \dots (2.08, \quad 1.25).$$

The reduced punctures will be

$$\frac{\rho}{2} \dots (1.95, -0.48) \dots \varphi,$$
$$\frac{\rho^2 - \rho}{2} \dots (0.13, \quad 1.73) \dots \psi.$$

The punctures ψ, $\psi - \phi$ and $\psi + \phi$ are found beyond the limits of the band $|\eta| < 1$. Thus the relative minimum adjacent to (1, 1, 1) belongs to the puncture ϕ. The parallel corresponding to the puncture ϕ contains the point $\rho/2$ with the space coordinates (1.30, −1.13, −0.17). Within the prism $|y| \leq 1$, $|z| \leq 1$, there will be only one point $\rho/2 + 1$ of this parallel. This point will be the relative minimum adjacent to (1, 1, 1) on OX. Division by $\rho/2 + 1$ takes the lattice $(1, \rho/2, \rho^2/2)$ into the lattice $(1, \rho, \rho^2)$. Consequently, the x-chain as it continues will be periodic. The unit ϵ_1 is equal to

$$(\rho^2 + 2\rho)\left(\frac{\rho}{2} + 1\right) = 2\rho^2 + 5\rho + 1.$$

For the determination of the unit ϵ_2 we must construct a z-chain by the same algorithm.

The punctures of the basis in the plane $x + y = 0$ will be

$$\rho \dots (-0.51, \quad 2.43),$$
$$\rho^2 \dots (-5.83, \quad 0.83).$$

The reduced basis of the lattice of punctures will be

$$\rho - 3\rho^2 \ldots (16.97, \quad -0.05) \ldots \varphi,$$
$$\rho - 2\rho^2 \ldots (11.14, \quad -0.78) \ldots \psi.$$

We must investigate points of the parallel corresponding to the punctures $\phi - \psi$, ψ and ϕ.

The parallel $\phi - \psi$ contains the point $-\rho^2$. Its space coordinates are $(-6.77, -5.12, -0.12)$. There exists a point in this parallel within the prism $|x| \leq 1$, $|y| \leq 1$, namely $-\rho^2 + 6$. It is useless to investigate the punctures ϕ and ψ now, since they are at a distance greater than 1 from the puncture $\phi - \psi$. Hence, the relative minimum adjacent to $(1, 1, 1)$ on OZ is $-\rho^2 + 6$. Division by $-\rho^2 + 6$ takes the original lattice into the lattice

$$\left(1, \ \frac{\rho}{2}, \ \frac{\rho^2}{2}\right)$$

Thus $-\rho^2 + 6$ is associated with the element $\rho^2 + 2\rho$ of the x-chain. The unit ϵ_2 is given by the relationship

$$\varepsilon_2 = \frac{-\rho^2 + 6}{\rho^2 + 2\rho} = 2\rho^2 - \rho - 11.$$

The example is solved.

PART B. THE CASE $D < 0$

§ 60. A THEOREM OF VORONOĬ ON NEIGHBORING RELATIVE MINIMA

After examining in detail in the preceding sections generalizations of the algorithm of continued fractions suggested by Voronoĭ for the case $n = 3$, $r = 0$, we now turn to the algorithm suggested by Voronoĭ for the case $n = 3$, $r = 1$, i.e., for the signature space $R_{3,1}$. We will consider a completely arbitrary three-dimensional lattice in $R_{3,1}$, one of whose points is the origin. We require only that the lattice satisfies the following two conditions: 1) the lattice contains no zero divisors, i.e., points different from the origin for which, if ξ, η, and ζ are the coordinates in $R_{3,1}$, then either $\xi + i\eta = 0$ or $\zeta = 0$; in other words, there are no points either on the axis ξ or in the plane ξ, η, i.e., the parameters $\rho = \sqrt{\xi^2 + \eta^2}$ and $|\zeta|$ of any point other than the point O are not equal to zero; 2) there are no points in the lattice that have identical parameters ρ other than points that are symmetric to each other with respect to the origin. We note that the lattices which will be most interesting to us below, namely the irreducible multiplicative lattices and the lattices rationally related to them, satisfy both of these conditions. Condition 1 is the condition of irreducibility, while Condition 2 is satisfied in view of the fact that if there were in the lattice two points ξ, η, ζ and $\bar{\xi}, \bar{\eta}, \bar{\zeta}$ for which $\rho = \bar{\rho}$, i.e., $\xi^2 + \eta^2 = \bar{\xi}^2 + \bar{\eta}^2$, then we would have $(\xi^2 + \eta^2)\zeta = n$ and $(\bar{\xi}^2 + \bar{\eta}^2)\bar{\zeta} = \bar{n}$, where n and $\bar{n}$, being the norms of these points, are rational, so that $\bar{\zeta} = \zeta\bar{n}/n$; but then $\bar{\xi} + i\bar{\eta} = (\xi + i\eta)\bar{n}/n$ and hence $\bar{\rho} = \pm\rho\bar{n}/n$, i.e., $\bar{n}/n = \pm 1$. But this means that either the point $\bar{\xi}, \bar{\eta}, \bar{\zeta}$ or the point $-\bar{\xi}, -\bar{\eta}, -\bar{\zeta}$ symmetric to it with respect to the origin will have a coordinate identical to ζ, and hence the difference of the point ξ, η, ζ and this point will have $\zeta = 0$, i.e., is the point O. Thus, for $\bar{\rho} = \rho$ either the point $\bar{\xi}, \bar{\eta}, \bar{\zeta}$ coincides with the point ξ, η, ζ or is symmetric to it with respect to the origin, i.e., is the point $-\xi, -\eta, -\zeta$.

In the signature space $R_{3,1}$ the normed body of a point is a right circular cylinder whose center is the origin and whose axis is the axis ζ. The given point will be located on the circumference of one of the bases. If the point M of a lattice satisfying Conditions 1 and 2 is a relative minimum of this lattice, i.e., if there are no points other than the point O (which lies in its center) within the normed cylinder of the lattice, then there is only one other point lying on its boundary besides the point M that lies on the circumference of one of its bases. This is the point $-M$ that is symmetric to M with respect to the origin, and it lies on the circumference of the other base, since otherwise there would be in the lattice two points nonsymmetric with respect to the origin and with identical ζ. But then their difference would give a zero divisor, which is impossible in view of Condition 1. We note further that in all the theory of relative minima it is sufficient to consider only points of the lattice in the upper half-space of $R_{3,1}$, i.e., only points with $\zeta > 0$, since both the lattice and the normed body are symmetric with respect to the origin, and every relative minimum has a relative minimum symmetric to it with respect to the origin.

If starting from some relative minimum ψ_1 we carry out the process described in §4 for any n and r, namely if in the given case $n = 3$, $r = 1$ we increase the radius of the normed cylinder without changing its height, then the first point ψ_2 with $\zeta > 0$ that intersects this cylinder (on its lateral surface) will be, in the first place, unique (in view of Condition 2), and secondly, it will be the relative minimum adjacent to ψ_1 in the direction of increasing ρ, i.e., there will be no relative minimum ψ^* for which $\rho_1 < \rho^* < \rho_2$. The point ψ_2 will be a relative minimum because its normed cylinder is a part of the cylinder which is being increased, and until it meets the point ψ_2 this cylinder remains empty inside (except for the point O). It is adjacent to ψ_1 in the direction of increasing ρ because if there were a relative minimum ψ^* with an intermediate value for ρ, then the height of its cylinder would be less than for ψ_2, since otherwise its cylinder would contain the point ψ_1, and ψ^* would not be a relative minimum, or else it would contain two points on one of its bases, which is impossible. But in this case, as the raduis of the cylinder of ψ_2 increases, the first point which would meet this cylinder would be, contrary to assumption, not the point ψ_2 but the point ψ^*. Repeating this process, starting in the same way from ψ_2, we next obtain the relative minimum ψ_3 adjacent to ψ_2 in the direction of increasing ρ, and so on.

Given a lattice in $R_{3,1}$ which satisfies Conditions 1 and 2, any algorithm for finding one relative minimum ψ_1 and then finding successive relative minima in the direction of increasing ρ is called by Voronoĭ a generalization of the algorithm of continued fractions in the signature space $R_{3,1}$.

(Voronoĭ also considers an algorithm for $R_{3,1}$ in which one looks for relative minima in the direction of increasing ζ, but we will not consider it.)

Let M be some nonzero point of the given lattice satisfying Conditions 1 and 2 that need not be a relative minimum, but which is *primary*, i.e., is such that there are no other points of the lattice on the segment OM. In such a case OM may be taken for one of the three vectors of the basis of the given lattice. Thus all the points of the lattice lie on straight lines parallel to OM, where each of these straight lines contains a uniform row of points such that the distance between two neighboring points on one of them is equal to the length of the segment OM. As in

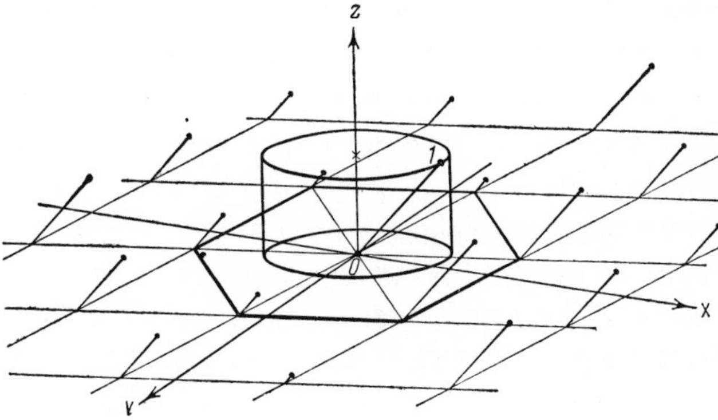

Figure 34

§15, we will call such a row of points a parallel of points. The straight lines containing these parallels of points pass through the points of a two-dimensional lattice constructed on the other two vectors of the basis of the given three-dimensional lattice. They also intersect the plane ξ, η in some two-dimensional lattice which we will denote by S and which is the projection of this two-dimensional lattice parallel to the direction of OM. Only one of the points of the given three-dimensional lattice is a point of the lattice S, namely the point O. In view of Condition 1 there are no more of its points in the remaining points of S. We will call the point of S in which the line of a parallel of points intersects the plane ξ, η the base of this parallel. The segment of each parallel (other than the parallel passing through the point O) from its base to the first point with positive ζ of the given three-dimensional lattice will be called the *pin* corresponding to this parallel, and the point of the given lattice the *head* of this pin, or the pinhead corresponding to the given point S. All the pins are parallel to the vector OM and are in length greater than zero and less than the length of OM (in Figure 34 the vector OM is denoted by 1, while the axes are denoted by x, y, z).

In the two-dimensional lattice S of bases of pins corresponding to the primary point M of the given three-dimensional lattice we consider the acute fundamental triangle, i.e., the so-called reduced triangle of Zelling (see Supplement I), namely that one of the six triangles meeting in the origin that covers the negative direction of the axis ξ. Let its vertices be the origin (0, 0) and the points (1, 0), (0, 1). (We write the coordinates of these points in the plane ξ, η, having chosen for coordinate vectors the sides of the triangle that go through the origin.) The heads of the seven pins inserted into the points (1, 0), (0, 1), (− 1, 0), (0, − 1), (1, − 1), (−1, 1), (1, 1) will be called "Voronoĭ pinheads"; that one of them which has the least ρ will be called the reduced Voronoĭ pinhead corresponding to the given primary point M of the lattice satisfying Conditions 1 and 2.

The algorithm suggested by Voronoĭ for the determination of successive relative minima situated in the direction of increasing ρ in the case $n = 3$, $r = 1$ is based on the following geometric theorem.

THEOREM. *If the reduced Voronoĭ pinhead ψ corresponding to the primary point M of the given lattice satisfying Conditions* 1 *and* 2 *lies outside the normed cylinder of the point M, then M is a relative minimum of the lattice and ψ is the relative minimum adjacent to M in the direction of increasing ρ. If ψ lies within the normed cylinder of the point M, then M is not a relative minimum, and thus there exists a point ψ lying inside the normed cylinder of M.*

For the proof of this remarkable theorem we will consider certain properties of systems of points that we call approximating lattices or approximately rectilinear systems of points. Let S be a two-dimensional lattice of points. We will associate every point in the plane of the lattice with identical and identically situated regions σ, each with respect to its own points.

By the approximating lattice S' we will mean the system of points that is such that each of them is either inside or on the boundary of its region σ, so that to each point of S there corresponds its region σ, while somewhere in each such region σ there is one and only one point of S'. Points of S' may be found in different places in the region σ, i.e., the system S' may in general not be a lattice. The region σ will be called the region of approximation, while the value of the radius r of the least circle that can be circumscribed around a point of S so that the whole region of approximation σ corresponding to this point will be inside the circle will be called the radius of approximation of the approximating lattice S' with respect to the lattice S.

In the general theory of two-dimensional lattices S we have the following theorems (see, for example, Supplement I): 1) a fundamental triangle of the lattice S can always be chosen, and moreover, in only one way (if we do not consider as distinct from it lattices homologous to it, i.e., those obtained from it by parallel translations and those symmetric to it with respect to the point O), as an acute triangle (but if it is a right triangle, then it may be chosen in two ways). Such a fundamental triangle is called reduced according to Zelling; 2) the shortest parameter a of the lattice S (i.e., the shortest segment connecting two points of S) is one of the sides of this triangle; 3) the least height h of the fundamental triangle reduced according to Zelling is not less than $a/\sqrt{2}$.

We note further that the six triangles of Zelling that meet in the point O form a hexagon which may be called the hexagon of Zelling, or the first hexagon of Zelling, and that in general the points of the lattice S are situated on the perimeters of the first, second, third, etc. hexagons of Zelling that are homothetic with respect to the origin and are obtained from the first by a homothetic expansion from the point O linearly, by a factor of two, three, and so on. (See Figure 36.)

Based on these properties of lattices, we may prove the following lemma about approximately rectilinear systems: *the point of the approximating lattice nearest to the point O of a lattice cannot lie beyond the nth reduced hexagon of the lattice, where* $n \leq (2r/a + 1)\sqrt{2}$.

PROOF. The point of the system S' nearest to the point O of the system S cannot be at a greater distance than $a + r$, where a is the least parameter of the system S and r is the radius of approximation of the system S' to the system S. Let the least distance from the point O to the perimeter of the first hexagon of Zelling be h. Then the corresponding distance for the second hexagon is $2h$, and so on. If the point of S' closest to the point O belongs to the nth hexagon of Zelling, then

$$nh - r \leq a + r,$$

from which it follows that

$$n \leq \frac{a + 2r}{h},$$

while

$$h \geq \frac{a}{\sqrt{2}},$$

and hence we obtain

$$n \leq \left(\frac{2r}{a} + 1\right) \sqrt{2}.$$

The application of this lemma on approximating lattices to the proof of the preceding theorem is based on the following. We project orthogonally onto the plane ξ, η all the pinheads of all the pins corresponding to the given primary point M of the three-dimensional lattice under consideration. We obtain in the plane ξ, η a nonrectilinear system of points S' (since the pins are of various lengths), which will approximate the two-dimensional lattice S of bases of pins. The region of approximation has the form of a segment coming from a point of S and coinciding in length and direction with the orthogonal projection of the segment OM onto the plane ξ, η. The radius of approximation will be the length of this projection, which we will denote by r. Let ψ be the Voronoĭ pinhead (out of the seven) that has the least ρ. If it lies within the normed cylinder of the point M, i.e., its orthogonal projection $\overline{\psi}$ onto the plane ξ, η lies inside

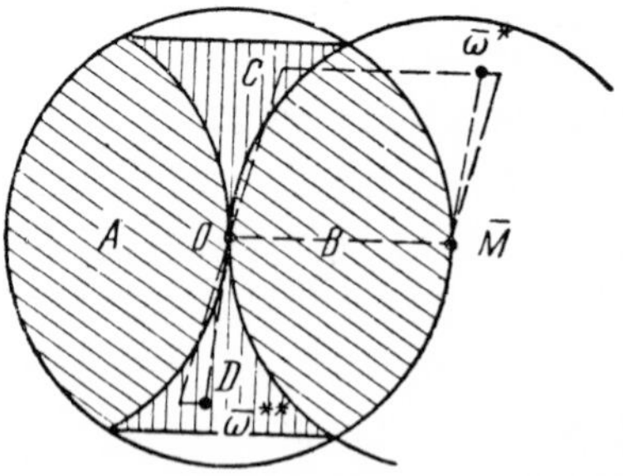

Figure 35

the circle with center at the point O and of radius r, then M is not a relative minimum, and ψ is a point lying within the normed cylinder of the point M. If we take this point ψ for a new point M, and so on, we finally obtain a point M such that the projection corresponding to it of the pinhead $\overline{\psi}$ does not lie within the circle r corresponding to it. We will show that in this case the least parameter a of the corresponding lattice S is not less than $r\sqrt{3}/2$, and then, putting this value into the formula of the lemma, we find that the number n of the hexagon of Zelling that may contain the pinhead of least radius ρ is ≤ 4. Then, having investigated each of the 60 points lying on the first four hexagons of Zelling, we will show that the nearest pinhead is one of the 7 Voronoĭ pinheads, namely the pinhead ψ, since we denoted by ψ the Voronoĭ pinhead with the least ρ. It will follow that if $\overline{\psi}$ lies outside the circle r, then ψ is a relative minimum, in view of the fact that as the radius increases, the normed cylinder of the point M can only encounter points of our lattice that have a ξ less than M has, i.e., only pinheads, while the pinhead out of the whole infinite set of pinheads with least ρ is the pinhead ψ. Moreover, it follows from this that ψ is the relative minimum adjacent to M.

Thus, we first show that if $\overline{\psi}$ lies outside the circle r, then $a \geq r\sqrt{3}/2$. If we assume that $\overline{\psi}$ lies outside the circle r, then a fortiori the projections of the other 6 Voronoĭ pinheads lie outside this circle, since their radii r are larger that the radius of $\overline{\psi}$, i.e., all seven Voronoĭ pinheads lie outside the circle r. We can see that the above inequality already follows from this. In fact, in this case the bases $(1, 0)$, $(0, 1)$, $(-1, 0)$, $(0, -1)$, $(1, -1)$, $(-1, 1)$ of the pins corresponding to them cannot lie within the crescents A and B (Figure 35), since if one of these points lay within the crescent B, then the point symmetric to it with respect to the origin would lie within the crescent A. But then the pinhead corresponding to this point would lie within the normed cylinder of the point M, which we have assumed is impossible. We will see that all these bases also lie outside of the regions C and D. In fact, if one of these bases lay inside one of these regions, for example, inside the region C, then the pinhead ω^* corresponding to it would be outside the cylinder of M; for if ψ lies outside the cylinder of M, then a fortiori the remaining six Voronoĭ pinheads, also do, since they have larger ρ. Hence its projection $\overline{\omega}^*$ would lie beyond the circle r on the segment starting from this base that is equal and parallel to the segment $\overline{OM}$. But in such a case, if we produce from the origin the vector equal to $\overline{\omega}^* \overline{M}$, we will obtain a projection $\overline{\omega}^{**}$ of the Voronoĭ pinhead corresponding to the base symmetric with respect to the origin to

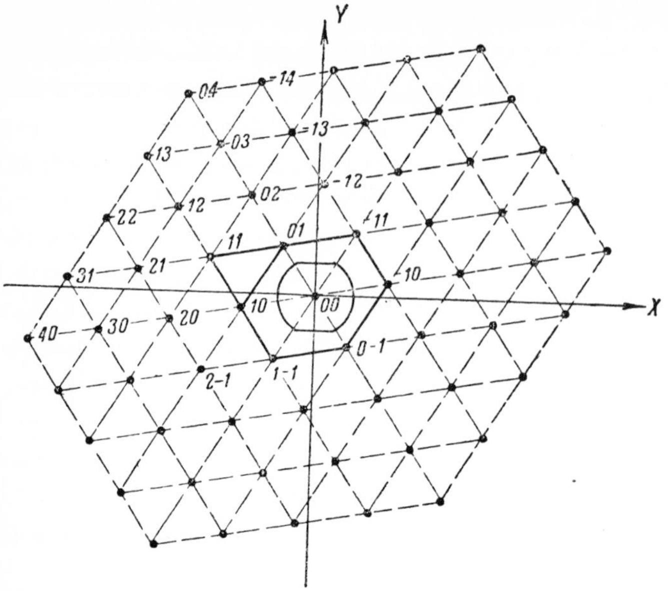

Figure 36

the one under consideration, and this pinhead ω^{**} will be inside the cylinder of M. Moreover, in the given case all the Voronoĭ pinheads must lie outside the cylinder of M. But the point of the lattice S of the bases of pins that is closest to the point O belongs to the first hexagon of Zelling, i.e., is one of the six points $(1, 0)$, $(0, 1)$, $(-1, 0)$, $(0, -1)$, $(1, -1)$, $(-1, 1)$, and hence the least parameter a of the lattice S is in this case no less than the distance from the origin to the perimeter of the region ν constructed from the pieces A, B, C, and D, i.e., it is not less than $r\sqrt{3}/2$.

We now apply this bound in the determination of the number of the hexagon of Zelling to which the pinhead with least ρ belongs. Considering as above the system S' of orthogonal projections of the pinheads onto the plane ξ, η (x, y) as approximating the lattice S, we obtain in this case from the formulas given in the lemma that $n \leq (4/\sqrt{3} + 1)\sqrt{2}$, i.e., $n < 4, 6 \cdots$, i.e., that when the pinhead ψ lies outside the cylinder of the point M, the pinhead with least ρ is not beyond the fourth hexagon of Zelling. Sixty points lie on the first, second, third, and fourth hexagons of Zelling. We will show that the pinhead with the least ρ cannot belong to 53 of these, and that it can only belong to the seven that are

Voronoĭ bases. As before, we will denote the bases of pins by coordinates (i, j) and projections of the corresponding pinheads by $(i, j)'$, so that the collection of points (i, j) gives the lattice S, and the collection of points $(i, j)'$ the system S'. The distance from the point $(i, j)'$ to the origin will be denoted by ρ_{ij}'. We will show that for each of the points $(i, j)'$ other than the points $(1, 0)'$, $(0, 1)'$, $(-1, 0)'$, $(0, -1)'$, $(1, -1)'$, $(-1, 1)'$, $(1, 1)'$ there is a point of S' closer to the

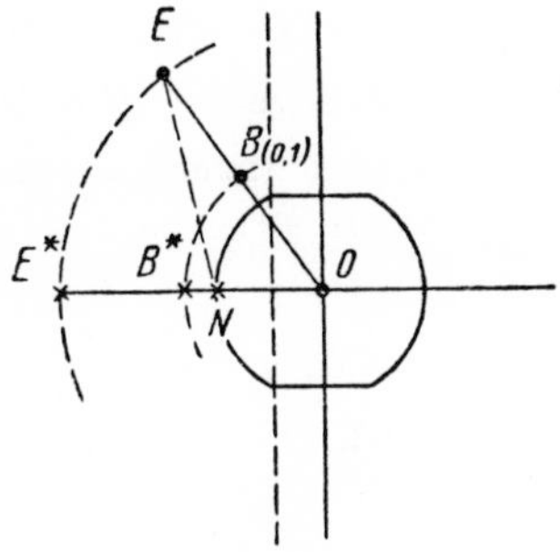

Figure 37

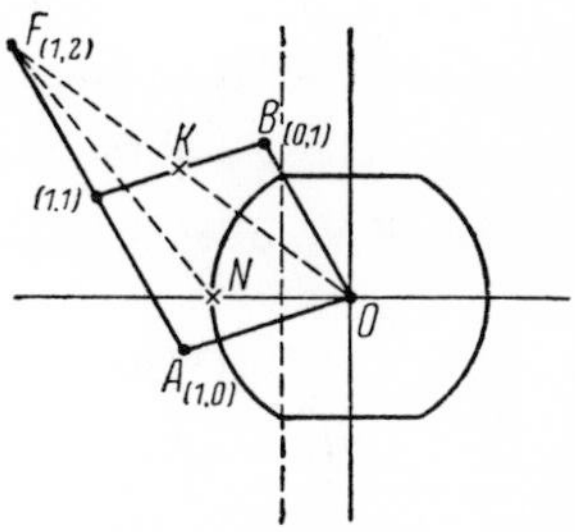

Figure 38

point O. In fact, for example, the point $E'(0, 2)'$ is further from the origin than the point $B'(0, 1)'$, which may be seen from Figure 37 if one takes into consideration that the point $(0, 1)$ lies outside the region ν and that the region S' approximating S is a segment coinciding with OM in length and direction. Hence, instead of the points S', E', and B', we may consider the points S, E, and B, calculating distances not to the point O, but from one of the compared points to the point nearest to it, and from another to the furthest point of the segment ON. For example, let B (Figure 37) lie to the left of $x = -\frac{1}{2}r$; in such a case the point of the segment NO nearest to the point E is the point N, and the furthest point from the point B is the point O, i.e., it is sufficient to show that $EN > BO$. This is true because B lies outside the region ν and to the left of $x = -\frac{1}{2}r$, and hence $BO > NO$, i.e., $E^*N > E^*B^*$; but in such a case $EN > E^*N > E^*B^* = B^*O = BO$. For the case when B lies to the right of $x = -\frac{1}{2}r$ the proof is analogous.

The points $(2, 0)'$, $(2, 2)'$, $(0, 3)'$, $(0, 4)'$, $(3, 0)'$, $(4, 0)'$ and so on may be excluded in the same way.

We now consider the point $F'(1, 2)'$. Again assuming that B lies to the left of $x = -\frac{1}{2}r$, we see that it is sufficient to show that $FN > BO$. But by an argument analogous to the preceding one, $FN > KO$ (Figure 38), where K is the midpoint of FO. But $KO > BO$ since the angle AOB is acute. We may analogously exclude the point F, comparing it with the point B' in the case when B lies to the right of $x = -\frac{1}{2}r$.

In the same way we may exclude the points $(2, 1)'$, $(1, 3)'$, $(-1, 3)'$, $(-1, 4)'$, and so on. There remain only the seven points $(1, 0)'$, $(0, 1)'$, $(-1, 0)'$, $(0, -1)'$, $(1, -1)'$, $(-1, 1)'$, $(1, 1)'$. Hence we obtain that M is a relative minimum, since of these seven points even the point $\bar{\psi}$ that has the smallest radius ρ is by assumption outside the circle r, and the point ψ is the relative minimum adjacent to M.

The theorem of Voronoĭ is thus proved in full.

§61. THE ALGORITHM OF VORONOĬ IN THE CASE $n = 3$, $r = 1$ FOR THE CALCULATION OF A CHAIN OF RELATIVE MINIMA IN THE DIRECTION OF INCREASING ρ, WHEN THE LATTICE IS RATIONALLY CONNECTED WITH AN IRREDUCIBLE MULTIPLICATIVE LATTICE IN $R_{3,1}$ OR IS SIMILAR TO SUCH A LATTICE

We assume that the lattice O consists of integer or fractional points of the cubic field Ω_{α}, where the point α satisfies the irreducible cubic equation $\zeta^3 = q\zeta + n$ that has integer coefficients q and n, and that has one real root α and two complex conjugate roots α' and α'', i.e., it has a negative discriminant $D = 4q^3 - 27n^2$. Let M be one of the "primary" points of the lattice O. We divide all the points of the lattice O by the point M, obtaining on division of the point M by itself the point 1, i.e., the point with coordinates $(1, 0, 1)$. We denote the lattice so obtained by O'. Since M was a primary point, we may take the point 1 for one of the points of the basis. Let the basis $[1, \phi, \psi]$ of the lattice O' have the form

$$\left[1, \frac{m + m'\alpha + m''\alpha^2}{\sigma}, \frac{n + n'\alpha + n''\alpha^2}{\sigma}\right],$$

when expressed in terms of α, where the numbers m, m', m'', n, n', n'' and σ are integers. Then it may be easily calculated that the positive binary quadratic form whose vector pair in the plane consists of vectors going from the point O to points of the plane that are projections parallel to the segment 01 of the second and the third point of this basis is

$$\Phi = Ax^2 + 2Bxy + Cy^2,$$

where

$$\left.\begin{aligned} A &= m'^2 + m'm''\alpha + m''^2(\alpha^2 - q), \\ B &= m'n' + (m'n'' + m''n')\frac{\alpha}{2} + m''n''(\alpha^2 - q), \\ C &= n'^2 + n'n''\alpha + n''^2(\alpha^2 - q), \end{aligned}\right\} \quad (1)$$

if we multiply it by σ. We note further that if $\theta = t + t'\alpha + t''\alpha^2$, then the square of the distance ρ from the point θ to the axis ζ is

$$\rho^2 = [(t + t''q)^2 - t'(t'q + t''n)] + [t''^2 n - tt']\alpha + [t'^2 - t''(t + t''q)]\alpha^2. \quad (2)$$

We obtain the following steps for the algorithm.

(I) If $m'n'' - m''n' < 0$, we replace the basis $[1, \phi, \psi]$ by the basis $[1, \psi, \phi]$. Geometrically this means that we choose for the first number that one of the two numbers ϕ and ψ which has the smaller argument in the plane ξ, η.

(II) We calculate by the formulas (1) the coefficients A, B, and C of the form $\Phi = (A, B, C)$. Geometrically the form (A, B, C) represents the vector pair defining the two-dimensional lattice Y corresponding to the given basis $[1, \phi, \psi]$ of the space lattice O'.

(III) If $B < 0$, then instead of A, B, and C, we take C, $-B$, and A and correspondingly we replace the basis $[1, \phi, \psi]$ by the basis $[1, -\psi, \phi]$.

(IV) If at least one of the conditions $A - B > 0$, $C - B > 0$ is not satisfied, then if $A < C$ we transform the form by the transformation $\begin{bmatrix} 1, & -\delta \\ 0, & 1 \end{bmatrix}$, and transform the basis correspondingly by the transformation $\begin{pmatrix} 1, & 0, & 0 \\ 0, & 1, & -\delta \\ 0, & 0, & 1 \end{pmatrix}$, where $\delta = [B/A]$; while if $C < A$ we transform the form by the transformation $\begin{bmatrix} 1, & 0 \\ -\delta, & 0 \end{bmatrix}$ where $\delta = [B/C]$. It is necessary to perform these two operations until it is not simultaneously true that $A - B > 0$ and $C - B > 0$. Then all three "reduction conditions" will be satisfied by the form, namely $A - B > 0$, $C - B > 0$, and $B > 0$.

All this exactly corresponds to the theory of reduction of a positive binary form as given, for example, in Supplement I. Geometrically steps (III) and (IV) signify the determination of a basic vector pair for the lattice S giving the acute triangle.

(V) If at least one of the inequalities $(m' - m''\alpha)/\sigma = b > 0$; $(n' - n''\alpha)/\sigma = d < 0$ is not satisfied, where σ, being an essentially positive number, need not be taken into consideration, then we choose out of the six pairs of numbers (b, d), $(-b, d)$, $(b-d, b)$, $(-b+d, -b)$, $(d, -b+d)$, $(-d, b-d)$ that unique pair for which both these inequalities are satisfied, and we transform the form (A, B, C) by the corresponding one of the six respective transformations

$$\begin{pmatrix}1&0\\0&1\end{pmatrix}\begin{pmatrix}-1&0\\0&-1\end{pmatrix}\begin{pmatrix}1&1\\-1&0\end{pmatrix}\begin{pmatrix}-1&-1\\1&0\end{pmatrix}\begin{pmatrix}0&-1\\1&1\end{pmatrix}\begin{pmatrix}0&1\\-1&-1\end{pmatrix}.$$

Geometrically this transformation signifies the choice, from the six fundamental acute triangles of the system S that meet in the point 0 and form the first hexagon of Zelling, of one triangle, namely the one covering the negative ξ-axis.

We note that in none of the inequalities of reduction, and also in none of the inequalities for b and d, can there be an equal sign, since from the irreducibility of the equation that is satisfied by α we would obtain in all cases, by equating to zero the coefficients of 1, α, and α^2, that either $m' = m'' = 0$ or $n' = n'' = 0$. But then the lattice O' would not be three-dimensional.

(VI) Let the basis $[1, \phi, \psi]$ be transformed into the basis $[1, \phi_1, \psi_1]$ by means of all the preceding transformations. Then we find rational numbers β and γ such that the numbers $\bar{\phi} = \phi_1 + \beta$ and $\bar{\psi} = \psi_1 + \gamma$ lie between zero and 1. Geometrically this signifies going to a parallel basis, the points $\bar{\phi}$ and $\bar{\psi}$ of which are the lowest points on the corresponding parallels, i.e., are the heads of the corresponding pins.

(VII) We calculate the numbers

$$a = \frac{2(m + m''q) - m'\alpha - m''\alpha^2}{2\sigma}; \qquad c = \frac{2(n + n''q) - n'\alpha - n''\alpha^2}{2\sigma},$$

where the numbers m, m', m'', n, n', n'', and σ corresponding to the basis $[1, \bar{\phi}, \bar{\psi}]$. Further, we assume that $\theta_0 = \bar{\phi}$ or $1 - \bar{\phi}$ (depending on which of the two numbers a or $1 - a$ is less than $\frac{1}{2}$), $\theta_1 = \bar{\psi}$ or $1 - \bar{\psi}$ (depending on which of the two numbers c or $1 - c$ is less than $\frac{1}{2}$), and if $\bar{\psi} - \bar{\phi} > 0$, then either $\theta_2 = \bar{\psi} - \bar{\phi}$ or $1 - \bar{\psi} + \bar{\phi}$ (depending on which of the two numbers $a - c$ or $c - a$ is less than $\frac{1}{2}$). If, however, $\bar{\psi} - \bar{\phi} > 0$, then $\theta_2 = \bar{\psi} - \bar{\phi}$ or $1 - \bar{\psi} + \bar{\phi}$ (depending on which of the two numbers $c - a$ or $a - c$ is less than $\frac{1}{2}$). After determining three numbers θ_0, θ_1, and θ_2 in this way, we discard their denominators, since the only thing that is important to us is the relative magnitudes of the distances ρ_0, ρ_1, and ρ_2 corresponding to the points θ_0, θ_1, and θ_2 that we calculate by (2). We find the least two of these $\rho_g < \rho_h$. However, if the conditions $\rho_2 > \rho_0$, $\rho_2 > \rho_1$ are satisfied simultaneously, and $\bar{\phi} + \bar{\psi} < 1$, $a + c < \frac{1}{2}$, then we must find a fourth number $\theta_3 = \bar{\phi} + \bar{\psi}$, calculate by (2) the ρ_3 corresponding to it, and then choose the two least $\rho_g < \rho_h$ from the three numbers ρ_0, ρ_2, ρ_3.

The points $1, \theta_g, \theta_h$ form a basis for the lattice O, where the second number θ_g is the relative minimum adjacent to 1 in the direction of increasing ρ if $\rho_g > 1$, while θ_h is the pinhead following θ_g at a distance ρ. If $\rho_g < 0$, the point θ_g lies inside the normed cylinder of the point 1.

The geometrical significance of this step is the following: $\bar{\phi}$ and $\bar{\psi}$ are the Voronoĭ pinheads corresponding to the bases (1, 0) and (0, 1); by (a, b) and (c, d) we denote the coordinates ξ, η of these bases; $1 - \bar{\phi}$ and $1 - \bar{\psi}$ are the Voronoĭ pinheads having bases $(-1, 0)$ and $(0, -1)$; as is easily seen, if $a < \frac{1}{2}$, then the pinhead $\bar{\phi}$ has a smaller $\bar{\phi}$ than $1 - \bar{\phi}$, and if $1 - a < \frac{1}{2}$, then the pinhead $1 - \bar{\phi}$ has the smaller ϕ; an analogous statement is true about the pinheads $\bar{\psi}$ and $1 - \bar{\psi}$; if $\bar{\phi} - \bar{\psi} > 0$, then $\bar{\phi} - \bar{\psi}$ is the pinhead $(-1, 1)$, and $1 - \bar{\phi} + \bar{\psi}$ is the pinhead $(1, -1)$, where obviously the first has the smaller ρ if $c - a < \frac{1}{2}$, while the second does if $a - c < \frac{1}{2}$; by these means we reject one Voronoĭ pinhead from each pair (1, 0) $(-1, 0)$, (0, 1) $(0, -1)$, $(1, -1)$ $(-1, 1)$ (the rejected one being clearly the further away) without using the long formula (2) for the calculation of ρ. We use only the calculation of a and c, which may be calculated much more easily than ρ; it remains only to calculate the ρ for the seventh Voronoĭ pinhead (1, 1). This may be done and then we can select from the three out of the first six pinheads that were not eliminated, and from the seventh pinhead, the one with least ρ. This will be the reduced Voronoĭ pinhead. However, the calculation may be reduced further. In fact, it is possible to show (we omit the proof) that the ρ_3 corresponding to the seventh head (1, 1) may be the smallest only if $\rho_2 > \rho_3$, $\rho_2 > \rho_1$, $\phi + \psi < 0$, and $a + c < \frac{1}{2}$. Thus only in this case is it necessary to calculate ρ_3; but on the other hand it is not necessary in this case to calculate ρ_2 (i.e., again because of our knowledge of the values of a and c we eliminate the calculation of one of the ρ). The points $1, \theta_g, \theta_h$ always form a basis in O, since clearly their bases form a fundamental triangle in the two-dimensional lattice S.

(VIII) We replace the basis $[1, \theta_g, \theta_h]$ by the basis $[1, \theta_h/\theta_g, 1/\theta_g]$, i.e., we divide the lattice O' by θ_g and bring it to the form

$$\left[1, \frac{m + m'\alpha + m''\alpha^2}{\sigma}, \frac{n + n'\alpha + n''\alpha^2}{\sigma}\right],$$

where we calculate the numbers m, m', m'', n, n', n'', and σ from analogous numbers for the basis $[1, \theta_g, \theta_h]$ by multiplying the numerators and denominators by ρ_g. The new basis thus obtained will be a basis of some new lattice O''.

Repeating the operations indicated, we obtain successive lattices O^{III}, O^{IV}, and so on.

If the primitive point M of the original lattice O is not a relative minimum in it, i.e., if 1 is not a relative minimum in O', then by the theorem of Voronoĭ, the reduced Voronoĭ pinhead θ_g will lie within the normed cylinder of the point 1. This point will be the point 1 in the lattice O'', and if it is again not a relative minimum in O'', then the reduced Voronoĭ pinhead of this lattice O'' will in turn lie within its normed cylinder, and consequently within the normed cylinder of the point M, and so on. Hence, in a finite number of steps we will arrive at a lattice O^l in which the point 1 is a relative minimum. Each of the successive lattices $O, O', O'', \cdots$ is obtained from the preceding one, and hence from the original lattice O, by the division by some point $R_{3,1}$, i.e., all these lattices are similar. Thus the point 1, which is a relative minimum in the lattice O^l, is obtained from some relative minimum ω of the original lattice by division by itself, and $O^l = (1/\omega)O$.

The lattice O, being rational with respect to an irreducible cubic multiplicative lattice, has multiplicative automorphisms, but in this case the chain of its relative minima repeats periodically, since each relative minimum determines the whole chain. Thus, starting with the lattice O^l, the lattices $O^l, O^{l+1}, O^{l+2}, \ldots$ will already repeat periodically, since, by the theorem of Voronoĭ, beginning with the lattice O^l reduced with respect to the point 1 of this lattice, the Voronoĭ pinhead will always be the relative minimum adjacent to 1 in the direction of increasing ρ. When 1 is a relative minimum of the lattice we will say that the basis $1, \theta_g, \theta_h$ is reduced according to Voronoĭ. Because of the uniqueness of the reduced basis of Voronoĭ for each given lattice (which follows from the rule for the choice of the points θ_g and θ_h), it follows that if the lattice O is rational with respect to an irreducible multiplicative cubic lattice, then the bases reduced according to Voronoĭ of the successive lattices $O^l, O^{l+1}, O^{l+2}, \cdots$ will repeat periodically, and two bases will be the same when the corresponding numbers m, m', m'', n, n', n'', and σ coincide.

§62. THE SOLUTION OF THE PROBLEM OF SIMILARITY OF LATTICES RATIONALLY CONNECTED WITH THE SAME IRREDUCIBLE CUBIC MULTIPLICATIVE LATTICE (I.E., WITH THE SAME CUBIC FIELD), OR OF LATTICES SIMILAR TO SUCH LATTICES

Let O_1 and O_2 be two lattices rationally connected with a given cubic field Ω_α. For one of these we calculate by the preceding algorithm a complete period of reduced Voronoĭ bases, while for the other we go up to the first Voronoĭ basis that occurs. Clearly the lattices O_1 and O_2 are similar if and only if the reduced basis of the second is included among the reduced bases of the first.

In fact, let O be some lattice. All the lattices similar to it which are obtained from it by division by its relative minima, i.e., those in which the point 1 is a relative minimum, will be called normalized lattices similar to it. If O is a lattice rational with respect to a multiplicative lattice, then it will have automorphisms, and hence a finite number of normalized lattices similar to itself.

The lattice $\bar{O}$ is clearly similar to the lattice O if and only if one of the normalized lattices similar to it is included among the normalized lattices similar to the lattice O.

§63. THE CALCULATION OF A BASIC MULTIPLICATIVE AUTOMORPHISM OF A LATTICE RATIONAL WITH RESPECT TO AN IRREDUCIBLE MULTIPLICATIVE LATTICE, OR SIMILAR TO SUCH A LATTICE, WHEN $n = 3$ AND $\tau = 1$

When $n = 3$ and $\tau = 1$ all the multiplicative automorphisms have the form $\epsilon = \pm \epsilon_0^m$ where ϵ_0 is some basic multiplicative automorphism equal to the least power of the basic multiplicative automorphism ϵ_0 (of the corresponding maximal lattice) that is an automorphism of the given lattice, and m assumes all possible ratioanl integer values positive, negative, and zero. This follows directly from the general theorem considered in §4 if we take into consideration that, other than the points 1 and -1, there are no points E in the maximal irreducible lattice where $n = 3$ and $\tau = 1$, all of whose parameters are equal to 1. In fact, if $E = \zeta$, $E' = \xi + i\eta$, $E'' = \xi - i\eta$, then the parameters of this point are $\rho = \sqrt{\xi^2 + \eta^2}$ and $|\zeta|$, and if $|\zeta| = 1$, then $\zeta = \pm 1$. In view of the irreducibility of the lattice, $E = \pm 1$, $E' = \pm 1$, and $E'' = \pm 1$, while all the multiplicative automorphisms of any lattice rationally connected with an irreducible multiplicative lattice are, as was shown in §4, automorphisms of the corresponding maximal lattice. If ϵ and η are multiplicative automorphisms of the given lattice, then clearly $\epsilon\eta$ is also a multiplicative automorphism of the lattice. If ϵ_0 is the basic multiplicative automorphism of the corresponding maximal lattice, and $\epsilon_0 = \epsilon_0^{\mu}$ is its least power that is a multiplicative automorphism of the given lattice, then $\epsilon_0^{k\mu}$, where k is any rational integer is also a multiplicative automorphism of the given lattice. Moreover, no power ϵ_0^t for which t is not divisible by μ can be a multiplicative automorphism of the given lattice, since otherwise, by multiplying it by $\epsilon_0^{k\mu}$ with a correspondingly chosen k, we would obtain a power ϵ_0^{ν} with an exponent $\nu < \mu$ which is also a multiplicative automorphism of the given lattice.

For the calculation of the basic automorphism ϵ_0 of the given lattice, it is clearly sufficient to calculate a complete period of its reduced Voronoĭ bases and to note that then the product of all the second numbers of all these bases (the first numbers are 1) will be ϵ_0. In fact, the second reduced lattice is similar to the original, and is obtained from the first by dividing it by its first relative minimum adjacent to 1 in the direction of increasing ρ, i.e., by the second number of its reduced Voronoĭ basis; the third is obtained analogously from the second by division by the second number of the reduced Voronoĭ basis, and so on. Finally, if the lth coincides with the first, i.e., the period comes to an end, then the lth is obtained from the $(l-1)$st by division of the $(l-1)$st by the second number of the reduced basis of the $(l-1)$st. Hence, the lth, coinciding with the first, is obtained from the first by division of the first by the indicated product of the second numbers of the reduced bases of the first, second, third, $\cdots$ and succeeding reduced lattices similar to the given one.

EXAMPLE. To find the period of the relative minima starting with 1 in the field $\Omega\sqrt[3]{19}$. The basis of this field, i.e., the basis of the lattice O' (see the example in §25), is $[1, \alpha, (1+\alpha+\alpha^2)/3]$, i.e., $m = 0$, $m' = 3$, $m'' = 0$, $n = 1$, $n' = 1$, $n'' = 1$, and $\sigma = 3$. The calculation of α gives $\alpha \approx 2.67$, $\alpha^2 \approx 7.12$.

STEP I. We have $m'n'' - m''n' = 3 > 0$, i.e., we leave the original basis.

STEP II. Calculating by formula (1) of §61 the coefficients A, B, and C of the form Φ, we obtain $\Phi = (9, 7.02, 10.79)$.

STEPS III and IV. These steps are not necessary, since the conditions $A - B > 0$, $C - B > 0$, and $B > 0$ are satisfied, i.e., this form is reduced.

STEP V. $b = m' - m'' \approx 3 > 0$ and $d = n' - n'' \approx -1.67 < 0$, i.e., the triangle corresponding to the given basis covers the negative semiaxis $-X$.

STEP VI. We find the rational integers β and γ from the conditions

$$0<\bar{\varphi}=\varphi_1+\beta=\alpha+\beta<1;\quad 0<\bar{\psi}=\psi_1+\gamma=\frac{1+\alpha+\alpha^2}{3}+\gamma<1,$$

and obtain $\beta = -2$, $\gamma = -3$, and hence $\bar{\phi} = -2 + \alpha$, $\bar{\psi} = (-8 + \alpha + \alpha^2)/3$.

STEP VII. We calculate the numbers a and c and obtain $a \approx -3.34$ and $c \approx -4.30$. Since $a < \frac{1}{2}$, we assume that $\theta_0 = \bar{\phi} = -2 + \alpha$; since $c < \frac{1}{2}$, then $\theta_1 = \bar{\psi} = (-8 + \alpha + \alpha^2)/3$; since $\bar{\phi} > \bar{\psi}$ and $c - a < \frac{1}{2}$, then $\theta_2 = 1 - \bar{\phi} - \bar{\psi} = (1 - 2\alpha + \alpha^2)/3$.

We calculate by formula (2) ρ_0, ρ_1, and ρ_2, obtaining $\rho_0 = 4 + 2\alpha + \alpha^2$, $\rho_1 = 5 + 3\alpha + \alpha^2$, and $\rho_2 = (13 + 7\alpha + \alpha^2)/3$, where $\rho_2 < \rho_0 < \rho_1$ and $1 < \rho_2$, i.e., the first reduced basis is

$$\left[1,\ \frac{1-2\alpha+\alpha^2}{3},\ -2+\alpha\right]. \tag{1}$$

STEP VIII. Transforming this basis by division by its middle member, and then by a cyclic transformation, we obtain the basis

$$\left[1,\ \frac{-7-\alpha+5\alpha^2}{36},\ \frac{13+7\alpha+\alpha^2}{36}\right]$$

for the lattice O''.

We repeat for this basis all eight steps.

I. Here $m'n'' - m''n' = -36 < 0$, i.e., we replace this basis by the basis

$$\left[1,\ \frac{13+7\alpha+\alpha^2}{36},\ \frac{-7-\alpha+5\alpha^2}{36}\right].$$

II. We calculate by the formulas (1) the quadratic form Φ and obtain (74.81, 73.99, 165.65).

III and IV. This form is reduced.

V. The additional conditions $b > 0$ and $d < 0$ are satisfied.

VI. We find the rational integers β and γ from $0 < (13 + 7\alpha + \alpha^2)/36 + \beta < 1$ and $0 < (-7 - \alpha + 5\alpha^2)/36 + \gamma < 1$ and we obtain $\beta = 1$, $\gamma = 0$, from which we get $\bar{\phi} = (-23 + 7\alpha + \alpha^2)/36$ and $\bar{\psi} = (-7 - \alpha + 5\alpha^2)/36$.

VII. $\bar{\phi} \approx 0.08$; $\psi \approx 0.72$; $a \approx -1.00$; $c \approx -0.65$; i.e.,

$$\theta_0=\frac{-23+7\alpha+\alpha^2}{36};\quad \theta_1=\frac{-7-\alpha+5\alpha^2}{36};\quad \theta_2=\frac{4-2\alpha+\alpha^2}{9}$$

and after calculation by the formulas (2) we obtain

$$\rho_0 = \frac{11 + 5\alpha + 2\alpha^2}{36}; \quad \rho_1 = \frac{4 + 13\alpha + \alpha^2}{36}; \quad \rho_2 = \frac{2+\alpha}{3}.$$

Since $\rho_2 > \rho_0$; $\rho_2 > \rho_1$, $\bar{\phi} + \bar{\psi} < 1$ and $a + c < \frac{1}{2}$, we calculate further $\theta_3 = \bar{\phi} + \bar{\psi} = (-5 + \alpha + \alpha^2)/6$ and correspondingly $\rho_3 = (1 + 4\alpha + \alpha^2)/6$.

Since $\rho_0 < \rho_1 < \rho_3$, we get that the basis

$$\left[1, \frac{-23 + 7\alpha + \alpha^2}{36}, \frac{-7 + \alpha + 5\alpha^2}{36}\right] \tag{2}$$

is the reduced basis of O'', i.e., the second reduced basis.

VIII. Transforming this by division by its middle member and then by a cyclic transformation, we again obtain the first reduced basis.

The reduced bases (1) and (2) thus represent a complete period of reduced bases.

The fundamental algebraic unit of the field $\Omega\sqrt[3]{19}$ is hence equal to

$$\varepsilon_0 = \frac{1 - 2\alpha + \alpha^2}{3} \cdot \frac{-23 + 7\alpha + \alpha^2}{36}$$

$$= \frac{-23 + 46\alpha - 23\alpha^2 + 7\alpha - 14\alpha^2 + 133 + \alpha^2 - 38 + 19\alpha}{108} = \frac{2 + 2\alpha - \alpha^2}{3}$$

§64. AN ALGORITHM FOR $D < 0$, BASED ON THE PARALLEL TRANSFORMATION OF A FACTORABLE FORM OF A LATTICE AND OF A FORM POLAR TO IT

In the preceding section we showed that the basic automorphism of a three-dimensional lattice of signature 1 (i.e., one having $D < 0$) that is rationally connected with a multiplicative lattice and contains the point (1, 0, 1) as a point in its basis, may be found by means of the steps indicated in §61.

1. The lattice is projected onto the complex plane XOY parallel to the rational direction. The projection will be a plane lattice.

2. The reduced hexagon of Zelling is found in the projection.

3. The pair of adjacent vertices ϕ and ψ lying on different sides of the "real axis" OX of the complex plane is located in the hexagon of Zelling. The remaining vertices will be $-\phi$, $-\psi$, $\phi - \psi$, and $\psi - \phi$.

4. For the vertices of the hexagon of Zelling and for the point $\phi + \psi$ we find the "pinheads"; that is, the points of the lattice closest to the plane XOY that have a positive real coordinate, and that are projected into the given points

of the projection.

5. From the "pinheads" corresponding to points of the projection symmetric with respect to the origin we choose the points closest to the real axis.

6. From the four points selected in such a manner, we choose the one closest to the axis OZ.

The point chosen as a result of these steps will be the relative minimum adjacent to (1, 0, 1) or, if the point (1, 0, 1) is not itself a relative minimum, then the chosen point will be an interior point for the normed cylinder of the point (1, 0, 1).

7. We divide the lattice by the chosen point and begin the process again with the lattice so obtained.

We continue the process until the original lattice is obtained again. The factor obtained in such a way will transform the lattice into itself and thus be a basic automorphism.

We give a means of carrying out all these steps without the approximate calculations of the coordinates of the points of the basis.

Under the given assumptions about the lattice (the lattice contains the point (1, 0, 1) as one of the points of its basis) the situation of the lattice is completely determined by the assignment of its Dirichlet form (see §§9 and 23).

We agree on the following notation. Coordinates of points of the lattice will be denoted by ρ, α, and β, considering ρ as the real coordinate and α and β as the components of the complex coordinates. The complex coordinates $\alpha \pm \beta i$ will be denoted by ρ' and ρ''. Points of the lattice will be denoted with the same letters used to denote their real coordinates. A basis of the lattice will be denoted by $(1, \rho_1, \rho_2)$. Coordinates of points of the lattice with respect to the basis will be correspondingly w, u, and v, and the Dirichlet form for the lattice will be written as in §23 in a triangular form

$$\begin{matrix} H, & K, & L, & M \\ & E, & F, & G \\ & & B, & C \\ & & & 1 \end{matrix}$$

which means

$$w^3 + w^2(Bu + Cv) + w(Eu^2 + Fuv + Gv^2) + Hu^3 + Ku^2v + Luv^2 + Mv^3.$$

The basis of the lattice and its Dirichlet form will repeatedly undergo transformations. We will denote the results of all the transformations in the same way, without indicating any change in the basis or in the coefficients of the form.

We keep in mind here that when subjecting the basis to a transformation with a certain matrix, we must subject the Dirichlet form to a transformation with the transposed matrix.

We turn to the consideration of the individual steps of the algorithm.

FIRST STEP. Projection of the lattice.

Let the Dirichlet form for the basis $[1, \rho_1, \rho_2]$ be

$$N(\rho) = \begin{matrix} HKLM \\ EFG \\ BC \\ 1 \end{matrix}$$

where $\rho = w + u\rho_1 + v\rho_2$.

The projection of the point ρ onto the complex plane parallel to the rational direction will have the coordinates

$$\xi = u(\alpha_1 - \rho_1) + v(\alpha_2 - \rho_2), \quad \eta = u\beta_1 + v\beta_2.$$

We associate with the lattice the binary cubic form

$$f(u, v) = \eta(\xi^2 + \eta^2) = \eta(\xi + i\eta)(\xi - i\eta) = \frac{1}{2i}(\rho' - \rho'')(\rho' - \rho)(\rho'' - \rho).$$

The form $f(u, v)$ has real coefficients. Moreover, it differs by only a constant factor from some form with rational coefficients which may be easily constructed, given the contravariant of Cayley for the original Dirichlet form.

In fact, the Cayley form differs by only a constant factor from the form

$$\begin{vmatrix} w & u & v \\ 1 & \rho_1' & \rho_2' \\ 1 & \rho_1'' & \rho_2'' \end{vmatrix} \cdot \begin{vmatrix} 1 & \rho_1 & \rho_2 \\ w & u & v \\ 1 & \rho_1'' & \rho_2'' \end{vmatrix} \cdot \begin{vmatrix} 1 & \rho_1 & \rho_2 \\ 1 & \rho_1' & \rho_2' \\ w & u & v \end{vmatrix}.$$

Setting $w = 0$ in the Cayley form, we obtain a form that differs by only a constant factor from the form

$$[u(\rho_2' - \rho_2'') - v(\rho_1' - \rho_1'')] \cdot [u(\rho_2'' - \rho_2) - v(\rho_1'' - \rho_1)] \cdot [u(\rho_2 - \rho_2') - v(\rho_1 - \rho_1')],$$

from which the form that interests us may be obtained by division by $2i$ and the replacement of v by u and of u by $-v$.

Thus, in order to find (with accuracy up to a constant real factor) the binary form corresponding to the projection of the original lattice, it is necessary to find the Cayley form

$$\begin{matrix} H'K'L'M' \\ E'F'G' \\ B'C' \\ A' \end{matrix}$$

and take its upper line (which is the same as setting w equal to 0) and compose the form

$$(M', \ -L', \ K', \ -H') = M'u^3 - L'u^2v + K'uv^2 - H'v^3.$$

This will be a form with rational coefficients from which the form $\eta(\xi^2 + \eta^2)$ differs by only a real constant factor.

When the original lattice is a ring, this form will coincide with the indexform of the ring and may be found without constructing the contravariant.

However, even in this case, in the second step of the algorithm, if after division by the relative minimum the lattice ceases to be a ring, then the construction of the contravariant is again necessary and must be calculated from the beginning.

SECOND STEP. Determination of the reduced hexagon of Zelling.

In order to find the hexagon of Zelling, it is sufficient to find one basis whose points form an acute triangle with the origin. There are six such bases and their points form the vertices of the hexagon of Zelling. The cubic binary form corresponding to such a basis will be said to be reduced. Without having recourse to approximate calculations the reduction of the cubic form may be carried out by the same method as in the analogous reduction for positive quadratic forms, using the inequality $bc - ad > 0$ for the coefficients given in §33, an inequality which is necessary and sufficient for the basic vectors to form an acute angle. Using this inequality we may reduce the cubic form as was done in §33, in a manner similar to the reduction of quadratic positive forms. We list these steps.

α) If at first $bc - ad < 0$, we perform the transformation $\begin{pmatrix} 1, & 1 \\ 0, & 1 \end{pmatrix}$ as many times as necessary to obtain for the first time that $bc - ad$ is positive.

β) We carry out the transformation $\begin{pmatrix} 1, & 0 \\ -1, & 0 \end{pmatrix}$ as many times as possible without destroying the positiveness of $bc - ad$.

γ) We carry out the transformation $\begin{pmatrix} 1, & -1 \\ 0, & 1 \end{pmatrix}$ as many times as possible without destroying the positiveness of $bc - ad$.

Then we alternate the operations β and γ until it is no longer possible to make any changes in this way.

The form obtained by these operations will be a reduced form.

Simultaneously we must transform the Dirichlet and Cayley forms, transforming the variables u and v in the Dirichlet form covariantly with transformations of the binary form, and the same variables in the Cayley form contravariantly.

THIRD STEP. It is first necessary for us to pass from one of the acute basic triangles to all the remaining ones. In order to do this it is necessary to make the transformation $\begin{pmatrix} 0, & -1 \\ 1, & -1 \end{pmatrix}$ five times. From the original form and the five new ones it is necessary to choose a form corresponding to the triangle whose vertices lie on opposite sides of the axis $O\xi$. The coordinates η_1 and η_2 of the vertices of such a triangle must be opposite in sign. From the formulas defining the coefficients of the form in terms of the basis we see that the signs of η_1 and η_2 coincide with the signs of the coefficients a and d. Hence it is necessary to choose from the six reduced forms the one for which the signs of a and d are different. There are two such forms, differing in sign. It is immaterial which of the two is chosen.

Having made a choice of a binary form, it is necessary to subject the Dirichlet and Cayley forms to the corresponding transformation.

The fourth, fifth, and sixth steps are next carried out from the beginning for the points ϕ and ψ of the chosen basis, and only then is our attention turned to the investigation of the points $\phi - \psi$ and $\phi + \psi$. We describe these steps for the points ϕ and ψ.

FOURTH STEP. Let

$$N(\varpi + u\varphi + v\psi) = \begin{matrix} HKLM \\ EFG \\ BC \\ 1 \end{matrix}$$

be the Dirichlet form after the first three steps.

We must now turn from the points ϕ and ψ to their "pinheads," i.e., to the points $\phi + t_1$ and $\psi + t_2$ with some integers t_1, and t_2 such that

$$0 < \phi + t_1 < 1; \quad 0 < \psi + t_2 < 1.$$

It is easy to find the numbers t_1 and t_2, since the sign of the real coordinate and the sign of the norm coincide.

But the norms of the numbers $t_1 + \phi$ and $t_2 + \psi$ are easy to find from the Dirichlet form:

$$N(t_1 + \phi) = t_1^3 + Bt_1^2 + Et_1 + H.$$

The least integer for which $N(t_1 + \phi) > 0$ is t_1. Hence t_1 will be the least integer larger than the root of the equation

$$t^3 + Bt^2 + Et + H = 0.$$

In the same way, t_2 will be the least integer larger than the root of the equation

$$t^3 + Ct^2 + Gt + M = 0.$$

To go to the basis consisting of the "pinheads" it is necessary to subject the Dirichlet form to the transformations

$$\begin{pmatrix} 1 & t_1 & 0 \\ 0 & 1 & 0 \\ 0 & 0 & 1 \end{pmatrix} \text{ and } \begin{pmatrix} 1 & 0 & t_2 \\ 0 & 1 & 0 \\ 0 & 0 & 1 \end{pmatrix}.$$

The Cayley form must be subjected to the contravariant transformations.

FIFTH STEP. If ρ is the "pin" for the projection of ω, then the pin of the projection of $-\omega$ will be $1 - \rho$. Thus, in order to carry out the fifth step, it is necessary to be able to choose from the points ρ and $1 - \rho$ that one which is closest to the axis OZ. The square of the distance from the point ρ to OZ id clearly equal to $\rho'\rho''$.

Similarly, the square of the distance from the point $1 - \rho$ to the axis OZ is equal to $(1 - \rho')(1 - \rho'')$. We form the difference of these squares,

$$\rho'\rho'' - (1 - \rho')(1 - \rho'') = \rho' + \rho'' - 1 = s - 1 - \rho,$$

where $s = \rho + \rho' + \rho''$.

This difference will be positive or negative, depending on the sign of its norm $N(s - 1 - \rho)$, which is easy to find, if we know the Dirichlet form and the expression for ρ in terms of the basis.

Thus, if $N(s - 1 - \rho) < 0$, then the point ρ is situated closer to OZ than $1 - \rho$, while if $N(s - 1 - \rho) > 0$, then the point ρ is further from OZ.

Applying this to the basis ϕ, ψ of the lattice at which we arrive after the first four steps, we obtain the following inequalities:

if $(E - B + 1)(B - 1) < H$, then ϕ is closer to OZ than $1 - \phi$,
if $(E - B + 1)(B - 1) > H$, then ϕ is further from OZ than $1 - \phi$,
if $(G - C + 1)(C - 1) < M$, then ψ is closer to OZ than $1 - \psi$,
if $(G - C + 1)(C - 1) > M$, then ψ is further from OZ than $1 - \psi$.

After examining these inequalities, we turn when necessary from the basis $[1, \phi, \psi]$ to one of the bases $[1, \phi, 1-\psi]$, $[1, 1-\phi, \psi]$, and $[1, 1-\phi, 1-\psi]$. Here is it necessary to subject the Dirichlet and Cayley forms to the corresponding transformations.

SIXTH STEP. Let

$$N(w+u\varphi+v\psi)=\begin{matrix}HKLM\\EFG\\BC\\1\end{matrix}$$

be the Dirichlet form after the fifth step.

We must clarify which of the points ϕ or ψ is situated closer to OZ. We form the difference of the squares of the distances from these points to OZ.

$$\varphi'\varphi''-\psi'\psi''=\frac{H}{\varphi}-\frac{M}{\psi}=\frac{H\psi-M\varphi}{\varphi\psi}.$$

The sign of this difference will coincide with the sign of its norm, which is easy to find from its Dirichlet form:

$$N(\varphi'\varphi''-\psi'\psi'')=\frac{N(H\psi-M\varphi)}{N(\varphi)\cdot N(\psi)}=\frac{MH^3-LMH^2+KM^2H-HM^3}{HM}=$$
$$=H^2-LH+KM-M^2.$$

Hence if $H^2-LH+KM-M^2<0$, the point ϕ lies closer to OZ than the point ψ, and conversely ψ is closer to OZ than ϕ for the inequality in the opposite direction.

After this we must pass (by means of the corresponding transformation of the Dirichlet form) from the basis $[1, \phi, \psi]$ to one of the bases $[1, \phi, \psi-\phi]$ and $[1, \phi-\psi, \phi]$, depending upon which of the points ϕ and ψ is situated closer to OZ. We then carry out again steps four, five, and six on the Dirichlet form so obtained.

If it turns out that the point $\pm(\phi-\psi)$ (or a point parallel to it) is closer to OZ than ϕ and ψ, then the calculations are finished. The closest point will be the relative minimum adjacent to 1 or a point inside the normed cylinder of the point 1. We end with a basis consisting of the point 1, the desired point, and one of the points ϕ, ψ and with the Dirichlet and Cayley forms corresponding to it.

SEVENTH STEP. Division by the desired point is obtained by division of the Dirichlet form by the norm of the desired point, which is equal to one of the derivatives of the Dirichlet form. After this, in order to preserve the uniqueness of the step, we make a complete cyclic permutation of the variables so as to preserve the name w for the coefficient of 1 in the expression $w + u\rho_1 + v\rho_2$ for points of the lattice in terms of the basis. For the Dirichlet form this permutation will simply look like a rotation of the triangular symbol consisting of the coefficients.

It is also necessary to "turn" the Cayley form in the same direction and through the same angle as the Dirichlet form. We need the Cayley form only in the construction of the binary form, and we are interested in the latter only up to a constant factor, so the Cayley form may be multiplied or divided by any desired quantity.

Having completed the seventh step, we repeat the process from the beginning until we obtain a Dirichlet form identical with the one obtained as the result of the first four steps the first time.

EXAMPLE. Find the basic unit of the field $\Omega(\sqrt[3]{19})$.

SOLUTION. The basis of the lattice is $\left[1,\ \rho,\ \dfrac{1+\rho+\rho^2}{3}\right]$, where $\rho = \sqrt[3]{19}$.

The Dirichlet form is

$$\begin{matrix} 19, & & 19, & & 0, & & 12 \\ & 0, & & -19, & & -6 & \\ & & 0, & & 1 & & \\ & & & 1. & & & \end{matrix}$$

The Cayley form is

$$\begin{matrix} 2, & & 1, & & -3, & & 3 \\ & 6, & & -17, & & -3 & \\ & & 6, & & 1 & & \\ & & & 40. & & & \end{matrix}$$

FIRST STEP. The form corresponding to the projection is

$$(3,\ 3,\ 1,\ -2).$$

SECOND STEP. $bc - ad > 0$:

$$(3,\ 3,\ 1,\ -2)\begin{pmatrix}1 & -1\\ 0 & 1\end{pmatrix} = (3,\ -6,\ 4,\ -3);\quad bc - ad < 0;$$
$$(3,\ 3,\ 1,\ -2)\begin{pmatrix}1 & 0\\ -1 & 1\end{pmatrix} = (3,\ -7,\ 7,\ -2);\quad bc - ad < 0.$$

The form $(3, 3, 1, -2)$ is reduced.

THIRD STEP. The form $(3, 3, 1, -2)$ itself has extreme coefficients with opposite signs.

FOURTH STEP. $t_1 = -2$; $t_2 = -3$. The new basis is $1,\ \rho - 2,\ (1 + \rho + \rho^2)/3 - 3$. The transformations of the Dirichlet form are

$$\begin{array}{rrrr} {}_{-2}19, & 19, & 0, & 12 \\ \nwarrow & 0, & -19, & -6 \\ & & 0, & 1 \\ & & & 1 \end{array} = \begin{array}{rrrr} 11, & 61, & 12, & 12 \\ & 12, & -23, & -6 \\ & & -6, & 1 \\ & & & 1 \end{array}$$

(the symbol $\overset{-2}{\nwarrow}$ designates the direction and the number with which we are carrying out Horner's method) and

$$\begin{array}{rrrr} 11, & 61, & 12, & 12 \\ & 12, & -23, & -6 \\ & & -6, & 1 \\ & & & 1 \end{array} \overset{-3}{\nearrow} = \begin{array}{rrrr} 11, & 25, & 27, & 12 \\ & 12, & 13, & 15 \\ & & -6, & -8 \\ & & & 1. \end{array}$$

The transformation of the Cayley form is

$$\underset{2}{\searrow}\begin{array}{rrrr} 2, & 1, & -3, & 3 \\ & 6, & -17, & -3 \\ & & 6, & 1 \\ & & & 40 \end{array} \underset{3}{\swarrow} = \begin{array}{rrrr} 2, & 1, & -3, & 3 \\ & 18, & -13, & -9 \\ & & 54, & -29 \\ & & & 92 \end{array} \underset{3}{\swarrow} = \begin{array}{rrrr} 2, & 1, & -3, & 3 \\ & 21, & -31, & 18 \\ & & -12, & -2 \\ & & & 5. \end{array}$$

FIFTH STEP.

$(E - B + 1)(B - 1) - H = -7 \cdot 19 - 11 < 0$; ρ_1 is closer to OZ than $1 - \rho_1$;
$(G - C + 1)(C - 1) - M = -9 \cdot 24 - 12 < 0$; ρ_2 is closer to OZ than $1 - \rho_2$.

We leave the forms unchanged.

SIXTH STEP.

$$H^2 - LH + KM - M^2 = 11^2 - 11 \cdot 27 + 25 \cdot 12 - 12^2 = -20 < 0.$$

ρ_1 is closer to OZ than ρ_2.

Now we must turn to the basis $[1, \rho_1, \rho_2 - \rho_1]$ and carry out steps four, five, and six. It is not necessary to construct the complete Dirichlet form for steps four and five. It is sufficient to construct its "right edge," i.e., the form

$$N(w + v(\rho_2 - \rho_1)) = w^3 - 2w^2v + 14wv^2 - v^3.$$

STEP 4'. $t_2 = 1$; $(1, \overset{\longrightarrow 1}{-2, 14}, -1) = (1, 1, 13, 12)$.

STEP 5'. $(G - C + 1)(C - 1) - M = -12 < 0$; $\rho_2 - \rho_1 + 1$ is closer to OZ than $\rho_1 - \rho_2$.

The Dirichlet form is

$$\begin{array}{rrrr} 11, & 25, & \overset{\rightarrow -1}{27,} & 12 \\ & 12, & 13, & 15 \\ & & -6, & -8 \\ & & & 1 \end{array} \overset{1}{\nearrow} = \begin{array}{rrrr} 11, & -8, & 10, & -1 \\ & 12, & -11, & 14 \\ & & -6, & -2 \\ & & & 1 \end{array} \overset{1}{\nearrow} = \begin{array}{rrrr} 11, & 4, & -7, & 12 \\ & 12, & -23, & 13 \\ & & -6, & 1 \\ & & & 1. \end{array}$$

SIXTH STEP. $H^2 - HL + KM - M^2 = 11^2 + 11 \cdot 7 - 4 \cdot 12 - 12^2 = 6 > 0$; $\rho_2 - \rho + 1$ is closer to OZ than ρ_1.

Hence $\rho_2 - \rho_1 + 1 = (1 - 2\rho + \rho^2)/3$ is the relative minimum next to 1.

The final Cayley form is

$$\begin{array}{ccccccc} 2, & & 1, & \overset{1\leftarrow}{} & -3, & & 3 \\ & 21, & & -31, & & 18 & \\ & & -12, & & -2 & & \\ & & & 5 & & & \end{array} \overset{\swarrow}{{}_{-1}} = \begin{array}{ccccccc} 3, & & 4, & & 6, & & 3 \\ & 8, & & 5, & & 18 & \\ & & -14, & & -2 & & \\ & & & 5 & & & \end{array} \overset{\swarrow}{{}_{-1}} = \begin{array}{ccccccc} 3, & & 4, & & 6, & & 3 \\ & 4, & & -7, & & 9 & \\ & & -13, & & -29 & & \\ & & & 22. & & & \end{array}$$

SEVENTH STEP.

The Dirichlet form is

$$\begin{array}{ccccccc} 1, & & -6, & & 12, & & 11 \\ & 1, & & -23, & & 4 & \\ & & 13, & & -7 & & \\ & & & 12. & & & \end{array}$$

We do not write the factor 1/12. We will remember it in the fifth step, the only step where this factor is needed.

The Cayley form is

$$\begin{array}{ccccccc} 22, & & -13, & & 4, & & 3 \\ & -29, & & -7, & & 4 & \\ & & 9, & & 6 & & \\ & & & 3. & & & \end{array}$$

The basis is $[1, 3/(\rho^2 - 2\rho + 1), \rho - 2/(\rho^2 - 2\rho + 1)] =$ $[1, (\rho^2 + 7\rho + 13)/36, (5\rho^2 - \rho - 7)/36]$.

FIRST STEP. The form corresponding to the projection is

$$(3, -4, -13, -22).$$

SECOND STEP. $bc - ad > 0$;

$$(3, -4, -13, -22)\begin{pmatrix} 1 & -1 \\ 0 & 1 \end{pmatrix} = (3, -13, 4, -16); \qquad bc - ad < 0;$$

$$(3, -4, -13\ -22)\begin{pmatrix} 1 & 0 \\ -1 & 1 \end{pmatrix} = (16, -44, 53, -22); \quad bc - ad < 0.$$

The form $(3, -4, -13, -22)$ is reduced.

THIRD STEP. The extreme coefficients of $(3, -4, -13, -22)$ have different signs.

FOURTH STEP. $t_1 = -1$; $t_2 = 0$.

The basis is $[1, (\rho^2 + 7\rho - 23)/36, (5\rho^2 - \rho - 7)/36]$.

The Dirichlet form is

$$\begin{array}{cccc} 1, & -6, & 12, & 11 \\ & 1, & -23, & 4 \\ & & 13, & -7 \\ & & & 12 \end{array} \ {\scriptstyle -1}\nwarrow \quad = \quad \begin{array}{cccc} 1, & 10, & 8, & 11 \\ & 11, & -9, & 4 \\ & & -23, & -7 \\ & & & 12. \end{array}$$

The Cayley form is

$$\begin{array}{cccc} 22, & -13, & 4, & 3 \\ & -29, & -7, & 4 \\ & & 9, & 6 \\ & & & 3 \end{array} \ \searrow{\scriptstyle -1} \quad = \quad \begin{array}{cccc} 22, & -13, & 4, & 3 \\ & 37, & -33, & 8 \\ & & 17, & -14 \\ & & & 5. \end{array}$$

FIFTH STEP.

$$(E-B+1)(B-1)-H=\frac{1}{144}[(11+23+12)(-23-12)-1\cdot 12]<0,$$

$$(G-C+1)(C-1)-M=\frac{1}{144}[(4+7+12)(-7-12)-11\cdot 12]<0.$$

Hence ρ_1 is closer to OZ than $1-\rho_1$ and ρ_2 is closer to OZ than $1-\rho_2$.

SIXTH STEP.

$$H^2-HL+KM-M^2=1-8+10\cdot 11-11^2<0;$$

ρ_1 is closer to OZ than ρ_2.

The preliminary calculation before the transfer to the basis $[1, \rho_1, \rho_2-\rho_1]$:

$$N(w+v\rho_2-v\rho_1)=12w^3+16w^2v+24wv^2+12v^3.$$

STEP 4′. $t_2=0$.

STEP 5′.

$$(G-C+1)(C-1)-M=\frac{1}{144}[(24-16+12)(16-12)-12^2]<0;$$

$\rho_2-\rho_1$ is closer to OZ than $1-\rho_2+\rho_1$.

STEP 6′.

The transfer to the basis $[1, \rho_1, \rho_2-\rho_1]$:

$$\begin{array}{cccc} 1, & \overset{\rightarrow\, -1}{10,} & 8, & 11 \\ & 11, & -9, & 4 \\ & & -23, & -7 \\ & & & 12 \end{array} \quad = \quad \begin{array}{cccc} 1, & 7, & -9, & 12 \\ & 11, & -31, & 24 \\ & & -23, & 16 \\ & & & 12 \end{array}$$

$$H^2-HL+KM-M^2=1+9+7\cdot 12-12^2<0;$$

ρ_1 is closer to OZ than $\rho_2-\rho_1$.

Preliminary calculation before the transfer to the basis $[1, \rho_1, \rho_1+\rho_2]$:

$$N(w + v\rho_1 + v\rho_2) = 12w^3 - 30w^2v + 6wv^2 + 30v^3.$$

S STEP 4″. $t_2 = 0$.

STEP 5″. $(G - C + 1)(C - 1) - M = \frac{1}{144}[-48 \cdot 31 - 30 \cdot 12] < 0$; $\rho_1 + \rho_2$ is closer to OZ than $1 - \rho_1 - \rho_2$.

STEP 6″.

The transfer to the basis $[1, \rho_1, \rho_1 + \rho_2]$:

$$\begin{array}{ccccccc} 1, & \overset{\longrightarrow 1}{10,} & 8, & 11 & & & \\ & 11, & -9, & 4 & & & \\ & & -23, & -7 & & & \\ & & & 12 & & & \end{array} = \begin{array}{cccc} 1, & 13, & 31, & 30 \\ & 11, & 13, & 6 \\ & & -23, & -30 \\ & & & 12 \end{array}$$

$$H^2 - HL + KM - M^2 = 1 - 31 + 13 \cdot 30 - 30^2 < 0;$$

ρ_1 is closer to OZ than $\rho_1 + \rho_2$.

Hence, ρ_1 is the relative minimum next to 1.

SEVENTH STEP.

The new basis is $[1, (5\rho^2 - \rho - 7)/(\rho^2 + 7\rho - 23), 36/(\rho^2 + 7\rho - 23)] = [1, (\rho^2 + 4\rho + 10)/3, (2\rho^2 + 5\rho + 11)/3]$.

The Dirichlet form is

$$\begin{array}{cccc} 11, & 4, & -7, & 12 \\ & 8, & -9, & -23 \\ & & 10, & 11 \\ & & & 1. \end{array}$$

The Cayley form is

$$\begin{array}{cccc} 3, & 8, & -14, & 5 \\ & 4, & -33, & 37 \\ & & -13, & 37 \\ & & & 22. \end{array}$$

We could now end our calculations, since our last basis is clearly equivalent to the original one. However, we will carry out the first four steps for a check.

FIRST STEP.

The projection is $(5, 14, 8, -3)$.

SECOND STEP. $bc - ad > 0$;

$$
\begin{array}{lll}
(5,\ 14,\ 8,\ -3)\begin{pmatrix}1 & -1\\ 0 & -1\end{pmatrix} & =(5,\ -1,\ -5,\ -2); & bc-ad>0;\\
(5,\ -1\ \ -5,\ -2)\begin{pmatrix}1 & -1\\ 0 & 1\end{pmatrix} & =(5,\ -16,\ 12,\ -3); & bc-ad<0;\\
(5,\ -1,\ -5,\ -2)\begin{pmatrix}1 & 0\\ -1 & 1\end{pmatrix} & =(3,\ 3,\ 1,\ -2); & bc-ad>0;\\
(3,\ 3,\ 1,\ -2)\begin{pmatrix}1 & 0\\ -1 & 1\end{pmatrix} & =(3,\ -5,\ 4,\ -2); & bc-ad<0;\\
(3,\ 3,\ 1,\ -2)\begin{pmatrix}1 & -1\\ 0 & 1\end{pmatrix} & =(3,\ -6,\ 4,\ -3); & bc-ad<0.
\end{array}
$$

Thus the form $(3,\ 3,\ 1,\ -2)$ is reduced.

The transformation of the Dirichlet form is

$$
\begin{array}{cccc}
11, & 4, & \overset{\rightarrow\ -1}{-7}, & 12\\
 & 8, & -9, & -23\\
 & & 10, & 11\\
 & & & 1
\end{array}
=
\begin{array}{cccc}
11, & -29, & 18, & 12\\
 & 8, & -25, & -6\\
 & & 10, & 1\\
 & & & 1
\end{array}
\qquad
\begin{array}{cccc}
11, & \overset{-1\ \leftarrow}{-29}, & 18, & 12\\
 & 8, & -25, & -6\\
 & & 10, & 1\\
 & & & 1
\end{array}
=
\begin{array}{cccc}
46, & -29, & -18, & 12\\
 & 27, & -13, & -6\\
 & & 9, & 1\\
 & & & 1.
\end{array}
$$

FOURTH STEP. $t_1 = -5$; $t_2 = -3$.

$$
\begin{array}{cccc}
46, & -29, & -18, & 12\\
{}_{-5}\ 27, & -13, & -6\ {}_{-3} & \\
 & 9, & 1 & \\
 & & 1 &
\end{array}
=
\begin{array}{cccc}
11, & 25, & 27, & 12\\
 & 12, & 13, & 15\\
 & & -6, & -8\\
 & & & 1.
\end{array}
$$

We obtain a form that coincides with the form obtained after the fourth step the first time. Hence the lattices of the first and third steps coincide.

The fundamental unit ϵ_0 is equal to

$$\frac{1-2\rho+\rho^2}{3}\cdot\frac{\rho^2+7\rho-23}{36}=\frac{-\rho^2+2\rho+2}{3}.$$

The problem is solved.

TABLE of fundamental units for all cubic fields having negative discriminants no larger than 379 in absolute value

(Calculated by B. Delone and K. Latyševa)

$-D$		
23	$\varepsilon^3 = -\varepsilon^2 + 1$	
31	$\varepsilon^3 = -\varepsilon + 1$	
44	$\varepsilon^3 = -\varepsilon^2 - \varepsilon + 1$	
59	$\varepsilon^3 = -2\varepsilon + 1$	
76	$\varepsilon^3 = \varepsilon^2 - 3\varepsilon + 1$	
83	$\varepsilon^3 = -2\varepsilon^2 - 2\varepsilon + 1$	
87	$\varepsilon^3 = -\varepsilon^2 - 2\varepsilon + 1$	
104	$\varepsilon^3 = \varepsilon^2 - 5\varepsilon + 1$	$\Delta = 2$
	$\varepsilon = -\rho^2 + \rho + 1$	
	$\rho^3 = \rho + 2$	
107	$\varepsilon^3 = 2\varepsilon^2 - 4\varepsilon + 1$	
108	$\varepsilon^3 = -3\varepsilon^2 - 3\varepsilon + 1$	
116	$\varepsilon^3 = -3\varepsilon^2 - 5\varepsilon + 1$	$\Delta = 2$
	$\varepsilon = \rho^2 - \rho - 1$	
	$\rho^3 = \rho^2 + 2$	
135	$\varepsilon^3 = -3\varepsilon + 1$	
139	$\varepsilon^3 = 4\varepsilon^2 - 6\varepsilon + 1$	
140	$\varepsilon^3 = 3\varepsilon^2 - 5\varepsilon + 1$	
152	$\varepsilon^3 = 5\varepsilon^2 - 9\varepsilon + 1$	$\Delta = 2$
	$\varepsilon = -\rho^2 + \rho + 3$	
	$\rho^3 = \rho^2 + 2\rho + 2$	
172	$\varepsilon^3 = 3\varepsilon^2 - 7\varepsilon + 1$	$\Delta = 2$
	$\varepsilon = -\rho^2 + 2\rho + 1$	
	$\rho^3 = 2\rho^2 + 2$	
175	$\varepsilon^3 = -2\varepsilon^2 - 3\varepsilon + 1$	
176	$\varepsilon^3 = -\varepsilon^2 - 3\varepsilon + 1$	
199	$\varepsilon^3 = \varepsilon^2 - 4\varepsilon + 1$	
200	$\varepsilon^3 = -7\varepsilon^2 - 13\varepsilon + 1$	$\Delta = 2$
	$\varepsilon = \rho^2 - \rho - 1$	
	$\rho^3 = 2\rho^2 - 3\rho + 4$	
204	$\varepsilon^3 = 5\varepsilon^2 - 11\varepsilon + 1$	$\Delta = 3$
	$\varepsilon = -\rho^2 + \rho + 1$	
	$\rho^3 = \rho^2 - \rho + 3$	
211	$\varepsilon^3 = 6\varepsilon^2 - 10\varepsilon + 1$	
212	$\varepsilon^3 = -\varepsilon^2 - 15\varepsilon + 1$	$\Delta = 8$
	$\varepsilon = 2\rho - 1$	
	$\rho^3 = \rho^2 - 4\rho + 2$	
216	$\varepsilon^3 = 9\varepsilon^2 - 21\varepsilon + 1$	$\Delta = 2$
	$\varepsilon = -\rho^2 - \rho + 1$	
	$\rho^3 = -3\rho + 2$	
231	$\varepsilon^3 = -4\varepsilon^2 - 5\varepsilon + 1$	
236	$\varepsilon^3 = 3\varepsilon^2 - 11\varepsilon + 1$	$\Delta = 4$
	$\varepsilon = \rho^2 - 3\rho + 1$	
	$\rho^3 = 2\rho^2 + \rho + 2$	
239	$\varepsilon^3 = -\varepsilon^2 - 8\varepsilon + 1$	$\Delta = 3$
	$\varepsilon = \rho^2 - \rho - 1$	
	$\rho^3 = \rho + 3$	
243	$\varepsilon^3 = -\varepsilon^2 - 12\varepsilon + 1$	
244	$\varepsilon^3 = -5\varepsilon^2 - 27\varepsilon + 1$	$\Delta = 16$
	$\varepsilon = -2\rho^2 + 10\rho - 7$	
	$\rho^3 = 5\rho^2 - 4\rho + 2$	
247	$\varepsilon^3 = -3\varepsilon^2 - 4\varepsilon + 1$	
255	$\varepsilon^3 = 5\varepsilon^2 - 8\varepsilon + 1$	
268	$\varepsilon^3 = 7\varepsilon^2 - 13\varepsilon + 1$	
279	$\varepsilon^3 = 2\varepsilon^2 - 5\varepsilon + 1$	
283	$\varepsilon^3 = -4\varepsilon + 1$	
300	$\varepsilon^3 = -7\varepsilon^2 - 23\varepsilon + 1$	$\Delta = 9$
	$\varepsilon = -\rho^2 + 5\rho - 5$	
	$\rho^3 = 4\rho^2 - 2\rho + 2$	
304	$\varepsilon^3 = -5\varepsilon^2 - 7\varepsilon + 1$	
307	$\varepsilon^3 = -5\varepsilon^2 - 19\varepsilon + 1$	$\Delta = 8$
	$\varepsilon = 2\rho - 1$	
	$\rho^3 = -\rho^2 - 3\rho + 2$	
324	$\varepsilon^3 = -15\varepsilon^2 - 57\varepsilon + 1$	$\Delta = 6$
	$\varepsilon = \rho^2 + \rho - 1$	
	$\rho^3 = 3\rho + 4$	
327	$\varepsilon^3 = -9\varepsilon + 1$	$\Delta = 3$
	$\varepsilon = -\rho^2 + 4\rho - 2$	
	$\rho^3 = 4\rho^2 - 3\rho + 3$	
331	$\varepsilon^3 = -2\varepsilon^2 - 4\varepsilon + 1$	
332	$\varepsilon^3 = 7\varepsilon^2 - 23\varepsilon + 1$	$\Delta = 8$
	$\varepsilon = -2\rho + 3$	
	$\rho^3 = +\rho^2 - 2\rho + 4$	
335	$\varepsilon^3 = -\varepsilon^2 - 4\varepsilon + 1$	
339	$\varepsilon^3 = 11\varepsilon^2 - 35\varepsilon + 1$	$\Delta = 8$
	$\varepsilon = -2\rho + 5$	
	$\rho^3 = 2\rho^2 + 3$	
351	$\varepsilon^3 = 3\varepsilon^2 - 6\varepsilon + 1$	
356	$\varepsilon^3 = 11\varepsilon^2 - 43\varepsilon + 1$	$\Delta = 16$
	$\varepsilon = -2\rho^2 + 2\rho + 13$	
	$\rho^3 = 7\rho + 8$	
364	$\varepsilon^3 = 3\varepsilon^2 - 19\varepsilon + 1$	$\Delta = 8$
	$\varepsilon = -2\rho + 1$	
	$\rho^3 = -4\rho + 2$	
367	$\varepsilon^3 = 4\varepsilon^2 - 7\varepsilon + 1$	
368	$\varepsilon^3 = -\varepsilon^2 - 7\varepsilon + 1$	$\Delta = 2$
379	$\varepsilon^3 = -10\varepsilon^2 - 26\varepsilon + 1$	$\Delta = 3$
	$\varepsilon = \rho^2 - 3$	
	$\rho^3 = \rho^2 - \rho + 4$	

TABLE of units for all purely cubic fields $\Omega(\alpha)$ where $\alpha = \sqrt[3]{a}$ for all a not greater than 70

(Calculated by A. Markov)

a	
2	$1+\alpha+\alpha^2$
3	$4+3\alpha+2\alpha^2$
5	$41+24\alpha+14\alpha^2$
6	$109+60\alpha+33\alpha^2$
7	$4+2\alpha+\alpha^2$
10	$\frac{23+11\alpha+5\alpha^2}{3}$
11	$89+40\alpha+18\alpha^2$
12	$55+24\sqrt[3]{12}+21\sqrt[3]{18}$
13	$94+40\alpha+17\alpha^2$
14	$29+12\alpha+5\alpha^2$
15	$\frac{5}{(5-2\alpha)^3}=5401+2190\alpha+888\alpha^2$
17	$324+126\alpha+49^2$
18	$55+24\sqrt[3]{12}+21\sqrt[3]{18}$
19	$\frac{14+5\alpha+2\alpha^2}{3}$
20	$11+4\sqrt[3]{20}+3\sqrt[3]{50}$
21	$\frac{3(3+\alpha)}{(3-\alpha)^4}=1705+618\alpha+224\alpha^2$
22	$\frac{1}{6}\left(\frac{2+\alpha}{3-\alpha}\right)^3=793+283\alpha+101\alpha^2$
23	$\frac{(1+\alpha)^6}{9(3-\alpha)^9}=2\,166\,673\,601+761\,875\,860\alpha+267\,901\,370\alpha^2$
26	$9+3\alpha+\alpha^2$
28	$9+3\alpha+\alpha^2$
29	$\frac{(19+6\alpha+2\alpha^2)^6}{3(70-32\alpha+3\alpha^2)^3}$
30	$\frac{3}{(\alpha-3)^3}=811+261\alpha+84\alpha^2$
31	$\frac{(1+\alpha)^2}{(\alpha-3)^5}=101\,209+32\,218\alpha+10\,256\alpha^2$
33	$\frac{(\alpha-1)^3}{(2+9\alpha-3\alpha^2)^5}$
34	$\frac{(4+\alpha)^3}{2(\alpha-3)^6}=334\,153+103\,146\alpha+31\,839\alpha^2$
35	$\frac{(1+\alpha)^3}{3(\alpha-2)(\alpha-3)^2}=\frac{278+85\alpha+26\alpha^2}{3}$
37	$100+30\alpha+9\alpha^2$
38	$\frac{2\cdot 3^2(8+\alpha)^3}{(\alpha-2)^6(\alpha-3)^3}=29\,071+8647\alpha+2572\alpha^2$
39	$\frac{3(1+\alpha)^2}{(4-\alpha)(\alpha-3)^3}=529+156\alpha+46\alpha^2$
41	$\frac{3^{10}(7+\alpha)^{12}(2+\alpha)^{21}}{(5-\alpha)^{42}}$
42	$\frac{7}{(7-2\alpha)^3}=21\,169+6090\alpha+1752\alpha^2$
43	$49+14\alpha+4\alpha^2$
44	$\frac{1}{2}\left(\frac{\alpha-2}{2\alpha-7}\right)^3=\frac{4007+1135\alpha+643\alpha^2}{3}$
45	$\frac{3^4(3+\alpha)^3}{(\alpha-3)^9}=1\,477\,441+415\,374\alpha+116\,780\alpha^2$
46	$\frac{3^2\cdot 2^2(2+\alpha)^3}{(4-\alpha)^9}=16\,449\,049+4\,590\,798\alpha+1\,281\,255\alpha^2$
47	$\frac{3(2+\alpha)^6(1+\alpha)^3}{(\alpha-3)^6(2\alpha-7)^6}$
50	$11+4\sqrt[3]{20}+3\sqrt[3]{50}$
51	$\frac{(3+\alpha)^6(\alpha-1)^3}{3(2\alpha-7)^6(\alpha-3)^3}=107\,846\,641+29\,081\,484\alpha+7\,841\,994\alpha^2$
52	$\frac{12}{(4-\alpha)^3}=209+56\alpha+15\alpha^2$
53	$\frac{(7+\alpha)^5(1+\alpha)^5}{3(4-\alpha)^5(5-\alpha)^5(2\alpha-7))^3}$
55	$\frac{5^5\cdot 7^{15}(7-\alpha)^{18}}{(4-\alpha)^{18}(\alpha-3)^{15}(\alpha-1)^{15}(5-\alpha)^{1}}$
57	$\frac{(3-\alpha)^4(8-\alpha)}{3(4-\alpha)^4(\alpha-1)(\alpha-3)(3\alpha-11)}=1\,460\,968+379\,620\alpha+98\,641\alpha^2$
58	$\frac{6}{(4-\alpha)^3}=929+240\alpha+62\alpha^2$
59	$\frac{(1+\alpha)^{15}}{3^5(3-3)^6(4-\alpha)^{15}}$
60	$\frac{4}{(4-\alpha)^3}=2161+552\alpha+141\alpha^2$
61	$\frac{3}{(4-\alpha)^3}=3905+992\alpha+252\alpha^2$
62	$\frac{2}{(4-\alpha)^3}=8929+2256\alpha+570\alpha^2$
63	$16+4\alpha+\alpha^2$
65	$16+4\alpha+\alpha^2$
66	$\frac{3}{(\alpha-4)^3}=9505+2352\alpha+582\alpha^2$
67	$\frac{2}{(\alpha-4)^3}=4289+1056\alpha+260\alpha^2$
68	$\frac{4}{(\alpha-4)^3}=2449+600\alpha+147\alpha^2$
69	$\frac{3^7\left(1+\sqrt[3]{69}\right)^{30}}{(3+\alpha)^6(6-\alpha)^{15}(\alpha-4)^{30}}$
70	$\frac{6}{(\alpha-4)^3}=1121+272\alpha+66\alpha^2$

CHAPTER V

THUE'S THEOREM

The most important general theorem on the representation of numbers by factorable forms in n variables (Dirichlet forms) is that, in general, a given number has either no representations or an infinite number of representations in case the form is irreducible in the rational field (except when $n = 1$, or when $n = 2$ and $r = 1$, which correspond to the only cases in which the number of "parameters" of points in the corresponding signature space is equal to 1). The same theorem holds in the representation of numbers by quadratic forms in two or more variables with the only exception of definite forms, in which case the numbers represented by the form are the lattice points on the finite surface of an n-dimensional ellipsoid.

The situation is entirely different when we consider binary forms of higher degree (binary quadratic forms are also Dirichlet forms and therefore are included in both of the above-mentioned theories). The number of representations of a given number by an irreducible binary form of degree greater than 2 is always finite. This fundamental fact was demonstrated in 1908 by the Norwegian mathematician Axel Thue (1868–1919). This result is a direct consequence of the fact that if ρ is an algebraic integer of the nth degree with $n > 2$, then there does not exist an infinite number of rational fractions y/x such that the difference $\rho - y/x$ is less than A/x^n in absolute value, where A is any given positive constant. Thue has also shown that there does not exist an infinitude of rational fractions y/x such that

$$\left|\rho - \frac{y}{x}\right| < \frac{A}{x^{n/2+1}},$$

and Siegel improved Thue's method to obtain this result with a smaller exponent ν, namely

$$\nu > \frac{n}{s+1} + s,$$

where s is that number chosen from $1, 2, \cdots, n-1$ which minimizes

$$\frac{n}{s+1} + s.$$

In the case of $n = 3$, which interests us most in this book, the numbers $1, 2, \cdots$ $\cdots, n-1$ are simply $1, 2$, and the corresponding

$$\frac{n}{s+1} + s$$

are

$$\frac{3}{2} + 1 \text{ and } \frac{3}{3} + 2,$$

so that Siegel's exponent $3/2 + 1$ is the same as Thue's. We shall consider in this chapter the proof of Thue's theorem that there is a finite number of representations of a given number by a binary form of degree greater than 2, using the geometrical exposition of Thue's method given by Tartakovskiĭ.

§65. THE HYPERBOLAS OF LIOUVILLE AND THUE

Let $f(x, y)$ be a binary form with integer coefficients, let a_0 be the coefficient of y^n and let $\rho, \rho_1, \rho_2, \cdots, \rho_{n-1}$ be the roots of the form, i.e., $f(x, y) = a_0 \cdot N(x\rho + y)$. Suppose that we have to solve the indeterminate equation $f(x, y) = \sigma$, where σ is a given rational integer. The absolute values of the factors $x\rho_k + y$ that correspond to the complex roots $\rho_k = a_k + ib_k$ are not less than $|b_k x|$, that is they tend to infinity as $|x|$ increases. If all the roots $\rho, \rho_1, \cdots$ $\cdots, \rho_{n-1}$ were complex, then obviously there would be no solutions in which x exceeds in absolute value some predetermined quantity, for example

$$\sqrt[n]{\frac{|\sigma|}{|a_0||b_1 b_2 \ldots b_n|}}.$$

In this case there is only a finite number of solutions x, y of the equation $f(x, y) = \sigma$ and they can all be found. Therefore if there are solutions with large $|x|$, then to each such solution must correspond at least one real root ρ such that

$$|x\rho + y| < \sqrt[n]{\left|\frac{\sigma}{a_0}\right|}.$$

Let

$$x\rho + y = \theta \cdot \sqrt[n]{\left|\frac{\sigma}{a_0}\right|},$$

where

$$-1<\theta<1.$$

Then we have

$$\sigma = a_0(x\rho+y)\prod_{k=1}^{n-1}(x\rho_k+y+x\rho-x\rho)$$

$$= a_0(x\rho+y)\,x^{n-1}\cdot\prod_{k=1}^{n-1}\left(\rho_k-\rho+\theta\frac{\sqrt[n]{\left|\frac{\sigma}{a_0}\right|}}{x}\right),$$

that is,

$$x\rho+y=\frac{\sigma}{a_0x^{n-1}\prod_{k=1}^{n-1}\left(\rho_k-\rho+\theta\frac{\sqrt[n]{\left|\frac{\sigma}{a_0}\right|}}{x}\right)},$$

and hence if $|x|$ is large, then $\left|\theta\frac{\sqrt[n]{\left|\frac{\sigma}{a_0}\right|}}{x}\right|$ is small and

$$|x\rho+y|=\frac{s}{|x|^{n-1}},$$

where s does not differ a great deal from the number

$$\frac{\sigma}{a_0\prod_{k=1}^{n-1}[(\rho_k-\rho)]}.$$

Hence if $|x|$ exceeds some ξ_L, then $L'<s<L$, where L' and L are certain positive constants depending only on the coefficients of the form $f(x, y)$, on the number σ to be represented and on the chosen bound ξ_L.

We shall consider geometrically the solutions x, y connected in this way with a given real root ρ of our form. In order to do this we lay out the quantity x on the ξ-axis and the quantity $x\rho+y$ on the η-axis. Then to all integer x, y will correspond points of a parallelogram lattice constructed on the points $(0, 0)$,

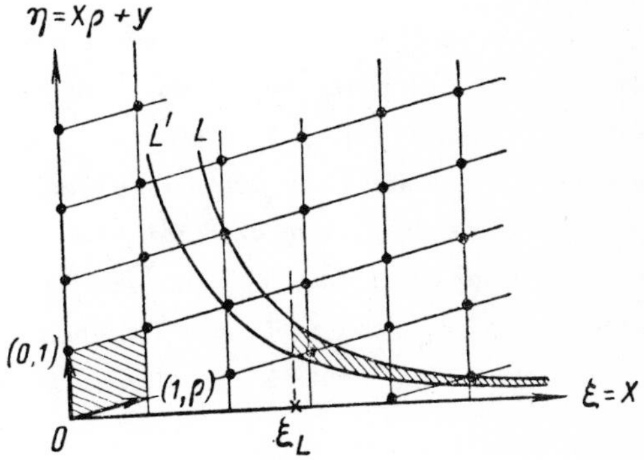

Figure 39

$(1, \rho)$ and $(0, 1)$. In this geometric interpretation the preceding result states that all the solutions for which $|x| > \xi_L$ lie between the "hyperbolas"

$$\eta = \frac{L'}{\xi^{n-1}} \text{ and } \eta = \frac{L}{\xi^{n-1}}.$$

The hyperbola L' was used by Liouville to prove the existence of transcendental numbers (1851). We shall use only the hyperbola L and call it the Liouville hyperbola. Thus all large solutions x, y lie under the Liouville hyperbola.

Thue's result consists in proving the existence of another hyperbola A,

$$\eta = \frac{1}{\xi^{\alpha}},$$

such that all sufficiently large solutions, for instance those for which $|x| > \xi_A$, lie above this hyperbola; moreover for $n > 2$, the exponent $\alpha < n - 1$. For every value of L, Thue's hyperbola will therefore be above the corresponding Liouville hyperbola for sufficiently large $|x|$. Thus if ξ_{AL} is the abscissa of the point of intersection of these two hyperbolas, there are no solutions with $|x|$ greater than the largest of the three positive numbers ξ_L, ξ_A, and ξ_{AL}. Thue himself has shown the existence of the A-hyperbola for the exponent

$$\alpha = \frac{n}{2} + \epsilon,$$

where ϵ is an arbitrarily small positive number, but it is sufficient for our purposes to take $\alpha = n - 1 - \epsilon$.

The hyperbola A of Thue is analogous to the hyperbola L' of Liouville by means of which he proved the existence of transcendental numbers, but it approaches the ξ-axis even more slowly. It is worthwhile to show the existence of such a hyperbola and to connect it with the hyperbola L of Liouville in order to obtain Thue's theorem.

As we shall see in §67, the essential point in Thue's (and Siegel's) proof of the existence of the hyperbola A is the assumption of the existence of a sufficiently "distant" (i.e., with large $|x|$) and sufficiently "good" rational approximation (i.e., in any case better than from continued fractions) to the root ρ, and such an approximation may actually fail to exist. However, if such an approximation does not exist then the equation $f(x, y) = \sigma$ cannot have large solutions, since large solutions would provide good approximations of this sort. Therefore, in this case Thue's theorem is also established.

§66. BOUNDARY SEQUENCES AND THE B-HYPERBOLA

In Thue's fundamental work, and in some special investigations of the impossibility of infinitely many representations by means of a binary cubic form, as well as in the corresponding works of Siegel devoted to the general Thue theorem, or to the special cases of the binary cubic form and the form $ax^n + by^n$, the proof of the existence of the A-hyperbola is carried out by first establishing the existence of an infinite sequence of integer points x, y of a lattice having the following properties:

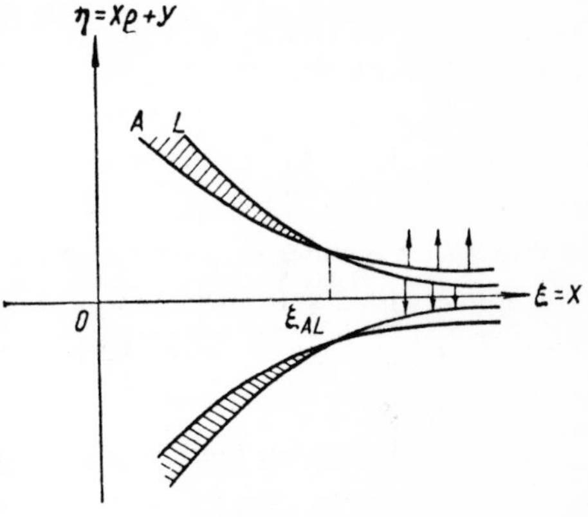

Figure 40

1°. The points approach the ξ-axis sufficiently close, although possibly not as close as by means of continued fractions.

2°. However, the points are located on ξ-axis sufficiently close to each other, i.e., they do not create large gaps (which a priori could arise from continued fractions).

3°. Also all these points are primitive, i.e., there are no integer points on the segments which connect these points to the origin. In other words the x and y of each point are relatively prime to each other. Tartakovskiĭ proposes to call this sequence of points a "boundary sequence."

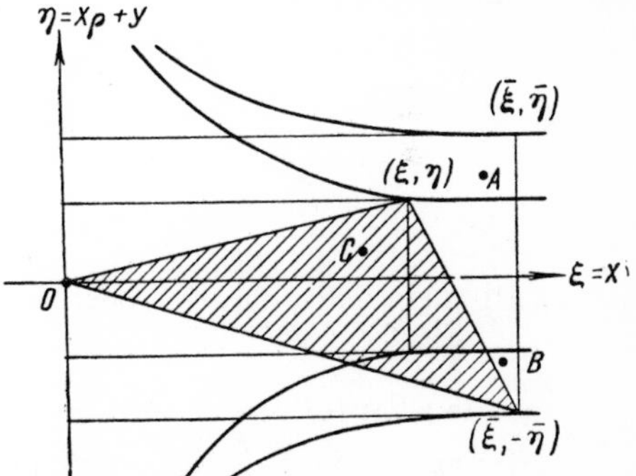

Figure 41

The right-hand half of the rectangle with center at the origin, with sides parallel to the coordinate axes and with one vertex at the point ξ, η (where $\xi > 0$) will be called the coordinate rectangle of ξ, η. We shall call the hyperbola $\eta = 1/\xi^{\beta}$ the B-hyperbola or the boundary hyperbola corresponding to a given α, if beginning with some point ξ the coordinate rectangle of every point of this hyperbola contains at least two distinct primitive points (x, y), and if the exponent of this hyperbola $\beta > 1/\alpha$. A boundary sequence will be a sequence of primitive approximations (x, y) such that there exists a B-hyperbola with the property that in every coordinate rectangle of the hyperbola there lie at least two such approximations.

We shall show (see Figure 41) that from the existence of the boundary sequence, i.e., from the existence of the B-hyperbola, follows the existence of the A-hyperbola. In fact, suppose that there exists an integer point C inside the A-hyperbola. Then this point would lie inside the coordinate rectangle of some point (ξ, η) on the A-hyperbola; for example, the point of intersection of A with the line OC. Consider the coordinate rectangle of some point $(\bar{\xi}, \bar{\eta})$ of the B-hyperbola with a sufficiently large $\bar{\xi}$ so that it contains two primitive integer points A and B. One of these two points does not lie on the line OC and therefore forms a parallelogram with the points O and C.

This parallelogram, being a parallelogram of our lattice of integer points, has an area not less than the area of the fundamental parallelogram of the lattice, which is equal to 1. But on the other hand, as can easily be seen, the area of this parallelogram is not less than the area of the parallelogram (half of which is shaded in Figure 41) constructed on the points $(0, 0)$, (ξ, η) and $(\bar{\xi}, -\bar{\eta})$. The area of this latter parallelogram is $|\xi\bar{\eta} + \bar{\xi}\eta|$ and is always < 1 if at the same time we have

$$|\xi\bar{\eta}| < \frac{1}{2} \text{ and } |\bar{\xi}\eta| < \frac{1}{2},$$

i.e., if

$$\sqrt[\alpha]{2\bar{\xi}}^{\,\frac{1}{\alpha}} < \xi < \frac{1}{2}\bar{\xi}^{\beta}.$$

But for all sufficiently large ξ one can fine $\bar{\xi}$ satisfying these inequalities if $\beta > 1/\alpha$.

Since in what follows it suffices that α be any fixed small quantity $< n - 1$, it is sufficient to show the existence of a boundary sequence for β for any small fixed quantity $> 1/(n - 1)$.

§67. TWO LEMMAS OF THUE

The most difficult part of Thue's theory is the proof of the existence of the boundary sequence. We shall give this proof only for $n = 3$ (although this shortens the demonstration only slightly) in the following three steps. First we shall prove Thue's lemma about polynomials, then we shall derive from this lemma the existence of a certain sequence of approximations, and finally we shall show that this sequence is a boundary sequence in our sense by establishing the existence of the B-hyperbola.

LEMMA I. *For every positive integer exponent m greater than 9 one can always find polynomials in t: $f_1(t)$, $f_2(t)$, $f_3(t)$, $P(t)$, and $Q(t)$ with rational integer coefficients such that $(\rho + t)^m \cdot [f_1(t)\rho^2 + f_2(t)\rho + f_3(t)] = \rho \cdot P(t) + Q(t)$, where the degrees of f_i do not exceed μ with*

$$\mu = \left[\frac{5}{8}(m-1)\right]$$

and the degrees of P and Q therefore do not exceed $m + \mu$, while the absolute values of all the coefficients of f_i are less than T^m, and all the coefficients of P and Q are less than S^m, where T and S depend only on the coefficients s, q, and n of $\rho^3 = s\rho^2 + q\rho + n$, but are independent of the exponent m.

PROOF. Consider $(\rho + t)^m$, where m is any positive integer exponent. Reducing the degrees by using the relation $\rho^3 = s\rho^2 + q\rho + n$ $(f = 0)$, we obtain

$$(\rho + t)^m = B_1^{(0)}(t)\rho^2 + B_2^{(0)}(t)\rho + B_3^{(0)}(t),$$

where the B's are polynomials in t with rational integer coefficients of degrees not exceeding m.

Similarly let

$$\rho(\rho + t)^m = B_1^{(1)}(t)\rho^2 + B_2^{(1)}(t)\rho + B_3^{(1)}(t),$$
$$\rho^2(\rho + t)^m = B_1^{(2)}(t)\rho^2 + B_2^{(2)}(t)\rho + B_3^{(2)}(t).$$

It is not hard to see that all the coefficients of the various powers of t in the B's do not exceed some number T_0^m, where T_0 depends only on the coefficients s, q, n of $f = 0$. Consider also all the functions $U(t) = C_1(t)\rho^2 + C_2(t)\rho + C_3(t)$, where C_1, C_2, C_3 are polynomials in t with rational integer coefficients whose absolute values do not exceed some number s, and with degrees not exceeding some number μ. We shall later specialize the numbers μ and s. There are altogether M such functions U, where $M = (2s + 1)^{3(\mu+1)}$.

We next multiply $(\rho + t)^m$ by all these U's and thus, after reducing the third and fourth powers of ρ by using $f = 0$, we obtain expressions of the kind

$$(\rho + t)^m \cdot U(t) = G_1(t)\rho^2 + G_2(t)\rho + G_3(t),$$

where

$$G_i(t) = B_i^{(0)}C_3 + B_i^{(1)}C_2 + B_i^{(2)}C_1 \quad (i = 1, 2, 3).$$

It is not hard to see that all the G's are polynomials in t of degree not higher than $m+\mu$, all of whose coefficients are integers less than N in absolute value, where $N = 3(m+1)sT_0^m$. We divide the interval $(-N, N)$ into h equal intervals I. We can then find

$$M_1 \geq \frac{M}{h}$$

polynomials U such that the first coefficients of all the G_1 corresponding to these U's lie inside a given interval I. Among these M_1 polynomials U we can in turn find at least

$$M_2 \geq \frac{M_1}{h} \geq \frac{M}{h^2}$$

U's in which the second coefficients of all the G_1's, corresponding to these functions U, lie inside an interval I (of course it might be a different interval from the one containing the first coefficients). Continuing this for all the $M+\mu+1$ coefficients of $G_1(t)$ we find

$$L \geq \frac{M}{h^{m+\mu+1}}$$

U's such that all the $G_1(t)$ corresponding to these L functions U have the coefficients of the same power of t lying in the same interval I. Let $L \geq 2$. Take two functions U_1 and U_2 out of these L functions. Let

$$(\rho+t)^m \cdot U_1 = G_1^{(1)}\rho^2 + G_2^{(1)}\rho + G_3^{(1)}; \quad (\rho+t)^m \cdot U_2 = G_1^{(2)}\rho^2 + G_2^{(2)}\rho + G_3^{(2)}).$$

Subtracting these equalities we obtain

$$(\rho+t)^m \cdot (U_1 - U_2) = (G_1^{(1)} - G_1^{(2)})\rho^2 + (G_2^{(1)} - G_2^{(2)})\rho + (G_3^{(1)} - G_3^{(2)}).$$

Suppose that $h > 2N$; then every interval I is less than 1 and all the coefficients of the difference $G_1^{(1)} - G_1^{(2)}$ are less than 1 in absolute value, but they are integers and therefore they must be zero, i.e., $G_1^{(1)} - G_1^{(2)} = 0$ and we obtain

$$(\rho+t)^m \cdot [f_1(t)\rho^2 + f_2(t)\rho + f_3(t)] = P(t)\cdot\rho + Q(t), \tag{1}$$

if we let

$$G_2^{(1)} - G_2^{(2)} = P(t); \quad G_3^{(1)} - G_3^{(2)} = Q(t); \quad U_1 - U_2 = f_1(t)\rho^2 + f_2(t)\rho + f_3(t).$$

The question remains whether there exists a number h such that $L \geq 2$ and $h > 2N$. Taking into consideration the values of L and N it is easily seen that these conditions lead to the following bounds on h:

$$3(m+1)2sT_0^m < h < (2s+1)^{\frac{3(\mu+1)}{m+\mu+1}}.$$

Hence if

$$3(m+1)\,2sT_0^m < (2s+1)^{\frac{3(\mu+1)}{m+\mu+1}} - 1,$$

then such an h can be found. The last inequality will hold if for instance

$$T_1^m < (2s+1)^{\frac{3(\mu+1)}{m+\mu+1}-1},$$

where $T_1 > 3\cdot 2T_0$, since $(3\cdot 2)^m > 3(m+1)$, and $2s+1 > 2s$. But if $m > 9$ and if $\mu = [5(m-1)/8]$, then $3(\mu+1)/(m+\mu+1) - 1 > 1/15$ and therefore the above inequality holds if $T_1^m < (2s+1)^{1/15}$ or if

$$2s+1 > T_1^{15m}.$$

Hence if $T > T_1^{15} > (6T_0)^{15}$, the inequalities will hold for all s such that $2s-1 \leq T^m < 2s+1$. The absolute value of each of the coefficients of P and Q is less than $2N < (2s-1)\,T_1^m < (TT_1)^m = S^m$, where $S = TT_1$, which completes the proof.

LEMMA II. *If x and y are integers such that $|\rho x + y| < 1$, then for every exponent $m > 9$ one can always find two pairs of integers B_0, C_0 and B_1, C_1 such that*

$$\frac{B_0}{C_0} \neq \frac{B_1}{C_1}$$

and such that $|B_0\rho + C_0|$ and $|B_1\rho + C_1|$ are less than $|[(\rho x + y)^{3/4}x^{5/8}H]|^{m-1}$, with $|B_0|$ and $|B_1|$ less than $D^{m-1}x^{13(m-1)/8+1}$, where H and D depend only on the coefficients s, q, n of the equation $\rho^3 = s\rho^2 + q\rho + n$, and do not depend on the exponent m.

This lemma is not hard to prove on the basis of the preceding one. We take the derivative with respect to t of both sides of the relation

$$P(t)\rho + Q(t) = (\rho + t)^m R(t), \tag{1}$$

where we have denoted by $R(t)$ the function $f_1(t)\rho^2 + f_2(t)\rho + f_3(t)$ and obtain

$$\rho P'(t) + Q'(t) = (\rho + t)^{m-1}[(\rho + t)R'(t) + mR(t)].$$

Multiplying this by $P(t)$ and subtracting the preceding equation multiplied by $P'(t)$, we obtain

$$Q(t)P'(t) - P(t)Q'(t) = (\rho + t)^{m-1}[(\rho + t)(P'(t)R(t) - R'(t)P(t)) - mP(t)R(t)]$$

and since the equation $f(\rho) = 0$ is irreducible we obtain

$$Q(t)P'(t) - P(t)Q'(t) = f(t)^{m-1}W(t),$$

where $W(t)$ is a polynomial in t. Since the degrees of $P(t)$ and $Q(t)$ do not exceed $m+\mu$, the degree γ of the polynomial W does not exceed

$$2(m+\mu-1) - 3(m-1) < \frac{m-1}{4}.$$

Consider all the expressions of the form

$$Z_{ab}(t) = \frac{d^a}{dt^a}P(t)\cdot\frac{d^b}{dt^b}Q(t) - \frac{d^b}{dt^b}P(t)\cdot\frac{d^a}{dt^a}Q(t)$$

for all a and b taken from $0, 1, 2, \cdots, \gamma, \gamma+1$. All these expressions cannot be simultaneously equal to zero for $t=-y/x$, i.e., all the $Z_{ab}(-y/x)$ cannot be equal to zero, since otherwise we would have

$$\frac{d^\lambda}{dt^\lambda}[f^{m-1}(t)W(t)] = 0$$

for all λ equal to $0, 1, 2, \cdots, \gamma$; but then

$$\left(t+\frac{y}{x}\right)^{\gamma+1}$$

would be a divisor of $f^{m-1}(t)W(t)$ and hence a divisor of $W(t)$, which is impossible since W is of degree γ. Let

$$Z_{ab}\left(-\frac{y}{x}\right) \neq 0$$

for $a=a_1$, $b=b_1$.

Consider the δth derivative of equation (1),

$$\rho P^{(\delta)}(t) + Q^{(\delta)}(t) = \frac{d^\delta}{dt^\delta}[(\rho+t)^m R(t)].$$

Every coefficient of P^δ and Q^δ is divisible by $1\cdot 2\cdot 3\cdots\delta$. Dividing the last relation by $\delta!$, after differentiation and substitution of $t=-y/x$ and noting that by assumption $|\rho x + y| < 1$ and that the coefficients of equation (1) are bounded by inequalities obtained in Lemma I, we get Lemma II by letting

$$\frac{x^{m-\mu-\delta}}{1\cdot 2\cdot 3\ldots\delta}Q^{(\delta)}\left(-\frac{y}{x}\right) = B, \quad \frac{x^{m+\mu-\delta}}{1\cdot 2\cdot 3\ldots\delta}P^{(\delta)}\left(-\frac{y}{x}\right) = C,$$

and taking for δ first a_1 and then b_1.

§68. THE DERIVATION OF THE EXISTENCE OF THE B-HYPERBOLA FROM THE LEMMAS

We shall now establish that the sequence of approximations obtained in Lemma II forms a boundary sequence by a method which will establish the existence of the B-hyperbola, i.e., of an hyperbola $\eta = 1/\xi^{\beta}$, where $\beta > 1/\alpha$ (i.e., $\beta > 1/2$), such that any of its coordinate rectangles contain at least two points of our lattice which do not lie on a straight line through the origin.

THEOREM. *The approximation sequence of Lemma* II *with* $x = x_0$, $y = y_0$, *where* (x_0, y_0) *is a sufficiently large solution, i.e., a sufficiently distant point lying between the two Liouville hyperbolas, is a boundary sequence.*

In fact, let (x_0, y_0) be a fixed distant point of our lattice lying between the two Liouville hyperbolas, i.e., such that $|x_0|$ is sufficiently large and $\rho x_0 + y_0 = \tau/x_0^2$, where $L' < \tau < L$. We denote by (ξ_{m+1}, η_{m+1}) the coordinates of the vertex of the coordinate rectangle in which by Lemma II (with $x = x_0$ and $y = y_0$) lie two approximations noncolinear with the origin in the case of the multiplier $(\rho + t)^{m+2}$, while by (ξ_m, η_m) we denote the corresponding coordinates obtained from the multiplier $(\rho + t)^{m-1}$. By Lemma II we then have

$$\xi_{m+1} = D^{m+1} x_0^{\frac{13}{8} m + \frac{13}{8} + 1}; \qquad |\eta_m| = \left| H x_0^{\frac{5}{8}} (\rho x_0 + y_0)^{\frac{3}{4}} \right|^m$$

or, if we take into consideration that $|\rho x_0 + y_0| = \tau x_0^{-2} < L x_0^{-2}$ and let

$$D = x_0^{\mu}, \quad HL^{\frac{3}{4}} = x_0^{\lambda},$$

we obtain

$$\xi_{m+1} = x_0^{\left(\frac{13}{8} + \mu\right) m + \frac{21}{8} + \mu}, \quad |\eta_m| < x_0^{\left(-\frac{7}{8} + \lambda\right) m}.$$

But if the point (x_0, y_0) is sufficiently distant, the exponents μ and λ are arbitrarily small and therefore for sufficiently large m the points $(\xi_{m+1}, |\eta_m|)$ lie below the hyperbola

$$\eta = \frac{1}{\xi^{\beta}},$$

where $\beta = 7/13 - \epsilon_1$, with $\beta > 1/2$. But this hyperbola is obviously such that each of its coordinate rectangles contains at least one of the coordinate rectangles (ξ_m, η_m) of Lemma II and therefore at least two points of the approximation sequence of Lemma II, noncolinear with the origin.

§69. INVESTIGATIONS OF V. A. TARTAKOVSKIĬ OF THE PROBLEM OF FINDING BOUNDS FOR THE SOLUTIONS BY MEANS OF THUE'S METHOD

On the basis of the previous discussion we determine a point ξ_{AL} from a solution (x_0, y_0) of $x_0\rho - y_0 = \tau/x_0^2$, with $0 < L' < |\tau| < L$. Let (x_1, y_1) be also a solution, i.e., let $x_1\rho - y_1 = \tau_1/x_1^2$ with $0 < L' < |\tau_1| < L$. By means of the solution (x_0, y_0) we construct the chain of approximations of Lemma II. For every $m > 9$ we have constructed two numbers $B_0\rho + C_0$ and $B_1\rho + C_1$ which are noncolinear with the origin. We shall denote by $\omega_m = B^{(m)}\rho - C^{(m)}$ that one of these two numbers which is noncolinear with the origin and with the point $x_1\rho - y_1$. Then it follows from the two equations

$$x_1\rho - \left(y_1 + \frac{\tau_1}{x_1^2}\right) = 0, \tag{1}$$

$$B^{(m)}\rho - (C^{(m)} + \omega_m) = 0 \tag{2}$$

that

$$\begin{vmatrix} x_1 & y_1 + \frac{\tau_1}{x_1^2} \\ B^{(m)} & C^{(m)} + \omega_m \end{vmatrix} = x_1 C^{(m)} - B^{(m)} y_1 + x_1\omega_m - B^{(m)}\frac{\tau_1}{x_1^2} = 0. \tag{3}$$

But $|x_1 C^{(m)} - B^{(m)} y_1| \geq 1$. We shall now establish the existence of a number $\bar{x}$ such that if $x_1 > \bar{x}$, then

$$|x_1\omega_m| < \frac{1}{2}, \tag{4}$$

$$\left| B^{(m)}\frac{\tau_1}{x_1^2}\right| < \frac{1}{2}. \tag{5}$$

It follows from (4) and (5) that (3) is impossible, i.e., that (1) and (2) cannot both hold, since (3) follows from them. Hence (1) is false, since (2) was established for a solution (x_0, y_0) in the previous section.

Since by Lemma II, we have that $|\omega_m|$ is less than

$$x_0^{\left(-\frac{7}{8}+\lambda\right)(m-1)+2}, \quad \text{a} \quad |B^{(m)}| < x^{\left(\frac{13}{8}+\mu\right)(m-1)+1},$$

it follows that if the conditions

$$\left| x_1 x_0^{\left(-\frac{7}{8}+\lambda\right)(m-1)+2}\right| < \frac{1}{2}, \tag{4'}$$

$$\left| x_0^{\left(\frac{13}{8}+\mu\right)(m-1)+1}\cdot\frac{\tau_1}{x_1^2}\right| < \frac{1}{2} \tag{5'}$$

hold, then conditions (4) and (5) also hold. We shall next show that if x_1 exceeds some $\bar{x}$, there exists an $m > 9$ satisfying the last conditions. The conditions for the existence of m can be put in the form

$$\psi(z) = \left(\frac{8}{7} + \lambda'\right)\frac{\ln x_1}{\ln x_0} + 3\frac{2}{7} + \lambda'' < m < \left(\frac{16}{13} + \mu'\right)\frac{\ln x_1}{\ln x_0} + \frac{5}{13} + \mu'' = \varphi(z), \quad (6)$$

where

$$z = \frac{\ln x_1}{\ln x_0}.$$

These conditions are obtained from (4′) and (5′) by taking logarithms. The quantities λ', λ'', μ', μ'', exactly like the corresponding λ, μ of the previous section, can be made arbitrarily small in absolute value for sufficiently large x_0.

We lay out z on the abcissa axis and on the ordinate axis the values ζ of the functions $\phi(z)$ and $\psi(z)$. If $z > \bar{z}$, then $\zeta_2 = \phi(z)$ exceeds $\zeta_1 = \psi(z)$ by more than a unit, and $\zeta_1 = \psi(z) > 9$, so that for every such z condition (6) is satisfied for an integer m. Solving the inequality

$$\left(\frac{8}{7} + \lambda'\right)z + 3\frac{2}{7} + \lambda'' + 1 < \left(\frac{16}{13} + \mu'\right)z + \frac{16}{13} + \mu'',$$

we see that it holds for sufficiently small λ', λ'', μ', μ'', i.e., for a sufficiently large x_0 it already holds for $z \geq 45$. Also in this case $\psi(z) > 9$. Hence for $z \geq 45$, i.e., for

$$x_1 \geq x_0^{45}$$

condition (6) is satisfied for some integer $m > 9$ (depending on x_1). Hence equation (1) does not hold, i.e., (x_1, y_1) is not a solution. It follows that solutions exceeding (x_0, y_0) can lie only between x_0 and x_0^{45}.

We next show that Lemmas I and II can be considerably simplified when m is less than a given constant m_0. In fact, in Lemma I it suffices to take $\mu = [m/2]$, since the value of μ was used in that lemma only once in the proof of the existence of the number h. For this it was necessary that the difference $3(\mu + 1)/(m + \mu + 1) - 1$ exceed a positive constant.

With $\mu = [m/2]$, and $m \leq m_0$ this will be the case for $m = 2\nu$. Then

$$\Delta = \frac{3\nu + 3 - 2\nu - \nu - 1}{3\nu + 1} > \frac{2}{\frac{3}{2}m_0 + 1}$$

while for $m = 2\nu + 1$,

$$\mu = \nu, \quad \Delta = \frac{3\nu + 3 - 2\nu - 1 - \nu - 1}{3\nu + 2} > \frac{1}{\frac{3}{2}m_0 + 1}.$$

Hence Lemma I holds for every positive $m \leq m_0$ with $\mu = [m/2]$.

Lemma II can be restated in this case as follows:

LEMMA IIa. *If x_0 and y_0 are integers such that $|\rho x_0 - y_0| < 1$, then for every positive exponent $m \leq m_0$ one can always find two pairs of integers B_0, C_0 and B_1, C_1 such that $B_0/C_0 \neq B_1/C_1$ and that $|B_0\rho + C_0|$ and $|B_1\rho + C_1|$ are less than $D\cdot|x_0\rho - y_0|^{m-1}\cdot x_0^{m/2}$ with $|B_0|$ and $|B_1|$ less than $H\cdot x_0^{(3/2)m}$.*

PROOF. Differentiating the equation

$$P(t)\rho + Q(t) = (\rho - t)^m \cdot R(t),$$

which was established by Lemma I we obtain

$$P'(t)\rho + Q'(t) = (\rho - t)^{m-1}\cdot[(\rho - t)R'(t) - mR(t)].$$

Multiplying this by $P(t)$ and subtracting from the previous equation multiplied by $P'(t)$ we find

$$Q(t)\cdot P'(t) - P(t)\cdot Q'(t) = (\rho - t)^{m-1}\cdot\{(\rho - t)[P(t)\cdot R'(t) - P'(t)\cdot R(t)] - mP'(t)\cdot R(t)\}.$$

Since the equation $f(z) = 0$ defining ρ is assumed to be irreducible, the polynomial in t with rational integer coefficients in the left-hand side of the last equation is divisible by $[f(t)]^{m-1}$. Denoting the quotient by $W(t)$ we obtain

$$Q(t)\cdot P'(t) - P(t)\cdot Q'(t) = [f(t)]^{m-1}\cdot W(t).$$

Here $W(t)$ is a polynomial with rational integer coefficients bounded by a number independent of x_0. Therefore, if x_0 is sufficiently large, the fraction $\bar{y}_0/\bar{x}_0$, being in its lowest terms, cannot be a root of the polynomial $W(t)$. (Here $\bar{y}_0 = y_0/(x_0, y_0)$ and $\bar{x}_0 = x_0/(x_0, y_0)$.) In fact $(x_0, y_0) \leq \sqrt[3]{\nu}$, where $\nu = f(x_0, y_0)$, i.e., $\bar{x}_0$ and $\bar{y}_0$ are sufficiently large if x_0 and y_0 are sufficiently large. But $\bar{x}_0$ and $\bar{y}_0$ would have to divide the end coefficients of $W(t)$ if $W(y_0/x_0) = 0$. Since $f(t)$ is irreducible it follows that $f(x_0/y_0) \neq 0$. Therefore

$$Q\left(\frac{y_0}{x_0}\right)\cdot P'\left(\frac{y_0}{x_0}\right) - P\left(\frac{y_0}{x_0}\right)\cdot Q'\left(\frac{y_0}{x_0}\right) \neq 0$$

and therefore we can take for the numbers $B_0\rho + C_0$ and $B_1\rho + C_1$ the following:

$$\rho x_0^{m+\mu}\cdot P\left(\frac{y_0}{x_0}\right) - x_0^{m+\mu}\cdot Q\left(\frac{y_0}{x_0}\right) = (x_0\rho - y_0)^m x_0^{\mu}\cdot R\left(\frac{y_0}{x_0}\right)$$

and

$$\rho x_0^{m+\mu-1}\cdot P'\left(\frac{y_0}{x_0}\right)-x_0^{m+\mu-1}\cdot Q'\left(\frac{y_0}{x_0}\right)$$
$$=(x_0\rho-y_0)^{m-1}x_0^{\mu}\left[\left(\rho-\frac{y_0}{x_0}\right)R'\left(\frac{y_0}{x_0}\right)-mR\left(\frac{y_0}{x_0}\right)\right].$$

From this it follows that

$$B_i<H\cdot x_0^{m+\left[\frac{m}{2}\right]}\leqslant H\cdot x_0^{\frac{3}{2}m}$$

and

$$|B_i\rho+C_i|<D\cdot|x_0\rho+y_0|^{m-1}x_0^{\left[\frac{m}{2}\right]}\leqslant D\cdot|x_0\rho+y_0|^{m-1}x_0^{\frac{m}{2}}.$$

This proves Lemma IIa.

Repeating the argument at the beginning of this section we see that (x_1, y_1) cannot be a solution of the indeterminate equation if there exists a positive integer m satisfying the conditions

$$\psi(z)=\frac{2}{3}\frac{\ln x_1}{\ln x_0}+\frac{4}{3}+\varepsilon<m<\frac{4}{3}\frac{\ln x_1}{\ln x_0}+\eta=\varphi(z),$$

where $z=\ln x_1/\ln x_0$ and where ϵ and η are arbitrarily small quantities for a sufficiently large x_0.

If $z=\ln x_1/\ln x\geq 3.6$, then $\phi(z)-\psi(z)>1$ and there exists a positive integer m satisfying the condition $\psi(z)<m<\phi(z)$. From this it follows that the x_1 of the solution cannot exceed $x_0^{3.6}$

To simplify the calculations we shall next assume that the irreducible polynomial $f(t)$ with root ρ is $f(t)=t^3-at-b$ (i.e., that the coefficient of t^2 is equal to zero).

We consider two numbers ω' and ω'' constructed from the solution (x_0, y_0),

$$\omega'=\rho x_0(3y_0^2-ax_0^2)-(2y_0^3+bx_0^3)=(\rho x_0-y_0)^2(-x_0\rho-2y_0)=B'\rho-C';$$
$$\omega''=\rho[3ay_0^4+18by_0^3x_0+6a^2y_0^2x_0^2+6aby_0x_0^3+(9b^2-a^3)x_0^4]$$
$$-[9by_0^4+8a^2y_0^3x_0+18aby_0^2x_0^2+18b^2y_0x_0^3+a^2bx_0^4]$$
$$=(y_0-\rho x_0)^3[9ax_0\rho^2+(3ay_0-9bx_0)\rho-(9by_0+8a^2x_0)]=B''\rho-C''.$$

We note that $B'<Cx_0^3$, $B''<Cx_0^4$, $|\omega'|<Cx_0^{-3}$, $|\omega''|<Cx_0^{-5}$. Here and below $C, C_0, C_1, C_2, \cdots$ will be constants which depend only on a, b and ν, where ν

is a number representable by the form, but do not depend on x_0.

We shall show that ω' and ω'' are not solutions. In fact

$$|x_0\rho+2y_0|=|x_0\rho-y_0+3y_0|>3y_0-1>\frac{x_0}{C_1}, \quad \text{i.e.,} \quad |\omega'|>\frac{x_0^{-3}}{C_2},$$

$$\begin{aligned}
&|9ax_0\rho^2+(3ay_0-9bx_0)\rho-(9by_0+8a^2x_0)|\\
&=|9a\rho(x_0\rho+y_0)+(12ay_0-9bx_0)\rho-(9by_0+8a^2x_0)|\\
&=|9a\rho(x_0\rho-y_0)-9b(x_0\rho-y_0)+12ay_0\rho-(18by_0+8a^2x_0)|\\
&=\left|(x_0\rho-y_0)\left[9a\rho-9b-\frac{8a^2}{\rho}\right]+\left[12a\rho-18b-\frac{8a^2}{\rho}\right]y_0\right|\\
&=\left|\frac{C_3}{x_0^2}+\frac{y_0}{\rho}(12a\rho^2-18b\rho-8a^2)\right|>\frac{x_0}{C_4}, \quad \text{i.e.,} \quad \omega''>\frac{x_0^{-5}}{C_5}.
\end{aligned}$$

On the other hand

$$\cdot\ |B'|=\left|x_0\left[3\left(x_0\rho-\frac{\tau}{x_0^2}\right)^2-ax_0^2\right]\right|=\left|x_0^3(3\rho^2-a)-6\tau\rho+\frac{3\tau^2}{x_0^3}\right|>C_6x_0^3,$$

and analogously

$$|B''|>C_7x_0^4.$$

All these inequalities are based on the fact that due to the irreducibility of of the equation $f(t)$ whose root is ρ, each of the three numbers

$$12a\rho^2-18b\rho-8a^2, \quad 3\rho^2-a, \quad 9a^2\rho+27ab\rho+(27b^2-a^3)$$

is different from zero. Hence $|B'|>C_6x_0^3$, $|\omega'|>x_0^{-3}/C_2$, i.e., (B', C') is not a solution.

Analogously $|B''|>C_7x_0^4$, $|\omega''|>x_0^{-5}/C_5$, i.e., (B'', C'') is not a solution.

We next show that ω' and ω'' are not colinear with the solution. In fact any integer multiple of ω' and ω'' cannot be a solution, since it gives a worse approximation to ρ than ω' or ω'' themselves. Neither can ω' and ω'' be multiples of a solution, since $d'=(B', C')$ and $d''=(B'', C'')$ are bounded by a constant d which does not depend on x_0 but only on the coefficients a, b, and on the size of the number ν which is represented by the form.

It is known that for any two binary forms

$$\varphi(x_0, y_0)=\sum_{k=0}^{m} a_kx_0^{m-k}y_0^k \quad \text{and} \quad \psi(x_0, y_0)=\sum_{l=0}^{n} b_lx_0^{n-l}y_0^l$$

two other binary forms

$$g(x_0, y_0) \text{ and } h(x_0, y_0),$$

can be found such that

$$g(x_0, y_0)\cdot\varphi(x_0, y_0)+h(x_0, y_0)\cdot\psi(x_0, y_0)=R_{\varphi,\psi}\cdot x_0^{m+n-1},$$

and also two binary forms $\bar{g}(x_0, y_0)$ and $\bar{h}(x_0, y_0)$ such that

$$\bar{g}(x_0, y_0)\cdot\varphi(x_0, y_0)+\bar{h}(x_0, y_0)\cdot\psi(x_0, y_0)=R_{\varphi,\psi}\cdot y_0^{m+n-1}.$$

The coefficients of the polynomials $g, h, \bar{g}, \bar{h}$ are polynomials in a_k and b_l with rational integer coefficients and $R_{\phi,\psi}$ is the resultant of the functions ϕ and ψ, i.e., it is also a polynomial in a_k, b_l with rational integer coefficients. Therefore

$$(\varphi(x_0, y_0),\ \psi(x_0, y_0))/(R_{\varphi,\psi}\cdot x_0^{m+n-1},\ R_{\varphi,\psi}\cdot y_0^{m+n-1})=R_{\varphi,\psi}\cdot(x_0, y_0)^{m+n-1}.$$

In our case if we take for ϕ and ψ first $B'(x_0, y_0)$ and $C'(x_0, y_0)$ and then $B''(x_0, y_0)$ and $C''(x_0, y_0)$, we have

$$R_{B', C'}=2\Delta, \quad R_{B'', C''}=-3\Delta^6,$$

where $\Delta = 4a^3 - 27b^2$, and therefore d' and d'' are less than

$$3\Delta^6\cdot(x_0, y_0)^7\leqslant 3\Delta^6\cdot\nu^{\frac{7}{3}}$$

(where ν is a number representable by the form).

The conditions that (x_1, y_1) cannot be a solution assume the form

$$|x_1\ \omega''|<\frac{1}{2};\quad \left|B''\frac{\tau_1}{x_1^2}\right|<\frac{1}{2}, \tag{7}$$

$$|x_1\ \omega'|<\frac{1}{2};\quad \left|B'\frac{\tau_1}{x_1^2}\right|<\frac{1}{2}. \tag{8}$$

Condition (7) will always be satisfied if a corresponding condition is satisfied in which ω'' is replaced by the larger number Cx_0^{-5} and B'' by the larger number Cx_0^{-4}. This gives the condition for x_1 not to be a solution in the form

$$C_8x_0^2<x_1<\frac{x_0^5}{C_9}.$$

Hence if x_1 is greater than $C_8x_0^2$, it cannot be a solution.

Analogously condition (8) will be satisfied if the corresponding condition in which ω' is replaced by the larger number Cx_0^{-3} and B' by the larger number Cx_0^3 is satisfied. This gives the condition for x_1 not to be a solution in the form

$$C_{10}x_0^{\frac{3}{2}} < x_1 < \frac{x_0^3}{C_{11}}.$$

Hence we obtain the final result:

If $x_1 > C_{10}x_0^{3/2}$, then (x_1, y_1) cannot be a solution.

We shall next prove that there can be no solutions in the interval $(x_0, C_{10}x_0^{3/2})$.

Every sufficiently large solution (x, y) is such that the ratio y/x is a convergent in the expansion of ρ in a continued fraction. Let y_0/x_0 be equal to one of the convergents p_n/q_n, i.e., $y_0 = dp_n$ and $x_0 = dq_n$, where $d = (x_0, y_0)$ is less than a constant not depending on x_0. Then

$$|q_n\rho - p_n| = \frac{1}{q_n\alpha_n + q_{n-1}},$$

where α_n is the nth complete quotient.

From this

$$q_n\alpha_n + q_{n-1} = \frac{1}{|q_n\rho - p_n|},$$

i.e.,

$$\alpha_n = \frac{1}{q_n|q_n\rho - p_n|} - \frac{q_{n-1}}{q_n} \geqslant \frac{d^2}{x_0|x_0\rho - y_0|} - 1 \geqslant \frac{d^2x_0}{C_{12}} - 1,$$

or

$$a_n = [\alpha_n] \geqslant \frac{x_0}{C_{13}}.$$

Hence $x_1 \geq p_{n+1} \geq x_0^2/C_{14}$, i.e., the very next convergent after p_n/q_n has a denominator which exceeds $C_{10}x_0^{3/2}$ and therefore so will all the other convergents.

Therefore a number M, depending only on the coefficients of the form and on the number represented by the form, can be found such that there exists only one solution (x, y) greater than M for each real root.

An analogous result can be obtained for binary forms of the same type but of higher degree.

§70. AN IMPROVEMENT ON SIEGEL'S THEOREM ON THE NUMBER OF SOLUTIONS OF $|f(x, y)| \le k$, WHERE $f(x, y)$ IS A BINARY CUBIC FORM OF POSITIVE DISCRIMINANT

1. **Statement of the problem. Elementary inequalities.** In the present section we give an exposition of Siegel's result on the number of solutions of the indeterminate equation $f(x, y) = k$, where $f(x, y)$ is a cubic form with integer coefficients. Siegel showed that the number of solutions of such an equation, when the form has a positive discriminant, does not exceed 10 in case the discriminant is sufficiently large with respect to the number k to be represented by the form.

We shall introduce some changes into Siegel's discussion and show that the number of primitive solutions (with x and y coprime) of the inequality

$$|f(x, y)| < k$$

does not exceed 10 (the solutions (x, y) and $(-x, -y)$ are not counted as distinct) if the magnitude of the discriminant of the form is sufficiently large with respect to k.

We begin as follows:

We introduce a ring of cubic numbers for which the form $f(x, y)$ is the index-form. We project the ring into the plane of zero trace, choosing the coordinate system and the scale in such a way that the complex coordinate projection of the point $(\omega, \omega', \omega'')$ is its Lagrange resolvent $\theta = \omega + \omega'\epsilon + \omega''\epsilon^2$, where $\epsilon = e^{2\pi i/3}$. In this projection the ring will project into a plane lattice of points with the area of the fundamental parallelogram equal to $\frac{1}{2}\sqrt{3\Delta}$, where Δ is the discriminant of the ring.

Let ω_1, ω_2 be the normal basis of the ring and let $\omega = x\omega_1 + y\omega_2 + z$ be a general element of the ring. We calculate the discriminant of ω in two ways. On the one hand

$$D(\omega) = \Delta \cdot [f(x, y)]^2,$$

while on the other hand

$$D(\omega) = [(\omega' - \omega'')(\omega'' - \omega)(\omega - \omega')]^2 = \frac{[(\theta - \bar\theta)(\theta\varepsilon - \bar\theta\varepsilon^2)(\theta\varepsilon^2 - \bar\theta\varepsilon)]^2}{(\varepsilon - \varepsilon^2)^6} = \frac{(\theta^3 - \bar\theta^3)^2}{-27}.$$

Here $\bar\theta = \omega + \omega'\epsilon^2 + \omega''\epsilon$.

Comparing the results we come to the conclusion that the solution of the inequality $[f(x, y)] \le k$ in integers is equivalent to the solution of the inequality

$$|\theta^3 - \bar\theta^3| \le 3k\sqrt{3\Delta}$$

in terms of the points of the lattice into which the ring of cubic numbers corresponding to the form $f(x, y)$ is projected.

The last inequality can be easily expressed geometrically. In order to do this we introduce polar coordinates $\theta = re^{i\phi}$. Then our inequality becomes

$$r^3 |\sin 3\varphi| \leqslant \frac{3}{2} k \sqrt{3\Delta}.$$

Solving this inequality is equivalent to finding all the points of the lattice in the region bounded by the curves $r^3 \sin 3\phi = \pm 3k\sqrt{3\Delta}/2$ (see Figure 42).

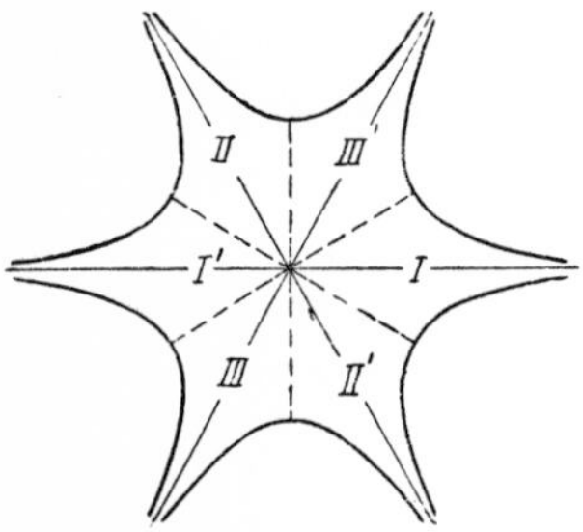

Figure 42

The dotted lines divide Figure 42 into 6 regions: I, I' II, II', III, III'. The pairs of regions symmetrical with respect to the origin correspond to solutions which we have agreed not to call distinct. Therefore it suffices to find the number of solutions in regions I, II, III.

In each of these the count proceeds in an analogous manner, since a permutation of ω, ω' and ω'' leads to a permutation of the three regions I, II, III. Therefore it is sufficient to find all the primitive points in the region I and to show that it cannot contain more than six points for a sufficiently large discriminant.

The region I can be defined by the supplementary inequality

$$|\phi| \leq \frac{\pi}{6}.$$

We next derive some simple inequalities for points of the lattice which are inside the region I. First of all we estimate the difference $\theta - \bar{\theta} = 2ri \sin\phi$. We have

$$|\theta - \bar{\theta}| = 2r|\sin\phi| \leq r \sin 3\phi,$$

since for $|\phi| < \pi/6$ we have $|2\sin\phi| \leq \sin 3\phi$. Hence

$$r^2 |\theta - \bar{\theta}| \leqslant \frac{3}{2} k \sqrt{3\Delta}. \tag{1}$$

Let θ_1 and θ_2 be two distinct primitive points of the lattice in the region I. Since they are not colinear with the origin the area of a parallelogram constructed on them is greater than or equal to the area of the fundamental parallelogram of the lattice. This leads us to the inequalities

$$\frac{1}{2}\sqrt{3\Delta} \leqslant r_1 r_2 |\sin(\varphi_1 - \varphi_2)| \leqslant r_1 r_2 (|\sin\varphi_1| + |\sin\varphi_2|)$$
$$\leqslant \frac{1}{2} r_1 r_2 (|\sin 3\varphi_1| + |\sin 3\varphi_2|) \leqslant \frac{3}{4} k\sqrt{3\Delta}\left(\frac{r_2}{r_1^2} + \frac{r_1}{r_2^2}\right),$$

from which

$$\frac{r_2}{r_1^2} + \frac{r_1}{r_2^2} \geqslant \frac{2}{3k}.$$

If $r_2 \geq r_1$, then $r_1/r_2^2 \leq r_2/r_1^2$ and hence

$$\frac{r_2}{r_1^2} \geqslant \frac{1}{3k}. \tag{2}$$

This is a "strong" inequality for large values of r_1 but a "weak" inequality for small values of r_1. In the latter case (2) may be replaced by the following:

$$\frac{1}{2}\sqrt{3\Delta} \leqslant r_1 r_2 |\sin(\varphi_1 - \varphi_2)| \leqslant r_1 r_2 \frac{\sqrt{3}}{2},$$

since

$$|\varphi_1 - \varphi_2| \leqslant \frac{\pi}{3}.$$

But $r_1 \leq \sqrt{3k \cdot r_2}$ and hence

$$r_2 \cdot \sqrt{3k \cdot r_2} \cdot \frac{\sqrt{3}}{2} \geqslant \frac{1}{2}\sqrt{3\Delta},$$

so that

$$r_2 \geqslant \left(\frac{\Delta}{3k}\right)^{\frac{1}{3}}. \tag{3}$$

We now arrange the points in the region I in increasing order of their radii-vectors:

$$r_1 \leqslant r_2 \leqslant r_3 \leqslant \ldots \leqslant r_s \leqslant r_{s+1} \leqslant \ldots.$$

It follows from (2) that

$$\frac{r_{s+1}}{3k} \geqslant \left(\frac{r_s}{3k}\right)^2, \tag{4}$$

from which

$$\frac{r_{s+m}}{3k} \geqslant \left(\frac{r_s}{3k}\right)^{2^m}.$$

For $s = 2$ we obtain

$$\frac{r_{m+1}}{3k} \geqslant \left(\frac{r_2}{3k}\right)^{2^{m-1}}.$$

Using inequality (3) for r_2 we obtain

$$\frac{r_{m+1}}{3k} \geqslant \left(\frac{\Delta}{81k^4}\right)^{2^{m-1}}. \tag{5}$$

The inequalities (3), (4) and (5) assume a more symmetric form if we let $r = (3k)^{1/3}\Delta^{1/6}t$. In fact they become

$$t_2 \geqslant \left(\frac{\Delta}{81k^4}\right)^{\frac{1}{6}}, \tag{3'}$$

$$t_{s+1} \geqslant \left(\frac{\Delta}{81k^4}\right)^{\frac{1}{6}} \cdot t_s^2, \tag{4'}$$

$$t_{m+1} \geqslant \left(\frac{\Delta}{81k^4}\right)^{\frac{2^m-1}{6}}. \tag{5'}$$

2. On the Thue-Siegel polynomials. In what follows we shall need some polynomials which resemble those of Thue. These are the polynomials $A_m(z)$, $B_m(z)$, $C_m(z)$ and $D_m(z)$ of the lowest degree which satisfy the conditions

$$\begin{aligned} A_m(x^3) - xB_m(x^3) &= (1-x)^m V_m(x), \\ C_m(x^3) - x^2 D_m(x^3) &= (1-x)^m W_m(x), \end{aligned} \tag{6}$$

where V_m and W_m are also polynomials.

We shall show that the following polynomials satisfy condition (6) for m even, $m = 2n$.

$$\begin{aligned} A_{2n}(z) &= \sum_{k=0}^{n} \binom{n-\frac{2}{3}}{k}\binom{n-\frac{1}{3}}{n-k} z^k; \\ B_{2n}(z) &= \sum_{k=0}^{n-1} \binom{n-\frac{1}{3}}{k}\binom{n-\frac{2}{3}}{n-1-k} z^k; \\ C_{2n}(z) &= \sum_{k=0}^{n} \binom{n-\frac{1}{3}}{k}\binom{n-\frac{2}{3}}{n-k} z^k; \\ D_{2n}(z) &= \sum_{k=0}^{n-1} \binom{n-\frac{2}{3}}{k}\binom{n-\frac{1}{3}}{n-1-k} z^k; \end{aligned} \tag{7}$$

while for m odd, $m = 2n+1$ we have

$$\begin{aligned} A_{2n+1}(z) &= \sum_{k=0}^{n} \binom{n+\frac{1}{3}}{k}\binom{n-\frac{1}{3}}{n-k} z^k; \\ B_{2n+1}(z) &= \sum_{k=0}^{n} \binom{n-\frac{1}{3}}{k}\binom{n+\frac{1}{3}}{n-k} z^k; \end{aligned} \tag{7'}$$

$$C_{2n+1}(z)=\sum_{k=0}^{n}\binom{n+\frac{2}{3}}{k}\binom{n-\frac{2}{3}}{n-k}z^k; \qquad (7')$$

$$D_{2n+1}(z)=\sum_{k=0}^{n}\binom{n-\frac{2}{3}}{k}\binom{n+\frac{2}{3}}{n-k}z^k$$

The quickest way to obtain the above formulas defining the polynomials is by making use of the theory of hypergeometric functions. Not wishing to introduce nonelementary considerations, we will show by mathematical induction that the polynomials (7) satisfy relations (6).

In order to do this we must introduce recurrence relations for these polynomials, and also relations between these polynomials and their derivatives.

The recurrence relations are

$$\begin{aligned} A_{m+1}(z)&=\alpha_m A_m(z)-\beta_m(1-z)A_{m-1}(z);\\ B_{m+1}(z)&=\alpha_m B_m(z)-\beta_m(1-z)B_{m-1}(z);\\ C_{m+1}(z)&=\gamma_m C_m(z)-\delta_m(1-z)C_{m-1}(z);\\ D_{m+1}(z)&=\gamma_m D_m(z)-\delta_m(1-z)D_{m-1}(z).\end{aligned} \qquad (8)$$

Here

$$\alpha_{2n}=2; \qquad \beta_{2n}=\frac{n-\frac{1}{3}}{n}; \qquad \gamma_{2n}=2; \qquad \delta_{2n}=\frac{n-\frac{2}{3}}{n};$$

$$\alpha_{2n+1}=\frac{2n+1}{n+1}; \quad \beta_{2n+1}=\frac{n+\frac{1}{3}}{n+1}; \quad \gamma_{2n+1}=\frac{2n+1}{n+1}; \quad \delta_{2n+1}=\frac{n+\frac{2}{3}}{n+1}.$$

while the relations between the polynomials and their derivatives are

$$\begin{aligned} 3A'_m(z)&=\lambda_m D_{m-1}(z);\\ B_m(z)+3zB'_m(z)&=\lambda_m C_{m-1}(z);\\ 3C'_m(z)&=\mu_m B_{m-1}(z);\\ 2D_m(z)+3zD'_m(z)&=\mu_m A_{m-1}(z).\end{aligned} \qquad (9)$$

Here

$$\lambda_{2n}=3n-2; \qquad \mu_{2n}=3n-1;$$
$$\lambda_{2n+1}=3n+1; \quad \mu_{2n+1}=3n+2.$$

Relations (8) and (9) can be easily checked, and from (8) and (9) relations (6) follow readily. Let us give the proof.

Relations (6) obviously hold for $m=1$ and $m=2$.

Suppose that they hold for all polynomials whose subscripts do not exceed m_0. We can then show that they hold for polynomials with subscripts $m_0 + 1$. This will prove (6) for all polynomials.

Relations (9) show that

$$[A_m(x^3) - xB_m(x^3)]' = -\lambda_m[C_{m-1}(x^3) - x^2 D_{m-1}(x^3)],$$
$$[C_m(x^3) - x^2D_m(x^3)]' = -\mu_m x[A_{m-1}(x^3) - xB_{m-1}(x^3)],$$

from which under the assumption that (6) holds for all $m \leq m_0$ we obtain

$$\begin{aligned} mV_m(x) - (1-x)\,V'_m(x) &= \lambda_m W_{m-1}(x), \\ mW_m(x) - (1-x)\,W'_m(x) &= \mu_m x V_{m-1}(x). \end{aligned} \qquad (9')$$

Now let $x = 1$. This gives

$$V_m(1) = \frac{\lambda_m}{m} W_{m-1}(1),$$

$$W_m(1) = \frac{\mu_m}{m} V_{m-1}(1).$$

Taking into consideration that

$$V_1(1) = 1; \quad W_1(1) = 2,$$

we obtain

$$\begin{aligned} V_{2n}(1) &= \frac{\lambda_{2n}\mu_{2n-1}\lambda_{2n-2}\cdots\lambda_2}{(2n)!}\cdot 2 = \frac{(3n)!}{3^n n!\,(2n)!}, \\ W_{2n}(1) &= \frac{\mu_{2n}\lambda_{2n-1}\mu_{2n-2}\cdots\mu_2}{(2n)!}\cdot 1 = \frac{(3n)!}{3^n n!\,(2n)!}, \\ V_{2n+1}(1) &= \frac{\lambda_{2n+1}\mu_{2n}\cdots\mu_2}{(2n+1)!}\cdot 1 = \frac{(3n+1)!}{3^n n!\,(2n+1)!}, \\ W_{2n+1}(1) &= \frac{\mu_{2n+1}\lambda_{2n}\cdots\lambda_2}{(2n+1)!}\cdot 2 = \frac{(3n+2)\cdot(3n)!}{3^n n!\,(2n+1)!}. \end{aligned} \qquad (10)$$

We now consider the expressions

$$A_{m_0+1}(x^3) - xB_{m_0+1}(x^3) \text{ and } C_{m_0+1}(x^3) - x^2D_{m_0+1}(x^3)$$

and show that they are both divisible by $(1 - x)^{m_0+1}$.

From (8)

$$\begin{aligned} A_{m_0+1}(x^3) - xB_{m_0+1}(x^3) &= \alpha_{m_0}[A_{m_0}(x^3) - xB_0(x^3)] \\ &\quad - \beta_{m_0}(1-x^3)[A_{m_0-1}(x^3) - xB_{m_0-1}(x^3)] \\ &= (1-x)^{m_0}[\alpha_{m_0}V_{m_0}(x) - \beta_{m_0}(1+x+x^2)\,V_{m_0-1}(x)], \\ C_{m_0+1}(x^3) - xD_{m_0+1}(x^3) &= (1-x)^{m_0}[\gamma_{m_0}W_{m_0}(x) - \delta_{m_0}(1+x+x^2)\,W_{m_0-1}(x)]. \end{aligned}$$

It is easily seen that the expressions in square brackets are divisible by $1 - x$.

In fact both of them are zero for $x = 1$, since

$$\alpha_{m_0} V_{m_0}(1) - 3\beta_{m_0} V_{m_0-1}(1) = 0,$$
$$\gamma_{m_0} W_{m_0}(1) - 3\delta_{m_0} W_{m_0-1}(1) = 0,$$

which can be readily checked by substituting the values of $V(1)$, $W(1)$, α, β, γ, δ separately for even and odd values of m_0.

This completes the proof of (6). We note some of the properties of the polynomials A_m, B_m, C_m, D_m, V_m, W_m which will be useful later.

PROPERTY 1. The polynomials $V_m(x)$ and $W_m(x)$ have positive coefficients.

PROOF. Let

$$V_m(x) = \sum v_m^{(k)} x^k, \quad W_m(x) = \sum w_m^{(k)} x^k.$$

The leading coefficients of V_m and W_m are obviously positive from (6).

It can be readily verified that the coefficients of the polynomials V_1, V_2, W_1, W_2 are also positive.

We now suppose that the coefficients of the polynomials $V_{m-1}(x)$ and $W_{m-1}(x)$ are positive and prove that this also holds for $V_m(x)$ and $W_m(x)$. This will prove Property 1.

Relations (9′) give

$$(m+k)\, v_m^{(k)} = (k+1)\, v_m^{(k+1)} + \lambda_m w_{m-1}^{(k)},$$
$$(m+k)\, w_m^{(k)} = (k+1)\, w_m^{(k+1)} + \mu_m v_{m-1}^{(k-1)}. \qquad (9'')$$

Since the numbers $\lambda_m v_{m-1}^{(k)}$ and $\mu_m v_{m-1}^{(k-1)}$ are positive we conclude that the coefficients $v_m^{(k)}$ and $w_m^{(k)}$ are also positive as long as $v_m^{(k+1)}$ and $w_m^{(k+1)}$ are positive. Therefore, since the leading coefficients of V_m and W_m are positive, it follows that all the $v_m^{(k)}$ and $w_m^{(k)}$ are positive.

PROPERTY 2.

$$|A_m(z)| < 2^{m-2},$$
$$|C_m(z)| < 2^{m-2},$$
$$|V_m(z)| < \left(\frac{3}{2}\right)^{m-2},$$
$$|W_m(z)| < \left(\frac{3}{2}\right)^{m-2},$$

the last inequality for $m > 3$ holds only if $|z| \le 1$.

PROOF. Because the coefficients of the polynomials A, C, V, and W are positive it follows that

$$|A_m(z)| \leq A_m(1); \quad |C_m(z)| \leq C_m(1);$$
$$|V_m(z)| \leq V_m(1); \quad |W_m(z)| \leq W_m(1).$$

The values of $V_m(1)$ and $W_m(1)$ are already known. The values of $A_m(1)$ and $C_m(1)$ can be easily found from (8). For $z = 1$ they are

$$A_{m+1}(1) = \alpha_m A_m(1); \quad C_{m+1}(1) = \gamma_m C_m(1).$$

Taking into consideration that $\alpha_m = \gamma_m \leq 2$ and that $A_2(1) = C_2(1) = 1$ we obtain

$$A_m(1) = C_m(1) = \alpha_{m-1}\alpha_{m-2} \ldots \alpha_2 < 2^{m-2}.$$

More precisely

$$A_{2n+1}(1) = C_{2n+1}(1) = \frac{(2n)!}{(n!)^2}; \quad A_{2n}(1) = C_{2n}(1) = \frac{(2n-1)!}{n!\,(n-1)!}.$$

For the polynomials $V_m(z)$ and $W_m(z)$ we have

$$V_{2n}(1) = W_{2n}(1) = \frac{(3n)!}{3^n n!\,(2n)!} = \frac{3n-1}{2n} \cdot \frac{3n-2}{2n-1} \cdot \frac{3n-4}{2n-2} \cdot \frac{3n-5}{2n-3} \cdots \frac{5}{4} \cdot \frac{4}{3} \cdot \frac{2}{2} \cdot \frac{2}{1}$$
$$< \left(\frac{3}{2}\right)^{2n-2} = \left(\frac{3}{2}\right)^{m-2},$$
$$V_{2n+1}(1) = \frac{(3n+1)!}{3^n \cdot n!\,(2n+1)!} < \frac{3n+1}{2n+1} \cdot \left(\frac{3}{2}\right)^{2n-2} < \left(\frac{3}{2}\right)^{2n-1},$$
$$W_{2n+1}(1) = \frac{3n+2}{2n+1} \cdot \frac{(3n)!}{3^n n!\,(2n)!} < \frac{3n+2}{2n+1} \cdot \frac{5}{3} \cdot \left(\frac{3}{2}\right)^{2n-4} < \left(\frac{3}{2}\right)^{2n-1}$$

for $n > 1$. This proves Property 2.

PROPERTY 3.

$$A_m(x^3)\,C_m(x^3) - x^3 B_m(x^3)\,D_m(x^3) \neq 0$$

for $x^3 \neq 1$.

PROOF.

$$A_m(x^3) - x\,B_m(x^3) = (1-x)^m V_m(x),$$
$$C_m(x^3) - x^2 D_m(x^3) = (1-x)^m W_m(x).$$

Multiplying the first equation by $C_m(x^3)$ and the second by $xB_m(x^3)$ and adding we get

$$A_m(x^3)\,C_m(x^3) - x^3 B_m(x^3)\,D_m(x^3) = (1-x)^m [C_m(x^3)\,V_m(x) + xB_m(x^3)\,W_m(x)].$$

The left-hand side is a polynomial of degree m in x^3. Since it is divisible by $(1-x)^m$, it must be divisible by $(1-x^3)^m$. The quotient is a constant different from zero since it is equal to $A_m(0) \cdot C_m(0)$. Hence

$$A_m(x^3)\,C_m(x^3) - x^3 B_m(x^3)\,D_m(x^3) = A_m(0)\,C_m(0)\,(1-x^3)^m \neq 0$$

with $x^3 \neq 1$, which establishes Property 3.

PROPERTY 4. For polynomials with odd subscripts we have

$$z^n A_{2n+1}\left(\frac{1}{z}\right) = B_{2n+1}(z),$$
$$z^n C_{2n+1}\left(\frac{1}{z}\right) = D_{2n+1}(z).$$

This is obvious.

PROPERTY 5. The coefficients of the polynomials A_{2n+1}, B_{2n+1}, C_{2n+1}, D_{2n+1} when multiplied by $M_n = 3^{[3n/2]}$ become integers. (The same is true of the corresponding polynomials with even subscripts.)

PROOF. Consider the binomial coefficient

$$\binom{n+\frac{1}{3}}{k} = \frac{(3n+1)(3n-2)\dots(3n+4-3k)}{3^k \cdot k!}.$$

Write $k! = 3^{\kappa} \cdot K$, where K is not divisible by 3. Denote by s the solution of the congruence

$$3s \equiv 1 \pmod{K}.$$

Then $(3n+1)(3n-2)\cdots(3n+4-3k) \equiv 3^k(n+s)(n+s-1)\cdots(n+s-(k-1)) \equiv 0 \pmod{K}$, since $(n+s)(n+s-1)\cdots(n+s-(k-1))$ is divisible by $k!$ and therefore by K: Hence $3^{k+\kappa}\binom{n+1/3}{k}$ is an integer. But $k+\kappa = k + [k/3] + [k/9] + \cdots < 3k/2$. Similarly we see that $3^{l+\lambda}\binom{n-1/3}{n-k}$ is an integer for

$$l+\lambda = n-k+\left[\frac{n-k}{3}\right]+\left[\frac{n-k}{9}\right]+\dots<\frac{3}{2}(n-k).$$

Therefore $3^{[3n/2]}\cdot\binom{n+1/3}{k}\binom{n-1/3}{n-k}$ is an integer, i.e., $M_n A_{2n+1}(z)$ has integer coefficients. Similarly we can see that $M_n C_{2n+1}(z)$ also has integer coefficients.

3. The construction of a boundary sequence.

LEMMA. *If θ is the resolvent of a number ω in a cubic field, then $\theta F_1(\theta^3, \bar\theta^3)$ and $\bar\theta^2 F_2(\theta^3, \bar\theta^3)$ are also resolvents of numbers in the same ring, if F_1 and F_2 are polynomials with rational integer coefficients.*

PROOF. Since θ^3 and $\bar{\theta}^3$ are roots of a quadratic equation with integer coefficients, it follows that

$$F_1(\theta^3, \bar{\theta}^3) = A + B\bar{\theta}^3; \quad F_2(\theta^3, \bar{\theta}^3) = C + D\theta^3$$

with rational integers A, B, C and D. Therefore taking into consideration that $\theta\bar{\theta}$ is a rational integer, the numbers $\theta F_1(\theta^3, \bar{\theta}^3)$ and $\bar{\theta}^2 F_2(\theta^3, \bar{\theta}^3)$ can be represented in the form $A_1\theta + B_1\bar{\theta}^2$ with rational integers A_1 and B_1. If θ is the resolvent of ω, then $\bar{\theta}^2 = (\omega + \omega'\epsilon^2 + \omega''\epsilon)^2 = \omega^2 + 2\omega'\omega'' + (\omega'^2 + 2\omega\omega'')\epsilon + (\omega''^2 + 2\omega\omega')\epsilon^2$ is the resolvent of the number $\omega^2 + 2\omega'\omega'' = 3\omega^2 - 2s\omega + 2q$ belonging to the same ring as ω. Since the resolvents form a lattice, it follows that $A_1\theta + B_1\bar{\theta}^2$ is the resolvent of some number in the ring, which completes the proof of the lemma.

We now give a construction of the "boundary sequence."

Let θ be a point of the region I which gives a solution of $|f(x, y)| \le k$. Consider the points

$$H_n = M_n A_{2n+1}\left(\frac{\bar{\theta}^3}{\theta^3}\right)\cdot \theta^{3n+1}, \quad K_n = M_n C_{2n+1}\left(\frac{\theta^3}{\bar{\theta}^3}\right)\cdot \bar{\theta}^{3n+2}.$$

Here $M_n = 3^{[3n/2]}$, A_{2n+1} and C_{2n+1} are the polynomials introduced in the preceding section.

The points H_n and K_n belong to the lattice which is a projection of the ring, since $M_n A_{2n+1}(\bar{\theta}^3/\theta^3)\theta^{3n}$ and $M_n C_{2n+1}(\theta^3/\bar{\theta}^3)\cdot\bar{\theta}^{3n}$ are polynomials in θ^3 and $\bar{\theta}^3$ with rational integer coefficients.

The points H_n and K_n are not collinear with the origin since

$$\begin{aligned} H_n\bar{K}_n - \bar{H}_n K_n = M_n^2 \theta^{6n+3}\Big[& A_{2n+1}\left(\frac{\bar{\theta}^3}{\theta^3}\right) C_{2n+1}\left(\frac{\bar{\theta}^3}{\theta^3}\right) \\ & - \left(\frac{\bar{\theta}}{\theta}\right)^{6n+3} A_{2n+1}\left(\frac{\theta^3}{\bar{\theta}^3}\right) C_{2n+1}\left(\frac{\theta^3}{\bar{\theta}^3}\right)\Big] \\ = M_n^2\theta^{6n+3}[A_{2n+1}(x^3) & C_{2n+1}(x^3) - x^3 B_{2n+1}(x^3) D_{2n+1}(x^3)] \neq 0, \end{aligned}$$

inasmuch as $x^3 = \bar{\theta}^3/\theta^3 \neq 1$.

We estimate the absolute values of H_n, K_n, $H_n - \bar{H}_n$, $K_n - \bar{K}_n$.

$$|H_n| = M_n \left| A_{2n+1}\left(\frac{\overline{\theta}^3}{\theta^3}\right)\right| \cdot |\theta|^{3n+1} < 3^{\frac{3}{2}n} \cdot 2^{2n-1} r^{3n+1};$$

$$|K_n| = M_n \left| C_{2n+1}\left(\frac{\theta^3}{\overline{\theta}^3}\right)\right| \cdot |\overline{\theta}|^{3n+2} < 3^{\frac{3}{2}n} \cdot 2^{2n-1} r^{3n+2};$$

$$|H_n - \overline{H}_n| = M_n \left| A_{2n+1}\left(\frac{\overline{\theta}^3}{\theta^3}\right)\theta^{3n+1} - A_{2n+1}\left(\frac{\theta^3}{\overline{\theta}^3}\right)\overline{\theta}^{3n+1}\right|$$

$$= M_n \left| A_{2n+1}\left(\frac{\overline{\theta}^3}{\theta^3}\right)\theta^{3n+1} - B_{2n+1}\left(\frac{\overline{\theta}^3}{\theta^3}\right)\theta^{3n}\overline{\theta}\right|$$

$$= M_n r^{3n+1}\left|1 - \frac{\overline{\theta}}{\theta}\right|^{2n+1} \cdot \left|V_{2n+1}\left(\frac{\overline{\theta}}{\theta}\right)\right|$$

$$< 3^{\frac{3}{2}n} \cdot r^n \cdot \left(\frac{3}{2}\right)^{2n-1} \cdot |\theta - \overline{\theta}|^{2n+1}.$$

But $|\theta - \overline{\theta}| \leq 3k\sqrt{3\Delta}/2r^2$.

Hence

$$|H_n - \overline{H}_n| < 3^{\frac{5n+1}{2}} \cdot \left(\frac{3}{2}\right)^{4n} \cdot k^{2n+1}\Delta^{n+\frac{1}{2}} r^{-3n-2}.$$

Similarly

$$|K_n - \overline{K}_n| < 3^{\frac{5n+1}{2}} \cdot \left(\frac{3}{2}\right)^{4n} \cdot k^{2n+1}\Delta^{n+\frac{1}{2}} r^{-3n-1}.$$

Let $\theta_1 = r_1 e^{i\phi}$ be any point in the region I. The point θ_1 is not collinear with one of the points H_n, K_n. Therefore the area of the fundamental parallelogram of the lattice does not exceed that of the parallelogram constructed on θ_1 and H_n, or, if this is zero, it does not exceed the area of the parallelogram constructed on θ_1 and K_n.

This leads us to one of the two following inequalities:

$$\frac{1}{2}\sqrt{3\Delta} \leq \frac{1}{2}|\theta_1\overline{H}_n - \overline{\theta}_1 H_n| \leq \frac{1}{2}|\theta_1 - \overline{\theta}_1| \cdot |\overline{H}_n| + \frac{1}{2}|\overline{\theta}_1| \cdot |\overline{H}_n - H_n|$$

$$< \frac{1}{2} \cdot \frac{3}{2} \cdot \frac{k\sqrt{3\Delta}}{r_1^2} \cdot 3^{\frac{3}{2}n} 2^{2n-1} r^{3n+1} + \frac{1}{2} r_1 3^{\frac{5n+1}{2}} \left(\frac{3}{2}\right)^{4n} \frac{k^{2n+1}\Delta^{n+\frac{1}{2}}}{r^{3n+2}},$$

or

$$\frac{1}{2}\sqrt{3\Delta} \leq \frac{1}{2}|\theta_1\overline{K}_n - \overline{\theta}_1 K_n|$$

$$< \frac{1}{2} \cdot \frac{3}{2} \cdot \frac{k\sqrt{3\Delta}}{r_1^2} 3^{\frac{3}{2}n} 2^{2n-1} r^{3n+2} + \frac{1}{2} r_1 3^{\frac{5n+1}{2}} \left(\frac{3}{2}\right)^{4n} \frac{k^{2n+1}\Delta^{n+\frac{1}{2}}}{r^{3n+1}}.$$

If the second inequality does not hold, then the first one cannot hold either. Therefore we will be interested only in the second one. It can be considerably simplified if we let $r = (3k)^{1/3}\Delta^{1/6}t$, $r_1 = (3k)^{1/3}\Delta^{1/6}t_1$, as we have done earlier in simplifying some more elementary inequalities. After some obvious simplifications we obtain

$$1 \leqslant \frac{1}{2} c_1^n k^{n+1} \Delta^{\frac{n}{2}} \left[\frac{t^{3n+2}}{t_1^2} + \frac{t_1}{t^{3n+1}} \right],$$

where c_1 is an absolute constant.

Let $t_1 = t^\nu$ and take $n = [\nu/2]$. Then

$$\frac{\nu}{2} - 1 \leqslant n \leqslant \frac{\nu}{2},$$

which gives

$$1 \leqslant c_1^{\frac{\nu}{2}} k^{\frac{\nu}{2}+1} \Delta^{\frac{\nu}{4}} t^{-\frac{\nu}{2}+2}.$$

This inequality is obviously impossible for $\nu \geq 4 + \epsilon$ and for sufficiently large t.

This proves that there is only a finite number of solutions of the inequality $|f(x, y)| \leq k$.

Suppose now that $\Delta \geq 81k^4$, and suppose that the inequality $|f(x, y)| \leq k$ has seven solutions in the region I. We take for t the number which corresponds to the fourth solution and for t_1 the one corresponding to the seventh solution. From (4′) and (5′) we have

$$t_1 \geqslant t^8, \quad \text{i.e.,} \quad \nu \geqslant 8,$$

$$t \geqslant \left(\frac{\Delta}{81k^4}\right)^{\frac{7}{6}}.$$

Taking this into account we obtain

$$1 \leqslant c_2^\nu k^{\frac{17}{6}\nu - \frac{25}{3}} \Delta^{\frac{7}{3} - \frac{\nu}{3}}.$$

This inequality is impossible if

$$\Delta > c_2^{\frac{3\nu}{\nu - 7}} k^{\frac{17\nu - 50}{2\nu - 14}}.$$

In order that it should always be impossible for $\nu \geq 8$ we must have

$$\Delta > c_3 \cdot k^{\frac{17 \cdot 8 - 50}{2 \cdot 8 - 14}} = c_3 k^{43}.$$

Hence if $\Delta > c_3 k^{43}$, then the inequality $|f(x, y)| \leq k$ cannot have more than six primitive solutions in the region I and therefore not more than 18 solutions altogether. The constant c_3 can be calculated. A rough estimate gives a number of the order of 10^{33}.

Using the same method it can be easily shown that if $f(x, y)$ is a cubic form of negative discriminant the inequality $|(f(x, y)| \leq k$ has not more than six primitive solutions for a sufficiently large discriminant.

In this case we must take for our projection coordinates the resolvents $\theta = \omega + \omega'\epsilon + \omega''\epsilon^2$ and $\bar{\theta} = \omega + \omega'\epsilon^2 + \omega''\epsilon$, which will both be real if ω is real and ω' and ω'' are complex conjugates.

The problem reduces to the enumeration of the points on the resolvent lattice in the region

$$|\theta^3 - \bar{\theta}^3| \leq 3k\sqrt{3\Delta}.$$

The role of r in the estimate will be played by the largest coordinate of the point. All the estimates are carried out in a manner similar to the above for positive discriminants, but with different constants.

4. A further improvement of Siegel's theorem. We now sharpen the result of the previous section by taking into consideration the even numbered polynomials which so far have not been included in the construction of the "boundary sequence."

We first prove a preliminary lemma.

LEMMA. *The product of the resolvents of two numbers in a cubic ring is a conjugate resolvent of a number in the same ring.*

PROOF. Let ω_1 and ω_2 be two numbers that form a normal basis of the ring and let

$$\varphi = x_1\omega_1 + y_1\omega_2 + z_1; \quad \psi = x_2\omega_1 + y_2\omega_2 + z_2$$

(where x_1, y_1, z_1 and x_2, y_2, z_2 are rational integers) be arbitrary numbers of the ring. We now denote by θ_1 and θ_2 the resolvents of the numbers ω_1 and ω_2. Then the product of the resolvents ϕ and ψ is

$$x_1x_2\theta_1^2 + (x_1y_2 + x_2y_1)\,\theta_1\theta_2 + y_1y_2\theta_2^2.$$

We have already shown (lemma in subsection 3 of this section) that θ_1^2 and θ_2^2 are conjugate resolvents of numbers in the ring. It remains to prove the same fact for $\theta_1\theta_2$. But

$$\theta_1\theta_2 = (\omega_1 + \omega_1'\varepsilon + \omega_1''\varepsilon^2)\,(\omega_2 + \omega_2'\varepsilon + \omega_2''\varepsilon^2) =$$
$$= \omega_1\omega_2 + \omega_1'\omega_2'' + \omega_1''\omega_2' + \varepsilon^2\,(\omega_1'\omega_2' + \omega_1''\omega_2 + \omega_1\omega_2'') + \varepsilon\,(\omega_1''\omega_2'' + \omega_1\omega_2' + \omega_1'\omega_2),$$

from which it follows that $\theta_1\theta_2$ is a conjugate resolvent of the number $\omega_1\omega_2 + \omega_1'\omega_2'' + \omega_1''\omega_2'$. This number belongs to the given cubic ring. In fact

$$\omega_1\omega_2+\omega_1'\omega_2''+\omega_1''\omega_2'=ad+\frac{\omega_1' ad}{\omega_1''}+\frac{\omega_1'' ad}{\omega_1'}=ad+ad\,\frac{\omega_1'^2+\omega_1''^2}{\omega_1'\omega_1''}$$

$$=ad+ad\,\frac{b^2-2ac-\omega_1^2}{\omega_1'\omega_1''}=ad+ad\,\frac{(b^2-2ac)\,\omega_1+\omega_1^3}{a^2d}$$

$$=ad+\frac{(b^2-2ac)\,\omega_1-b\,\omega_1^2+ac\omega_1-a^2d}{a}$$

$$=\frac{(b^2-ac)\,\omega_1-b\,(b\omega_1-ac+a\omega_2)}{a}$$

$$=bc-c\omega_1-b\omega_2.$$

Here a, b, c, d are the coefficients of the index-form of the ring.

This proves the lemma.

We now turn to the polynomials with even subscripts.

In constructing the boundary sequence with polynomials of odd subscripts we made use of the lower bound of the absolute value of the quantity

$$\theta_1\theta^{3n+1}\cdot M_{2n+1}\left[\frac{\bar\theta_1}{\theta_1}A_m\left(\frac{\bar\theta^3}{\theta^3}\right)-\frac{\bar\theta}{\theta}\,B_m\left(\frac{\bar\theta^3}{\theta^3}\right)\right],$$

provided it is different from zero.

The existence of the lower bound follows from the fact that this absolute value is a doubled area of the fundamental parallelogram based on the two points θ_1 and $\theta^{3n+1}M_{2n+1}A_m(\bar\theta^3/\theta^3)$ of the resolvent lattice.

If we construct the corresponding quantity

$$U_{2n}=\theta_1\theta^{3n}\cdot M_{2n}\left[\frac{\bar\theta_1}{\theta_1}\,A_{2n}\left(\frac{\bar\theta^3}{\theta^3}\right)-\frac{\bar\theta}{\theta}\,B_{2n}\left(\frac{\bar\theta^3}{\theta^3}\right)\right],$$

for polynomials with even subscripts, it does not have such a simple geometric interpretation, but it is nevertheless bounded from below by a number which depends only on the discriminant of the region.

In fact since A_{2n} is a polynomial of degree n and B_{2n} is a polynomial of degree $n-1$ it follows from the lemma proved above that U_{2n} is a conjugate resolvent of one of the numbers in the ring, i.e., it is a point symmetric with respect to the real axis with one of the points of the lattice which is a projection of the ring.

Furthermore it is easily seen that $U_{2n}\neq 0$.

In fact if $U_{2n} = 0$, we would have

$$\frac{\overline{\theta}_1}{\theta_1} A_{2n}\left(\frac{\overline{\theta}^3}{\theta^3}\right) = \frac{\overline{\theta}}{\theta} B_{2n}\left(\frac{\overline{\theta}^3}{\theta^3}\right). \qquad (*)$$

This equality would have to hold for complex conjugates and therefore

$$\frac{\theta_1}{\overline{\theta}_1} A_{2n}\left(\frac{\theta^3}{\overline{\theta}^3}\right) = \frac{\theta}{\overline{\theta}} B_{2n}\left(\frac{\theta^3}{\overline{\theta}^3}\right).$$

But from the properties of the polynomials A_{2n} and B_{2n} proved above we have

$$A_{2n}\left(\frac{\theta^3}{\overline{\theta}^3}\right) = \frac{\theta^{3n}}{\overline{\theta}^{3n}} C_{2n}\left(\frac{\overline{\theta}^3}{\theta^3}\right),$$

$$B_{2n}\left(\frac{\theta^3}{\overline{\theta}^3}\right) = \frac{\theta^{3n-3}}{\overline{\theta}^{3n-3}} D_{2n}\left(\frac{\overline{\theta}^3}{\theta^3}\right),$$

from which

$$\frac{\theta_1}{\overline{\theta}_1} C_{2n}\left(\frac{\overline{\theta}^3}{\theta^3}\right) = \frac{\overline{\theta}^2}{\theta^2} D_{2n}\left(\frac{\overline{\theta}^3}{\theta^3}\right).$$

Multiplying termwise the last equality by (*) we would have

$$A_{2n}\left(\frac{\overline{\theta}^3}{\theta^2}\right) C_{2n}\left(\frac{\overline{\theta}^3}{\theta^3}\right) = \frac{\overline{\theta}^3}{\theta^3} B_{2n}\left(\frac{\overline{\theta}^3}{\theta^3}\right) D_{2n}\left(\frac{\overline{\theta}^3}{\theta^3}\right),$$

which is impossible since

$$A_{2n}(x)\, C_{2n}(x) - x \cdot B_{2n}(x) \cdot D_{2n}(x) = A_{2n}(0) \cdot C_{2n}(0)\,(1 - x)^{2n} \neq 0$$

for $x = \overline{\theta}^3/\theta^3 \neq 1$. Hence $U_{2n} \neq 0$ and is a point conjugate with one of the points of the resolvent lattice.

From this it follows that

$$|U_{2n}| \geqslant \left(\frac{3}{2}\sqrt{3\Delta}\right)^{\frac{1}{3}},$$

since all the points of the resolvent lattice lie on the curves $r^3\,|\sin 3\phi| = 3/2\,k\sqrt{3\Delta}$ for rational integer values of k and therefore the absolute value of every point of the resolvent lattice $r \geq (3/2\sqrt{3\Delta})^{1/3}$.

Hence

$$\left|\theta_1 \theta^{3n} M_{2n} \cdot A_{2n}\left(\frac{\overline{\theta}^3}{\theta^3}\right) \cdot \frac{\overline{\theta}_1}{\theta_1} - \frac{\overline{\theta}}{\theta} B_{2n}\left(\frac{\overline{\theta}^3}{\theta^3}\right)\right| \geqslant \left(\frac{3}{2}\sqrt{3\Delta}\right)^{\frac{1}{3}}.$$

We denote as before $|\theta| = r$; $\theta_1 = r_1$. From the last inequality, we obtain

$$\left(\frac{3}{2}\sqrt{3\Delta}\right)^{\frac{1}{3}} \leqslant M_{2n} r_1 r^{3n}\left[\left|A_{2n}\left(\frac{\overline{\theta}^3}{\theta^3}\right)\right| \cdot \left|\frac{\overline{\theta}_1}{\theta_1} - 1\right| + \left|1 - \frac{\overline{\theta}}{\theta}\right|^{2n} \cdot \left|V_{2n}\left(\frac{\overline{\theta}}{\theta}\right)\right|\right]$$

$$\leqslant M_{2n}[r^{3n}A_{2n}(1)\cdot|\overline{\theta}_1 - \theta_1| + r^n r_1 \cdot |\theta - \overline{\theta}|^{2n}\cdot V_{2n}(1)]$$

$$\leqslant M_{2n}\left[\frac{3}{2}k\sqrt{3\Delta}\cdot A_{2n}(1)\cdot\frac{r^n}{r_1^2} + \left(\frac{3}{2}k\sqrt{3\Delta}\right)^{2n}\cdot V_{2n}(1)\cdot\frac{r_1}{r^{3n}}\right].$$

By going from r and r_1 to t and t_1 we obtain

$$1 \leqslant c^n k^{n+\frac{1}{3}} \Delta^{\frac{n}{2}}\left[\frac{t^{3n}}{t_1^2} + \frac{t_1}{t^{3n}}\right], \tag{12}$$

or letting $t_1 = t^\nu$

$$1 \leqslant c^n k^{n+\frac{1}{3}} \Delta^{\frac{n}{2}} (t^{3n-2\nu} + t^{\nu-3n}). \tag{**}$$

We compare this with the inequality obtained previously for polynomials with odd subscripts, namely

$$1 \leqslant c_1{}^n k^{n+1} \Delta^{\frac{n}{2}} (t^{3n+2-2\nu} + t^{\nu-3n-1}). \tag{* * *}$$

The first of these gives the best results when ν is close to an even integer $2n$, while the second gives the best results when ν is close to an odd integer $2n+1$. We divide up the region of possible values for ν into the intervals $2n - \alpha \leq \nu \leq 2n + \alpha$ and $2n + 1 - \beta \leq \nu \leq 2n + 1 + \beta$ surrounding all integers. These intervals cover all real numbers if we let $\alpha + \beta = 1$. We shall choose the numbers α and β later in the most advantageous manner. For every value of ν we shall find an appropriate value of n. We will have

$$\frac{\nu - \alpha}{2} \leqslant n \leqslant \frac{\nu + \alpha}{2},$$

if ν is an interval surrounding an even number, and

$$\frac{\nu - 1 - \beta}{2} \leqslant n \leqslant \frac{\nu - 1 + \beta}{2},$$

if ν is in an interval surrounding an odd number.

In the first case (**) gives

$$1 \leqslant c_2^\nu k^{\frac{\nu}{2}+\frac{1}{3}+\frac{\alpha}{2}} \cdot \Delta^{\frac{\nu+\alpha}{4}} \cdot t^{-\frac{\nu}{2}+\frac{3\alpha}{2}}, \tag{A}$$

while in the second case (* * *) gives

$$1 \leqslant c_2^\nu k^{\frac{\nu}{2}+\frac{1}{2}+\frac{\beta}{2}} \Delta^{\frac{\nu-1+\beta}{4}} t^{-\frac{\nu}{2}+\frac{1}{2}+\frac{3\beta}{2}}. \tag{B}$$

Suppose that t corresponds to the fourth solution in the region I. Then from the elementary inequalities in subsection 1 of this section it follows that $t \geq (\Delta/81k^4)^{7/6}$, and therefore

$$1 \leqslant c_3^{\nu} \cdot k^{\frac{17}{6}\nu + \frac{1}{3} + \frac{13}{2}\alpha} \cdot \Delta^{2\alpha - \frac{\nu}{3}},$$

or

$$1 \leqslant c_3^{\nu} \cdot k^{\frac{17}{6}\nu - \frac{11}{6} - \frac{13}{2}\beta} \cdot \Delta^{2\beta + \frac{1}{3} - \frac{\nu}{3}}.$$

We now show that for a sufficiently large Δ the number of points in the region I does not exceed 5. In fact for the sixth solution $\nu \geq 4$ if $\Delta \geq 81k^4$. The inequalities cannot hold if

$$\Delta > c_3^{\frac{\nu}{\frac{\nu}{3} - 2\alpha}} \cdot k^{\frac{\frac{17}{6}\nu + \frac{1}{3} - \frac{13}{2}\alpha}{\frac{\nu}{3} - 2\alpha}},$$

$$\Delta > c_3^{\frac{\nu}{\frac{\nu}{3} - 2\beta - \frac{1}{3}}} \cdot k^{\frac{\frac{17}{6}\nu - \frac{11}{6} - \frac{13}{2}\beta}{\frac{\nu}{3} - 2\beta - \frac{1}{3}}},$$

as long as $\nu > 6\alpha$ and $\nu > 6\beta + 1$ and therefore they cannot hold if

$$\Delta > c_4 \cdot k^{\frac{\frac{35}{3} - \frac{13}{2}\alpha}{\frac{4}{3} - 2\alpha}},$$

$$\Delta > c_4 \cdot k^{\frac{\frac{19}{2} - \frac{13}{2}\beta}{1 - 2\beta}},$$

as long as $\alpha < 2/3$, $\beta < 1/2$.

If we take $\alpha = 94/163$, $\beta = 69/163$, the inequalities do not hold and therefore there does not exist a sixth solution in the region I with

$$\Delta > c_4 k^{44}.$$

5. Bounds for all but one solution of $|f(x, y)| \leq k$ in the region I, and lowering of the bound for the number of solutions.[1]

The inequality (1) of the previous section can be replaced by a much stronger one, namely

---

[1] This subsection was supplied by the author to replace the original one.

$$1 \leq \frac{1}{2} c_1^n k^{n+\frac{2}{3}} \Delta^{\frac{n}{2}-\frac{1}{6}} \left[\frac{t^{3n+1}}{t_1^2} + \frac{t_1}{t^{3n+2}} \right], \tag{11'}$$

provided the point H_n is not collinear with the point θ_1 and the origin.

Let us clarify the question as to when this is possible. Let $Q_n = H_n/q_n$ be a primitive point on a ray containing H_n. Then if θ_1 lies on this ray we have

$$|Q_n^3 - \overline{Q}_n^3| \leq 3k\sqrt{3\Delta}$$

and

$$|H_n^3 - \overline{H}_n^3| \leq q_n^3 \cdot 3k\sqrt{3\Delta}.$$

But

$$|H_n^3 - \overline{H}_n^3| = M_n^3 \left| A_{2n+1}^3 \left(\frac{\overline{\theta}^3}{\theta^3} \right) \theta^{9n+3} - A_{2n+1}^3 \left(\frac{\theta^3}{\overline{\theta}^3} \right) \overline{\theta}^{9n+3} \right|$$

$$= M_n^3 |\theta^3 - \overline{\theta}^3|^{2n+1} \cdot |\theta|^{3n} \cdot \left| V_{2n+1}\left(\frac{\overline{\theta}}{\theta}\right) \cdot V_{2n+1}\left(\frac{\epsilon\overline{\theta}}{\theta}\right) \cdot V_{2n+1}\left(\frac{\epsilon^2\overline{\theta}}{\theta}\right) \right|$$

$$\geq C_1(n)\,\Delta^{n+\frac{1}{2}} r^{3n},$$

since $V_{2n+1}(\overline{\theta}/\theta)$, $V_{2n+1}(\epsilon\overline{\theta}/\theta)$ and $V_{2n+1}(\epsilon^2\overline{\theta}/\theta)$ for sufficiently large $r > C_2(n)$ are arbitrarily close to the nonzero numbers $V_{2n+1}(1)$, $V_{2n+1}(\epsilon)$ and $V_{2n+1}(\epsilon^2)$.

Furthermore it is not hard to estimate q_n. It is clear that q_n is an integer, since it is a common divisor of the forms H_n and $\overline{H}_n$, which are forms of the $(3n+1)$st degree with integer coefficients in θ and $\overline{\theta}$ respectively. These forms are relatively prime and hence q_n must be a divisor of $C_3(n)\,a^{3n+1}$, where $C_3(n)$ is the resultant of the two forms and a is the greatest common divisor of θ and $\overline{\theta}$ (in the corresponding field). Let $\theta^3 - \overline{\theta}^3 = 3k_0\sqrt{-3\Delta}$, where $|k_0| \leq k$; then a^3 is a divisor of $3k_0\sqrt{-3\Delta}$, and hence q_n^6 divides $[C_3(n)]^6 (27k_0^2\Delta)^{3n+1}$, from which $q_n \leq C_3(n)\,(27k^2\Delta)^{n/2+1/6}$.

Hence (11′) fails to hold only if

$$C_1(n)\,\Delta^{n+\frac{1}{2}} r^{3n} \leq C_4(n) k^{3n+2} \Delta^{\frac{3}{2}n+1}$$

and

$$r \leq C_5(n)\,k^{1+\frac{2}{3n}} \Delta^{\frac{1}{6}+\frac{1}{6n}}.$$

We cannot guarantee that the opposite inequalities hold simultaneously since $C_5(n)$ grows very fast with n. However, for $n = 1, 2, \cdots, n_0$ these inequalities will hold as soon as

$$r \geq C_5(n_0) K^{\frac{5}{3}} \Delta^{\frac{1}{3}}.$$

We denote by P_{2n+1}, P_{2n} and P'_{2n+1} the "forbidden intervals" for t_1 which occur if we require that both the summands of the right-hand sides of (11), (12) and (11′) are less than ½. These intervals are

$$P_{2n+1} = \left[c_1^{\frac{n}{2}} k^{\frac{n}{2}+\frac{1}{2}} \Delta^{\frac{n}{4}} t^{\frac{3}{2}n+1},\ c_1^{-n} k^{-n-1} \Delta^{-\frac{n}{2}} t^{3n+1} \right],$$

$$P_{2n+1} = \left[c_1^{\frac{n}{2}} k^{\frac{n}{2}+\frac{1}{3}} \Delta^{\frac{n}{4}-\frac{1}{12}} t^{\frac{3}{2}n+\frac{1}{2}},\ c_1^{-n} k^{-n-\frac{2}{3}} \Delta^{-\frac{n}{2}+\frac{1}{6}} t^{3n+2} \right],$$

$$P_{2n} = \left[c_1^{\frac{n}{2}} k^{\frac{n}{2}+\frac{1}{6}} \Delta^{\frac{n}{4}} t^{\frac{3}{2}n},\ c_1^{-n} k^{-n-\frac{1}{3}} \Delta^{-\frac{n}{2}} t^{3n} \right].$$

These are in fact intervals for $t > c_1 k^2 \Delta^{1/2}$.

The interval P_{2n} overlaps P_{2n+1} for

$$t > c_1^{1+\frac{2}{3n-2}} k^{1+\frac{11}{3(3n-2)}} \Delta^{\frac{1}{2}+\frac{1}{3n-2}}.$$

The interval P_{2n} overlaps P'_{2n+1} for

$$t > c_1^{1+\frac{1}{3n-1}} k^{1+\frac{7}{3(3n-1)}} \Delta^{\frac{1}{2}+\frac{1}{3(3n-1)}}.$$

The interval P_{2n+1} overlaps P_{2n+2} for

$$t > c_1^{1+\frac{2}{3n-1}} k^{1+\frac{13}{3(3n-1)}} \Delta^{\frac{1}{2}+\frac{1}{3n-1}}.$$

The interval P'_{2n+1} overlaps P_{2n+2} for

$$t > ck^{1+\frac{5}{3(3n+1)}} \Delta^{\frac{1}{2}-\frac{1}{3(3n+1)}}.$$

Let us also take into consideration the interval

$$P_1 = [t,\ c_2 k^{-\frac{2}{3}} \Delta^{\frac{1}{6}} t^2],$$

which is forbidden in view of the fundamental inequality.

The interval P_1 overlaps P_2 for

$$t > c_3 k^{\frac{8}{3}} \Delta^{\frac{1}{6}}.$$

Hence for $t > c_4 k^{8/3} \Delta^{2/3}$, the intervals P_1, P_2, P'_3, P_4, P'_5, P_6, P_7, P_8, ... overlap and cover the whole real axis. Therefore if $t > c_4 k^{8/3} \Delta^{2/3}$ and

$t > c_5 k^{7/3}\Delta^{1/6}$, there exist solutions in the region I for which $t_1 > t$. The second of these inequalities follows from the first for a sufficiently large Δ.

The inequality

$$|r^3 \sin 3\phi| \leq \frac{3}{2} k\sqrt{3\Delta}$$

has not more than one primitive solution (not counting the symmetric ones) with $r \leq \sqrt{\sqrt{3}/2}\,\Delta^{1/4}$, since if there were two solutions, noncollinear with the origin, then the area of the fundamental parallelogram would be less than $3\sqrt{3\Delta/2}$.

We denote by θ_0 the point which provides such a solution if it exists. Not counting θ_0, the least solution in the region I has $r > \sqrt{\sqrt{3}/2}\,\Delta^{1/4}$. From elementary inequalities we conclude that for the next solution $r > c_6 k^{-1}\Delta^{1/2}$ and for the next $r > c_7 k^{-3}\Delta$, and therefore $t > c_8 k^{-10/3}\Delta^{5/6}$.

It is clear that for $\Delta > c_9 k^{36}$ and a sufficiently large c_9 we have

$$c_8 k^{-\frac{10}{3}}\Delta^{\frac{5}{6}} > c_4 k^{\frac{8}{3}}\Delta^{\frac{2}{3}}.$$

Therefore for $\Delta > c_9 k^{36}$, the region I (and therefore also the regions II and III) cannot contain more than three primitive solutions of the inequality $|f(x, y)| \leq k$, not counting the solution given by the point θ_0. The total number of solutions does not exceed 10 for $\Delta > c_9 k^{36}$.

Similar considerations for forms of negative discriminant give 4 as the limit for the number of solutions with a sufficiently large $|\Delta|$.

These results were obtained in a student paper of A. E. Gel'man in 1949.

CHAPTER VI

ON INDETERMINATE EQUATIONS OF THE THIRD DEGREE IN TWO UNKNOWNS

PART A. INTEGER SOLUTIONS

Some of the important problems in the theory of cubic irrationals are equivalent to the problem of solving the indeterminate equation of the third degree of the form $f(X, Y) = \sigma$ in rational integers, where f is a given binary form with rational integer coefficients a, b, c, d and σ is a given rational integer. For instance the question of whether a given ring of cubic integers has a power basis, or whether a given cubic field has a power basis can be reduced to the solution of such an indeterminate equation. Also the question of whether there exist cubic equations with a given discriminant and other related problems can be reduced to such equations, as well as some other remarkable problems in the elementary theory of numbers, such as the distributions of squares and cubes. This problem can be stated as follows: given a rational integer k, do there exist arbitrarily large squares and cubes such that the distance between them does not exceed k, or on the other hand, can a place in the natural sequence of squares and cubes be found such that beyond it all the differences are greater than k? The theory of indeterminate equations of the third degree shows that the second alternative is true. It also shows that the number of such squares and cubes whose differences do not exceed k is bounded as a function of k. It is a curious fact that all the knowledge to date does not give a method for finding all these squares and cubes.

The theory of the indeterminate equation $f(X, Y) = \sigma$ of the third degree in two variables, i.e., the theory of binary cubic forms is as yet quite incomplete. In fact the problem of representing numbers by such forms has not been completely solved. It is true that Thue's remarkable theorem shows that the number of such representations is always finite. However, in terms of the usual requirements of an arithmetical theory this theorem should be regarded only as the first step that leads to many further questions.

The first requirement is to find an exact upper bound for the number of representations.

The second is to find a finite, and if possible a practical algorithm that would give in any special case either all the representations, if they exist, or else show that there are no representations, if this is the case.

The first problem is completely solved in the paper of B. Delone, *On the number of representations of a number by a binary cubic form with negative discriminant* (Izv. Akad. Nauk SSSR Ser. Mat. 16 (1922), 253–272), at least for the case of negative discriminant. As to the second question, a practical method is given for the same case in Delone's paper *Über den Algorithmus der Erhöhung* (J. Leningrad Math. Soc. 1 (1927), 257–267), where an algorithm is presented which either found all solutions in the special cases to which it was applied or showed that they did not exist. However, the theory of this algorithm is incomplete, since one cannot be certain that the algorithm always terminates, although it has terminated for all of the many examples to which it was applied. Some special cases of these equations were completely solved by Delone, Nagell and Faddeev.

We shall consider in the present chapter all that has been done on the representation of numbers by the form $f(X, Y)$, i.e., on the solution in rational integers of the cubic indeterminate equation of the type

$$aX^3 + bX^2Y + cXY^2 + dY^3 = \sigma.$$

§71. THE SOLUTION OF THE INDETERMINATE EQUATION $aX^3 + Y^3 = 1$

1. The reduction of the problem to binomial units. We can suppose that a is a rational integer which is not a perfect cube and we will look for all the solutions of

$$aX^3 + Y^3 = 1 \tag{1}$$

in rational integers X, Y. The solution $X = 0$, $Y = 1$ will be called trivial.

From the identity

$$aX^3 + Y^3 = (X\sqrt[3]{a} + Y)(X\zeta\sqrt[3]{a} + Y)(X\zeta^2\sqrt[3]{a} + Y) \quad (\text{where } \zeta = e^{\frac{2\pi i}{3}})$$

we see that to every solution X, Y of (1) corresponds some positive (i.e., of norm $+1$) algebraic unit of the form $X\sqrt[3]{a} + Y$ with rational integers X, Y, and conversely that to every such unit corresponds a solution of (1). We shall next consider positive units of the form $A(\sqrt[3]{a})^2 + B\sqrt[3]{a} + C$, where A, B, C are rational integers, i.e., positive units of the ring $[(\sqrt[3]{a})^2, \sqrt[3]{a}, 1]$ with the power basis $(\sqrt[3]{a})^2, \sqrt[3]{a}, 1$. For brevity we will denote this ring by $O\sqrt[3]{a}$. We shall call *binomial* the units which do not contain the term $c(\sqrt[3]{a})^2$, i.e., those of the form $B\sqrt[3]{a} + C$. The problem of finding solutions of (1) is thus reduced to the problem of finding all binomial units in the ring $O(\sqrt[3]{a})$.

2. On the units in the ring $O\sqrt[3]{a}$. The equation $X^3 = a$ has one real root and two complex conjugate roots. All the units in the ring $O\sqrt[3]{a}$ can therefore be obtained as all possible rational powers of one so-called fundamental unit of this ring. If ϵ is any unit different from ± 1, then $\epsilon, -\epsilon, 1/\epsilon, -1/\epsilon$ are also units. Moreover, out of these four units there is obviously only one greater than 0 and less than 1, and this unit will be called a positive direct unit while its reciprocal will be called a positive inverse unit. Of the four units thus connected with the fundamental unit of the ring $O\sqrt[3]{a}$ we will denote by ϵ_0 the one which satisfies the inequality $0 < \epsilon_0 < 1$, and we shall call it the positive direct fundamental unit, while its inverse $\eta_0 = \epsilon_0^{-1}$ will be called the positive inverse fundamental unit of the ring $O\sqrt[3]{a}$. All the positive direct units of the ring $O\sqrt[3]{a}$ are obviously positive integer powers of the direct fundamental unit, while the positive inverse units are the same integer powers of the inverse fundamental unit. The problem of solving (1) now reduces to finding all those positive exponents m for which either ϵ_0^m or η_0^m is a binomial unit.

3. On the powers of the positive inverse fundamental unit.

THEOREM I. *All three coefficients of any inverse unit are positive.*

The theorem is obvious geometrically, for the planes constructed on the vectors $\overrightarrow{01}$, $\overrightarrow{0\sqrt[3]{a}}$, $\overrightarrow{0(\sqrt[3]{a})^2}$, have the highest point of intersection with the surface $(x^2 + y^2)z = 1$ at the height $z = \sqrt[3]{4}$. But there are only two points between $z = 1$ and $z = \sqrt[3]{4}$ on the surface of $(x^2 + Y^2)z = 1$ which belong to irreducible cubic maximal lattices O, namely the points which belong to lattices with discriminants -23 and -31. But the lattices of $O\sqrt[3]{a}$, which lie in the upper part (i.e., with $z > 1$) of the surface $(x^2 + Y^2)z = 1$, i.e., all the inverse units, lie in a positive trihedral vector-triplet $\overrightarrow{01}$, $\overrightarrow{0\sqrt[3]{a}}$, $\overrightarrow{0(\sqrt[3]{a})^2}$. Hence if $A(\sqrt[3]{a})^2 + B\sqrt[3]{a} + C$ is a direct unit of the ring $O\sqrt[3]{a}$, then all three coefficients

$$A' = B^2 - AC; \quad B' = A^2a - BC; \quad C' = C^2 - ABa \tag{2}$$

of the inverse unit are positive.

From this it follows that we need to look for binomial units only among the powers of the direct fundamental unit.

4. On powers of units of the type $B\sqrt[3]{a}+C$ or $A(\sqrt[3]{a})^2+C$.

THEOREM II. *No rational integer power of a unit of the type* $B\sqrt[3]{a}+C$ *or of the type* $A(\sqrt[3]{a})^2+C$ *can be binomial.*

We must show that all powers of units of the type $B\sqrt[3]{a}+C$ and $A(\sqrt[3]{a})^2+C$ are units of the form $M(\sqrt[3]{a})^2+P\sqrt[3]{a}+Q$ with $M \neq 0$. In fact if $(B\sqrt[3]{a}+C)^m$ or $(A(\sqrt[3]{a})^2+C)^m$ have $M=0$, then we would have one of the following conditions from $(B\sqrt[3]{a}+C)^m$:

Either

$$\xi^{\lambda}+\xi^{\lambda-1}\cdot(C^3)\cdot\frac{m(m-1)(m-2)}{1\cdot2\cdot3}+\ldots+(C^3)^{\lambda}\cdot\frac{m(m-1)}{1\cdot2}=0,$$

if $m=3\lambda+2$, or

$$\xi^{\lambda-1}\cdot\frac{m(m-1)}{1\cdot2}+\xi^{\lambda-2}(C^3)\frac{m(m-1)(m-2)(m-3)(m-4)}{1\cdot2\cdot3\cdot4\cdot5}+\ldots+$$
$$+(C^3)^{\lambda-1}\cdot\frac{m(m-1)}{1\cdot2}=0,$$

if $m=3\lambda+1$, or

$$\xi^{\lambda-1}\cdot m+\xi^{\lambda-2}\cdot(C^3)\cdot\frac{m(m-1)(m-2)(m-3)}{1\cdot2\cdot3\cdot4}+\ldots+(C^3)^{\lambda-1}\cdot\frac{m(m-1)}{1\cdot2}=0,$$

if $m=3\lambda$, where ξ stands for B^3a.

For $(A(\sqrt[3]{a})^2+C)^m$ we get

$$\xi^{\lambda}\cdot m+\xi^{\lambda-1}\cdot(C^3)\cdot\frac{m(m-1)(m-2)(m-3)}{1\cdot2\cdot3\cdot4}+\ldots+(C^3)^{\lambda}\cdot m=0,$$

in case $m=3\lambda+2$,

$$\xi^{\lambda}+\xi^{\lambda-1}\cdot(C^3)\cdot\frac{m(m-1)(m-2)}{1\cdot2\cdot3}+\ldots+(C^3)^{\lambda}\cdot m=0,$$

if $m=3\lambda+1$, and

$$\xi^{\lambda-1}\cdot\frac{m(m-1)}{1\cdot2}+\xi^{\lambda-2}\cdot(C^3)\cdot\frac{m(m-1)(m-2)(m-3)(m-4)}{1\cdot2\cdot3\cdot4\cdot5}+\ldots+$$
$$+(C^3)^{\lambda-1}\cdot m=0,$$

if $m=3\lambda$, where ξ now stands for A^3a^2.

In view of the fact that $B\sqrt[3]{a}+C$ and $A(\sqrt[3]{a})^2+C$ are units, we have $B^3a+C^3=\pm1$, and $A^3a^2+C^3=\pm1$, from which it follows that B^3a and A^3a^2 are relatively prime to C, i.e., that ξ and C are relatively prime. If we suppose that $a>2$, we get from this that $|C|>1$.

Let π be a prime divisor of C, and suppose that the binomial coefficient of the highest power of ξ in that one of the six equations under consideration is divisible exactly by π^{κ}. In each of the remaining binomial coefficients we preserve the first two factors in the numerator, i.e., $m(m-1)$, and the last two in the denominator and divide all the other factors in the denominator into the numerator, which can always be done, since for every $n > 0$ and $0 < k \leq n$ the binomial coefficient $n(n-1)(n-2)\cdots(n-k+1)/k!$ is an integer. The first term of our equation is divisible by exactly the κth power of π, while the remaining terms must contain π to a higher power, since the power to which it could appear in either of the remaining two factors in the denominator is less than the power introduced by the fact that π divides C. Even if $\pi = 2$, we have $\pi^3 > 5$, $\pi^6 > 8$, $\pi^9 > 11$, etc. Moreover, the integer obtained by dividing the denominator into the numerator can also contain π as a factor. Therefore all the terms except the first contain at least $\pi^{\kappa+1}$ as a factor, while the first term is divisible only by π^{κ}, which is impossible.

In case $a = 2$ we have $|C| = 1$ and the above argument does not hold. But this case has to do with the equation $2x^3 + y^3 = 1$, which was solved by Euler, who showed by Fermat's method of infinite descent that the equation has no other solutions than $x = 0$, $y = 1$ and $x = 1$, $y = -1$, not only in integers but even in rationals. The theorem is true for $a = 2$ and therefore is proved in all cases.

5. On the square of a unit.

THEOREM III. *The square of an irrational unit of the ring* $O(\sqrt[3]{a})$ *cannot be a binomial unit.*

PROOF. Let $M(\sqrt[3]{a})^2 + P\sqrt[3]{a} + Q$ be a unit whose square is of the form $B\sqrt[3]{a} + C$; then

$$M^3a^2 + P^3a + Q^3 - 3MPQa = 1 \tag{3}$$

and

$$P^2 + 2MQ = 0. \tag{4}$$

We will show that (3) and (4) do not have any simultaneous solutions in rational integers M, P, Q other than $M = P = 0$, $Q = 1$ or $P = Q = 0$, $M = 1$, $a = 1$, which do not satisfy our conditions since in these cases either the unit under consideration is rational or else $a = 1$, contrary to assumption. From (4) we obtain

either 1. $Q = \gamma^2$, $M = -2\alpha^2$, $P = \pm 2\alpha\gamma$,

or 2. $Q = -\gamma^2$, $M = 2\alpha^2$, $P = \pm 2\alpha\gamma$,

or 3. $Q = 2\gamma^2$, $M = -\alpha^2$, $P = \pm 2\alpha\gamma$,

or 4. $Q = -2\gamma^2$, $M = \alpha^2$, $P = \pm 2\alpha\gamma$.

Substituting these into (3) we obtain respectively

$$-8t^2 \pm 20t\gamma^3 + \gamma^6 = +1, \tag{5}$$
$$-8t^2 \pm 20t\gamma^3 + \gamma^6 = -1, \tag{6}$$
$$t^2 \pm 20t\gamma^3 - 8\gamma^6 = +1, \tag{7}$$
$$t^2 \pm 20t\gamma^3 - 8\gamma^6 = -1, \tag{8}$$

where we have denoted $a\alpha^3$ by t. From (5) we have $t = \pm\frac{1}{4}(5\gamma^3 \pm \sqrt{27\gamma^6 - 2})$, and therefore $27\gamma^6 - 2$ must be a square, let us say z^2, i.e., $z^2 + 2 = \sigma^3$ where $\sigma = 3\gamma^2$, or $(z + \sqrt{-2})(z - \sqrt{-2}) = \sigma^3$. The numbers $z + \sqrt{-2}$ and $z - \sqrt{-2}$ cannot have a common factor prime to 2. Since σ is odd, the numbers $z + \sqrt{-2}$ and $z - \sqrt{-2}$ must be relatively prime and therefore are cubes of algebraic integers in $\Omega(\sqrt{-2})$, but in $\Omega(\sqrt{-2})$ all the ideals are principal ideals and there are only the two units $+1$ and -1. All the numbers in the field $\Omega(\sqrt{-2})$ are of the form $u + v\sqrt{-2}$, where u and v are rational integers. Therefore we have

$$z + \sqrt{-2} = (u + v\sqrt{-2})^3 = u^3 + 3u^2v\sqrt{-2} - 6uv^2 - 2v^3\sqrt{-2}.$$

From this we obtain $3u^2v - 2v^3 = v(3u^2 - 2v^2) = 1$, i.e., $v = \pm 1$ and hence $3u^2 - 2 = \pm 1$ or $u = \pm 1$ and therefore $z = u^3 - 6uv^2 = \pm 5$, from which $\gamma = \pm 1$ and $t = \pm\frac{1}{4}(5 \pm 5) = 0$. But if $t = 0$, then $\alpha = 0$ and we have

$$M = 0, \quad P = 0, \quad Q = 1.$$

It would then follow from equation (6) that $\gamma^6 \equiv -1 \pmod 4$, which is impossible.

Equation (7) can be written in the form

$$u^2 - 4 \cdot 27\gamma^6 = 1$$

if we let $t \pm 10\gamma^3 = u$; it can also be written

$$\frac{u-1}{2} \cdot \frac{u+1}{2} = \dot{\sigma}^3,$$

where $\sigma = 3\gamma^2$. But u is odd since t is odd from (7), and therefore $(u-1)/2$ and $(u+1)/2$ are two consecutive rational integers which must both be cubes, and from this it follows that one of them must be zero. Therefore $\sigma = 0$ and $\gamma = 0$ and we have

$$P = 0, \quad Q = 0, \quad M = 1, \quad a = 1.$$

Equation (8) gives $t^2 \equiv -1 \pmod 4$, which is impossible.

6. On the cube of a unit.

THEOREM IV. *The cube of an irrational unit of the ring $O(\sqrt[3]{a})$ cannot be* *a binomial unit.*

PROOF. Let $M(\sqrt[3]{a})^2 + P\sqrt[3]{a} + Q$ be a unit so that

$$M^3a^2 + P^3a + Q^3 - 3MPQa = 1, \tag{9}$$

and suppose that $(M(\sqrt[3]{a})^2 + P\sqrt[3]{a} + Q)^3$ is a binomial unit, i.e., the coefficient of $(\sqrt[3]{a})^2$ is zero, i.e.,

$$M^2Pa + P^2Q + MQ^2 = 0. \tag{10}$$

We will show that the equations (9) and (10) do not have other simultaneous solutions in rational integers M, P, Q except $M = P = 0$, $Q = 1$ or $M = Q = 0$, $P = 1$, $a = 1$ or $P = Q = 0$, $M = 1$, $a = 1$, which do not satisfy our conditions since in these cases either the unit is rational or $a = 1$, contrary to our hypothesis.

Let δ be the g.c.d. of M and P. We see from (9) that Q is prime to a and δ. It follows from (10) that $M = \delta^2 \cdot m$, $P = \delta \cdot p$, where m and p are relatively prime, since otherwise δ would not be the g.c.d. of M and P.

By (10)

$$-m^2\delta^4p\delta a = Q(p^2\delta^2 + m\delta^2Q), \quad \text{or} \quad -m^2\delta^3pa = Q(p^2 + mQ).$$

But m is relatively prime to p and therefore to $p^2 + mQ$. Therefore $Q = m^2q$ and $-m^2\delta^3pa = m^2q(p^2 + m^3q)$, or $-p\delta^3a = q(p^2 + m^3q)$. But q is relatively prime to δ and a, since q divides Q and therefore $p = qs$ and $-qs\delta^3a = q(q^2s^2 + m^3q)$, or $-s\delta^3a = q(qs^2 + m^3)$. But since q is relatively prime to δ and a we have $s = qe$ and $-qe\delta^3a = q(q^3e^2 + m^3)$, or $-e\delta^3a = q^3e^2 + m^3$. But e divides s and therefore it divides p and is relatively prime to m from which it follows that $e = \pm 1$. Thus we obtain

$$\mp \delta^3a = q^3 + m^3, \; M = m\delta^2, \; P = \pm q^2\delta, \; Q = m^2q, \; MPQ = \pm m^3q^3\delta^3.$$

Substituting this into (9) we get

$$m^3\delta^6a^2 \pm q^6\delta^3a + m^6q^3 \mp 3m^3q^3\delta^3a = 1.$$

But $\delta^3 = \mp(q^3 + m^3)/a$; this gives

$$m^3(m^3 + q^3)^2 - (m^3 + q^3)\,q^6 + m^6q^3 + 3m^3q^3(m^3 + q^3) = 1,$$

or, letting $m^2q = \lambda$, $m^3 - q^3 = \mu$, we get the equation

$$9\lambda^3 + \mu^3 = 1, \tag{11}$$

i.e., a special equation of our type with $a = 9$. The direct positive fundamental unit of the ring $O(\sqrt[3]{9})$ is $\sqrt[3]{9}-2$, which is a binomial unit. Therefore, by Theorems I and II equation (11) has only one nontrivial solution $\lambda = 1$, $\mu = -2$ besides the trivial solution $\lambda = 0$, $\mu = 1$. Since $m^3 - q^3 = \mu$, the solution $\lambda = 1$, $\mu = -2$ gives $m = -1$, $q = 1$ and therefore $\delta = 0$, i.e., $M = P = 0$, $Q = 1$. The solution $\lambda = 0$, $\mu = 1$ gives either $m = 0$, $q = -1$ or $m = 1$, $q = 0$, i.e., $M = Q = 0$, $P = 1$, $a = 1$ or $P = Q = 0$, $M = 1$, $a = 1$.

7. The proof of the fundamental theorem. We have just shown that the square or the cube of a unit cannot be a solution. In order to prove this for a fifth power we would have to show that there do not exist rational numbers M, P, Q, a such that M and P are not both zero and $a > 1$, satisfying the two equations

$$M^3a^2 + P^3a + Q^3 - 3MPQa = 1$$

and

$$5M^4Qa^2 + 10M^3P^3a^2 + 30M^2PQ^2a + 20MP^2Qa + 5MQ^4 + P^5a + 10P^2Q^3 = 0.$$

These equations are fairly complicated and it is not clear how this is to be accomplished. However, if we make use of all the foregoing theorems the method given below works for any power of a unit and gives a complete solution of equation (1).

Let $A(\sqrt[3]{a})^2 + B\sqrt[3]{a} + C$ be any unit of the ring $O(\sqrt[3]{a})$, and let $[A(\sqrt[3]{a})^2 + B\sqrt[3]{a} + C]^m = M(\sqrt[3]{a})^2 + P\sqrt[3]{a} + Q$. Then it is easily seen that

$$3(\sqrt[3]{a})^2 \cdot M = [A(\sqrt[3]{a})^3 + B\sqrt[3]{a} + C]^m + \zeta\cdot[A\zeta^2(\sqrt[3]{a})^2 + B\zeta\sqrt[3]{a} + C]^m + \zeta^2[A\zeta(\sqrt[3]{a})^2 + B\zeta^2\sqrt[3]{a} + C]^m,$$

where ζ, as before, is $\sqrt[3]{1} = e^{2\pi i/3}$.

Let $M = 0$. We consider separately the cases $m = 3y + 2$ and $m = 3y + 1$. We need not consider the case $m = 3y$ in view of Theorem IV.

First let $m = 3y + 2$ and $M = 0$; then we have

$$[A\zeta(\sqrt[3]{a})^2 + B\sqrt[3]{a} + C\zeta^2]^m + [A\zeta^2(\sqrt[3]{a})^2 + B\sqrt[3]{a} + C\zeta]^m = -[A(\sqrt[3]{a})^2 + B\sqrt[3]{a} + C]^m.$$

By Theorem III we can suppose that m is odd, and in this case $[\zeta^2 A(\sqrt[3]{a})^2 + B\sqrt[3]{a} + \zeta C] + [\zeta A(\sqrt[3]{a})^2 + B\sqrt[3]{a} + \zeta^2 C]$ is a divisor of $[A(\sqrt[3]{a})^2 + B\sqrt[3]{a} + C]^m$, and therefore is an algebraic unit, i.e., $-A(\sqrt[3]{a})^2 + 2B\sqrt[3]{a} - C$ is a unit and we have $-A^3a^2 + 8B^3a - C^3 - 6ABCa = \pm 1$.

On the other hand

$$A^3a^2 + B^3a + C^3 - 3ABCa = 1.$$

Adding this to the preceding equation we get

$$9aB(B^2 - AC) = 2 \text{ or } 0,$$

i.e., either $B^2 - AC = 0$ or $B = 0$. But $B^2 - AC$ is a coefficient of the inverse unit (see (2)) and therefore by Theorem I it cannot be zero. Hence $B = 0$, so that the original unit was binomial; but by Theorems I and II none of the powers greater than the first of a binomial unit can be binomial. Since we are considering the case $m = 3y + 2$, it follows that $M \neq 0$. In case $m = 3y + 1$ and $M = 0$ we have

$$[A(\sqrt[3]{a})^2 + \zeta B\sqrt[3]{a} + \zeta^2 C]^m + [A(\sqrt[3]{a})^2 + \zeta^2 B\sqrt[3]{a} + \zeta C]^m$$
$$= -[A(\sqrt[3]{a})^2 + B\sqrt[3]{a} + C]^m,$$

from which we get in an analogous fashion that $2A(\sqrt[3]{a})^2 - B\sqrt[3]{a} - C$ is a unit, and again by equating the two relations

$$8A^3a^2 - B^3a - C^3 - 6ABCa = \pm 1 \text{ and } A^3a^2 + B^3a + C^3 - 3ABCa = 1,$$

we get $9aA(A^2a - BC) = 2$ or 0. But $A^2a - BC$ is again a coefficient of an inverse unit, which is different from zero. Thus we obtain $A = 0$, or that the unit under consideration is of the form $B\sqrt[3]{a} + C$ and is itself a binomial unit, and hence none of its powers greater than the first can be binomial units by Theorem II. However, in case $m = 3y + 1$, it is possible to have $M = 0$ but only, as we have seen, for $m = 1$. By Theorem I the only nontrivial solution of (1) is the direct positive fundamental unit of the ring $O(\sqrt[3]{a})$, if it happens to be a binomial unit. This results in the following general theorem giving the complete solution of equation (1).

THEOREM V. *The indeterminate equation $aX^3 + Y^3 = 1$, where a is a rational integer which is not a perfect cube, has, besides the trivial solution $X = 0$, $Y = 1$, at most one nontrivial solution in integers X, Y. This nontrivial solution exists if and only if the direct positive fundamental unit of the ring $O(\sqrt[3]{a})$ is a binomial unit, i.e., is of the form $B_0\sqrt[3]{a} + C_0$, in which case the solution is $X = B_0$, $Y = C_0$.*

§72. THE GENERALIZATION OF THE METHOD OF §71 TO THE EQUATION $I(X, Y) = 27$

The method given for the solution of the equations considered in the preceding section can be applied to the solution of a fairly general class of indeterminate cubic equations and even to some quartic equations.

In the first place the method of §71 was generalized by the Norwegian mathematician Nagell, who solved completely the indeterminate equations $aX^3 + bY^3 = c$ with $c = 1$ and 3. Further generalizations are due to Faddeev. We shall not consider equations of the Nagell type separately, since they are special cases of a wider class of equations that we will consider in the next section.

Here we will consider the problem of finding units in a cubic field of negative discriminant, lying in the plane of zero trace.

This problem is equivalent to solving the indeterminate equation

$$I(X, Y) = 27,$$

where $I(X, Y)$ is the cubic covariant of the index-form of the maximal ring of the field.

In fact let

$$f(X, Y) = aX^3 + bX^2Y + cXY^2 + eY^3$$

be the index-form of the maximal ring. We can take for a basis of the ring $[1, \omega_1, \omega_2]$, where ω_1 and ω_2 are respectively roots of the equations

$$\omega_1^3 = b\omega_1^2 - ac\omega_1 + a^2e, \quad \omega_2^3 = c\omega_2^2 - be\omega_2 + ae^2.$$

The cubic covariant

$$\begin{aligned} I(X, Y) = {} & (27a^2e - 9abc + 2b^3)X^3 + (27abe - 18ac^2 + 3b^2c)X^2Y \\ & + (-27ace + 18b^2e - 3bc^2)XY^2 + (-27ae^2 + 9bce - 2c^3)Y^3 \end{aligned}$$

can be represented in the form

$$N[(3\omega_1 - b)X - (3\omega_2 - c)Y],$$

from which it follows that every solution of the equation $I(X, Y) = 27$ determines a unit ϵ of the maximal ring satisfying the relation

$$\epsilon + \epsilon' + \epsilon'' = 0,$$

i.e., lying in the plane of zero trace.

In fact if $I(X, Y) = N[(3\omega_1 - b)X - (3\omega_2 - c)Y] = 27$, then $bX + cY$ is a multiple of 3 and the integer

$$\epsilon = \frac{1}{3}[(3\omega_1 - b)X - (3\omega_2 - c)Y]$$

is a unit of the maximal ring, which obviously lies in the plane of zero trace.

Conversely, if the unit $\epsilon = Z + X\omega_1 - Y\omega_2$ lies in the plane of zero trace, then X, Y, and Z satisfy the relation $3Z + bX - cY = 0$, from which it follows that

$$3\epsilon = (3\omega_1 - b)\, X - (3\omega_2 - c)\, Y,$$

and therefore X and Y give a solution of the equation

$$I(X, Y) = 27.$$

It is necessary to point out that the solution of $I(X, Y) = 27$, where $I(X, Y)$ is a cubic covariant of any binary cubic form (not necessarily of the index-form of the maximal ring) can also be reduced to the problem of finding units in the plane of zero trace by the same considerations.

We now take up this problem. As before we shall call the unit ϵ of a cubic ring of negative discriminant a direct unit if $0 < \epsilon < 1$ and an inverse unit if $\epsilon > 1$.

LEMMA 1. *With the exception of the unit ϵ satisfying the equation $\epsilon^3 = \epsilon + 1$, there exist no inverse units in the plane of zero trace.*

PROOF. Every unit lying in the plane of zero trace satisfies the equation

$$\epsilon^3 = - q\epsilon + 1.$$

This equation has a negative discriminant for $q \geq - 1$. For $q = - 1$, ϵ is an inverse unit, while for $q = 0$ the equation is reducible. Finally for $q \geq 1$, ϵ is a direct unit, since $\phi(0) = - 1$, $\phi(1) = q$ are of different sign and therefore there is a root ϵ of the equation $\phi(z) = z^3 + qz - 1 = 0$ between 0 and 1. This proves the lemma.

LEMMA 2. *A unit which is a cube of another unit cannot lie in the plane of zero trace.*

PROOF. Let $\epsilon = \eta^3$, where η is a root of the equation $\eta^3 = s\eta^2 - q\eta + 1$. Then $\epsilon + \epsilon' + \epsilon'' = s^3 - 3sq + 3$. Obviously the rational integer $\epsilon + \epsilon' + \epsilon'' = s^3 - 3sq + 3$ cannot be divisible by 9 and therefore cannot be zero. This proves the lemma.

LEMMA 3. *A unit which is the fourth power of another unit cannot lie in the plane of zero trace, with the single exception of the unit ϵ satisfying the equation $\epsilon^3 = - 1040\epsilon + 1$, which is equal to η^4, where $\eta^3 = 2\eta^2 - 6\eta + 1$.*

PROOF. Let $\epsilon = \eta^4$, where η satisfies the equation $\eta^3 = s\eta^2 - q\eta + 1$. Then

$$\epsilon + \epsilon' + \epsilon'' = s^4 - 4s^2q + 4s + 2q^2.$$

If ϵ lies in the plane of zero trace, then

$$s^4 - 4s^2q + 4s + 2q^2 = 0.$$

From this it follows that s and q are both even. Letting $s = 2s_1$, $q = 2q_1$ we have

$$2s_1^4 - 4s_1^2q_1 + s_1 + q_1^2 = 0,$$

from which

$$q_1 = 2s_1^2 \pm \sqrt{2s_1^4 - s_1}.$$

In order that the last equation should hold it is necessary that $s_1(2s_1^3 - 1)$ be a perfect square and therefore that $2s_1^3 - 1 = \pm v^2$.

It is easily seen that the equation $2s_1^3 - 1 = v^2$ has a unique solution $s_1 = 1$ to which corresponds $q_1 = 1$ or $q_1 = 3$. The equation $2s_1^3 - 1 = -v^2$ has the single solution $s_1 = 0$ to which correpsonds $q_1 = 0$.

Hence if $\epsilon = \eta^4$ lies in the plane of zero trace, then η must satisfy one of the equations

$$\eta^3 = 2\eta^2 - 6\eta + 1, \quad \eta^3 = 2\eta^2 - 2\eta + 1.$$

The second of these equations is reducible, while the first gives the single exception stated in the lemma. This proves the lemma.

LEMMA 4. *A positive power of a number lying in the plane of zero trace cannot lie in the plane of zero trace, with the exception of the powers of the numbers given by the equations:*

$$\eta^3 = -\eta + 1; \quad \eta^3 = -6\eta + 12; \quad \eta^3 = -4\eta + 4;$$
$$\eta^3 = -30\eta + 60; \quad \eta^3 = -2\eta + 2; \quad \eta^3 = -3\eta + 9;$$
$$\eta^3 = -3\eta + 3; \quad \eta^3 = -5\eta + 5; \quad \eta^3 = -30\eta + 30.$$

PROOF. Let η be a number in the plane of zero trace and let $\eta^3 = -q\eta + n$ be the equation satisfied by η.

Denote by s_m the sum $\eta^m + \eta'^m + \eta''^m$. By the well-known Waring's formula for sums of powers, s_m can be written in the form

$$s_m = \sum_{2\alpha + 3\beta = m} \frac{m}{(\alpha + \beta)} \cdot \frac{(\alpha + \beta)!}{\alpha!\beta!} (-q)^\alpha n^\beta.$$

The summation is taken over all non-negative integers α, β for which

$$2\alpha + 3\beta = m.$$

Expanding the right-hand side in ascending powers of n we consider separately the cases in which m is even and odd. In the first case we write $m = 2l$

and in the second we write $m = 2l + 3$. We obtain

$$s_{2l} = \sum_{s=0}^{\left[\frac{l}{3}\right]} \frac{2l}{l-s} \cdot \frac{(l-s)!}{(2s)!\,(l-3s)!} (-q)^{l-3s} n^{2s}$$
$$= 2\cdot(-q)^l + \frac{2l\,(l-2)}{1\cdot 2}(-q)^{l-3}\cdot n^2$$
$$+ \frac{2l\,(l-3)\,(l-4)\,(l-5)}{1\cdot 2\cdot 3\cdot 4}(-q)^{l-6}\cdot n^4 + \ldots$$

$$s_{2l+3} = \sum_{s=0}^{\left[\frac{l}{3}\right]} \frac{2l+3}{l-s+1} \cdot \frac{(l-s+1)!}{(2s+1)!\,(l-3s)!} (-q)^{l-3s}\cdot n^{2s+1}$$
$$= \frac{2l+3}{1}(-q)^l n + \frac{(2l+3)\,(l-1)\,(l-2)}{1\cdot 2\cdot 3}(-q)^{l-3}\cdot n^3 + \ldots$$

We let $q^3 = q_1\delta$, $n^2 = n_1\delta$, where δ is the greatest common divisor of q^3 and n^2 and equate s_m to zero. After obvious simplifications we obtain

$$2q_1^{l_1} - \frac{2l\,(l-2)}{1\cdot 2} q_1^{l_1-1} n_1 + \frac{2l\,(l-3)\,(l-4)\,(l-5)}{1\cdot 2\cdot 3\cdot 4} q_1^{l_1-2} n_1^2 - \ldots = 0 \qquad (\alpha)$$
$$\left(\text{for } m = 2l; \qquad l_1 = \left[\frac{l}{3}\right]\right)$$

$$\frac{2l+3}{1} q_1^{l_1} - \frac{(2l+3)\,(l-1)\,(l-2)}{1\cdot 2\cdot 3} q_1^{l_1-1} n_1 + \ldots = 0 \qquad (\beta)$$
$$\left(\text{for } m = 2l+3; \; l_1 = \left[\frac{l}{3}\right]\right).$$

The equation (α) is obviously impossible for n_1 different from 1 or 2, since n_1 must be a divisor of $2q_1$, while q_1 and n_1 are relatively prime to each other. Moreover for $n_1 = 2$, the equation (α) is impossible for even l, since in this case all the terms on the left-hand side except the first are divisible by 4, while the first term is not. If l is odd all the terms beginning with the third are divisible by 8. Letting $n_1 = 2$ we have the congruence

$$2q_1^{l_1-1}\,[q_1 + 1 - (l-1)^2] \equiv 0 \pmod 8,$$

from which $q_1 \equiv 3 \pmod 4$.

Hence equation (α) is possible only with $n_1 = 1$ and $n_1 = 2$. In the second case we must have $q_1 \equiv 3 \pmod 4$.

We now turn to equation (β).

It is obviously impossible for even n_1, since n_1 must divide $2l + 3$. It is also impossible for any n_1 having an odd prime factor greater than 3 and for an

n_1 which is a multiple of 3^2, since in all these cases the first term is divisible by a lower power of the prime under consideration than all the remaining terms in the sum. This is easily seen by simple calculations.

Therefore equation (β) holds only if $n_1 = 1$ or $n_1 = 3$, where the second case is possible only if $m = 2l + 3$ is a multiple of 3. We now write s_m in increasing powers of q. In doing so we must separate three cases according to whether m is of the form $3k$, $3k + 2$, or $3k + 4$:

$$s_{3k} = \sum_{s=0}^{\left[\frac{k}{2}\right]} \frac{3k}{k+s} \cdot \frac{(k+s)!}{(3s)!\,(k-2s)!} (-q)^{3s} \cdot n^{k-2s} = 3n^k - \frac{3k \cdot k\,(k-1)}{1 \cdot 2 \cdot 3} q^3 n^{k-2}$$
$$+ \frac{3k\,(k+1)\,k\,(k-1)\,(k-2)\,(k-3)}{1 \cdot 2 \cdot 3 \cdot 4 \cdot 5 \cdot 6} q^6 n^{k-4} - \ldots$$

$$s_{3k+2} = \sum_{s=0}^{\left[\frac{k}{2}\right]} \frac{3k+2}{k+s+1} \cdot \frac{(k+s+1)!}{(3s+1)!\,(k-2s)!} (-q)^{3s+1} \cdot n^{k-2s} = -\frac{3k+2}{1} q n^k$$
$$+ \frac{(3k+2)\,(k+1)\,k\,(k-1)}{1 \cdot 2 \cdot 3 \cdot 4} q^4 n^{k-2} - \ldots$$

$$s_{3k+4} = \sum_{s=0}^{\left[\frac{k}{2}\right]} \frac{3k+4}{k+s+2} \cdot \frac{(k+s+2)!}{(3s+2)!\,(k-2s)!} (-q)^{3s+2} \cdot n^{k-2s} = \frac{(3k+4)\,(k+1)}{1 \cdot 2} q^2 n^k$$
$$- \frac{(3k+4)\,(k+2)\,(k+1)\,k\,(k-1)}{1 \cdot 2 \cdot 3 \cdot 4 \cdot 5} q^5 n^{k-2} + \ldots .$$

We equate s_m to zero, using as before

$$q_1 = \frac{q^3}{\delta}, \quad n_1 = \frac{n^2}{\delta}, \quad \delta = (q^3, n^2).$$

After simplification we arrive at the equations

$$3n_1^{k_1} - \frac{3k \cdot k\,(k-1)}{1 \cdot 2 \cdot 3} n_1^{k_1-1} q_1 +$$
$$+ \frac{3k\,(k+1) \cdot k\,(k-1)\,(k-2)\,(k-3)}{1 \cdot 2 \cdot 3 \cdot 4 \cdot 5 \cdot 6} n^{k_1-2} q_1^2 - \ldots = 0 \qquad (\gamma)$$
$$\left(\text{for } m = 3k, \qquad k_1 = \left[\tfrac{k}{2}\right]\right),$$

$$\frac{3k+2}{1} n_1^{k_1} - \frac{(3k+2)\,(k+1)\,k\,(k-1)}{1 \cdot 2 \cdot 3 \cdot 4} n_1^{k_1-1} q_1 + \ldots = 0 \qquad (\delta)$$
$$\left(\text{for } m = 3k+2, \; k_1 = \left[\tfrac{k}{2}\right]\right),$$

$$\frac{(3k+4)\,(k+1)}{1 \cdot 2} n_1^{k_1} - \frac{(3k+4)\,(k+2)\,(k+1)\,k\,(k-1)}{1 \cdot 2 \cdot 3 \cdot 4 \cdot 5} n_1^{k_1-1} q_1 + \ldots = 0. \qquad (\varepsilon)$$

We note that n_1 must be equal to 1, 2, or 3 in (γ), while n_1 can be only 1 or 2 in (δ) and (ϵ).

Equation (γ) is obviously impossible for q_1 different from 1 or 3.

Equation (δ) is possible only if $q_1 = 1$, 2, or 4, since in case q_1 is divisible by a prime $p \geq 3$, or by 2^3, all the terms in the sum on the left-hand side, except the first, are divisible by a higher power of p (or of 2) than the first term.

Let $q_1 = 4$ in (δ). Then n_1 must be 1. It is easily seen that all the summands on the left-hand side of (δ) starting with the third are divisible by 16 in this case. Therefore we have the congruence

$$3k+2-\frac{(3k+2)(k+1)k(k-1)}{6}\equiv 0 \pmod{16}.$$

This congruence can hold only with even k. Letting $k = 2k_1$ we have

$$9k_1+3-(3k_1+1)k_1(4k_1^2-1)\equiv 0 \pmod 8.$$

This congruence in turn can hold only for odd k_1. In this case $4k_1^2 \equiv 4 \pmod 8$ and the last congruence is equivalent to

$$(3k_1+1)(1-k_1)\equiv 0 \pmod 8,$$

from which $k \equiv 1 \pmod 4$ and $m = 6k_1 + 2 \equiv 0 \pmod 8$.

Equation (ϵ) is impossible if q_1 is divisible by a prime $p > 5$, and for q divisible by 3^2, 2^2 and 5^2, since in all these cases the first term is divisible by a lower power of the prime than all the other terms.

Letting $q_1 = 3n$ and combining the first two terms we arrive at the conclusion that (ϵ) holds only for $n_1 \equiv n \pmod 3$. Finally letting $q_1 = 5n$ and combining the first two terms we see that (ϵ) holds for $n_1 \equiv n \pmod 5$, $m \equiv 1 \pmod 5$ and for $n_1 \equiv -n \pmod 5$, $m \equiv 0 \pmod 5$.

Summarizing these results we find that s_m is equal to zero only for the following values of n_1, q_1 and m:

n_1	3	2	2	1	1	1	1	1	1
q_1	1	3	15	4	2	3	5	30	1
m	$\equiv 0(3)$	$\equiv 0(6)$	$\equiv 0(10)$	$\equiv 0(8)$					

All these cases were listed as exceptions in the statement of the lemma.

REMARK. In the case $n_1 = 2$, $q_1 = 3$, we must have m a multiple of 6. But $s_6 = 0$ and the equation satisfied by η^6, where $\eta^3 = -6\eta + 12$, is not among the exceptions. Therefore η^6 is the only power of η found in the plane of zero trace. Similarly among the powers of the numbers given by the equations

$$\eta^3 = -30\eta + 60 \quad (n_1 = 2,\ q_1 = 15), \quad \eta^3 = -4\eta + 4 \quad (n_1 = 1,\ q_1 = 4)$$

only η^{10} can be found in the plane of zero trace for the first equation and only η^8 for the second. A more detailed study of (β) shows that for $n_1 = 3$, $q_1 = 1$ we must have m a multiple of 9. But η^9, where $\eta^3 = -3\eta + 9$, is in the plane of zero trace. Hence, except for η^9 there are no other powers of η in the plane of zero trace.

The study of the remaining five exceptions can be reduced, as we shall see in the next section, to the solution of some very concrete indeterminate equations, which can be solved by the algorithm which will be discussed in §75. This investigation shows that on the plane of zero trace will be found η^{11} for $n_1 = q_1 = 1$ and η^{13} for $n_1 = 1$, $q_1 = 2$.

Therefore finally we have only six exceptions. In the plane of zero trace will be found

η^6, where $\eta^3 = -6\eta + 12$; η^8, where $\eta^3 = -4\eta + 4$; η^{10}, where $\eta^3 = -30\eta + 6$;
η^9, where $\eta^3 = -3\eta + 9$; η^{11}, where $\eta^3 = -\eta + 1$; η^{13}, where $\eta^3 = -2\eta + 2$.

In this section we needed Lemma 4 only for units, i.e., for $n = 1$. In the next section we shall need it for $n_1 = 1$. We nevertheless gave the lemma in a more general form as it seems of interest in itself.

THEOREM. *Only the direct fundamental unit or its square can be found in the plane of zero trace, except for*

$$\epsilon_0^{-1}, \ \textit{where}\ \epsilon_0^3 = -\epsilon_0^2 + 1,$$

$$\epsilon_0^4, \ \textit{where}\ \epsilon_0^3 = 2\epsilon_0^2 - 6\epsilon_0 + 1,$$

$$\epsilon_0^{11}, \ \textit{where}\ \epsilon_0^3 = -\epsilon_0 + 1.$$

PROOF. Let ϵ_0 be the direct fundamental unit and let $\epsilon = \epsilon_0^m$ lie in the plane of zero trace

$$\epsilon_0^m + \epsilon_0'^m + \epsilon_0''^m = 0,$$

where m is non-negative, except for a single exception given in Lemma 1, and is not a multiple of 4, except for the single exception given in Lemma 3. Suppose that m is divisible by the odd prime p. Let $\epsilon_0^{m/p} = \eta$. Then

$$\eta^p + \eta'^p + \eta''^p = 0.$$

From this it follows that the number $\eta' + \eta''$ is a unit. Let $\eta^3 = s\eta^2 - q\eta + 1$ be the equation satisfied by η. Since $\eta' + \eta''$ is a unit, $N(\eta' + \eta'') = N(s - \eta) = qs - 1 = +1$. Therefore either $qs = 2$ or $qs = 0$.

The condition $qs = 2$ leads to four equations for η of which only one, namely $\eta^3 = \eta^2 - 2\eta + 1$ is of negative discriminant and has a real root between 0 and 1.

If $qs = 0$, then either $q = 0$ or $s = 0$.

If $s = 0$, then by Lemma 4, $q = 1$ and $p = 11$.

If $q = 0$, then η is a direct unit only for $s = -1$.

This case must be treated separately.

The two cases which need additional consideration both lead to finding units in the plane of zero trace in a region with discriminant -23.

The corresponding indeterminate equation

$$x^3 + 2x^2y + 9xy^2 + 25y^3 = 1$$

has the unique solution $x = 1$, $y = 0$, which can be seen using the algorithm "of ascent." To this solution corresponds the unique unit η^{-1} of this region, lying in the plane of zero trace where $\eta^3 = -\eta^2 + 1$. This completes the proof of the theorem.

It follows from this theorem that in order to solve the equation $I(X, Y) = 27$ one must find the direct fundamental unit ϵ_0 of the region to which belong the roots of the form

$$f(x, y) = ax^3 + bx^2y + cxy^2 + ey^3.$$

If this unit, or its square, lies in the plane of zero trace and belongs to the ring generated by the roots of $f(x, y)$, then $I(x, y) = 27$ has a unique solution (except for $D = -31$) which can be obtained from the representation of 3ϵ in the form $(3\omega_1 - b)x - (3\omega_2 - c)y$, where ϵ is a unit in the plane of zero trace. In the contrary case (with two exceptions) the equation $I(x, y) = 27$ has no solutions.

§73. FURTHER GENERALIZATIONS OF THE METHODS OF §71

We shall now solve by the same method a wide class of indeterminate equations. Before defining this class we must first give a lemma about the general cubic indeterminate equation of the form $f(x, y) = 1$, where $f(x, y)$ is a cubic form.

LEMMA 1. *In order that the equation* $f(x, y) = 1$ *have a solution it is necessary (but not sufficient) that the form* $f(x, y)$ *be primitive (i.e., its coefficients do not have a common factor different from* 1) *and that it can be represented as a norm of a linear function with coefficients in a ring defined by the form* (for the proof see subsection 1 of §76).

We note that in order to represent the form $f(x, y)$ as a norm of a linear function with coefficients in the ring O, corresponding to the form $f(x, y)$, it is necessary and sufficient that $O^* = O$, where O^* is the lattice polar to the lattice which represents the ring O.

Hence it makes sense to consider only those equations $f(x, y) = 1$ for which $f(x, y) = N(\lambda x + \mu y)$, where λ and μ are numbers belonging to the field corresponding to the form $f(x, y)$. The solution of such equations is equivalent to finding units of rings of the form $\lambda x + \mu y$. From a geometrical point of view the solution of the equation $f(x, y) = 1$ is equivalent to finding units in the plane $\lambda x + \mu y$ which go through the origin.

Let $\epsilon = \lambda x + \mu y$ be a unit giving a solution of the equation $f(x, y) = 1$. We bring in the conjugate numbers $\epsilon' = \lambda' x + \mu' y$, $\epsilon'' = \lambda'' x + \mu'' y$. There is obviously a relation between the units $\epsilon, \epsilon', \epsilon''$ of the form

$$\phi \cdot \epsilon + \phi' \cdot \epsilon' + \phi'' \cdot \epsilon'' = 0,$$

where $\phi = \lambda' \mu'' - \lambda'' \mu'$, $\phi' = \lambda'' \mu - \lambda \mu''$, $\phi'' = \lambda \mu' - \lambda' \mu$.

The numbers ϕ, ϕ', ϕ'' depend only on the form of the equation $f(x, y)$, but not on the selected solution.

We will give a solution of $f(x, y) = 1$ for which the numbers ϕ, ϕ', ϕ'' are associated, i.e., they differ only by multipliers which are units in the case of forms with negative discriminant.

To clarify the question as to what equation can be included in the class under consideration we prove the following lemma.

LEMMA 2. *If* $f(x, y) = N(\lambda x + \mu y)$ *is primitive and is decomposable into linear factors with algebraic integer coefficients (of any degree) such that*

$$f(x, y) = (\alpha_1 x + \beta_1 y)(\alpha_2 x + \beta_2 y)(\alpha_3 x + \beta_3 y)$$

and the numbers $\alpha_1\beta_2 - \alpha_2\beta_1$, $\alpha_2\beta_3 - \alpha_3\beta_2$, $\alpha_3\beta_1 - \alpha_1\beta_3$ *are associated, then the numbers* ϕ, ϕ', ϕ'' *are also associated.*

PROOF. Consider two decompositions of $f(x, y)$, into factors, namely,

$f(x, y) = (\lambda x + \mu y)(\lambda' x + \mu' y)(\lambda'' x + \mu'' y) = (\alpha_1 x + \beta_1 y)(\alpha_2 x + \beta_2 y)(\alpha_3 x + \beta_3 y).$
These two decompositions can differ only by constant multipliers. Hence

$$\lambda = \epsilon_1 \alpha_1;\ \lambda' = \epsilon_2 \alpha_2;\ \lambda'' = \epsilon_3 \alpha_3;$$

$$\mu = \epsilon_1 \beta_1;\ \mu' = \epsilon_2 \beta_2;\ \mu'' = \epsilon_3 \beta_3.$$

The form $f(x, y)$ is primitive, and therefore the numbers α_1, β_1 are relatively prime and one can find algebraic integers γ, δ such that $\alpha_1 \gamma + \beta_1 \delta = 1$.

Therefore $\epsilon_1 = \lambda \gamma + \mu \delta$ is an algebraic integer, being the result of addition and multiplication of algebraic integers. From the same considerations we can show that $1/\epsilon_1$, ϵ_2, $1/\epsilon_2$, ϵ_3, $1/\epsilon_3$ are algebraic integers and therefore that ϵ_1, ϵ_2, ϵ_3 are units.

The numbers ϕ, ϕ', ϕ'' differ from the numbers $\alpha_2\beta_3 - \alpha_3\beta_2$, $\alpha_3\beta_1 - \alpha_1\beta_3$, $\alpha_1\beta_2 - \alpha_2\beta_1$ only by multipliers $\epsilon_2\epsilon_3$, $\epsilon_3\epsilon_1$, $\epsilon_1\epsilon_2$, which are units. Therefore if the latter are associated, so are ϕ, ϕ', ϕ'' which proves the lemma.

Now we can easily show that the equations $ax^3 + by^3 = 1$ belong to the class of indeterminate equations under consideration. In fact

$$ax^3 + by^3 = (x\sqrt[3]{a} + y\sqrt[3]{b})(x\sqrt[3]{a} + y\sqrt[3]{b}\,\zeta)(x\sqrt[3]{a} + y\sqrt[3]{b}\,\zeta^2),$$

where $\zeta = e^{2\pi i/3}$. The determinants $\alpha_2\beta_3 - \alpha_3\beta_2$, $\alpha_3\beta_1 - \alpha_1\beta_3$, $\alpha_1\beta_2 - \alpha_2\beta_1$ are respectively equal to $\sqrt[3]{ab}\,(\zeta^2 - \zeta)$, $\sqrt[3]{ab}\,(1 - \zeta^2)$, $\sqrt[3]{ab}\,(\zeta - 1)$ and are obviously associated.

In the same way we can show that the equations $ax^3 + by^3 = 3$ with $a \not\equiv \pm b \pmod 9$ and $I(x, y) = 27$ can also be reduced to equations of this type. The equation $ax^3 + y^3 = 1$, being a special case of $ax^3 + by^3 = 1$, belongs to our class. However, we shall see that the equations $ax^3 + y^3 = 1$ and $I(x, y) = 27$ occupy a unique position and require special treatment, which has already been given in the foregoing sections.

We now take up the solution of equations of this class.

Let $f(x, y)$ be primitive and representable in the form $N(\lambda x + \mu y)$, where the numbers $\phi = \lambda'\mu'' - \lambda''\mu'$, $\phi' = \lambda''\mu - \lambda\mu''$, $\phi'' = \lambda\mu' - \lambda'\mu$ are associated. As we have already seen in the solution of the equation $f(x, y) = 1$, this problem is equivalent to the problem of finding units in the "plane"

$$\phi \cdot \epsilon + \phi' \cdot \epsilon' + \phi'' \cdot \epsilon'' = 0. \qquad (*)$$

The number ϕ does not belong to the cubic field to which belongs the root of the form f; however the numbers ϕ^2 and $\phi'\phi''$ do belong to this field. Multiplying (*) by $\phi\phi'\phi''$, we obtain

$$\nu\epsilon + \nu'\epsilon' + \nu''\epsilon'' = 0,$$

where $\nu = \phi^2\phi'\phi''$ belongs to the cubic field and ν' and ν'' are the conjugates of ν. We denote by l the norm of ν. It is obvious that ν, ν', ν'' are associated with each other and therefore also with $\sqrt[3]{l}$. In this way the solution of the indeterminate equations of the type under consideration is reduced to the following problem:

To find all numbers ω belonging to a cubic field and lying in the plane of zero trace

$$\omega + \omega' + \omega'' = 0,$$

which together with their conjugates are associated with $\sqrt[3]{l}$, is a given rational integer.

We note that for the equation $ax^3 + by^3 = 1$ we have $l = ab$. Without loss of generality we can assume that l is positive and free of cubic factors. We can let $l = fg^2$, where f and g are square free.

We denote by L the totality of all the numbers in the cubic field under consideration which, as well as their conjugates, are divisible by $\sqrt[3]{l}$. By $\bar{L}$ we denote all the numbers in the field which together with their conjugates are divisible by $\sqrt[3]{\bar{l}}$, where $\bar{l} = f^2g$. The sets L and $\bar{L}$ are obviously ideals. Further we denote by L_0 and $\bar{L}_0$ all the numbers having zero trace which belong respectively to L and $\bar{L}$. Then L_0 and $\bar{L}_0$ obviously have binomial bases. We denote these by $[\nu_1, \nu_2]$ and $[\bar{\nu}_1, \bar{\nu}_2]$.

It is easily seen that every number belonging to L can be represented in the form $(x\nu_1 + y\nu_2 + z)/3$, where x, y, z are rational integers, and where z is divisible by fg. In fact let ν be any number belonging to the ideal L. We let $\nu + \nu' + \nu'' = z$. The rational integer z is divisible by $\sqrt[3]{l}$ and therefore by fg. Furthermore $3\nu - z$ obviously belongs to L_0. Therefore $3\nu - z = x\nu_1 + y\nu_2$ with rational integer x and y. Therefore ν is actually equal to $(x\nu_1 + y\nu_2 + z)/3$. Analogously, every number belonging to the ideal $\bar{L}$ can be written in the form $(x\bar{\nu}_1 + y\bar{\nu}_2 + z)/3$.

Let $\omega = x\nu_1 + y\nu_2$ be a number in the plane of zero trace giving a solution of our problem, i.e., associated with $\sqrt[3]{l}$. The number $\eta = \omega/\sqrt[3]{l}$ is a unit in the field which is the union of the fields $\Omega(\omega)$ and $\Omega(\sqrt[3]{l})$. This field will in general be a field of the ninth degree. The number η can belong to $\Omega(\omega)$ only in two cases, namely either if $l = 1$, or if $\Omega(\omega)$ coincides with $\Omega(\sqrt[3]{l})$.

Both of these cases have already been considered. In fact if $l = 1$, then the problem reduces to finding units in the plane of zero trace. If $\Omega(\omega)$ coincides with $\Omega(\sqrt[3]{l})$, then the problem reduces to the solution of the equation $x^3 + ly^3 = 1$. In fact a basis for the plane of zero trace for the field $\Omega(\sqrt[3]{l})$ is formed by $\sqrt[3]{l}$ and $\sqrt[3]{l}$ and therefore the set L_0 consists of numbers of the form $x\sqrt[3]{l} + y\sqrt[3]{l}$, which are divisible by $\sqrt[3]{l}$. Among these numbers the ones which are associated with $\sqrt[3]{l}$ have the property that

$$N(x + y\sqrt[3]{l}) = x^3 + ly^3 = 1.$$

We exclude these two cases from consideration.

We now introduce the unit

$$\epsilon = \eta^3 = \frac{\omega^3}{l}.$$

This unit belongs to the basic cubic field and is not the cube of any unit in the same field (of course the cases $l = 1$ and $\Omega(\omega) = \Omega(\sqrt[3]{l})$ are excluded).

Units of the form ω^3/l, where ω is a number in the plane of zero trace will be called units of the desired type.

Concerning these units we shall now prove a few theorems from which the complete solution of our problem can be easily obtained.

THEOREM 1. *The unit* $\epsilon = \omega^3/l$, *where* ω *is a number in the plane of zero trace, cannot be an inverse unit, with a finite number of exceptions.*

PROOF. Let $\eta = \sqrt[3]{\epsilon} = \omega/\sqrt[3]{l}$, $\eta' = \omega'/\sqrt[3]{l}$, $\eta'' = \omega''/\sqrt[3]{l}$. The numbers η, η', η'' are roots of an equation of the form

$$\eta^3 = -q\sqrt[3]{l}\,\eta + 1,$$

where q is a rational integer. This equation has one real root η and two complex conjugate roots η' and η'' and therefore the discriminant of the equation is negative, or

$$-4lq^3 - 27 < 0.$$

This is possible only if $q > 0$, with the exception of $q = -1$, $l = 1, 2, 3, 4, 5, 6$.

But for $q > 0$, the real root η of the equation $\eta^3 = -q\sqrt[3]{l}\,\eta + 1$ satisfies the inequality $0 < \eta < 1$. Therefore also $0 < \epsilon < 1$, which proves the theorem.

THEOREM 2. *A positive power of a unit of the form* $\omega/\sqrt[3]{l}$, *where* ω *is a number in the plane of zero trace, cannot be a unit of the same form; neither can it be a unit of the form* $\omega/\sqrt[3]{l}$, *except for* η^8, *where* $\eta = \omega/\sqrt[3]{4}$, $\omega^3 = -4\omega + 4$, *and* η^{13}, *where* $\eta = \omega/\sqrt[3]{2}$, $\omega^3 = -2\omega + 2$.

PROOF. If $(\omega/\sqrt[3]{l})^n = \omega_1/\sqrt[3]{l}$ or $\omega_1/\sqrt[3]{l}$, then ω^n is a number in the plane of zero trace. But by Lemma 4 of the preceding section a power of a number in the plane of zero trace cannot be a number in the plane of zero trace, with six exceptions. From the fact that ω is such that $\omega/\sqrt[3]{l}$ is a unit it follows that ω is a root of $\omega^3 = -q\omega + n$, where $n = l$ and q is divisible by $\sqrt[3]{l^2}$, and therefore q^3 is divisible by η^2. Moreover $l \neq 1$. These conditions are satisfied only by the two out of the six exceptions that appear in the statement of the theorem.

THEOREM 3. *A unit of the form* ω^3/l, *where* ω *is a number in the plane of zero trace, cannot be an odd power of another unit, with a finite number of exceptions.*

PROOF. Let $\omega^3/l = (x\nu_1 + y\nu_2)^3/l = \epsilon^p$, where ϵ is a unit in the field $\delta(\omega)$, and suppose that this field does not belong to the list of exceptions to Theorems 1 and 2.

Let p be an odd number. It cannot be a multiple of 3 and hence $p \equiv \pm 1 \pmod 6$.

We consider in detail the case $p \equiv 1 \pmod 6$. Let $p = 6k + 1$.

The unit ϵ must be a direct fundamental unit. Consider the unit $\epsilon^{1/3} = \sqrt[3]{\epsilon^p} \cdot \epsilon^{-2k} = \omega\epsilon^{-2k}/\sqrt[3]{l}$. The number $\omega_1 = \omega\epsilon^{-2k}$ obviously belongs to the ideal L and therefore can be represented in the form $(x_1\nu_1 + y_1\nu_2 + z_1)/3$ with z_1 divisible by fg.

Hence

$$\eta = \varepsilon^{\frac{1}{3}} = \frac{x_1\nu_1 + y_1\nu_2 + z_1}{3\sqrt[3]{l}} = \frac{\omega_1}{\sqrt[3]{l}},$$

$$\eta^p = \varepsilon^{\frac{p}{3}} = \frac{\omega}{\sqrt[3]{l}}.$$

Consider the numbers $\eta' = \omega_1'/\sqrt[3]{l}$, $\eta'' = \omega_1''/\sqrt[3]{l}$.

They satisfy the equation

$$\eta^p + \eta'^p + \eta''^p = 0,$$

from which it follows that $\eta' + \eta'' = (z_1 - \omega_1)/\sqrt[3]{l}$ is an algebraic unit and therefore $z_1 - \omega_1$ is associated with $\sqrt[3]{l}$.

On the other hand ω_1 is a root of the equation

$$\omega_1^3 = z_1\omega_1^2 - q\omega_1 + l,$$

with z_1 divisible by fg and q divisible by l.

Since the norm $N(z_1 - \omega_1) = \pm l$, the coefficients z_1 and q_1 are related by

$$N(z_1 - \omega_1) = z_1^3 - z_1^3 + qz_1 - l = \pm l,$$

from which either

$$qz_1 = 2l,$$

or

$$qz_1 = 0.$$

The first equality is possible only for a finite number of values of q, z_1 and l. The second is possible for $q = 0$ or for $z_1 = 0$.

If $q = 0$, then $1/\omega_1 + 1/\omega_1' + 1/\omega_1'' = 0$ and therefore $\bar{\omega}_1 + \bar{\omega}_1' + \bar{\omega}_1'' = 0$, where $\bar{\omega}_1 = fg/\omega_1 = \sqrt[3]{\bar{l}}\,\eta^{-1}$ is an algebraic integer associated with $\sqrt[3]{\bar{l}}$ and lying in the plane of zero trace. This is impossible with a finite number of exceptional cases, since the inverse unit $1/\epsilon = 1/\eta^3$ cannot be of the form $\bar{\omega}_1^3/\bar{l}$ with $\bar{\omega}_1$ lying in the plane of zero trace.

If $z_1 = 0$, then $\omega_1 + \omega_1' + \omega_1'' = 0$ and therefore ω_1 lies in the plane of zero trace and

$$\left(\frac{\omega_1}{\sqrt[3]{l}}\right)^p = \frac{\omega}{\sqrt[3]{l}}.$$

This is impossible by Theorem 2, with a finite number of exceptions. This proves the theorem for $p \equiv 1 \pmod 6$.

In the second case of $p \equiv -1 \pmod 6$ the theorem is proved in a similar way, so that we omit the proof.

It follows from the preceding that the only units of the form $(x\nu_1 + y\nu_2)^3/l$ are the units ϵ_0^{2k}, where ϵ_0 is a direct fundamental unit of the field. Hence a given field can have only one such unit; for if there were two such units one of them would have to be a power of the other, which is impossible.

We will now show that if this unit exists it can be found in a finite number of steps, or else it can be shown not to exist.

In order to do this we first prove the following theorem.

THEOREM 4. *The indeterminate equation*

$$m^2u^6 - 2^s n^2 v^6 = 1$$

has no solutions $u, v,$ *for given odd* m *and* n *if* $s \geq 8k + 4$, *where* k *is the number of distinct odd divisors of* n.

PROOF. From every solution of the equation

$$m^2u^6 - 2^s n^2 v^6 = 1$$

one can "descend" to the solution of another equation of the same type.

In fact the equation

$$m^2u^6 - 2^s n^2 v^6 = 1$$

can be rewritten in the form

$$\frac{mu^3+1}{2} \cdot \frac{mu^3-1}{2} = 2^{s-2}n^2v^6,$$

from which it follows, since $(mu^3 + 1)/2$ and $(mu^3 - 1)/2$ are relatively prime, that

$$\frac{mu^3 \pm 1}{2} = 2^{s-2}n_1^2 v_1^6; \quad \frac{mu^3 \mp 1}{2} = m_1^2 u_1^6,$$

where $(m_1, 2n_1) = 1$, $m_1 n_1 = n$, $u_1 v_1 = v$.

From this it follows that

$$m_1^2 u_1^6 - 2^{s-2} n_1^2 v_1^6 = \mp 1.$$

The minus sign on the right-hand side is obviously impossible for $s \geq 4$. Therefore we have actually "descended" to a new equation

$$m_1^2 u_1^6 - 2^{s_1} n_1^2 v_1^6 = 1$$

of the same type as the original one in which v_1 is a divisor of v, and we have $m_1 n_1 = n$, $(m_1, 2n_1) = 1$ and $s_1 = s - 2$. From this equation one can descend to the next one, and so forth until the exponent of 2 becomes less than 2.

Such a descent can be of two kinds.

The descent of the first kind is such that if $m_1 = 1$, then $n_1 = n$.

The descent of the second kind has $m_1 > 1$. In this case n_1 will contain fewer prime divisors than n, in view of the fact that m_1 and n_1 are relatively prime and $n_1 = n/m_1$.

We shall now show that we cannot have four descents of the first kind in a row. In fact, suppose that there are four descents of the first kind one after another. Then the following five equations would have solutions

$$\begin{aligned} m^2u^6 - 2^s\, n^2\, v^6 &= 1, \\ u_1^6 - 2^{s-2}\, n^2\, v_1^6 &= 1, \\ u_2^6 - 2^{s-4}\, n^2\, v_2^6 &= 1, \\ u_3^6 - 2^{s-6}\, n^2\, v_3^6 &= 1, \\ u_4^6 - 2^{s-8}\, n^2\, v_4^6 &= 1. \end{aligned}$$

However this is impossible. In fact a solution of the second and fifth equations can be considered as a solution of the equation

$$x^3 - Ay^3 = 1 \quad (A = 2^{s-8}\, n^2)$$

with $x = u_2^2$, $y = 4v_1^2$ for the second equation and $x = u_4^2$, $y = v_4^2$ for the fifth.

These solutions of the equation $x^3 - Ay^3 = 1$ are distinct, since v_4 is a divisor of v_1. But we know that the equation $x^3 - Ay^3 = 1$ cannot have more than one solution with $xy \neq 0$.

Hence the assumption that it is possible to have four descents of the same kind in a row leads to a contradiction and therefore in any four descents there must be at least one descent of the second kind. Therefore the number n loses at least one odd prime factor in every four descents. After $4k$ descents n will lose all its odd prime factors and we will arrive at the equation

$$m_{4k}^2\, u_{4k}^6 - 2^t v_{4k}^6 = 1,$$

where $t = s - 4k \geq 4$.

Repeating the descent one more time we arrive at the equation

$$u_{4k+1}^6 - 2^{t-2}\, v_{4k+1}^6 = 1.$$

This equation obviously has no solutions since $t - 2 \geq 2$ and the equations

$$x^3 - 4y^3 = 1, \quad x^3 - 8y^3 = 1 \text{ and } x^3 - 16y^3 = 1$$

have no solutions with $xy \neq 0$. This proves the theorem.

The descent used in this argument is due to Nagell.

THEOREM 5. *Units of the desired type* $\epsilon = (x\nu_1 + y\nu_2)^3/l$ *can be found only among the powers*

$$\epsilon_0^{4^s} \quad or \quad \epsilon_0^{2\cdot 4^s}$$

with $s \leq (4k + 8)/3$, *where* k *is the number of distinct prime divisors of* l.

PROOF. First of all we note that for the existence of the unit

$\epsilon = (x\nu_1 + y\nu_2)^3/l$ it is necessary that the fundamental unit ϵ_0 or its square ϵ_0^2 be of the form ω_1^3/l, where ω_1 is a number of the fundamental cubic region associated with $\sqrt[3]{l}$. In fact if we let $(x\nu_1 + y\nu_2)^3/l = \epsilon_0^{2^k}$, it is obvious that $2^k \equiv 1 \pmod 3$ for even k, and that $2^k \equiv 2 \pmod 3$ for odd k. Let $2^k = 3t + \sigma$, $\sigma = 1$ or 2. We obtain

$$\varepsilon_0^{\frac{\sigma}{3}} = \frac{(x\nu_1 + y\nu_2)\,\varepsilon_0^{-t}}{\sqrt[3]{l}} = \frac{\omega_1}{\sqrt[3]{l}}.$$

Let $\epsilon_0^{\sigma/3} = \eta_0$, $\epsilon^{1/3} = \eta$. From the above discussion it follows that

$$\eta = \eta_0^{4^s}.$$

Consider the equations one of whose roots is

$$\eta_0,\ \eta_1 = \eta_0^4,\ \eta_2 = \eta_0^{16}, \ldots,\ \eta_s = \eta_0^{4^s}, \ldots.$$

These equations are

$$\eta_0^3 = a_0 \sqrt[3]{l}\,\eta_0^2 - b_0 \sqrt[3]{l}\,\eta_0 + 1,$$
$$\eta_1^3 = a_1 \sqrt[3]{l}\,\eta_1^2 - b_1 \sqrt[3]{l}\,\eta_1 + 1,$$

etc. The coefficients of these equations are related by

$$a_{s+1} = a_s^4 f^2 g - 4a_s^2 b_s f g + 2b_s^2 g + 4a_s,$$
$$b_{s+1} = b_s^4 f g^2 - 4b_s^2 a_s f g + 2a_s^2 f + 4b_s.$$

For a unit of the desired type $a_s = 0$.

We will now show that either a_s and b_s are divisible by 2^{2s-1} for $s \geq 1$, or else there are no solutions to our problem. In order to do this we consider several cases.

Let $l = fg^2$ be odd and let a_0 also be odd. Then obviously all a's are odd and hence $a_s = 0$ is impossible. Suppose now that $l = fg^2$ is odd, while a_0 is even, but b_0 is odd. In this case all the b's are odd and all $a_s \equiv 2 \pmod 4$. Hence also in this case $a_s = 0$ is impossible. Now if a_0 and b_0 are both even, then a_1 and b_1 are divisible by 8 and a_2, b_2 by 32, etc.

Finally let $l = fg^2$ be an even number; then a_1, b_1 are both even, a_2, b_2 are divisible by 8, etc., a_s, b_s are both divisible by 2^{2s-1}.

Now suppose that $a_{s+1} = 0$ for $s + 1 > (4k + 8)/3$.

This leads to the indeterminate equation

$$a_s^4 f^2 g - 4a_s^2 b_s fg + 2b_s g + 4a_s = 0.$$

From this equation it follows that $4a_s$ is divisible by g. Since a_s is also divisible by 2^{2s-1} we can be assured that a_s is divisible by $2^{2s-2}g$. Let $a_s = 2^{2s-2}g\alpha$. After substitution and simplification we get

$$2^{8s-9}l^2\alpha^4 - 2^{4s-3}\alpha^2 l b_s + b_s^2 + 2^{2s-1}\alpha = 0,$$

from which

$$(b_s - 2^{4s-4}\alpha^2 l)^2 = 2^{2s-1}\alpha(2^{6s-8}l^2\alpha^3 - 1).$$

The numbers $2^{2s-1}\alpha$ and $2^{6s-8}l^2\alpha^3 - 1$ are relatively prime and their product is a perfect square. Hence

$$\alpha = \pm 2u^2,$$
$$2^{6s-8}l^2\alpha^3 - 1 = \pm v^2.$$

where the plus and minus signs correspond. The plus sign must be discarded. Substituting $\alpha = -2u^2$ in the second equation we obtain

$$2^{6s-5}l^2u^6 = v^2 - 1,$$

from which

$$\frac{v-1}{2}\cdot\frac{v+1}{2} = 2^{6s-7}l^2u^6.$$

The numbers $(v-1)/2$ and $(v+1)/2$ are relatively prime. Therefore

$$\frac{v\pm 1}{2} = m^2u_1^6; \quad \frac{v\mp 1}{2} = 2^{6s-7}n^2v_1^6,$$

where $mn = l$, $u_1v_1 = u$.

Subtracting we obtain

$$m^2u_1^6 - 2^{6s-7}n^2v_1^6 = \pm 1,$$

where the minus sign on the right-hand side must be discarded.

But by Theorem 4 the last equation has no solutions.

In fact $s+1 > (4k+8)/3$, $6s-7 > 8k+3$ and therefore

$$6s - 7 \geq 8k + 4.$$

The number n contains not more than l prime factors. Hence the equation

$$m^2u_1^6 - 2^{6s-7}n^2v_1^6 = 1$$

satisfies the conditions of Theorem 4 and therefore has no solutions.

§74. THE GENERALIZATION OF THE METHOD OF §71 TO THE EQUATION $x^4 - Ay^4 = \pm 1$

These equations were first solved by Professor V. A. Tartakovskiǐ in his paper *Auflösung der Gleichung* $x^4 - \rho y^4 = 1$ (Izv. Akad. Nauk SSSR (1926)) by a method different from the one which we will give here.

1. The equation

$$x^4 - Ay^4 = \pm 1 \tag{1}$$

can be transformed into

$$(x^2 + xy\sqrt[4]{-4A} + y^2\sqrt{-A})(x^2 - xy\sqrt[4]{-4a} + y^2\sqrt{-A}) = \pm 1. \tag{2}$$

The number $x^2 + xy\sqrt[4]{-4A} + y^2\sqrt{-A}$ belongs to the ring $O(\sqrt[4]{-4A})$ with the basis $[1, \sqrt[4]{-4A}, \sqrt{-A}, \sqrt{-A}\sqrt[4]{-4A}]$ in the field $\Omega\sqrt[4]{-4A}$ and in view of (2) is a unit of this ring of a special type in which the term $\sqrt{-A}\sqrt[4]{-4A}$ is missing.

In this way every solution of (1) defines a trinomial unit of the type $a + b\sqrt[4]{-4A} + c\sqrt{-A}$ of the ring $O(\sqrt[4]{-4A})$. It is not hard to see that conversely every trinomial unit of this type determines a solution of equation (1).

In fact, let $\epsilon = a + b\sqrt[4]{-4A} + c\sqrt{-A}$ be a unit.

Then the norm

$$N(\epsilon) = \epsilon\epsilon'\epsilon''\epsilon''' = (a^2 - Ac^2)^2 + 4A(ac - b^2)^2$$

must be equal to 1. For this we must have

$$ac - b^2 = 0, \tag{3}$$

$$a^2 - Ac^2 = \pm 1. \tag{4}$$

We see from (4) that $(a, c) = 1$ and therefore by (3)

$$a = \pm x^2, \quad b = \pm xy, \quad c = \pm y^2.$$

Substituting into (4) we obtain

$$x^4 - Ay^4 = \pm 1.$$

Therefore the problem of finding trinomial units in the ring $O(\sqrt[4]{-4A})$ is equivalent to solving equation (1).

2. We study next the properties of the units in the ring $O(\sqrt[4]{-4A})$.

First of all we note that the field $\Omega(\sqrt[4]{-4A})$ and therefore also the ring

$O(\sqrt[4]{-4A})$ have by Dirichlet's theorem a unique fundamental unit, whose positive and negative integer powers give all the units.

Let $\epsilon = a + b\sqrt[4]{-4A} + c\sqrt{-A} + d\sqrt{-A}\sqrt[4]{-4A}$ be any unit of the ring $O(\sqrt[4]{-4A})$. Its conjugates are

$$\begin{aligned}\varepsilon' &= a + bi\sqrt[4]{-4A} + c\sqrt{-A} + di\sqrt{-A}\sqrt[4]{-4A},\\ \varepsilon'' &= a - b\sqrt[4]{-4A} + c\sqrt{-A} - d\sqrt{-A}\sqrt[4]{-4A},\\ \varepsilon''' &= a - bi\sqrt[4]{-4A} + c\sqrt{-A} + di\sqrt{-A}\sqrt[4]{-4A}\end{aligned}$$

and its norm is

$$N(\varepsilon) = (a^2 - Ac^2 + 4Abd)^2 + 4A(ac - b^2 + Ad^2)^2 = 1.$$

Therefore

$$a^2 - Ac^2 + 4Abd = \pm 1, \tag{5}$$
$$ac - b^2 + Ad^2 = 0. \tag{6}$$

The second conjugate unit ϵ'' belongs to the same ring as ϵ. It is easily verified that

$$\epsilon\epsilon'' = (a^2 - Ac^2 + 4Abd) + 2\sqrt{-A}(ac - b^2 - Ad^2) = \pm 1.$$

Therefore

$$\epsilon'' = \pm\frac{1}{\epsilon}. \tag{7}$$

We shall call ϵ a direct unit if $|\epsilon| > 1$, and an inverse unit if $|\epsilon| < 1$. It follows from (7) that if the direct unit ϵ is trinomial, then the inverse unit $1/\epsilon$ is also trinomial and conversely. Hence it is sufficient to find all trinomial units among the positive powers of the direct fundamental unit.

We note the following inequality. If ϵ is a direct unit, then $|\epsilon| > 2\sqrt[4]{4A} - 1$. In fact

$$\epsilon - \epsilon'' = 2\sqrt[4]{-4A}\,(b + d\sqrt{-A})$$

and therefore

$$|\epsilon - \epsilon''| = 2\sqrt[4]{4A}\,\sqrt{b^2 + Ad^2}.$$

Since ϵ is a direct unit $|\epsilon''| = |1/\epsilon| < 1$ and therefore

$$|\epsilon| \geq |\epsilon - \epsilon''| - |\epsilon''| > 2\sqrt[4]{4A} - 1.$$

3. THEOREM 1. *An odd power of a trinomial unit of the type*

$$a + b\sqrt[4]{-4A} + c\sqrt{-A}$$

cannot be a trinomial unit of the same type.

PROOF. Let $\epsilon = a + b\sqrt[4]{-4A} + c\sqrt{-A}$; then

$$\epsilon'' = a - b\sqrt[4]{-4A} + c\sqrt{-A}$$

and

$$\epsilon^2 = \epsilon(\epsilon'' + 2b\sqrt[4]{-4A}) = \pm 1 + 2b\epsilon\sqrt[4]{-4A}.$$

Therefore

$$(\pm 1)^n \varepsilon^{2n} = (1 \pm 2b\varepsilon\sqrt[4]{-4A})^n = 1 \pm \frac{n}{1}\cdot 2b\varepsilon\sqrt[4]{-4A}$$
$$+ \frac{n(n-1)}{1\cdot 2}\cdot 8b^2\varepsilon^2\sqrt{-A} \pm \frac{n(n-1)(n-2)}{1\cdot 2\cdot 3}\cdot 16b^3\varepsilon^3\sqrt{-A}\sqrt[4]{-4A} + \dots$$
$$+ \frac{n(n-1)\dots(n-k+1)}{k!}\, 2^k b^k \left(\sqrt[4]{-4A}\right)^k\cdot\varepsilon^k + \dots .$$

Multiplying both sides of the equality by ϵ'' we obtain

$$(\pm 1)^{n+1}\varepsilon^{2n-1} = \varepsilon'' + n\cdot 2b\sqrt[4]{-4A} \pm \frac{n(n-1)}{1\cdot 2}\, 8b^2\varepsilon\sqrt{-A}$$
$$+ \frac{n(n-1)(n-2)}{1\cdot 2\cdot 3}\, 16b^3\varepsilon^2\sqrt{-A}\sqrt[4]{-4A} \pm \dots$$
$$\pm \frac{n(n-1)\dots(n-k+1)}{k!}\cdot 2^k b^k(\sqrt[4]{-4A})^k\varepsilon^{k-1} + \dots$$
$$= a - b\sqrt[4]{-4A} + c\sqrt{-A} + n\cdot 2b\sqrt[4]{-4A}$$
$$+ n(n-1)\cdot 4b^2\sqrt{-A}\,(a + b\sqrt[4]{-4A} + c\sqrt{-A})$$
$$\pm \frac{n(n-1)(n-2)}{3}\cdot 8b^3\sqrt{-A}\sqrt[4]{-4A}\,(\pm 1 + 2ab\sqrt[4]{-4A}$$
$$+ 4b^2\sqrt{-A} + 2bc\sqrt{-A}\sqrt[4]{-4A}) + \dots$$
$$\pm \frac{n(n-1)\dots(n-k+1)}{k!}\cdot 2^k b^k(\sqrt[4]{-4A})^k\varepsilon^{k-1} + \dots .$$

In order that ϵ^{2n-1} be trinomial it is necessary that the coefficient of $\sqrt{-A}\sqrt[4]{-4A}$ on the right-hand side of the above equality be zero, i.e.,

$$n(n-1)\cdot 4b^3 + \frac{n(n-1)(n-2)}{3}\cdot 8b^3 + \dots$$
$$+ \frac{n(n-1)\dots(n-k+1)}{k!}\, 2^k b^k H_k + \dots = 0. \qquad (8)$$

Here H_k denotes the coefficient of $\sqrt{-A}\sqrt[4]{-4A}$ in $(\sqrt{-4A})^k\epsilon^{k-1}$. Obviously H_k is divisible by 4 for $k \geq 4$. We divide (8) by $4b^3$ and introduce the notation $G_k = \frac{1}{4}H_k\, b^{k-3}$.

Then

$$n(n-1)+\frac{n(n-1)(n-2)}{3}\cdot 2+\dots \tag{9}$$
$$+\frac{n(n-1)\dots(n-k+1)}{k!}2^k G_k+\dots=0.$$

Equation (9) is obviously impossible. In fact, let 2^σ be the highest power of 2 in $n(n-1)$. Then the second term $2n(n-1)(n-2)/3$, as well as all the other terms, contains 2 to a power not less than $\sigma+1$, since it is well known that $k!$ contains 2 to at most the $(k-1)$st power. Hence the left-hand side of (9) is not divisible by $2^{\sigma+1}$ and therefore cannot be zero.

Hence setting equal to zero the coefficient of $\sqrt{-A}\sqrt[4]{-4A}$ in $(\pm 1)^{n+1}\epsilon^{2n-1}$ we have arrived at a contradiction. This proves Theorem 1.

THEOREM 2. *An odd power of a trinomial unit of the type*

$$a+c\sqrt{-A}+d\sqrt{-A}\sqrt[4]{-4A}$$

cannot be a trinomial unit of the type $a'+b'\sqrt[4]{-4A}+c'\sqrt{-A}$.

PROOF. Let

$$\epsilon=a+c\sqrt{-A}+d\sqrt{-A}\sqrt[4]{-4A};$$

then

$$\epsilon''=a+c\sqrt{-A}-d\sqrt{-A}\sqrt[4]{-4A}$$

and

$$\epsilon^2=\pm 1+2d\sqrt{-A}\sqrt[4]{-4A}\cdot\epsilon.$$

Furthermore

$$(\pm 1)^n\varepsilon^{2n}=(1\pm 2d\sqrt{-A}\sqrt[4]{-4A}\varepsilon)^n$$
$$=1\pm 2nd\sqrt{-A}\sqrt[4]{-4A}\,\varepsilon$$
$$+\frac{n(n-1)}{1\cdot 2}\cdot 4d^2\cdot(-A)\sqrt{-4A}\,\varepsilon^2\pm\dots$$
$$\pm\frac{n(n-1)\dots(n-k+1)}{k!}2^k d^k(\sqrt{-A}\sqrt[4]{-4A}\varepsilon)^k+\dots.$$

Hence multiplying by ϵ'' we obtain

$$(\pm 1)^{n+1}\varepsilon^{2n-1}=\varepsilon''+2nd\sqrt{-A}\sqrt[4]{-4A}$$
$$\pm\frac{n(n-1)}{1\cdot 2}\cdot 8d^2(-A)\sqrt{-A}\varepsilon\pm\dots$$
$$\pm\frac{n(n-1)\dots(n-k+1)}{k!}2^k d^k(\sqrt{-A}\sqrt[4]{-4A})^k\varepsilon^{k-1}+\dots=$$

$$= a + c\sqrt{-A} + d\sqrt{-A}\sqrt[4]{-4A} + 2nd\sqrt{-A}\sqrt[4]{-4A}$$
$$\pm \frac{n(n-1)}{1\cdot 2} 8d^2(-A)\sqrt{-A}(a + c\sqrt{-A} + d\sqrt{-A}\sqrt[4]{-4A})$$
$$\pm \ldots \pm \frac{n(n-1)\ldots(n-k+1)}{k!} 2^k d^k (\sqrt{-A}\sqrt[4]{-4A})^k \varepsilon^{k-1} + \ldots$$

Setting the coefficient of $\sqrt{-A}\sqrt[4]{-4A}$ equal to zero we obtain

$$(2n+1)d + \frac{n(n-1)(n-2)}{1\cdot 2\cdot 3} \cdot 8d^3 H_3 + \ldots \pm \frac{n(n-1)\ldots(n-k+1)}{k!} 2^k d^k H_k + \ldots = 0. \qquad (10)$$

We denote by H_k the coefficient of

$$\sqrt{-A}\sqrt[4]{-4A} \text{ in } (\sqrt{-A}\sqrt[4]{-4A})^k \cdot \epsilon^{k-1}.$$

Dividing out d in (10) we obtain the equation

$$(2n+1) + \frac{n(n-1)(n-2)}{3} 4d^2 H_3 + \ldots \pm \frac{n(n-1)\ldots(n-k+1)}{k!} 2^k d^{k-1} H_k + \ldots = 0,$$

which is obviously impossible, because the first term $2n + 1$ is odd, while all the other terms are even.

THEOREM 3. *The equation* $x^4 - 2y^4 = -1$ *has the unique solution* $x = \pm 1$, $y = \pm 1$. *The equation* $x^4 - 2y^4 = +1$ *has no solutions other than the trivial ones* $x = \pm 1$, $y = 0$.

PROOF. The solution of the equations $x^4 - 2y^4 = \pm 1$ can be reduced to finding trinomial units in $O(\sqrt[4]{-8})$.

It can be easily established that $\epsilon_0 = 1 + \sqrt[4]{-8} + \sqrt{-2}$ is a unit in $O(\sqrt[4]{-8})$. This unit determines the solution $x = \pm 1$, $y = \pm 1$ of the equation

$$x^4 - 2y^4 = -1.$$

We show that ϵ_0 is the fundamental unit of $O(\sqrt[4]{-8})$. In fact

$$|\epsilon_0| \approx 3.40,$$

but we have seen in subsection 2 that the absolute value of any unit must exceed

$$2\sqrt[4]{8} - 1 \approx 2.36.$$

From this it follows that ϵ_0 cannot be a power of any unit and therefore must itself be the fundamental unit. Since ϵ_0 is a trinomial unit, its odd powers cannot be trinomial units. The theorem will be proved if we can show that among the even powers of ϵ_0 there are no trinomial units.

We have

$$\varepsilon_0^2 = -1 + 2\sqrt[4]{-8}\cdot\varepsilon_0$$

and

$$\varepsilon_0^{2n}(-1)^n = 1 - 2n\sqrt[4]{-8}\,\varepsilon_0 + \frac{n(n-1)}{1\cdot 2}\cdot 8\sqrt{-2}\,\varepsilon_0^2 - \dots$$

$$\pm\frac{n(n-1)\dots(n-k+1)}{k!}\,2^k(\sqrt[4]{-8})^k\varepsilon_0^k + \dots$$

$$= 1 - 2n\sqrt[4]{-8}\,(1 + \sqrt[4]{-8} + \sqrt{-2})$$

$$+\frac{n(n-1)}{1\cdot 2}\cdot 8\sqrt{-2}\,(1 + 2\sqrt[4]{-8} + 4\sqrt{-2} + 2\sqrt{-2}\sqrt[4]{-8}) + \dots$$

$$\pm\frac{n(n-1)\dots(n-k+1)}{k!}\cdot 2^k(\sqrt[4]{-8})^k\varepsilon_0^k + \dots$$

Equating to zero the coefficient of $\sqrt{-2}\,\sqrt[4]{-8}$ and dividing by 2 we obtain

$$-n + 4n(n-1) + \dots \pm \frac{n(n-1)\dots(n-k+1)}{k!}\cdot 2^{k-1}H_k + \dots = 0, \tag{11}$$

where H_k is the coefficient of $\sqrt{-2}\,\sqrt[4]{-8}$ in $(\sqrt[4]{-8})^k\,\epsilon^k$.

It is obvious that for $k \geq 3$, we have H_k even. If n is divisible by 2^σ, then $4n(n-1)$ is divisible by $2^{\sigma+2}$ and all the other terms in the left-hand side of (11) are divisible by at least $2^{\sigma+1}$, since n is divisible by 2^σ, and $k!$ is divisible by at most 2^{k-1}, while H_k is even. Hence the equation cannot hold and the theorem follows.

THEOREM 4. *The square of a unit in* $O(\sqrt[4]{-4A})$ *cannot be a trinomial unit.*

PROOF. Suppose the contrary. Let

$$\epsilon = a + b\sqrt[4]{-4A} + c\sqrt{-A} + d\sqrt{-A}\,\sqrt[4]{-4A}$$

be a unit in $O(\sqrt[4]{-4A})$ and let $\epsilon^2 = a' + b'\sqrt[4]{-4A} + c'\sqrt{-A}$.

But

$$\varepsilon^2 = a^2 - Ac^2 - 4bdA + 2(ab - cdA)\sqrt[4]{-4A}$$
$$+ 2(b^2 - Ad^2 + ac)\sqrt{-A} + 2(ad + bc)\sqrt{-A}\,\sqrt[4]{-4A}.$$

Therefore

$$ad + bc = 0,$$

or

$$\frac{a}{b} = \frac{c}{-d},$$

from which

$$a = km, \quad c = kn,$$
$$b = lm, \quad d = -ln. \tag{12}$$

On the other hand, since ϵ is a unit,

$$a^2 - Ac^2 + 4Abd = \pm 1, \tag{5}$$
$$ac - b^2 + Ad^2 = 0. \tag{6}$$

Substituting the values of a, b, c, d from (12) into (5) and (6) we obtain

$$k^2m^2 - Ak^2n^2 - 4Al^2mn = \pm 1, \tag{5'}$$
$$k^2mn - l^2m^2 + Al^2n^2 = 0. \tag{6'}$$

From (5′) we see that

$$(k, l) = 1; \ (m, n) = 1; \ (k, A) = 1; \ (m, A) = 1.$$

From (6′) we see that Al^2n^2 is divisible by n and l^2m^2 is divisible by n, so that l^2 is divisible by m and n and hence by their product mn, since $(m, n) = 1$. On the other hand k^2mn is divisible by l^2, so that mn is divisible by l^2, from which it follows that

$$mn = \pm l^2.$$

Therefore

$$m = \sigma_1 u^2; \ n = \sigma_2 v^2; \cdot l = uv,$$

where

$$\sigma_1 = \pm 1, \ \sigma_2 = \pm 1.$$

Substituting this into (5′) and (6′) we obtain

$$k^2(u^4 - Av^4) - 4A\sigma_1\sigma_2u^4v^4 = \pm 1, \tag{5''}$$
$$k^2\sigma_1\sigma_2u^2v^2 - u^2v^2(u^4 - Av^4) = 0. \tag{6''}$$

From (6″) it follows that

$$k^2 = \sigma_1\sigma_2(u^4 - Av^4). \tag{13}$$

Substituting into (5″) we obtain

$$(u^4 - Av^4)^2 - 4Au^4v^4 = \pm 1,$$

or

$$u^8 - 6Au^4v^4 + A^2v^4 = \pm 1,$$

from which

$$Av^4 = 3u^4 \pm \sqrt{8u^8 \pm 1}, \tag{14}$$

and therefore

$$8u^8 \pm 1 = t^2. \tag{15}$$

The minus sign in (15) can be discarded since a square of an odd number cannot be in the form $8N - 1$.

Therefore

$$8u^8 = (t-1)(t+1),$$

from which

$$t \mp 1 = 2p^8; \quad t \pm 1 = 4q^8; \quad u = pq. \tag{16}$$

It follows from (16) that

$$p^8 - 2q^8 = \mp 1. \tag{17}$$

But by Theorem 3 the solutions of (17) are

$$p = 1, \quad q = 0,$$

$$p = 1, \quad q = 1$$

and there are no others.

The first solution gives $n = 0$, which is obviously impossible. The second gives $u = 1$ and hence, by (14), $Av^4 = 6$ or 0. The solution $Av^4 = 0$ gives $a = \pm 1$;

$$b = c = d = 0$$

since $\epsilon_0 = \pm 1$; while $Av^4 = 6$ gives after substitution in (13) the impossible equation

$$k^2 = -5\sigma_1\sigma_2.$$

This proves the theorem.

THEOREM 5. *No odd power of the fundamental unit, except the first, can be trinomial.*

PROOF. Suppose on the contrary that

$$\epsilon_0^n = a' + b' \sqrt[4]{-4A} + c' \sqrt{-A},$$

where n is an odd number.

Consider separately the cases

$$n = 4m + 1,$$

$$n = 4m - 1.$$

First let

$$n = 4m + 1$$

and

$$\epsilon_0 = a + b \sqrt[4]{-4A} + c \sqrt{-A} + d \sqrt{-A} \sqrt[4]{-4A};$$

then

$$\varepsilon_0^{4m+1} = a' + b' \sqrt[4]{-4A} + c' \sqrt{-A}, \tag{18}$$

$$(\varepsilon_0''')^{4m+1} = a' - b' i \sqrt[4]{-4A} - c' \sqrt{-A}. \tag{19}$$

Multiplying (19) by i and subtracting from (18) we obtain

$$\begin{aligned}\varepsilon_0^{4m+1} - i(\varepsilon_0''')^{4m+1} &= a'(1-i) + c'(1+i)\sqrt{-A} \\ &= (1-i)(a' + ic'\sqrt{-A}) = (1-i)(a' - c'\sqrt{A}).\end{aligned} \tag{20}$$

The left-hand side of (20)

$$\varepsilon_0^{4m+1} - i(\varepsilon_0''')^{4m+1} = \varepsilon_0^{4m+1} - (i\varepsilon_0''')^{4m+1}$$

is divisible by the number

$$\begin{aligned}\lambda &= \varepsilon_0 - i\varepsilon_0'' \\ &= a + b\sqrt[4]{-4A} + c\sqrt{-A} \\ &\quad + d\sqrt{-A}\sqrt[4]{-4A} - i(a - bi\sqrt[4]{-4A} - c\sqrt{-A} + di\sqrt{-A}\sqrt[4]{-4A}) \\ &= a(1-i) + c(1+i)\sqrt{-A} + 2d\sqrt{-A}\sqrt[4]{-4A} \\ &= (1-i)(a + ci\sqrt{-A} + d\cdot(1+i)\cdot\sqrt{2}\sqrt[4]{A^3}\, e^{\frac{2\pi i}{4}}) \\ &= (1-i)(a - c\sqrt{A} - 2d\sqrt[4]{A^3}).\end{aligned}$$

Therefore $a' - c' \sqrt{A}$ is divisible by $a - c\sqrt{A} - 2d\sqrt[4]{A^3}$. It is easily seen that $a' - c' \sqrt{A}$ is a unit in the field $\Omega\sqrt{A}$, since as we have seen in subsection 1, $a' = \pm x^2$, $c' = \pm y^2$, where x, y is a solution of

$$x^4 - Ay^4 = \pm 1,$$

which can be written as

$$(x^2 - y^2\sqrt{A})(x^2 + y^2\sqrt{A}) = \pm 1.$$

Therefore the number $\lambda = a - c\sqrt{A} - 2d\sqrt[4]{A^3}$ is a unit in the field $\Omega(\sqrt[4]{A})$ and its norm must be ± 1; hence

$$N(\lambda) = (a^2 + Ac^2)^2 - 4A(ac + 2Ad^2)^2 = \pm 1. \tag{21}$$

On the other hand

$$a^2 - Ac^2 + 4Abd = \pm 1, \tag{5}$$

$$ac - b^2 + Ad^2 = 0. \tag{6}$$

Eliminating b from (5) and (6) we obtain

$$(a^2 - Ac^2)^2 \mp 2(a^2 - Ac^2) + 1 - 16A^2d^2(ac + Ad^2) = 0. \tag{22}$$

Subtracting (22) from (21) we obtain

$$\pm 2(a^2 - Ac^2) - 1 = \pm 1,$$

from which

$$a^2 - Ac^2 = 0 \text{ or } \pm 1.$$

Substituting into (5) we obtain

$$4Abd = \pm 2, \ \pm 1, \text{ or } 0,$$

from which $b = 0$, or $d = 0$, since

$$4Abd = \pm 2, \ \pm 1,$$

which is obviously impossible.

Analogously, for $n = 4m + 3$ we arrive at the conclusion that in this case either $b = 0$ or $d = 0$, which is impossible, since we know from Theorems 1 and 2 that among the odd powers of units of the type

$$a + b\sqrt[4]{-4A} + c\sqrt{-A}$$

and

$$a + c\sqrt{-A} + d\sqrt{-A}\sqrt[4]{-4A}$$

there are no trinomial units of the type

$$a' + b' \sqrt[4]{-4A} + c' \sqrt{-A}.$$

This proves the theorem.

5. Combining the results of subsection 4 we see that the fundamental unit is the only trinomial unit in $O(\sqrt[4]{-4A})$. Therefore, the equation $x^4 - Ay^4 = \pm 1$ can have only one nontrivial solution, which is given by the fundamental unit if this unit is trinomial.

This method can be generalized to the equations

$$ax^4 - by^4 = 1, 2, 4, 8$$

in the same way as the method for the solution of $ax^3 + y^3 = 1$ was generalized to the equations considered in §73, among which in particular were the equations $ax^3 + by^3 = 1$ and 3 previously solved by Nagell.

§75. ON THE NUMBER OF SOLUTIONS OF THE INDETERMINATE EQUATION $AX^3 + BX^2Y + CXY^2 + EY^3 = \sigma$, WHERE THE FORM (A, B, C, E) IS IRREDUCIBLE AND IS OF NEGATIVE DISCRIMINANT

1. Reduction to the problem with $\sigma = 1$. If $\sigma \neq 1$, then, as has been shown by Lagrange (*Nouvelle méthode pour résoudre les problèmes indeterminées en nombre entires*, Mémoires de Berlin, Vol. 24, 1770), the solution of the equation $AX^3 + BX^2Y + CXY^2 + EY^3 = \sigma$ can be reduced to the solution of the system of equations of the type $A_iX^3 + B_iX^2Y + C_iXY^2 + E_iY^3 = 1$, where $i = 1, 2, \cdots, k$ and k does not exceed σ.

In fact, let the given equation be

$$AX^3 + BX^2Y + CXY^2 + EY^3 = \sigma. \tag{1}$$

Lagrange notes that one can suppose that X and σ are relatively prime, since if $X = X'\delta$, and $\sigma = \sigma'\delta$, where δ is any prime factor of σ, then either Y is divisible by δ in which case we could divide out δ^3, or else E is divisible by δ. Writing $E = E'\delta$ and dividing out δ we arrive at a representation of σ' by the form $(A\delta^2, B\delta, C, E')$.

Furthermore, Lagrange states, Let X, Y be any solution; then since X and σ are relatively prime we can find numbers $\overline{Y}$ and θ such that $\sigma\overline{Y} + \theta \cdot X = Y$ and $-\sigma/2 < \theta \leq \sigma/2$. Substituting this Y into (1) we obtain

$$(A + B\theta + C\theta^2 + E\theta^3)\, X^3 + (B + 2C\theta + 3E\theta^2)\, \sigma X^2Y + (C + 3E)\, \sigma^2XY^2 + E\sigma^3Y^3 = \sigma,$$

all of whose terms except the first are divisible by σ. But X is relatively prime to σ and therefore $A + B\theta + C\theta^2 + E\theta^3$ must be divisible by σ. Hence θ must satisfy the congruence $A + B\theta + C\theta^2 + E\theta^3 \equiv 0 \pmod{\sigma}$, and for every root θ_i of this congruence we obtain after division by σ an equation of the type

$$A_i X^3 + B_i X^2 \bar{Y} + C_i X \bar{Y}^2 + E_i \bar{Y}^3 = 1, \tag{2}$$

where

$$A_i = \frac{A + B\theta_i + C\theta_i^2 + E\theta_i^3}{\sigma}; \qquad B_i = B + 2C\theta_i + 3E\theta_i^2;$$

$$C_i = (C + 3E\theta_i)\sigma; \qquad E_i = E\sigma^2.$$

Thus if we find all the X, $\bar{Y}$ satisfying all the equations (2) we will obtain all the solutions X, Y of (1) with X prime to σ, where $Y = \sigma\bar{Y} + \theta_i X$. All the equations for which X is not prime to σ can be reduced, as we have seen above, by dividing out the common factor in the equations in which the reduced X and σ are prime to each other, and these equations in turn can be reduced to equations of type (2).

2. The reduction of the problem of the number of representations of a number by an integer form to the representations of unity. Hence the problem of finding all the representations of a number σ by a binary cubic form (A, B, C, E) is reduced to the problem of finding all representations of the number 1 by a finite number of these forms and therefore the problem of representing σ by a given form reduces to the problem of representing 1 by such forms. Let (A, B, C, E) be one of these forms. There are two possibilities. Either this form does not represent 1 and hence the number of representations of 1 is zero, or else it represents 1, i.e., there exist values $x = \beta$, $y = \delta$ such that $A\beta^3 + B\beta^2\delta + C\beta\delta^2 + E\delta^3 = 1$, but in that case β and δ are relatively prime and we can find numbers α and γ such that $\alpha\delta - \beta\gamma = 1$. If we now transform this form (A, B, C, E) by a unimodular transformation with integer coefficients $\begin{pmatrix}\alpha & \beta \\ \gamma & \delta\end{pmatrix}$, then the last coefficient of the transformed form will be $A\beta^3 + B\beta^2\delta + C\beta\delta^2 + E\delta^3$ and therefore will be equal to 1. We will write the transformed form as $(n, -q, s, 1)$. A form in which one of the end coefficients is unity (we shall always make it the last) will be called an "integer" form. Hence if (A, B, C, E) represents 1, it is equivalent to some integer form, and the number of representations of 1 by the given form is equal to the number of representations of 1 by the equivalent integer form. We do not say that we can find the form $(n, -q, s, 1)$ for any given form (A, B, C, E)

but only that in case the form (A, B, C, E) represents 1, then the equivalent integer form $(n, -q, s, 1)$ exists.

3. The reduction of the problem of the number of representations to the problem of finding binomial units. From the identity

$$X^3n - X^2Yq + XY^2s + Y^3 = (X\rho + Y)(X\rho' + Y)(X\rho'' + Y),$$

where ρ, ρ', ρ'' are the roots of the cubic equation $\rho^3 = s\rho^2 + q\rho + n$, we see that to every solution of the equation

$$nX^3 - qX^2Y + sXY^2 + Y^3 = 1 \tag{3}$$

corresponds a positive (i.e., with norm $+1$) unit of the type $X\rho + Y$ of the ring $O(\rho) = [\rho^2, \rho, 1]$, i.e., a positive binomial unit, and conversely.

In case $D = s^2q^2 - 18sqn + 4q^3 - 4s^3n - 27n^2 < 0$, which is the only case which we will consider corresponding to one real root ρ and two complex conjugate roots ρ', ρ'', all the positive units of the ring $O(\rho)$ are rational integer powers of one so-called fundamental unit of the ring. As before, the fundamental unit ϵ_0 satisfying the inequalities $0 < \epsilon_0 < 1$ will be called the positive direct fundamental unit. (These positive direct fundamental units are tabulated at the end of Chapter IV for all rings $O(\rho)$ with negative discriminants D not greater than 379 in absolute value.) In this case all the positive units ϵ of the ring $O(\rho)$ are positive rational integer powers of this fundamental unit ϵ_0 and of its inverse $\eta_0 = \eta_0^{-1}$, i.e., every such unit is either ϵ_0^m or η_0^m. In case $D < 0$ the whole problem of the number of representations reduces to finding those positive exponents m for which either ϵ_0^m or η_0^m is a binomial unit in ρ, i.e., of the type $P\rho + Q$.

By a solution of the form we mean a set of rational integer values X, Y which when substituted into the form make it equal to 1, but for brevity the binomial unit which gives this solution will also be called a solution of the form.

4. On the inverse solutions. In this subsection we consider the powers of the inverse unit with positive integer m.

THEOREM. *Among the positive rational integer powers of the inverse unit there can be only a finite number of binomial units and these can be readily found.*

The case $D < 0$, i.e., when there is one pair of complex roots, corresponds to the signature space (x, y, z) $R_{3,1}$; i.e., the positive units of the lattice $[\rho^2, \rho, 1]$ lie on the surface $(x^2 + y^2)z = 1$. The binomial numbers $X\rho + Y$ lie on the plane $x + Hy + z = 0$, where, as can be easily verified, $H = [2(3q + s^2)\rho + sq + 9n]/|\sqrt{D}|$.

t is easily seen that the surface $(x^2+y^2)\,z=1$ containing the units has no points in common with the surface of all binomial points for $z>\sqrt[3]{H^2+1}$. Therefore the set of powers η_0^m can contain binomial units only for exponents m which do not exceed $l=\lg\sqrt[3]{H^2+1}/\lg\eta_0$. After the fundamental unit ϵ_0 of the ring $O(\rho)$ has been calculated, we can find l, and then calculate all η_0^m for $m\le l$ and thus find all inverse solutions of the equation $(n,\,-q,\,s,\,1)=1$, or show that there are none.

REMARK. It is possible, without calculating the unit, to find a lower bound for the inverse of the fundamental unit $\eta_0=\eta_0^{-1}$ depending on the discriminant of the ring, provided $|D|>27$, since the surface on which all the points of a given discriminant lie is given by the equation $((x+z)^2+y^2)\,y=\pm\frac{1}{2}\sqrt{|D|}$ and, as can be easily seen, this surface does not intersect the surface of the units $(x^2+y^2)z=1$ for $z=1$, but is either lower or higher. For example, for $|D|>54$, the least z of the upper intersection exceeds 2. For large $|D|$, the growth of z is like $\sqrt[3]{\frac{1}{4}|D|}$. This bound on η_0 from below is valid for all rings except one, since there is only one ring defined by the equation $\rho^3=-\rho^2+1$ whose discriminant -23 is less than 27 in absolute value. The true values of η_0 are slightly larger than this bound. We give a table of equations satisfied by the smallest inverse units η_0 and their discriminants, the units thesmelves being approximated from below.

$z^3=z+1$	1.3	-23
$z^3=z^2+1$	1.4	-31
$z^3=z^2+z+1$	1.8	-44
$z^3=2z^2+1$	2.2	-59
$z^3=3z^2-z+1$	2.7	-76
$z^3=2z^2+2z+1$	2.8	-83
$z^3=3z^2+1$	3.1	-135
$z^3=3z^2+z+1$	3.3	-176
$z^3=4z^2-2z+1$	3.5	-107
$z^3=3z^2+2z+1$	3.6	-175
$z^3=4z^2-z+1$	3.8	-199
$z^3=3z^2+3z+1$	3.8	-108
....	....	......

These geometric considerations are not helpful in finding direct solutions, since the surface on which the units lie intersects the surface containing all the binomial points in an infinite line for $z<1$, and it is not at all clear from this point of view why it could not contain even an infinite number of points of the parallelepipidal lattice $O(\rho)$. The only reasons so far discovered for the impossibility of this are of a purely arithmetical nature.

5. **On the solutions of equivalent integer forms.** Let $(n,\,-q,\,s,\,1)$ and $(\bar n,\,-\bar q,\,\bar s,\,1)$ be two equivalent integer forms and $\begin{pmatrix}\alpha & \beta\\ \gamma & \delta\end{pmatrix}$ be the transformation which carries the first form into the second. In this case $(\beta,\,\delta)$ is a solution of the first form, i.e., $n\beta^3-q\beta^2\delta+s\beta\delta^2+\delta^3=1$, and σ, γ are two rational integers such that $\alpha\delta-\beta\gamma=1$. It is easily seen that if we take two other numbers α', γ'

satisfying this equation, then we obtain another form $(\bar{n}', -\bar{q}', \bar{s}', 1)$, which is parallel to the form $(\bar{n}, -\bar{q}, \bar{s}, 1)$, i.e., can be obtained from it by the substitution $\begin{pmatrix} 1 & 0 \\ r & 1 \end{pmatrix}$. We shall say that the form $(\bar{n}, -\bar{q}, \bar{s}, 1)$, as well as all the forms parallel to it, can be obtained from the integer form $(n, -q, s, 1)$ by means of its solution β, δ.

Let $X = \beta_1, Y = \delta_1$; $X = \beta_2, Y = \delta_2$; $\cdots$; $X = \beta_i, Y = \delta_i$; $\cdots$ be all the successive solutions of the integer form $(n, -q, s, 1)$ corresponding to the powers $\epsilon_0^{m_1}, \epsilon_0^{m_2}, \cdots, \epsilon_0^{m_i}, \cdots$ of the positive direct unit with $m_1 < m_2 < \cdots < m_i < \cdots$, and let there be no solutions with intermediate values of the exponents. By the theorem of subsection 4, the first exponent m_1 must be negative if there exist inverse solutions, and zero if there are no inverse solutions. As to the question whether there exists a last term, this is equivalent to the question whether there is a finite number of solutions. If we assume the well-known theorem of Thue, then it is known that this series of exponents is finite. But we are constructing this theory independently of Thue's theorem and therefore we cannot make this assertion at this time. Let β_k, δ_k be one of the solutions. Then the equivalent integer form $(\bar{n}, -\bar{q}, \bar{s}, 1) = (n, -q, s, 1) \begin{pmatrix} \alpha_k & \beta_k \\ \gamma_k & \delta_k \end{pmatrix}$ has solutions $X = \delta_k\beta_i - \beta_k\delta_i$, $Y = -\gamma_k\beta_i + \alpha_k\delta_i$ (for $i = 1, 2, \cdots$). If ρ and $\bar{\rho}$ are respectively roots of $\rho^3 = s\rho^2 + q\rho + u$ and $\bar{\rho}^3 + \bar{s}\bar{\rho}^2 + \bar{q}\bar{\rho} + \bar{n}$, then we have $\bar{\rho} = (\alpha_k\rho + \gamma_k)/(\beta_k\rho + \delta_k)$ and therefore the solutions of the second form are

$$(\delta_k\beta_i - \beta_k\delta_i)\bar{\rho} + (-\gamma_k\beta_i + \alpha_k\delta_i) = \frac{(\alpha_k\delta_k - \beta_k\gamma_k)(\beta_i\rho + \delta_i)}{\beta_k\rho + \delta_k} = \frac{\beta_i\rho + \delta_i}{\beta_k\rho + \delta_k}.$$

In this way we have the following theorem.

THEOREM. *If an integer form is transformed into an equivalent integer form by means of the solution* $\epsilon_0^{m_k}$ *of the first form, then the solutions of the second integer form may be obtained from the solutions* $\epsilon_0^{m_1}, \epsilon_0^{m_2}, \cdots, \epsilon_0^{m_i}$ *of the first form by division by* $\epsilon_0^{m_k}$, *i.e., they are* $\epsilon_0^{m_1 - m_k}, \epsilon_0^{m_2 - m_k}, \cdots, \epsilon_0^{m_i - m_k} \cdots$.

6. On the reduction to an integer form having no inverse solutions. Using the above theorems one can transform an integer form having inverse solutions into an equivalent integer form which has no inverse solutions. In order to do this it is sufficient to calculate the fundamental unit ϵ_0^m and then to find, using the method of subsection 4, an inverse solution with the largest in absolute value (negative) exponent m_1 and then to transform the given form using this solution

We shall always suppose in what follows that this transformation has been made and that the form has no inverse solutions.

7. **On the powers of binomial units.**

THEOREM. *No power of a unit of the type* $b\rho + c$, *where* $b \neq \pm 1$, *can be a binomial unit.*

In other words we must show that all the powers of a unit of the type $b\rho + c$ with $b \neq \pm 1$ are of the type $M\rho^2 + P\rho + Q$, where $M \neq 0$.

In fact, if $M = 0$ in $(b\rho + c)^m$, then

$$\frac{m(m-1)}{1\cdot 2} c^{m-2} + \frac{m(m-1)(m-2)}{1\cdot 2\cdot 3} bc^{m-3} s + \frac{m(m-1)(m-2)(m-3)}{1\cdot 2\cdot 3\cdot 4} b^2 c^{m-4}(q+s^2) + \ldots = 0.$$

Since $b\rho + c$ is a unit, b and c are relatively prime. Suppose first that b has a prime divisor π greater than 3 and let $m(m-1)/1\cdot 2$ be divisible exactly by π^k. We leave the first two factors, namely $m(m-1)$ in the numerators and the last two factors in the denominators of the binomial coefficients and divide all the remaining factors of the denominators into the numerators. The first term is divisible exactly by π^k, while in all the other terms the power of π which may be lost because it enters into the last two terms of the denominators is less than that gained from the corresponding power of b, since even for $\pi = 5$, we have $\pi > 3$, $\pi^2 > 4$, $\pi^3 > 5$, etc. Moreover π may be contained in the integer obtained as the result of cancellation of the rest of the denominator into the numerator and from the factors arising from the coefficients n, q, s of the form. Therefore all the terms, except the first are divisible at least by π^{k+1}, while the first term is divisible exactly by π^k, which is impossible.

The case remains where b consists exclusively of powers of 2 and 3. In case b is divisible by 3^2 while $m(m-1)/1\cdot 2$ is divisible exactly by 3^k, the successive terms are divisible at least by 3^{k+1}, since $3^2 > 3$, $3^4 > 4$, $3^6 > 5$, etc. If b is even while $m(m-1)/1\cdot 2$ is divisible exactly by 2^k, then $(m(m-1)(m-2)/1\cdot 2\cdot 3)\, bc^{m-3}s$ and $(m(m-1)(m-2)(m-3)/1\cdot 2\cdot 3\cdot 4)\, b^2c^{m-4}(q+s^2)$ are divisible at least by 2^{k+1}, since one of the numbers $m-2$ or $m-3$ must be even. All the other terms are also divisible by 2^{k+1}, since $2^3 > 5$, $2^4 > 6$, etc.

We are left with the case $b = 3$. In this case we obtain from $c^3 + sc^3b - qcb^2 + nb^3 = 1$ that $c^3 \equiv c \equiv 1 \pmod 3$, i.e., $c = 3y + 1$. If we substitute this c

and $b = \pm 3$, we get $s \equiv 0 \pmod 3$. Therefore we see that if $m(m-1)/1\cdot 2$ is divisible exactly by 3^k, then $(m(m-1)(m-2)/1\cdot 2\cdot 3)\, bc^{m-3} s$ is divisible at least by 3^{k+1} and all the other terms are also divisible at least by 3^{k+1}, since $3^2 > 4$, $3^3 > 5$, etc.

REMARK. In case $b = \pm 1$, a power of a binomial unit $b\rho + c$ may also be binomial, which can easily be seen by examples.

8. **The algorithm of ascent.** We now develop a method which we call the algorithm of ascent. Let $\epsilon_0 = a\rho^2 + b\rho + c$ and let $\epsilon_0^{m_i} = P_i\rho + Q_i$ be all the solutions of the equation $(n, -q, s, 1) = 1$, where we do not suppose that we know whether this number is finite or infinite. If we write $\epsilon_0'^{m_i} = P_i\rho' + Q_i$ and $\epsilon_0''^{m_i} = P_i\rho'' + Q_i$ for the conjugate roots ρ', ρ'' and subtract, we obtain $\epsilon_0'^{m_i} - \epsilon_0''^{m_i} = P_i(\rho' - \rho'')$, from which we see that the P_i for all the solutions are divisible by $(\epsilon_0' - \epsilon_0'')/(\rho' - \rho'') = -a\rho + b + as$. Therefore we have

$$P_i = (-a\rho + b + as)\cdot(\varepsilon_0'^{m_i-1} + \varepsilon_0'^{m_i-2}\varepsilon_0'' + \dots + \varepsilon_0'\varepsilon_0''^{m_i-2} + \varepsilon_0''^{m_i-1}),$$

or, since the second factor on the right is a symmetric function with rational integer coefficients of ρ' and ρ'',

$$P_i = (-a\rho + b + as)\cdot(A_i\rho^2 + B_i\rho + C_i),$$

where the numbers A_i, B_i, C_i are rational integers. From this we obtain

$$A_ib - B_ia = 0; \quad -A_iaq + B_i(b + as) - C_ia = 0; \quad -A_ian + (b + as)C_i = P_i,$$

from which

$$A_i = \frac{a^2P_i}{N(-a\rho + b + as)}; \quad B_i = \frac{abP_i}{N(-a\rho + b + as)}; \quad C_i = \frac{(b^2 + abs + a^2q)P_i}{N(-a\rho + b + as)}.$$

But the greatest common divisor of $(a^2, ab, b^2 + abs + a^2q)$ is $(a, b)^2$. Letting $(a, b) = \delta$, i.e., $a = a_1\delta$, $b = b_1\delta$, we see that all the P_i of all the solutions are divisible by κ, where $\kappa = |\delta\cdot N(-a_1\rho + b_1 + a_1 s)|$. If $\kappa > 1$, this means that all the solutions are of the type $\bar{P}_i\bar{\rho} + Q_i$, where $\bar{\rho} = \kappa\rho$ and $\bar{P}_i = P_i/\kappa$. Therefore they all lie in a "higher" ring $O(\bar{\rho}) = O(\kappa\rho)$. The fundamental unit $\bar{\epsilon}_0$ of the ring $O(\bar{\rho})$ is the least power ϵ_0^{μ} of the fundamental unit ϵ_0 of the ring $O(\rho)$ which lies in the ring $O(\bar{\rho})$, i.e., whose coefficients of ρ^2 and ρ are divisible respectively by κ^2 and κ. If κ is relatively prime to the index of ρ in Ω_ρ, then μ is a divisor of $\phi(\kappa^2)$, where ϕ is Euler's totient function in Ω_ρ, since by Fermat's theorem in Ω_ρ we have $\epsilon_0^{\phi(\kappa^2)} \equiv 1 \pmod{\kappa^2}$, i.e., $\epsilon_0^{\phi(\kappa^2)}$ is of the form

$\kappa^2(t_1\rho^2 + t_2\rho + t_3) + 1$. If κ is relatively prime to the index of ρ, we can suppose that t_1, t_2, t_3 are integers, i.e., in this case $\epsilon_0^{\phi(\kappa^2)}$ already lies in $O(\bar{\rho})$. In case κ is not relatively prime to the index of ρ it is also easy to find the exponent μ. The problem is now reduced to finding those powers of ϵ_0 which are binomial in $\bar{\rho}$, i.e., are of the type $P_i\bar{\rho} + Q_i$. Repeating this argument we go on to rings $O(\bar{\bar{\rho}})$, $O(\bar{\bar{\bar{\rho}}})$, etc. In this way we go to higher and higher rings, looking for solutions until finally we arrive at a κ^* which is 1. This can happen only if the corresponding number $-a^*\rho^* + b^* + a^*s^*$ is either a rational or an algebraic unit.

REMARK. It can happen that the fundamental unit of the ring $O(\rho)$ already has coefficients of ρ^2 and ρ which are respectively divisible by ν^2 and $\nu \neq 1$, in which case ϵ_0 is already in the higher ring $O(\nu\rho)$ with respect to $O(\rho)$. In this case we can start with the ring $O(\nu\rho)$, adjoining ν to ρ. This can happen at any stage of the algorithm in calculating the fundamental unit in a higher ring, in which case we proceed in the same way. Thus sometimes, besides the multipliers κ, there may also be some "supplementary" multipliers ν, which make the ring even "higher."

9. THEOREM. *The number* $-a\rho + b + as$ *cannot be an algebraic unit in a higher ring.*

The algorithm of ascent stops if and only if at some step the quantity $-a\rho + b + as$ is an ordinary rational or algebraic unit (although the ring under consideration may not be the given ring but a higher one, we omit starring the letters for simplicity). We shall show that $-a\rho + b + as$ can be an algebraic unit only before the first ascent, i.e., only in the given ring. We shall always suppose that the form has been transformed so as not to have inverse solutions. In that case, if $-a\rho + b + as$ is an algebraic unit, then, being a binomial unit, it must be plus or minus a positive rational integer power μ of the positive direct fundamental unit of the corresponding ring $O(\rho)$, i.e., $\pm\epsilon_0^{\mu}$, where $\mu > 1$, since if $\epsilon_0 = a\rho^2 + b\rho + c$ we would have $-a\rho + b + as = \pm(a\rho^2 + b\rho + c)$ or $a = b = c = 0$, which is impossible.

Now let $\eta_0 = \epsilon_0^{-1}$. A simple calculation shows that $\pm\eta_0^{\mu} = 1/(-a\rho + b + as) = a\epsilon_0 + a'$, where $a' = abs + b^2 - a^2q - ac$. From this we get $\pm\eta_0^{\mu+1} = a'\eta_0 + a$. If we now suppose that the ring $O(\rho)$ has been "heightened," i.e., $\rho = k\rho_0 + r$, where $k > 1$, r is a rational integer and ρ_0 is an algebraic integer, we obtain

$$\eta_0 = \epsilon_0^{-1} = a'\rho^2 + b'\rho + c' = k \cdot \theta + c'',$$

where θ is an algebraic integer and c'' is a rational integer. Therefore

$\eta_0^{\mu+1} = (k\theta + c'')^{\mu+1}$. In this way we obtain $\pm (k\theta + c'')^{\mu+1} = a'\eta_0 + a = a'k\theta + (a'c'' + a)$, which is impossible by the theorem in subsection 7.

REMARK. We shall suppose that the number $-a\rho + b + as$ is neither a rational nor an algebraic unit, so that at least the first step of the ascent can be carried out. We shall now see how the algorithm of ascent progresses and what consequences we can derive from it.

10. CASE 1. The quantity $-a^*\rho^* + b^* + a^*s^*$ is not a unit at any step of the algorithm. If the number $-a^*\rho^* + b^* + a^*s^*$ is never a unit, then the P_i of all the solutions must be divisible by κ, $\kappa\bar{\kappa}$, $\kappa\bar{\kappa}\bar{\bar{\kappa}}$, $\kappa\bar{\kappa}\bar{\bar{\kappa}}\bar{\bar{\bar{\kappa}}}$, etc., i.e., every P_i exceeds any number given in advance and hence the equation $(n, -q, s, 1) = 1$ has no solutions in this case.

11. CASE 2. The quantity $-a^*\rho^* + b^* + a^*s^*$ becomes a unit at some stage of the algorithm. From the theorem of subsection 9 and from the fact that we have assumed that the first step is possible, it follows that it is an ordinary unit, $+1$ or -1. If $-a^*\rho^* + b^* + a^*s^* = \pm 1$, we have $a^* = 0$, $b^* = \pm 1$. Hence all the solutions are binomial units of the ring $O(\rho^*)$ having the fundamental unit $\xi_0^* = a^*\rho^{*2} + b^*\rho^* + c^*$, i.e., $\pm\rho^* + c^*$. But since we have assumed that our form is already transformed as in subsection 6 so as not to have any inverse solutions, all the solutions must be positive rational integer powers of the fundamental unit ϵ_0^* of $O(\rho^*)$, and these solutions are binomial, i.e., of the type $P^*\rho^* + Q$. Let $\rho^* = k\rho$, where k is the product of all the ascent multipliers κ and all the supplementary multipliers ν, and in the case under consideration $k > 1$. We obtain $(\pm k\rho + c^*)^m = P_k^*\rho + Q$, which is impossible in view of the theorem in subsection 7 for any $m > 1$. The equation under consideration $(n, -q, s, 1) = 1$ has therefore besides the trivial solution $X = 0$, $Y = 1$ one more solution $\pm k\rho + c^*$ and no other solutions.

12. The case in which $-a\rho + b + as$ is a unit for the original equation. If $-a\rho + b + as$ is an ordinary unit, i.e., if $-a\rho + b + as = \pm 1$, then $a = 0$, $b = \pm 1$ and the positive fundamental unit of the ring $O(\rho)$ is $\epsilon_0 = a\rho^2 + b\rho + c = \pm\rho + c$. But in this case the given integer form is parallel to an integer form whose root is ϵ_0. Let that form be $(1, -t, r, 1)$, i.e., suppose that ϵ_0 is a root of the equation $z^3 = rz^2 + tz + 1$. This form has the two end coefficients equal to 1. Such a form will be called reversible. We shall consider the theory of such reversible forms in subsections 13–23 below.

We next suppose that $-a\rho + b + as = \epsilon$ is an algebraic unit. We can write the fundamental direct positive unit $\epsilon_0 = a\rho^2 + b\rho + c$ of $O(\rho)$ as a linear fractional function of ρ (see §12) as $\epsilon_0 = (\alpha\rho + \beta)/(\gamma\rho + \delta)$. Then it can be easily calculated that $\alpha = \pm(abs + b^2 - a^2q - ac)$; $\beta = \pm(acs + bc - a^2n)$; $\gamma = \pm(-a)$; $\delta = \pm(b + as)$. We select the sign in such a way that $N(\gamma\rho + \delta) = \pm N(\epsilon) = \pm 1$. If again $z^3 = rz^2 + tz + 1$ is the equation satisfied by ϵ_0, then the form

$$\begin{aligned}(1, -t, r, 1) &= (X\varepsilon_0 + Y)(X\varepsilon_0' + Y)(X\varepsilon_0'' + Y)\\ &= N\left(X\frac{\alpha\rho+\beta}{\gamma\rho+\delta} + Y\right) = N(X(\alpha\rho+\beta) + Y(\gamma\rho+\delta))\cdot\frac{1}{N(\gamma\rho+\delta)}\\ &= N[(X\alpha + Y\gamma)\rho + (X\beta + Y\delta)]\\ &= (\bar{X}\rho + \bar{Y})(\bar{X}\rho' + \bar{Y})(\bar{X}\rho'' + \bar{Y}) = (n, -q, s, 1),\end{aligned}$$

where we let $\bar{X} = \alpha X + \gamma Y$, $\bar{Y} = \beta X + \delta Y$ and where $z^3 = sz^2 + qz + n$ is the equation satisfied by ρ.

In this way we see that $(1, -t, r, 1) = (n, -q, s, 1)\begin{pmatrix}\alpha & \beta\\ \gamma & \delta\end{pmatrix}$, and since $\alpha\delta - \beta\gamma = \pm 1$, the form $(n, -q, s, 1)$ is equivalent to the reversible form $(1, -t, r, 1)$.

Hence the case in which the given equation is such that $-a\rho + b + as$ is a rational or algebraic unit, and as a result the ascent algorithm cannot even get started, is equivalent to a reversible equation.

13. On the reduction of a reversible equation to the fundamental reversible equation. If the given equation is reversible, i.e., if $n = 1$, then ρ is an algebraic unit, but ρ may not be the fundamental unit of the ring $O(\rho)$. For example the root ϵ of $z^3 = z^2 - 2z + 1$ is a unit but not a fundamental unit of the ring $O(\epsilon)$. The fundamental unit of the ring $O(\epsilon)$ is $\epsilon_0 = \epsilon^2 - \epsilon + 1$ and we have $\epsilon = \epsilon_0^2$. From the fact that ϵ_0 is in $O(\epsilon)$ it follows that $D_{\epsilon_0} \geq D_\epsilon$, and from the fact that ϵ is a power of ϵ_0 it follows that $D_\epsilon \geq D_{\epsilon_0}$, i.e., $D_{\epsilon_0} = D_\epsilon$. By repeating the arguments developed in subsection 12 we can show that if ϵ_0 satisfies the equation $z^3 = rz^2 + tz + 1$, then the forms $(1, -t, r, 1)$ and $(1, -q, s, 1)$ are equivalent and we can find the substitution $\begin{pmatrix}\alpha & \beta\\ \gamma & \delta\end{pmatrix}$ which carries one into the other, i.e., the transformation from a given reversible equation to the fundamental reversible equation equivalent to it.

14. On solutions with even exponents of reversible forms. Let $(1, -q, s, 1)$ be the fundamental direct reversible form (i.e., a form such that a root of the equation $z^3 = sz^2 + qz + 1$ is the direct fundamental unit of the ring corresponding to to this form). All its solutions will be positive integer powers of the direct fundamental unit ϵ and its inverse η, where ϵ is a root of $z^3 = sz^2 + qz + 1$. We consider separately the odd and even powers. We start with the even powers. If we look for solutions of the type $(\epsilon^2)^{m_i}$ we will obtain the result, as in subsection 8, that all the P_i of these solutions are divisible by

$$\frac{\epsilon'^2 - \epsilon''^2}{\epsilon' - \epsilon''} = \epsilon' + \epsilon''.$$

If $N(\epsilon' + \epsilon'') \neq \pm 1$, we will get a number κ, different from 1, which must divide all the P_i of all these solutions. Analogously, all the P_i of all the solutions $(\eta^2)^{m_i}$ must be divisible by

$$\frac{\eta'^2 - \eta''^2}{\epsilon' - \epsilon''},$$

but we have

$$\frac{\eta'^2 - \eta''^2}{\varepsilon' - \varepsilon''} = \frac{\frac{1}{\varepsilon'^2} - \frac{1}{\varepsilon''^2}}{\varepsilon' - \varepsilon''} = -\frac{\varepsilon'^2 - \varepsilon''^2}{(\varepsilon'\varepsilon'')^2 (\varepsilon' - \varepsilon'')},$$

i.e.,

$$N\left(\frac{\eta'^2 - \eta''^2}{\varepsilon' - \varepsilon''}\right) = N(\varepsilon' + \varepsilon'')$$

and therefore all these P_i must also be divisible by κ. Therefore all the direct and inverse solutions with even exponents are binomial units of the higher ring $O(\kappa\epsilon)$. Conversely every binomial unit of the ring $O(\kappa\epsilon)$ is a solution of the reversible equation under consideration.

15. **On reversed forms.** Every reversible form has, besides the trivial solution 1, also a solution ϵ. If we transform the reversible form using the solution ϵ, i.e., by the transformation $\begin{Bmatrix} \alpha & 1 \\ \gamma & 0 \end{Bmatrix}$, where we take $\alpha = 0$, $\gamma = -1$, we obtain by subsection 5 a "reversed" form $(1, s, -q, 1)$, i.e., a form obtained by writing the coefficients of the given form in reverse order.

16. **Solutions of reversible forms with odd exponents.** In order to study the solutions $P_i\epsilon + Q_i$ corresponding to odd exponents m_i we use the reversed form. By subsection 5 all the solutions of the given form with odd exponents correspond to solutions of the reversed form with even exponents, and conversely. These solutions are

$$\frac{1}{\epsilon}(P_i\epsilon + Q_i) = Q_i\eta + P_i.$$

All the Q_i of all the direct solutions are divisible by $(\epsilon'^2 - \epsilon''^2)/(\eta' - \eta'')$, but we have

$$N\left(\frac{\varepsilon'^2-\varepsilon''^2}{\eta'-\eta''}\right)=N(\varepsilon'+\varepsilon''),$$

and therefore if $N(\epsilon'+\epsilon'')\neq\pm 1$, all these Q_i must be divisible by $\epsilon>1$. Analogously, all the Q_i of the inverse solutions must divisible by $(\eta'^2-\eta''^2)/(\eta'-\eta'')$, but we have

$$N\left(\frac{\eta'^2-\eta''^2}{\eta'-\eta''}\right)=N(\varepsilon'+\varepsilon''),$$

and therefore all the Q_i of all these solutions must also be divisible by κ. We thus see that all the solutions with odd exponents of the given reversible form, whether direct or inverse, are binomial units in the ring $O(\kappa\eta)$. Conversely, every binomial unit of the ring $O(\kappa\eta)$ is a solution of the given reversible equation with P_i and Q_i interchanged.

17. **The nonequivalence of the two forms to which a reversible form is reduced in case $N(\epsilon'+\epsilon'')\neq\pm 1$.** If $N(\epsilon'+\epsilon'')\neq\pm 1$, a solution of the reversible equation $(1,-q,s,1)=1$ can be reduced in this way to the solution of the two "higher" equations

$$(\kappa^3,-q\kappa^2,s\kappa,1)=1 \text{ and } (\kappa^3,s\kappa^2,-q\kappa,1)=1.$$

It can be easily seen that these forms are not equivalent. In fact, if this were the case the roots $\kappa\epsilon$ and $\kappa\eta$ of these forms could be expressed in terms of each other, but this is impossible since $\epsilon=\eta^2+q\eta+s$ and $\kappa\epsilon=\kappa\eta^2+\kappa q\eta+\kappa s$ and it is impossible to find three rational integers A, B, C such that $A\kappa^2\eta^2+B\kappa\eta+C=\kappa\eta^2+\kappa q\eta+\kappa s$.

18. **On the cases in which $N(\epsilon'+\epsilon'')=\pm 1$.** Hence we can replace the problem of the solution of a reversible equation by the solution of two "higher" equations to which the algorithm of ascent is applicable. But we still have the exceptional cases with $N(\epsilon'+\epsilon'')=\pm 1$ when this cannot be done. In these cases we have $N(\epsilon'+\epsilon'')=N(s-\epsilon)=sq+1$, but $sq+1$ if $s=0$ or if $q=0$. These two cases will be considered in subsections 19 and 20. The case $sq+1=-1$ implies $sq=-2$, i.e., $s=1$, $q=-2$; $s=-1$, $q=2$; $s=2$, $q=-1$, or $s=-2$, $q=1$, with discriminants -23, $+49$, -23, $+49$ respectively. There are only two equations with negative discriminant and these are equivalent to the equation $z^3=-z^2+1$, which is again of the type $q=0$. Therefore we must study the reversible equations with $s=0$, $q=0$.

19. **On the powers of a root of the equation $z^3=qz+1$, where $q\neq 1$.** Let

ϵ be a root of the reversible equation $z^3 = qz + 1$ and consider the solutions which are the powers ϵ^m for positive m. If the coefficient M of ϵ^2 in ϵ^m is equal to zero we have, as can be easily seen, one of the following relations:

(1) if $m = 3\gamma + 2$,

$$1 + q^3 \frac{(\gamma - 1)\gamma(\gamma + 1)}{1 \cdot 2 \cdot 3} + q^6 \frac{(\gamma - 3)(\gamma - 2)(\gamma - 1)(\gamma + 1)(\gamma + 2)}{1 \cdot 2 \cdot 3 \cdot 4 \cdot 5 \cdot 6} + \ldots = 0;$$

(2) if $m = 3\gamma + 1$,

$$\gamma + q^3 \frac{(\gamma - 2)(\gamma - 1)\gamma(\gamma + 1)}{1 \cdot 2 \cdot 3 \cdot 4}$$
$$+ q^6 \frac{(\gamma - 4)(\gamma - 3)(\gamma - 2)(\gamma - 1)\gamma(\gamma + 1)(\gamma + 2)}{1 \cdot 2 \cdot 3 \cdot 4 \cdot 5 \cdot 6 \cdot 7} + \ldots = 0;$$

(3) if $m = 3\gamma$,

$$\frac{\gamma(\gamma - 1)}{1 \cdot 2} + q^3 \frac{(\gamma - 3)(\gamma - 2)(\gamma - 1)\gamma(\gamma + 1)}{1 \cdot 2 \cdot 3 \cdot 4 \cdot 5}$$
$$+ q^6 \frac{(\gamma - 5)(\gamma - 4)(\gamma - 3)(\gamma - 2)(\gamma - 1)\gamma(\gamma + 1)(\gamma + 2)}{1 \cdot 2 \cdot 3 \cdot 4 \cdot 5 \cdot 6 \cdot 7 \cdot 8} + \ldots = 0.$$

It is obvious that if $|q| \neq 1$, then the case $m = 3y + 2$ is impossible. As to the other two cases, we note that a prime p appears in $m!$ to a degree not exceeding $(m - 1)/(p - 1)$. If we let $p^m/m! = \bar{p}^m$, we see that the fraction $\bar{p}^m$, after cancellation of the highest possible powers of p, will still have p in the numerator to a degree at least

$$\left[m - \frac{m-1}{p-1}\right],$$

where the square brackets denote as usual the greatest integer. The second and third relations can now be written

$$\bar{q} \cdot \gamma + \bar{q}^4 (\gamma + 1) \ldots (\gamma - 2) + \bar{q}^7 (\gamma + 2) \ldots (\gamma - 4) + \ldots = 0;$$
$$\bar{q}^2 \gamma (\gamma - 1) + \bar{q}^5 (\gamma + 1) \ldots (\gamma - 3) + \bar{q}^8 (\gamma + 2) \ldots (\gamma - 5) + \ldots = 0.$$

Suppose first that $|q|$ is a prime p greater than 3. In this case the first term is not divisible by as high a power of p as are the remaining terms, since

$$\left[4 - \frac{3}{p-1}\right] > \left[4 - \frac{3}{3}\right] = 3$$

and

$$\left[m - \frac{m-1}{p-1}\right]$$

does not decrease as m increases. The first relation is therefore impossible. Moreover

$$\left[5-\frac{4}{p-1}\right]\geqslant\left[5-\frac{4}{4}\right]=4,$$

i.e., the second relation is also impossible.

If $|q| = 3$ and if y is divisible exactly by 3^k, then the first term of the first relation is divisible by 3^{k+1}, and the second by at least $3^{k+[4-3/2]} = 3^{k+2}$, while the succeeding terms, since

$$\left[m-\frac{m-1}{2}\right]$$

does not decrease with increasing m, are also divisible by at least 3^{k+2}. Therefore the first relation is also impossible for $|q| = 3$. The second relation also does not hold for $|q| = 3$, since if exactly 3^k divides $y(y-1)$, then the first term is divisible exactly by 3^{k+2}, the second at least by 3^{k+4}, the third at least by $3^{k+[8-7/2]} = 3^{k+4}$, and all the others at least by 3^{k+4}. Finally if $|q| = 2$ and y is divisible exactly by 2^k, then the first term of the first relation is divisible exactly by 2^{k+1}, and all the other terms by still higher powers of 2, since after cancellation of 2^m the denominators are odd and the second and third terms have in the numerator, besides the factor $y(y-1)$, at least two other consecutive integers and therefore at least one more factor 2. The same is true of the second relation. If $|q|$ is not a prime, we can make the argument for a prime factor p of $|q|$. If p again divides $|q|p^{-1}$, then all the other terms will be divisible by a higher power of p than that dividing the first term. We see in this way that among the powers ϵ^m of the root ϵ of the equation $z^3 = qz + 1$, $|q| \neq 1$ and $m > 1$, there are no binomial units other than ϵ^3, which is equal to $q\epsilon + 1$.

20. Solutions of direct reversible equations in case $s = 0$, $q \neq -1$. If $z^3 = qz + 1$ is a direct reversible equation it follows from $D = 4q^3 - 27 < 0$ that $q = 1$, 0 or < 0. But $q = 1$ gives the reversed equation, while $q = 0$ gives a reducible equation. The equation $z^3 = -z + 1$ will be considered in subsection 21. Now we will take up the remaining case $q < -1$. All the direct solutions are powers of ϵ with positive exponents m. By subsection 19 there are only two such solutions, namely ϵ and $\epsilon^3 = q\epsilon + 1$. All the positive inverse solutions are powers of the inverse unit $\eta = \epsilon^{-1} = \epsilon^2 - q$ which are binomial in ϵ. We can now apply to these solutions the results of subsection 4 by showing that $\eta > \sqrt[3]{H^2 + 1}$, so that there are no inverse solutions. In fact the inequality $\eta > \sqrt[3]{H^2 + 1}$ is satisfied, for we can write

$$\varepsilon^2 - q > \sqrt[3]{\left[\frac{3}{\sqrt{|D|}}(2q\varepsilon + 3)\right]^2 + 1},$$

or

$$\varepsilon^6 + 3|q|\varepsilon^4 + 3|q|^2\varepsilon^2 + |q|^3 - 1 > \frac{9}{|D|}(4|q|^2\varepsilon^2 - 12|q|\varepsilon + 9),$$

or

$$|q|^2\varepsilon^2 + |q|\varepsilon + |q|^3 > \frac{36}{|D|}q^2\varepsilon^2 - \frac{108}{|D|}|q|\varepsilon + \frac{81}{|D|}$$

This inequality holds because for $q < -1$, $|D| \geq 59$ and hence

$$|q|^2\varepsilon^2 > \frac{36}{|D|}|q|^2\varepsilon^2.$$

Furthermore

$$|q|\varepsilon > -\frac{108}{|D|}|q|\varepsilon \quad \text{и} \quad |q|^3 > \frac{81}{|D|}.$$

Thus we see that the direct fundamental equation $z^3 = qz + 1$ with $q \neq -1$ has no solutions except the following: the trivial solution 1 and the obvious solutions ϵ and $\epsilon^3 = q\epsilon + 1$.

21. The solutions of the equation $(1, 1, 0, 1) = 1$. Let $\epsilon^m = M_m\epsilon^2 + P_m\epsilon + Q_m$. We calculate a small table of powers of ϵ^m. We see that besides the first power and the cube, the eighth power is also binomial. We shall show that there are no other binomial powers. In fact, suppose that there exists such a power, for instance $\epsilon^m = P_m\epsilon + Q_m$; then m must have one of the eight forms $m = 8\gamma + r$, where $r = 0$, 1, 2, 3, 4, 5, 6, 7, i.e., ϵ^m is of the form $(3\epsilon - 2)^\gamma \cdot \epsilon^r$. But we have

m	M_m	P_m	Q_m
1	0	1	0
2	1	0	0
3	0	—1	1
4	—1	1	0
5	1	1	—1
6	1	—2	1
7	—2	0	1
8	0	3	—2
....	.....	.....	.....

$$(3\varepsilon - 2)^\gamma = (-2)^\gamma + \gamma(-2)^{\gamma-1}\cdot 3\varepsilon$$
$$+ \frac{\gamma(\gamma-1)}{1\cdot 2}(-2)^{\gamma-2}\cdot 3^2\varepsilon^2 + \frac{\gamma(\gamma-1)(\gamma-2)}{1\cdot 2\cdot 3}(-2)^{\gamma-3}3^3\varepsilon^3 + \ldots$$

and therefore M_m for various values of r is of the form:

$$r = 0;\quad \frac{\gamma(\gamma-1)}{1\cdot 2}(-2)^{\gamma-2}\cdot 3^2 + \frac{\gamma(\gamma-1)(\gamma-2)}{1\cdot 2\cdot 3}(-2)^{\gamma-3}3^3 M_3$$
$$+ \frac{\gamma(\gamma-1)(\gamma-2)(\gamma-3)}{1\cdot 2\cdot 3\cdot 4}(-2)^{\gamma-4}3^4 M_4 + \cdots;$$

$$r=1;\quad \gamma(-2)^{\gamma-1}\cdot 3+\frac{\gamma(\gamma-1)}{1\cdot 2}(-2)^{\gamma-2}\cdot 3^2 M_3 + \frac{\gamma(\gamma-1)(\gamma-2)}{1\cdot 2\cdot 3}(-2)^{\gamma-3}3^3 M_4+\dots;$$

and so on.

In all these cases $M_m = 0$ is impossible, as can be easily seen by examining the terms as to their divisibility by powers of 3, as was done in subsections 7 and 19, taking into consideration that M_4, M_5, M_6, M_7 are not divisible by 3, while $M_8 = 0$. Therefore the equation $(1, 1, 0, 1) = 1$ has no direct solutions except for ϵ, ϵ^3 and ϵ^8. As to inverse solutions, application of the method of subsection 4 shows that there are none. Therefore all the solutions of $(1, 1, 0, 1) = 1$ are the following: $\epsilon^0 = 1$, $\epsilon^1 = \epsilon$, $\epsilon^3 = -\epsilon + 1$, $\epsilon^8 = 3\epsilon - 2$.

22. The case $q = 0$. The equation $z^3 = sz^2 + 1$ can be a direct equation (i.e., its root can be a direct unit, satisfying the inequality $\epsilon < 1$) only if $s < 0$, but its discriminant is $-4s^3 - 27$ and can be less than zero only if $s > -2$. The case $q = 0$ therefore leads to only one equation with $s = -1$, i.e., the equation $(1, 0, -1, 1) = 1$.

23. The solution of the equation $(1, 0, -1, 1) = 1$. We begin again with the calculation of the powers of $\epsilon^m = M_m\epsilon^2 + P_m\epsilon + Q_m$. We have carried out this calculation to $m = 120$ (thus for example $\epsilon^{120} = 11275550\cdot\epsilon^2 + 9734175\cdot\epsilon - 13773374$), but we have found no further solutions after ϵ^{14}. We shall show that indeed there are no further solutions. In fact, if there were a solution greater than ϵ^{14} it would be of one of the forms $(4\epsilon - 3)^\gamma\cdot\epsilon^r$, where $r = 1, 2, 3, 4, 5, 6, 7, 8, 9, 10, 11, 12, 13$. We have relation

$$(4\epsilon-3)^\gamma=(-3)^\gamma+\gamma(-3)^{\gamma-1}\cdot 4\epsilon + \frac{\gamma(\gamma-1)}{1\cdot 2}(-3)^{\gamma-2}\cdot 4^2\epsilon^2+\dots.$$

Multiplying this by ϵ^r we obtain for the coefficient of ϵ^2

$$M_r(-3)^\gamma+M_{r+1}\gamma(-3)^{\gamma-1}\cdot 4+M_{r+2}\frac{\gamma(\gamma-1)}{1\cdot 2}\cdot(-3)^{\gamma-2}4^2+\dots=M_m. \tag{1}$$

m	M_m	P_m	Q_m
[1]	0	1	0
2	1	0	0
3	−1	0	1
4	1	1	−1
[5]	0	−1	1
6	−1	1	0
7	2	0	−1
8	−2	−1	2
9	1	2	−2
10	1	−2	1
11	−3	1	1
12	4	1	−3
13	−3	−3	4
[14]	0	4	−3

Obviously, this coefficient is not zero in case $r = 2, 3, 4, 6, 7, 8, 9, 10, 11, 13$, since in these cases, as can be seen from the table, M_r is not a multiple of

4. In the cases $r = 1$ and $r = 5$ we have $M_r = 0$ and $M_{r+1} = 1$ or -1. In fact, if γ is divisible exactly by 2^k, then the first nonzero term $M_{r+1} \cdot \gamma(-3)^{\gamma-1} \cdot 4$ is divisible by 2^{k+2}, and all the other terms are divisible by still higher powers of 2, which can be easily seen by the method of subsection 7. The case $r = 0$ gives

$$\frac{\gamma(\gamma-1)}{1\cdot 2}(-3)^{\gamma-2}\cdot 4^2 + M_3 \frac{\gamma(\gamma-1)(\gamma-2)}{1\cdot 2\cdot 3}\cdot(-3)^{\gamma-3}\cdot 4^3 + \ldots,$$

which by a similar argument cannot be zero. Only the case $r = 12$ remains. Here the investigation of the coefficients of (1) is not helpful since $M_{12} = 4$ and $M_{13} = -3$ and therefore both these terms may be divisible by the same power of 2. However, in this case we can write ϵ^m as $(4\epsilon - 3)^\gamma \epsilon^{-2}$, where $\epsilon^{-2} = \epsilon + 1$ and in this way obtain the coefficient of ϵ^2 in the expansion of ϵ^m as

$$\gamma\cdot 4(-3)^{\gamma-1} + M_3 \frac{\gamma(\gamma-1)}{1\cdot 2}\cdot 4^2(-3)^{\gamma-2} + M_4 \frac{\gamma(\gamma-1)(\gamma-2)}{1\cdot 2\cdot 3} 4^3(-3)^{\gamma-3} + \ldots$$
$$+ \frac{\gamma(\gamma-1)}{1\cdot 2}\cdot 4^2(-3)^{\gamma-2} + M_3 \frac{\gamma(\gamma-1)(\gamma-2)}{1\cdot 2\cdot 3} 4^3(-3)^{\gamma-3} + \ldots.$$

Now if γ is divisible exactly by 2^k, then the first term is divisible exactly by 2^{k+2} and all the other terms by at least 2^{k+3}, and therefore this coefficient also cannot be equal to zero. Therefore there are no direct solutions for $m > 14$. The application of the method discussed in subsection 4 shows that there is only one inverse solution $\epsilon^{-2} = \epsilon + 1$. Therefore all five solutions of $(1, 0, -1, 1) = 1$ are given by

$$\epsilon^{-2} = \epsilon + 1,\quad \epsilon^0 = 1,\quad \epsilon^1 = \epsilon,\quad \epsilon^5 = -\epsilon + 1,\quad \epsilon^{14} = 4\epsilon - 3.$$

24. The summary of the above results. From all the results obtained in subsections 1–23 it follows that:

1°. The number of solutions of the general equation $(A, B, C, E) = 1$, if this number is greater than zero, is equal to the number of solutions of some "integer" equation $(n, -q, s, 1) = 1$ equivalent to it, but in general we do not know how to obtain this equation from the given one

$$(A, B, C, E) = 1.$$

2°. For every integer equation $(n, -q, s, 1) = 1$ we can find "reversible" equation $(1, -t, r, 1) = 1$ equivalent to it. In order to do this it is sufficient to find the fundamental unit of the corresponding ring.

3°. If the equation $(n, -q, s, 1) = 1$ is not equivalent to a reversible equation, then the algorithm of ascent can be started and it will either never terminate, in which case the equation has only one "trivial" solution (0, 1), or it will terminate, but we do not know where, and then the equation will have two solutions: the trivial one, and another one which we can obtain if we can carry out the algorithm of ascent to its conclusion.

4°. If the equation is equivalent to a reversible one, then this reversible equation can be reduced to two "higher" equations, each of which is nonequivalent to the reversible equation and therefore can be solved.

5°. This is impossible only in certain special cases, but all of these have been solved above and none of them have more than four solutions (including the trivial solution).

6°. Only one equation has five solutions.

7°. Infinitely many equations, for example the equation $(1, -q, 0, 1) = 1$ with $|q| > 1$, have three solutions.

We note that the question of whether a given general equation $(A, B, C, E) = 1$ is equivalent to a reversible equation $(1, -t, r, 1) = 1$ can always be solved, for the ring corresponding to the form (A, B, C, E) is the same as the ring corresponding to the form $(1, -t, r, 1)$ as a result of the forms being equivalent. Therefore, if we calculate the fundamental unit of the ring corresponding to (A, B, C, E) and if its discriminant is not equal to the discriminant of the form (A, B, C, E), then the form is not equivalent to the reversible form, but if the discriminants are equal, then the form is equivalent to the reversible form whose root is this unit ϵ.

As a result of all this we can state the following fundamental theorem.

THEOREM. *The number of solutions in integers X, Y of the indeterminate equation $(A, B, C, E) = 1$, where (A, B, C, E) is an irreducible binary cubic form with integer coefficients of negative discriminant, is generally not more than 2, and is equal to 3 or 4 only if the form is equivalent to a reversible form. Only one class of forms with discriminant -23 has five solutions. No such equation has more than five solutions.*

After reducing the problem by means of the algorithm of ascent to reversible forms, we have also studied these forms by means of the algorithm of ascent, dividing the solutions into those having even and odd exponents. Nagell suggested a different, very clever and basically geometrical method for handling reversible forms which shows that such forms, except in three cases, cannot have more than three solutions. This somewhat improves the above theorem, which did not show whether there exist infinitely many nonequivalent reversible equations having four solutions. We now consider this addition by Nagell, giving it a geometrical exposition.

25. On powers of the direct fundamental unit in $O(\epsilon)$ which are binomial in ϵ. We begin with the theorem:

If ϵ is the direct fundamental unit in the ring $O(\epsilon)$, then there are no binomial inverse units, except for $D = -23$.

In fact, for a given discriminant D_ϵ, the plane of binomial units based on 1 and ϵ and the surface of all units $(x^2 + y^2) z = 1$ have points in common not higher than a certain height H_ϵ, which can be easily calculated. For the existence of binomial inverse units it is necessary that $H_\epsilon \geq H_D$, where H_D is the height of the lowest point of intersection of the discriminant surface D_ϵ with the upper part of the surface of units. In order that $H_\epsilon \geq H_D$ it is necessary, as can be easily seen, that ϵ should lie on the line of intersection of the surface of the units with the surface D_ϵ sufficiently far from the origin, i.e., that ϵ be sufficiently small, but calculations show that in this case, beginning say with $D = -59$, we already have ϵ^{-1} greater than H_ϵ. Therefore there are no binomial in ϵ inverse units for $|D_\epsilon| \geq 59$. The cases $D = -44, -31, -23$ can be considered specially by means of the method in subsection 4, with the result that there is only one inverse unit binomial in ϵ, where ϵ is the direct fundamental unit of the ring $O(\epsilon)$ for $D = -23$, satisfying the equation $\epsilon^3 = -\epsilon^2 + 1$, and $\epsilon^{-2} = \epsilon + 1$.

THEOREM. *If $|D_\epsilon| > 44$, then among the powers ϵ^m with non-negative integer exponents of the direct fundamental unit ϵ of the ring $O(\epsilon)$ there exists, besides the trivial units $\epsilon^0 = 1$, $\epsilon' = \epsilon$ binomial in ϵ, at most one other unit binomial in ϵ.*

In fact, let $\epsilon^\mu = b\epsilon + c$, where μ is the least exponent greater than 1 for which ϵ^m is binomial in ϵ and suppose also that $\epsilon^{\mu'} = B\epsilon + C$ is binomial in ϵ, where $\mu' > \mu$. Then $\mu' = \mu \cdot \nu + \tau$, where ν and τ are rational integers and $0 \leq \tau \leq \mu - 1$. We will show that if $|D_\epsilon| > 59$, then $\tau \geq 2$. In fact, if $\tau = 0$ then we would have $(b\epsilon + c)^\nu = B\epsilon + C$ and by the lemma in subsection 7, we would have $b = \pm 1$, i.e., $0 < \pm\epsilon + c < 1$. But $0 < \epsilon < 1$ and therefore $c = 1$ and $b\epsilon + c = -\epsilon + 1$.

However, if $-\epsilon + 1$ is a positive unit and if $z^3 = rz^2 + tz + 1$, then $\epsilon - 1$ satisfies the equation

$$(x + 1)^3 = r(x + 1)^2 + t(x + 1) + 1$$

and therefore

$$-N(\epsilon-1)=N(-\epsilon+1)=-1=r+t+1-1,$$

i.e., $r+t=-1$ and

$$D_\epsilon=r^4-6r^3+7r^2+6r-31.$$

But this D_ϵ is negative only for $r=-1, 0, 1, 2, 3, 4$, with the corresponding $D_\epsilon=-23, -31, -23, -23, -31, -23$.

Suppose now that $\tau=1$. Then we have $(b\epsilon+c)^\nu\cdot\epsilon=A\epsilon+B$. Since the coefficient of ϵ^2 must be zero it follows that if $\epsilon^3=r\epsilon^2+t\epsilon+1$, then

$$\nu bc^{\nu-1}+\frac{\nu(\nu-1)}{1\cdot 2}b^2c^{\nu-2}r+\sum_{k\geq 3}\binom{\nu}{k}b^kc^{\nu-k}\lambda_k=0,$$

where λ_k are rational integers. Cancelling out νb we obtain

$$c^{\nu-1}+\frac{1}{2}(\nu-1)bc^{\nu-2}r+\sum_{k\geq 3}\binom{\nu-1}{k-1}\frac{b^{k-1}}{k}\cdot c^{\nu-k}\cdot\lambda_k=0.$$

Suppose that b is divisible by an odd prime π. Then the sum Σ is also divisible by π, since $\pi^{k-1}\geq 3^{k-1}>k$ for all $k\geq 3$. The second term $\frac{1}{2}(\gamma-1)bc^{\nu-2}r$ is also divisible by π, i.e., c must also be divisible by π, but this is impossible because b and c are prime to each other, since $b\epsilon+c$ is a unit. If b is even, then Σ is also even, since $2^{k-1}>k$ for $k\geq 3$. The second term is also even, either if b is a multiple of 4, or if r is even, but in this case c is also even, which is impossible. There remains only the case $|b|=2$ and r odd, since b cannot be divisible by an odd prime. But if $|b|=2$, then $\epsilon^m=b\epsilon+c=\pm 2\epsilon+c$ and therefore since $0<\epsilon<1$ and $0<\epsilon^\mu<1$, it follows that $|c|<3$, i.e., the only possibility is $b\epsilon+c=\pm(2\epsilon-1)$. Let us find the discriminants D_ϵ for which $2\epsilon-1$ is a unit. We have $N(2\epsilon-1)=2r+4t+7$, and letting $N(2\epsilon-1)=-1$ we have $r=-2t-4$, so that r is even and not odd. If $N(2\epsilon-1)=1$ we have $r=-2t-3$ and the discriminant $D_\epsilon=4t^3+t^2(2t+3)^2+4(2t+3)^3+18t(2t+3)-27$, which is negative only if $t=-1, -2, -3, -4, -5$. The case $t=-3$ leads to a reducible equation, while the cases $t=-4$ and -5 give $1<\epsilon$, but we supposed that ϵ is the direct fundamental unit. The case $t=-2$ gives the equation $\epsilon^3=-\epsilon^2-2\epsilon+1$, so that ϵ, although a unit, is not the fundamental unit of the ring $O(\epsilon)$ but a square of the fundamental unit of this ring. There remains only one case $t=-1$, which gives $\epsilon^3=-\epsilon^2-\epsilon+1$ with discriminant -44, and this has four solutions $\epsilon^0=1$, $\epsilon^1=\epsilon$, $\epsilon^4=2\epsilon-1$, $\epsilon^{17}=-103\epsilon+56$. By our fundamental theorem these are the only solutions.

Hence if we let $\epsilon^\tau = u\epsilon^2 + v\epsilon + w$ we have $u \neq 0$, since $\tau > 1$ and $< \mu$, where ϵ^μ is the least power of ϵ with $\mu > 1$ which is binomial in ϵ. Therefore we have

$$(b\epsilon + c)^\nu \cdot (u\epsilon^2 + v\epsilon + w) = B\epsilon + C,$$

with $u \neq 0$. Expanding on the left side by the binomial theorem, multiplying out and setting the coefficient of ϵ^2 equal to zero, we obtain

$$u[c^\nu + \nu c^{\nu-1}br + \ldots] + v\left[\nu c^{\nu-1}b + \frac{\nu(\nu-1)}{1\cdot 2}c^{\nu-2}b^2r + \ldots\right]$$
$$+ w\left[\frac{\nu(\nu-1)}{1\cdot 2}c^{\nu-2}b^2 + \frac{\nu(\nu-1)(\nu-2)}{1\cdot 2\cdot 3}c^{\nu-3}b^3r + \ldots\right] = 0,$$

from which we get $uc^\nu \equiv 0 \pmod b$. But since $b\epsilon + c$ is a unit, b and c are relatively prime and therefore u is divisible by b, i.e.,

$$|u| \geq |b|. \tag{1}$$

We now show that $\tau = \mu - 1$ is impossible. In fact, if this were the case,

$$u\varepsilon^2 + v\varepsilon + w = \varepsilon^{\mu-1} = \frac{\varepsilon^\mu}{\varepsilon} = \frac{b\varepsilon + c}{\varepsilon},$$

or

$$u\varepsilon^3 + v\varepsilon^2 + w\varepsilon = b\varepsilon + c,$$

i.e.,

$$(ur + v)\varepsilon^2 + (ut + w)\varepsilon + u = b\varepsilon + c,$$

from which

$$u = c$$

and therefore $u \equiv 0 \pmod b$ and since b and c are relatively prime we must have $b = \pm 1$, but as we have seen earlier $b \neq \pm 1$ for $|D_\epsilon| > 31$. Therefore we have the inequality

$$\tau \leq \mu - 2. \tag{2}$$

Inequalities (1) and (2), as can easily be seen from the geometric considerations that follow, are incompatible for $|D_\epsilon| > 44$. In fact, since $\tau \leq \mu - 2$ and since the distances of points from the z-axis are multiplicative, if we denote by $\{\ \}$ the distance of a point from the z-axis, we have the following inequality:

$$\{u\varepsilon^2 + v\varepsilon + w\} \leqslant \frac{\{b\varepsilon + c\}}{\{\varepsilon^2\}}. \tag{3}$$

Now let the x, y coordinates of the projection of ϵ on the X, Y-plane parallel to the rational direction be (α, β) and let the coordinates of the projection of ϵ^2 be (γ, δ). In this case the coordinates of the projection of $M\epsilon^2 + P\epsilon + Q$ are $(M\gamma + P\alpha, M\delta + P\beta)$ since the addition of Q merely translates the point parallel to the rational direction. Since the distance from a point to the z-axis differs from the distance of such a projection by not more than a point on the z-axis, we have

$$\{u\gamma + v\alpha,\ u\delta + v\beta\} - \varepsilon^{\tau} \leqslant \frac{|b|\,\{\alpha, \beta\} + \varepsilon^{\mu}}{\{\alpha, \beta\}^2 - \varepsilon^2}. \tag{4}$$

We replace v in $\{u\gamma + v\alpha, u\delta + v\beta\}$ by the v^* which minimizes this distance, i.e., we replace this distance by the distance h from the origin to the line $x = u\gamma + v^*\alpha$, $y = u\delta + v^*\beta$, where v^* is a variable parameter. The usual equation of this line is of the form $x\beta + y\alpha + (\alpha\delta - \beta\gamma)\,u = 0$, i.e.,

$$h = \left|\frac{u\,(\alpha\delta - \beta\gamma)}{\sqrt{\alpha^2 + \beta^2}}\right|.$$

Thus we obtain from (4) the stronger inequality

$$\frac{|u|\cdot|\alpha\delta - \beta\gamma|}{\sqrt{\alpha^2 + \beta^2}} - \varepsilon^{\tau} \leqslant \frac{|b|\sqrt{\alpha^2 + \beta^2} + \varepsilon^{\mu}}{\alpha^2 + \beta^2 - \varepsilon^2},$$

or, since by (1) we have $|u| \geq |b|$ and since $|\alpha\delta - \beta\gamma|$ is easily seen to be the volume of the basic parallelepiped of the lattice $[\epsilon^2, \epsilon, 1]$, namely, $\frac{1}{2}\sqrt{|D_\epsilon|}$, and taking into consideration that τ and μ are greater than 2, we obtain the inequality

$$u\varepsilon^2 < \alpha^2 + \beta^2$$

and

$$\sqrt{|D_\varepsilon|} \leqslant \left(2(1 + \varepsilon^2)\sqrt{\alpha^2 + \beta^2} + \frac{\varepsilon^2}{\sqrt{\alpha^2 + \beta^2} - 1}\right),$$

from which it follows that

$$|D_\varepsilon| < 44.$$

Combining the two theorems which we have just proved we see that the reversible equation $(1, r, -t, 1) = 1$ can have at most three solutions if the discriminant $|D| > 44$. We note that infinitely many equations may have three solutions, for example the equations $(1, 0, -t, 1) = 1$, discussed in subsection 20, always have three solutions. As to the equations with discriminants -44, -31, and -23, the two latter ones were completely solved in subsections 21 and 23 and have four and five solutions respectively. The equation with discriminant

$D = -44$, as was pointed out above, has the four solutions ϵ^0, ϵ^1, ϵ^4, ϵ^{17}, and since by the fundamental theorem it cannot have more than four solutions, these must be all the solutions.

We collect all the above results into the final theorem.

THEOREM. *The number of solutions in integers* X, Y *of the indeterminate equation* $(A, B, C, E) = 1$, *where* (A, B, C, E) *is an irreducible, binary cubic form with integer coefficients and with negative discriminant, is in general not greater than* 2. *It can have three solutions only if the form is equivalent to a reversible form, in which case it must have either two or three solutions and there will be infinitely many classes for which it will have three solutions. Only for two classes of forms with discriminants* -44 *and* -31 *does the equation have four solutions, and it has five solutions for the single class of determinant* -23. *No such equation can have more than five solutions.*

We thus have the following table for the number of solutions:

if the form is not equivalent to a reversible form,	0	
	1	
	2	if the form is equivalent to a reversible form,
	3	
	4	if $D = -44$ and -31,
	5	if $D = -23$.

§76. FURTHER INVESTIGATIONS ON THE ALGORITHM OF ASCENT

In the proof of the above fundamental theorem on the number of representations of a number by a binary cubic form of negative discriminant use was made of a special computational process which we called the algorithm of ascent. This algortihm was developed only for integer forms, i.e., forms, one of whose end coefficient is equal to 1. This is sufficient for the problem of finding the number of solutions, since in case the form under consideration is not equivalent to an integer form, there are no representations of the number 1, and therefore we need only consider integer forms. The algorithm as it stands is insufficient, however, for the problem of actually finding the solutions for a general binary cubic form of negative discriminant, and therefore it becomes necessary to develop this algorithm also for noninteger forms. This can be done. The algorithm of ascent can be considered as a method of successive approximations to the solution. The complete solution would be obtained if we had a method of deciding in advance at what step of the algorithm we can stop looking for further solutions. We propose below two such criteria for stopping, which occurred in the first few steps of the algorithm of ascent in all the examples to which the algorithm was applied. However we do not have a bound for the number of steps necessary before one or the other of our criteria is applicable.

1. On a sufficient condition for the indeterminate equation $(A, B, C, E) = 1$ to have a solution. Let $AX^3 + BX^2Y + CXY^2 + EY^3 = (A, B, C, E) = \Phi(X, Y)$ be a given binary cubic form and let ω_1 and ω_2 be roots of the equations $\omega_1^3 - B\omega_1^2 + AC\omega_1 - A^2E = 0$ and $\omega_2^3 - C\omega_2^2 + BE\omega_2 - AE^2 = 0$, respectively, where $\omega_1\omega_2 = AE$. The module $[\omega_1, \omega_2, 1]$, as was shown in §15, is a ring. We shall denote this ring by $O(\Phi)$ or $O[\omega_1, \omega_2, 1]$. The discriminant of this ring is equal to the discriminant of Φ. The same ring corresponds to equivalent forms. As is easily seen, the form Φ can be represented (in the field $\Omega(\omega_1)$) as the norm of a number of the type $\lambda X + \mu Y$, where λ and μ are integers in the field $\Omega(\omega_1)$. For example, if the form Φ is primitive, i.e., if the coefficients A, B, C, E have no common factor, then λ and μ have no common factor, and $\rho = \lambda/\mu$ is a root of the equation $N(\rho - Y) = A - BY + CY^2 - EY^3 = 0$, i.e., λ/μ is a general cubic fractional number. If the field $\Omega(\omega_1)$ has more than one class of ideals, then one can always find in it an unlimited number of fractions which, when reduced to their lowest terms in the field, will still retain common ideal factors in the numerator and denominator and therefore will not be relatively prime. In case the form Φ represents the number 1, it is equivalent to an "integer" form, i.e., to a form with $E = 1$, for example, $(A, B, C, E) = (n, -q, s, 1)_{\begin{pmatrix}\alpha & \beta\\ \gamma & \delta\end{pmatrix}}$; and if ρ is a root of $\rho^3 = s\rho^2 + q\rho + n$, we will obtain $(A, B, C, E) = N_\Omega(\lambda X + \mu Y)$, where $\lambda = \alpha\rho + \gamma$ and $\mu = \beta\rho + \delta$; i.e., in this case Φ has an "integer decomposition" in its ring $O(\Phi) = O(\rho^2, \rho, 1)$. If Φ is primitive, which we will always suppose in the future, then the numbers λ and μ are relatively prime. We have $\lambda/\mu = \omega_2/E$ and therefore $E = \mu j$, $\omega_2 = \lambda j$, where j is a number of $\Omega(\omega_1)$. The number $\alpha E - \beta\omega_2$ of the ring $O(\Phi)$ is equal to $(\alpha\mu - \beta\lambda)\cdot j = j$, since $\alpha\mu - \beta\lambda = 1$, i.e., j is a number in the ring $O(\Phi)$. The ideal (ω_2, E) of the ring $O(\Phi)$ must therefore be the principal ideal as well as an element of the ring $O(\Phi)$. If the form Φ is given, then using the methods of Chapters II and IV we can find out whether (ω_2, E) is a principal ideal or not in $\Omega(\omega_1)$ and in case it is, we can find the corresponding algebraic integer j of the ring, if it exists. In fact, if (ω_2, E) is the principal ideal in $\Omega(\omega_1)$, which is equal to an integer I of $\Omega(\omega_1)$, then the number j, if it

exists, is equal to $l \cdot \epsilon$, where ϵ is some unit in $\Omega(\omega_1)$. Let the discriminant of Φ be negative. Then all the units in $\Omega(\omega_1)$ are powers of the fundamental unit l_0. Let l_0^μ be the least power of l_0 lying in the ring $O(\Phi)$, i.e., $l_0^\mu = \epsilon_0$, where ϵ_0 is the fundamental unit of the ring $O(\Phi)$. Then j does not exist if there is no element of $O(\Phi)$ among the numbers $l, ll_0, ll_0^2, \cdots, ll_0^{\mu-1}$. Otherwise j can be found among these μ numbers.

If j is found, then $\lambda = \omega_2/j$ and $\mu = E/j$, or else they differ from these numbers by the same multiplier; and this multiplier is a unit ϵ in the ring $O(\Phi)$, since if $\lambda\epsilon$ and $\mu\epsilon$ are in the ring $O(\Phi)$, then $\alpha\mu\epsilon - \beta\lambda\epsilon$ is also in the ring.

Therefore in order that $\Phi(X, Y) = 1$ *have a solution it is necessary to have such a decomposition of* Φ *in its own ring.*

Examples show, however, that this condition is not sufficient.

2. On two congruences which have to be satisfied by all the solutions P, Q of the equation $\Phi(X, Y) = 1$ in case Φ is an irreducible binary cubic form with integer coefficients and negative discriminant. We suppose that our necessary condition is satisfied and we let $\lambda = r\omega_1 + s\omega_2 + t$, $\mu = u\omega_1 + v\omega_2 + w$. If $\Phi(P, Q) = 1$, then $\lambda P + \mu Q$ is a positive unit in the ring $O(\Phi)$. If the discriminant of the form Φ is negative, then the ring $O(\Phi)$ has only one independent fundamental unit. Let $\epsilon_0 = a\omega_1 + b\omega_2 + c$ be the direct positive fundamental unit, i.e., the fundamental unit satisfying the condition $0 < \epsilon_0 < 1$. The nine rational integers $a, b, c;\ r, s, t;\ u, v, w$ can be calculated by the methods of Chapters II and IV. We have $\lambda P + \mu Q = \epsilon_0^m$. Since the plane of binomial numbers $\lambda X + \mu Y$ intersects the upper part of the surface of units in a finite piece of a curve we can find all the solutions with $m < 0$, as it was done in subsection 4 of §75. If the highest solution is ϵ_0^{-k}, then if we take for λ and μ the quantities $\lambda\epsilon_0^{-k}$ and $\mu\epsilon_0^{-k}$, which can always be done, we arrive at a new integer decomposition of the form Φ which has no solutions with a negative exponent m. For every solution P, Q we will then have

$$\begin{aligned}\lambda P + \mu Q &= (rP + uQ)\,\omega_1 + (sP + vQ)\,\omega_2 + (tP + wQ)\\ &= F\omega_1 + G\omega_2 + H = \varepsilon = \varepsilon_0^m = (a\omega_1 + b\omega_2 + c)^m,\end{aligned}$$

where $m > 0$. If we write these equations for the conjugate rings and subtract, we get

$$\begin{aligned}F(\omega_1' - \omega_1'') + G(\omega_2' - \omega_2'') &= \varepsilon_0'^m - \varepsilon_0''^m = (\varepsilon_0' - \varepsilon_0'')(U\omega_1 + V\omega_2 + W)\\ &= [a(\omega_1' - \omega_1'') + b(\omega_2' - \omega_2'')](U\omega_1 + V\omega_2 + W),\end{aligned}$$

where U, V, W are also rational integers. We have

$$\omega_1' - \omega_1'' = \frac{AE(\omega_2'' - \omega_2')}{\omega_2' \cdot \omega_2''} = \frac{AE\omega_2(\omega_2'' - \omega_2')}{AE^2} = -\frac{\omega_2}{E}(\omega_2' - \omega_2''),$$

therefore after simplification we obtain

$$-F\omega_2 + EG = (-a\omega_2 + Eb)(U\omega_1 + V\omega_2 + W).$$

The comparison of coefficients gives three equations, and if we solve them we obtain $\Delta \cdot U = a(bF - aG)$, $\Delta \cdot V = b(bF - aG)$, $\Delta \cdot W = b(aC - bE)G + a(aA - bB)F$, where $\Delta = a^3A - a^2bB + ab^2C - b^3E$. Let $\delta = (a, b)$ and $a = a_1\delta$, $b = b_1\delta$, and let $\Delta/\delta^3 = \kappa$; we then obtain

$$\kappa \cdot \delta \cdot U = a_1(b_1F - a_1G);$$

$$\kappa \cdot \delta \cdot V = b_1(b_1F - a_1G);$$

$$\kappa \cdot \delta \cdot W = b_1(a_1C - b_1E)G + a_1(a_1A - b_1B)F.$$

From the first two equations, in view of $(a_1, b_1) = 1$, we obtain

$$b_1F - a_1G \equiv 0 \pmod{\kappa\delta},$$

or

$$P \cdot K + QL \equiv 0 \pmod{\kappa\delta}, \tag{1}$$

where $K = \begin{vmatrix} a_1 & b_1 \\ r & s \end{vmatrix}$; $L = \begin{vmatrix} a_1 & b_1 \\ u & v \end{vmatrix}$, while the third one gives

$$P \cdot \mathrm{K} + Q\mathrm{L} \equiv 0 \pmod{\varkappa\delta},$$

where $\mathrm{K} = \begin{vmatrix} Ca_1b_1 - Eb_1^2 & Ba_1b_1 - Aa_1^2 \\ r & s \end{vmatrix}$, $\mathrm{L} = \begin{vmatrix} Ca_1b_1 - Eb_1^2 & Ba_1b_1 - Aa_1^2 \\ u & v \end{vmatrix}$.

All the solutions P, Q of $\Phi(x, y) = 1$ must satisfy congruences (1) and (2).

3. The case in which the congruences (1) and (2) are identities. Let λ and μ enter into the decomposition of Φ in $O(\Phi)$; then $\lambda_k = \lambda\epsilon_0^k$ and $\mu_k = \mu_0^k$ give a similar decomposition. If we denote the numbers K, L, K, L of this decomposition by K_k, L_k, K_k, L_k, then it is easy to calculate that $K_1 \equiv Kc + \delta\mathrm{K}$, $L_1 \equiv Lc + \delta\mathrm{L}$ and $\mathrm{K}_1 \equiv \mathrm{K}c + \delta \cdot K \cdot \phi$, $\mathrm{L}_1 \equiv \mathrm{L}c + \delta L\phi$ modulo $\kappa\delta$, where $\phi = -ACa_1^2 + (AE + BC)a_1b_1 - BEb_1^2$. If the congruences (1) and (2) are identities, i.e., if $K \equiv L \equiv \mathrm{K} \equiv \mathrm{L} \equiv 0 \pmod{\kappa\delta}$, then the congruences are also identities for K_k, L_k, K_k, L_k. Let σ be a common divisor of K and L; then σ divides

$\begin{vmatrix} r & s \\ u & v \end{vmatrix}$, since a_1 and b_1 are relatively prime. The number $\begin{vmatrix} r & s \\ u & v \end{vmatrix}$ is the index of the module $[\lambda, \mu, 1]$ with respect to the module $[\omega_1, \omega_2, 1]$.

We suppose that the equation $\Phi(x, y) = 1$ has a solution. In this case $\lambda = (\alpha\rho + \gamma)\cdot\epsilon$, $\mu = (\beta\rho + \delta)\cdot\epsilon$, where ϵ is a unit of the ring $[\omega_1, \omega_2, 1] = [\rho^2, \rho, 1]$ since $\alpha\mu - \beta\lambda = \epsilon$. Let $\epsilon = \mathrm{A}\rho^2 + \mathrm{B}\rho + \Gamma$. Then we have

$$\begin{vmatrix} r & s \\ u & v \end{vmatrix} = \begin{vmatrix} \mathrm{A}\alpha s + \mathrm{B}\alpha + \mathrm{A}\gamma, & \mathrm{A}\alpha q + \Gamma\alpha + \mathrm{B}\gamma \\ \mathrm{A}\beta s + \mathrm{B}\beta + \mathrm{A}\delta, & \mathrm{A}\beta q + \Gamma\beta + \mathrm{B}\delta \end{vmatrix} = \begin{vmatrix} \alpha & \beta \\ \gamma & \delta \end{vmatrix} \begin{vmatrix} \mathrm{A}s + \mathrm{B}, & \mathrm{A} \\ \mathrm{A}q + \Gamma, & \mathrm{B} \end{vmatrix}$$
$$= \mathrm{AB}s + \mathrm{B}^2 - \mathrm{A}^2 q - \mathrm{A}\Gamma = \mathrm{A}',$$

where A' is the coefficient of ρ^2 of the inverse positive unit $\eta = \epsilon^{-1}$. Every common divisor of K and L therefore divides A'. Hence if $K \equiv L \equiv 0 \pmod{\kappa\delta}$ and if σ is the product of all the distinct prime factors of κ, then A' must be divisible by $\sigma\cdot\delta$. The number $N[\mathrm{A}'(s-\rho) + \mathrm{B}']$ is the index of the unit η with respect to the ring $O(\rho)$, and since η is a positive integer power of ϵ_0^{-1} it must be divisible by the index $\kappa\delta^3$ with respect to $O(\rho)$ of the unit ϵ_0. But it is easily seen that A' and B' have δ as a common factor, i.e., $\mathrm{A}' = \mathrm{A}_1'\cdot\delta$, $\mathrm{B}' = \mathrm{B}_1'\cdot\delta$ and therefore the number $N[\mathrm{A}_1'(s-\rho) + \mathrm{B}_1']$ must be divisible by κ. But since $\mathrm{A}_1' \equiv 0 \pmod{\kappa}$, it follows that $\mathrm{B}_1'^3 \equiv 0 \pmod{\kappa}$ and hence $\mathrm{B}_1' \equiv 0 \pmod{\sigma}$. Thus if (1) is an identity, then σ is a divisor of A_1' and B_1'.

We now consider (1) and (2) with K_1, L_1, K_1, L_1, which are now also identities. Therefore, if we let $\epsilon\epsilon_0 = \mathrm{A}''\rho^2 + \mathrm{B}''\rho + \Gamma''$ and $\epsilon_0 = \bar{a}\rho^2 + \bar{b}\rho + \bar{c}$, then A_1'' and B_1'' must also be divisible by σ. If we now express A_1'' and B_1'' in terms of A', B', Γ' and $\bar{a}$, $\bar{b}$, $\bar{c}$ we obtain the result, by letting $\bar{a} = \bar{a}_1\delta$ and $\bar{b} = \bar{b}_1\delta$, that $\bar{a}_1\Gamma$ and $\bar{b}_1\Gamma$ are divisible by σ. But $(\bar{a}_1, \bar{b}_1) = 1$, since it is easily seen that $(\bar{a}, \bar{b}) = (a, b) = \delta$ and Γ cannot be divisible by σ if $\sigma > 1$; therefore $\sigma = 1$. From this it follows that $\kappa = \pm 1$. The number $u = a_1\omega_1 + b_1\omega_2$ of $O(\Phi)$ therefore has index ± 1 with respect to $O(\Phi)$ and, consequently, the form $(\bar{n}, -\bar{q}, \bar{s}, 1)$, whose root is $\bar{\rho}$, is an integer form equivalent to Φ.

We have thus found a solution of $\Phi = 1$. We shall now show that we have simultaneously discovered a second solution.

In fact from $K \equiv L \equiv \mathrm{K} \equiv \mathrm{L} \equiv 0 \pmod{\kappa\delta}$ it follows easily that $r \equiv s \equiv u \equiv v \equiv 0 \pmod{\kappa\delta}$. Thus for instance $K\cdot(Ba_1b_1 - Aa_1^2) - \mathrm{K}b_1 = (-Aa_1^3 + Ba_1^2b_1 - Ca_1b_1^2 + Eb_1^3)\cdot s = -\kappa s$, i.e., if K and K are divisible by $\kappa\delta$, then s is divisible by δ. Hence in this case $\mathrm{A}' = \begin{vmatrix} r & s \\ u & v \end{vmatrix} \equiv 0 \pmod{\delta^2}$. The unit η, and therefore also the unit ϵ, lies in this case in the ring $O(\delta\rho)$. Let $\epsilon = \epsilon_0^\tau$, i.e., $\epsilon = A_1\delta^2\rho^2 + B_1\delta\rho + \Gamma = (\bar{a}_1\delta\rho^2 + \bar{b}_1\delta\rho + \bar{c})^\tau$. Equating the coefficient of ρ^2 we obtain $\tau\bar{a}_1\bar{\delta}\bar{c}^{\tau-1} \equiv 0 \pmod{\delta^2}$. But $(\bar{c}, \delta) = 1$, and we can also suppose that $(\tau, \delta) = 1$, since λ, μ can always be replaced by $\lambda\epsilon_0^k$, $\mu\epsilon_0^k$, while τ is replaced by $\tau - k$, where k can be chosen so that $(\tau - k, \delta) = 1$. Therefore $\bar{a}_1 \equiv 0 \pmod{\delta}$ and therefore the unit ϵ_0 itself lies in this case in the ring $O(\delta\rho)$. The index of ϵ_0 with respect to $O(\delta\rho)$ is $\pm\delta^3$, since $\kappa = \pm 1$. The unit ϵ_0 is therefore a unit of the ring $O(\delta\rho)$ with index ± 1 with respect to this ring. The form $(\delta^3 n - \delta^2 q, \delta s, 1)$ is therefore equivalent to some reversible form corresponding to the ring $O(\delta\rho)$ is therefore equivalent to some reversible form $(1, -q', s', 1)$. The equation $(\delta^3 n, -\delta^2 q, \delta s, 1) = 1$ has therefore two solutions, namely $(0,1)$ and (X_1, Y_1) and, consequently, the equation $(n, -q, s, 1) = 1$ has the two solutions $(0, 1)$ and $(\delta X_1, Y_1)$, so that the equation $(A, B, C, E) = 1$ also has two solutions since $(A, B, C, E) \sim (n, -q, s, 1)$.

THEOREM. *If the congruences* (1) *and* (2) *are identically satisfied and if* $\kappa \neq \pm 1$, *then* $\Phi(X, Y) = 1$ *has no solutions. If however* $\kappa = \pm 1$, *then it has two solutions, which can both be found. Moreover, the solution of the equation* $\Phi(X, Y) = 1$ *is reduced to the solution of the reversible equation* $(1, -q', s', 1) = 1$, *which can be solved.*

4. The algorithm of ascent. Suppose that both the congruences (1) and (2) are identically satisfied. Denote by d the greatest common divisor of K, L and $\kappa\delta$, and let $K = d \cdot K'$, $L = dL'$, $\kappa\delta = d\kappa'$. Then we will have $PK' + QL' \equiv 0 \pmod{\kappa'}$. Now if $(K', L') = d'$ and $K' = K''d'$, $L' = L''d'$, then we will have $(d', \kappa') = 1$ and therefore $PK'' + QL'' \equiv 0 \pmod{\kappa'}$, where $(K'', L'') = 1$. If we transform the form (A, B, C, E) into the form (A', B', C', E') by means of the transformation $\begin{pmatrix} \alpha & -L'' \\ \gamma & K'' \end{pmatrix}$, where $\alpha K'' + \gamma L'' = 1$, we obtain $A'P'^3 + B'P'^2Q' + C'P'Q'^2 + E'Q'^3 = 1$, where $P' \equiv 0 \pmod{\kappa'}$, since $P' = PK'' + QL''$.

Let $P' = \bar{P} \cdot \kappa'$ and $\bar{A} = A' \cdot \kappa'^3$, $\bar{B} = B' \cdot \kappa'^2$, $\bar{C} = C' \cdot \kappa'$, $\bar{E} = E$; then we get the equation $(\bar{A}, \bar{B}, \bar{C}, \bar{E}) = 1$ to which the solution of the equation $(A, B, C, E) = 1$ is reduced. The discriminant of the form $(\bar{A}, \bar{B}, \bar{C}, \bar{E})$ is κ'^6 times as large as that of the form (A, B, C, E) and $\kappa' \neq \pm 1$, since we have assumed that the congruences (1) is not an identity. In a similar way we can transform the form $(\bar{A}, \bar{B}, \bar{C}, \bar{E})$ into the form $(\bar{\bar{A}}, \bar{\bar{B}}, \bar{\bar{C}}, \bar{\bar{E}})$ and so on. This process will terminate only if at some step the corresponding form has no integer decomposition in its own ring, in which case the equation $(A, B, C, E) = 1$ has no solutions, or if at some step the congruences (1) and (2) become identities, in which case the equation $(A, B, C, E) = 1$ either has no solutions or else has two solutions, which will be found at this stage of the algorithm.

5. The first case, when the equation $\Phi(X, Y) = 1$ has a unique solution. In this case, which happens very often, the algorithm of ascent never terminates, as shown by the theorem of subsection 3. We shall not pursue here the study of this rather remarkable circumstance.

6. The second case, when the equation $\Phi(X, Y)$ has at least two solutions. In this case, as will be clear from the geometrical considerations discussed in the next subsection, the congruences (1) and (2) become identities at some step of the algorithm of ascent.

7. Approximations to the solutions by means of the algorithm of ascent. Let X, Y be all possible pairs of rational integers. We consider them as points with respect to some fixed coordinate system, so that they form a parallelogrammatic lattice. The points P, Q, whose integer coordinates satisfy the congruence $PK' + QL' \equiv 0 \pmod{\kappa'}$, i.e., they satisfy the indeterminate equation $PK'' + QL'' = t\kappa'$, where t is a rational integer, obviously form a sublattice of this lattice. Each step of the algorithm of ascent leads to a sublattice of the previous lattice, the area of whose basic parallelogram is at least twice the area of the previous one. These lattices have the point (0, 0) in common. If we have a solution (P_1, Q_1), then the process consists in removing from the lattice (X, Y) each time a row of points parallel to the row (0, 0) (P_1, Q_1). This process can continue indefinitely, which will be the case, as we have shown, if there is only one solution. However, if there are two solutions (P_1, Q_1) and (P_2, Q_2), then the area of the successive basic parallelograms cannot surpass the area of the parallelogram constructed on the points (0, 0), (P_1, Q_1) and (P_2, Q_2), since these points lie in all the lattices, and therefore the algorithm must terminate. If we can find the closest point to (0, 0) in each of these lattices and if there is a unique solution, then it will appear in this sequence of minima.

8. The calculation of the numbers λ and μ for "higher" forms. Suppose that λ and μ have been calculated for the given form $\Phi(X, Y)$ by the method of subsection 1 and that the ϵ_0 has been found. If in accordance with subsection 4 we transform the form Φ into $\bar{\Phi}$ by means of the transformation $\begin{pmatrix} \alpha & -L'' \\ \gamma & K'' \end{pmatrix}$, then $\gamma' = \alpha\lambda + \gamma\mu$, $\mu' = \mu K'' - \lambda L''$.

Suppose that this has been accomplished, so that $\lambda' = \lambda$, $\mu' = \mu$. In this case

$$(A,\ B,\ C,\ E)=N(\lambda x+\mu y);$$
$$(\bar{A},\ \bar{B},\ \bar{C},\ \bar{E})=N(\lambda\varkappa' X+\mu Y)=(A\varkappa'^3.\ B\varkappa'^2,\ C\varkappa',\ E).$$

The basis corresponding to this "higher" form is $\bar{\omega}_1 = \kappa'^2\omega_1$, $\bar{\omega}_2 = \kappa'\omega_2$. The numbers $\lambda\kappa''$, μ in the decomposition of $\bar{\Phi}$ in $O(\Phi)$ become $\bar{\lambda}$, $\bar{\mu}$ in the decomposition of $\bar{\Phi}$ in its own ring $O(\bar{\Phi})$ and therefore $\bar{\lambda} = \lambda\kappa'\epsilon_0^{\tau}$, $\bar{\mu} = \mu\epsilon_0^{\tau}$, where τ is a rational integer exponent $< \nu$, if ϵ_0^{ν} is the least power of ϵ_0 lying in $O(\bar{\Phi})$.

9. The criteria for termination. It may happen that the equation $\Phi(X, Y) = 1$ has no solutions. Therefore it is necessary to find a criterion which will guarantee that after a certain number of steps it is useless to pursue the algorithm of ascent, as there are no further solutions. If we could find such a criterion the problem would be solved, but this we have not been able to do. However, we can point out two criteria which appear in the first few steps of all the numerical examples which we have considered, although we cannot guarantee their appearance before some definite step given in advance. In the first place it may happen that at some step the form will not have a decomposition in its own ring, which can always be checked by the method of subsection 8. In the second place it may happen that at some step the congruences (1) and (2) are incompatible, which will be the case if and only if $\begin{vmatrix} r & s \\ u & v \end{vmatrix}$ is not divisible by δ.

10. Two examples. Consider the form (2, 0, 3, 2) with $D = -648$. Then $\omega_1^3 + 6\omega_1 - 8 = 0$ and $\omega_2^3 - 3\omega_2 - 8 = 0$, where $\omega_1 - 1 = \epsilon$ is a unit. The numbers λ and μ of the ring $O(2, 0, 3, 2)$ must have norm 2. However, using known methods considered for instance in § 22, it can be shown that the ring $O(2, 0, 3, 2)$ does not contain numbers with norm 2. The form (2, 0, 3, 2) therefore has no decomposition in its own ring. Therefore, the first criterion for the termination of the algorithm holds and the form (2, 0, 3, 2) = 1 has no solutions. Now consider the form (3, 3, 4, 2) with $D = -516$. Here $\omega_1^3 - 3\omega_1^2 + 12\omega_1 - 18 = 0$, $\omega_2^3 - 4\omega_2^2 + 6\omega_2 - 12 = 0$. We compute the numbers λ and μ. They are $\lambda = -3 + \omega_2$, $\mu = 2 - \omega_1$. The fundamental unit of the ring $O(3, 3, 4, 2)$ is $\epsilon_0 = 23 - 7\omega_2$, and $\delta = 7$, while $\begin{vmatrix} r & s \\ u & v \end{vmatrix} = 1$ is not divisible by 7. Therefore congruences (1) and (2) are incompatible; that is, the second criterion holds and the equation (3, 3, 4, 2) = 1 has no solutions. (Incidentally this is the form with negative discriminant of smallest absolute value which fails to represent the number 1 for nontrivial reasons, i.e.,

not because the form is imprimitive or has even end coefficients and odd middle coefficients; i.e., a form having 2 for greatest common divisor of all of the numbers which it represents, so that the ring has a common divisor of all of its indices).

11. The algorithm of ascent in the case of an "integer" form. If the form Φ is an integer form, i.e., one of its end coefficients is 1, for instance $\Phi = (n, -q, s, 1)$, then we have $K = a_1$, $L = 0$, $K = a_1 b_1 s - b_1^2$, $L = 0$ (in case the fundamental unit of the ring $O(\Phi)$ is $a\rho^2 + b\rho + c$, where $\rho^3 = s\rho^2 + q\rho + n$ and $a = a_1\delta$, $b = b_1\delta$ with $(a_1, b_1) = 1$). Therefore since $(a_1, b_1) = 1$, congruences (1) and (2) both reduce to the single congruence $P \equiv 0 \pmod{\kappa\delta}$ and we obtain the algorithm of ascent discussed in §75.

12. The termination criterion in the case of an integer form. In this case the criterion of subsection 9 is never applicable. There exists, however, another criterion. If the coefficients a and b of the fundamental unit $\epsilon_0 = a\rho^2 + b\rho + c$ are divisible respectively by k^2 and k, where k is a rational integer, then ρ can be replaced by ρk and we can look for binomial units in ρk instead of in ρ. The unit for which such a k does not exist will be called "reduced." We next prove the following theorem.

No positive integer, power ϵ_0^m of a reduced unit ϵ_0 can be binomial if the coefficients a, b have an odd prime factor π in common.

In fact let $a = a_1\pi$, $b = b_1\pi$, with $a_1 \not\equiv 0 \pmod{\pi}$; then the coefficient of ρ^2 in ϵ_0^m is

$$m \cdot c^{m-1} \cdot \pi \cdot a_1 + \frac{m(m-1)}{1 \cdot 2} c^{m-2} \cdot \pi^2 \cdot A_2 + \frac{m(m-1)(m-2)}{1 \cdot 2 \cdot 3} c^{m-3} \pi^3 A_3 + \cdots,$$

where $A_2, A_3, \cdots$ are rational integers. This coefficient cannot be zero, since $(a_1, \pi) = 1$ and $(c, \pi) = 1$ and therefore if m is divisible exactly by π^τ, we have $\pi^2 > 3$, $\pi^3 > 4$, etc. if $\pi > 2$. We shall call every common divisor of the coefficients a, b of a unit a "divisor" of the unit.

Let ϵ_0^μ be the least power of the fundamental unit ϵ_0 having the divisor π. Two cases may arise: either the coefficient of ρ^2 in ϵ_0^μ is divisible only by π, or it is divisible at least by π^2. In the first case we will call π a divisor of the first kind, and in the second case, of the second kind with respect to ϵ_0. It is easily seen that if ϵ_0^m has a divisor π, then ϵ_0^m is a power of ϵ_0^μ. Hence we can make the following statement: *If at some step of the algorithm of ascent (not necessarily at the first step) the multiplier of ascent π is a prime of the first kind with respect to the given fundamental unit, then there are no solutions with positive m and the calculation can stop.* In all the cases to which the algorithm was applied, a multiplier π which was a prime of the first kind appeared in one of the early steps, usually at the first or second step, and therefore this method always solved the equation. We have not been able to prove, however, that in general a multiplier of the first kind must appear at some stage of the algorithm, if there are no solutions.

In view of the fact that for large π it is difficult to calculate ϵ_0^{μ} modulo π^2, we make use in these cases of the following two determinants. For brevity, we introduce these determinants without proof. We shall suppose that π is not a divisor of the discriminant of ρ. In this case the prime π is decomposable in $\Omega(\rho)$ either into the product of three distinct prime ideals of the first degree $\pi = \mathfrak{p}_1 \mathfrak{p}_2 \mathfrak{p}_3$, or into the product of an ideal of the second degree $\mathfrak{q}$ by an ideal of the first degree $\mathfrak{p}$, namely $\pi = \mathfrak{q}\cdot\mathfrak{p}$, but π cannot be a prime ideal, since it is a divisor of the norm of the binomial number $-a\rho + b + as$.

A necessary and sufficient condition that π be of the second kind with respect to ϵ in case $\pi = \mathfrak{p}_1 \mathfrak{p}_2 \mathfrak{p}_3$ is that $\Delta \equiv 0 \pmod{\pi}$, while in case $\pi = \mathfrak{q}\cdot\mathfrak{p}$, it is that $\nabla \equiv 0 \pmod{\pi}$, where the determinants Δ and ∇ are

$$\Delta = \begin{vmatrix} \sigma_1 + \dfrac{\psi(x_1)(2ax_1+b)}{\varepsilon_1\cdot f'(x_1)}, & x_1, & 1 \\ \sigma_2 + \dfrac{\psi(x_2)(2ax_2+b)}{\varepsilon_2\cdot f'(x_2)}, & x_2, & 1 \\ \sigma_3 + \dfrac{\psi(x_3)(2ax_3+b)}{\varepsilon_3\cdot f'(x_3)}, & x_3, & 1 \end{vmatrix}.$$

Here

$$f(x) = x^3 - sx^2 - qx - n = (x-x_1)(x-x_2)(x-x_3) + \pi\psi(x);\ \sigma_i = \frac{\varepsilon_1^{\pi-1}-1}{\pi};$$

$$\varepsilon_i = ax_i^2 + bx_i + c \text{ (where } x_i = x_1, x_2, x_3);\ f'(x) = 3x^2 - 2sx - q].$$

$$\nabla = \begin{vmatrix} \dfrac{\varepsilon_1^{\pi-i}-1}{\pi} + \dfrac{\psi(x_1)(2ax_1+b)}{\varepsilon_1 f'(x_1)}, & x_1, & 1 \\ \dfrac{(A-B\theta)^{\pi+1}-\nu}{\nu\pi} + \dfrac{\psi(\beta')(2a\beta'+b)}{(A+B\theta)\cdot f'(\beta')}, & \beta', & 1 \\ \dfrac{(A+B\theta)^{\pi+1}-\nu}{\nu\pi} + \dfrac{\psi(\beta'')(2a\beta''+b)}{(A-B\theta)\cdot f'(\beta'')}, & \beta'', & 1 \end{vmatrix},$$

where

$$f(x) = (x-x_1)(x^2+hx+k) + \pi\cdot\psi(x);\qquad -\pi < h < \pi;\quad h = 2h_1;$$

$$\theta = \sqrt{h_1^2 - k};\ \beta' = -h_1 + \theta;\ \ \beta'' = -h_1 - \theta;\ \ a\beta'^2 + b\beta' + c = A + B\theta;$$

$$\nu = A^2 - B^2(h_1^2 - k);\ \varepsilon_1 = ax_1^2 + bx_1 + c;\ \ f'(x) = 3x^2 - 2sx - q.$$

13. **Example.** Consider the form $(2, 6, 3, 1) = 1$ with $D = -216$. (For this form there exists a considerable literature of its own, since it is connected with the equation $U^3 - V^2 = -2$. In vol. 25 of Math. Zeit., A. Brauer gave a solution of this equation, having discovered a special method of solving equations of the form $U^3 - V^2 = -k$ for $k = 2$. However, we were already able in 1920 to solve not only this equation but all equations of the type $(A, B, C, E) = 1$ with, for example, $D < 0$ and $|D| < 300$.) Here $(2, 6, 3, 1) \sim (2, 3, 0, 1)$, and $\rho^3 = -3\rho + 2$, $\epsilon_0 = -\rho^2 - \rho + 1$, $-a\rho + b + as = \rho - 1$, $\kappa = 2, \delta = 1$, so that for the first multiplier of ascent we have $\pi = 2$. We must consider the ring $O(\bar{\rho})$, where $\bar{\rho} = 2\rho$. We obtain $\epsilon_0^2 = -\bar{\rho}^2 - 3\bar{\rho} + 5$, $-\bar{a}\bar{\rho} + \bar{b} + \overline{as} = \bar{\rho} - 3$, and therefore the second multiplier of ascent is $\bar{\pi} = 47$. Since 47 is somewhat large, we use the above determinants. Since $47 = \mathfrak{q} \cdot \mathfrak{p}$, we must calculate $\nabla \cdot x^3 + 3x - 2 = (x - 25)(x^2 - 22x + 111) + 47(x^2 - 14x + 59)$; in other words, we now have $x_1 = 25$, $\epsilon_1 = 649$, $\sigma = (649^{46} - 1)/47 \equiv 34 \pmod{47}$, $\beta' + 11 + \theta$, where $\theta = \sqrt{10}$, $A + B\theta = -141 - 23\theta$, $\nu \equiv 872 \pmod{47^2}$, and

$$872^{-1} \cdot 47^{-1}[(-141 + 23\theta)^{48} - 872] \equiv 10\theta - 2 \pmod{47}.$$

We therefore get $\nabla \equiv 18\theta \not\equiv 0 \pmod{47}$. The prime 47 is therefore of the first kind with respect to $\epsilon_0 = -\rho^2 - \rho + 1$ and therefore the equation $(2, 6, 3, 1) = 1$ has no solutions. (We note that of all the equations with $|D| < 300$, this particular equation leads to the most troublesome calculations. In all the other cases it was not necessary to calculate Δ or ∇.)

§77. ON INTEGER CUBIC EQUATIONS WITH A GIVEN DISCRIMINANT

We shall call a cubic equation $z^3 = sz^2 + qz + n$ an "integer" cubic equation if its coefficients s, q, n are rational integers.

THE PROBLEM. *To find all cubic equations, or what is the same thing, all cubic irrationals, having a given discriminant* D. This problem is obviously equivalent to the problem of representation of numbers by binary cubic forms, for if one finds all the maximal rings whose discriminants are divisors of D which differ from D only for square factors Δ^2, then the problem reduces to the representation of the numbers Δ by the index-forms of the corresponding rings.

If $z^3 = sz^2 + qz + n$ is an integer equation with a given discriminant D, then all the integer equations "parallel" to it, i.e., the equations that are obtained from this equation by the linear translation of z to $z + r$, where r is a rational integer, have obviously the same discriminant. To every solution of the index-form $= \Delta$ corresponds a whole "parallel" of these equations, for if $[1, \omega_1, \omega_2]$ is a basis of the corresponding ring and if $r + x\omega_1 + y\omega_2$ is a general number of the ring, then x and y will be the variables of the index-form, which will be determined, while r remains indeterminate. From this "parallel" of equations one can select a representative equation having the least s in absolute value, i.e., the unique equation in a given parallel of equations for which $s = -1, 0$, or 1.

Since we have found for all $-300 < D < 0$ all the solutions of the equation $f(x, y) = 1$ by means of the algorithm of ascent (see the following table of solutions) we can also give a corresponding table of representatives of the "parallels" of integer cubic equations with these discriminants. The beginning of this table follows the table of solutions. It is interesting to note how "large" is the "smallest" of the equations of the fourth parallel corresponding to the discriminant -44.

§78. ON THE EQUATION $U^3 - V^2 = k$

It is very remarkable that our basic problem of representation of numbers by binary cubic forms is very closely connected with the problem of the distribution of squares and cubes in the natural sequence of integers. In fact it is equivalent to the problem of finding squares and cubes differing by a given number k, i.e., to the problem of solving in integers U, V the indeterminate equation

$$U^3 - V^2 = k, \tag{1}$$

where k is a given integer.

In fact we will next show (in subsection 1) that if we find all the solutions of all the equations $f_i(x, y) = 1$, where f_i are the representatives of all the classes of binary cubic forms whose discriminants are $108k$ (these representatives can easily be found using the method of §30), we can then find all the solutions of (1). From this it follows incidentally that equation (1) has only a finite number of solutions.

On the other hand we will show (in subsection 2) that in order to find all the solutions of the equation

$$f(x, y) = 1, \tag{2}$$

where f is a binary cubic form whose discriminant is D, it is sufficient to find all solutions of (1) for $k = 16 \cdot 27D$.

1. Multiplying both sides of (1) by 108, we note that we can then write

$4(3U)^3 - 27(2V)^2 = 108k$. Let U, V be a solution of (1). To it corresponds the binary cubic form $x^3 - 3Uxy^2 - 2Vy^3 = (1, 0, -3U, -2V)$ whose discriminant is $108k$. The problem of solving equation (1) is obviously equivalent to the problem of finding all the forms of the type $(1, 0, -3U, -2V)$, where U and V are rational integers having discriminant $108k$. We find the representatives of all the classes of binary cubic forms of discriminant $108k$. If $f(x, y)$ is one of these forms and if a form of the type $(1, 0, -3U, -2V)$ is contained in its class so that $(1, 0, -3U, -2V) = f(x, y)_{\begin{pmatrix}\alpha & \beta\\ \gamma & \delta\end{pmatrix}}$, then $f(\alpha, \gamma) = 1$, i.e., $x = \alpha$, $y = \gamma$ is a solution of $f(x, y) = 1$. Conversely, if $x = \alpha$, $y = \gamma$ is a solution, then choosing β and δ such that $\alpha\delta - \beta\gamma = 1$ we can transform the given form f into an equivalent form having the coefficient of x^3 equal to 1. It is obvious that for given α and γ, the choice of β and δ is not unique. In fact, if β_0, δ_0 is a suitable choice for β, δ, then the other choices are

$$\beta = \beta_0 + t\alpha, \quad \delta = \delta_0 + t\gamma$$

with integer t. From this it follows that

$$\begin{pmatrix}\alpha & \beta\\ \gamma & \delta\end{pmatrix} = \begin{pmatrix}\alpha & \beta_0\\ \gamma & \delta_0\end{pmatrix}\begin{pmatrix}1 & t\\ 0 & 1\end{pmatrix}.$$

Therefore the forms obtained from the form $f(x, y)$ by the substitution $\begin{pmatrix}\alpha & \beta\\ \gamma & \delta\end{pmatrix}$ for given α, γ and various values of β, δ will all be "parallel" to each other, i.e., they can be obtained from each other by the substitution $\begin{pmatrix}1 & t\\ 0 & 1\end{pmatrix}$. Therefore to every solution α, γ of the equation $f(x, y) = 1$ corresponds a set of parallel forms equivalent to $f(x, y)$ and having 1 for the coefficient of x^3. This set of forms cannot have more than one form with the coefficient of x^2y equal to zero. Hence in order to solve (1) it is sufficient:

α) To find a representative form $f(x, y)$ of every class of forms with determinant $108k$. This problem is solved in a finite number of steps. We note that in doing so we must find not only the irreducible forms but also the reducible ones.

β) To solve the equation $f(x, y) = 1$. This equation for $D < 0$, i.e., for $k < 0$, can in many cases be solved by the "algorithm of ascent" (probably always, but this has not been proved). In case of a reducible f it is easily solved.

γ) Starting with each solution (α, γ), to choose β, δ such that $\alpha\delta - \beta\gamma = 1$ and to transform the form $f(x, y)$ into a form with leading coefficient unity.

δ) For each of these forms to find a parallel form of the type $x^3 + qxy^2 - ny^3$, if this is possible, or to show that there is no such form.

ϵ) From the forms thus obtained, to select those for which

$$q \equiv 0 \pmod 3,$$
$$n \equiv 0 \pmod 2,$$

and then $U = -q/3$, $V = n/2$ will be a solution of (1). This method gives all the solutions.

If the form $f(x, y)$ is reducible then it is either nonequivalent to a form of the type $x^3 + qxy^2 - ny^3$, or, if it is equivalent to such a form, it can be replaced by it and our problem is reduced to seeking solutions of $x^3 + qxy^2 - ny^3 = 1$. But if f is reducible, then this form is also reducible and it can be written as $(x + ry)(x^2 + gxy + ty^2)$ and therefore we must find simultaneous solutions in integers x, y of either

$$\left.\begin{aligned} x + ry &= 1, \\ x^2 + gxy + ty^2 &= 1, \end{aligned}\right\}$$

or of

$$\left.\begin{aligned} x + ry &= -1, \\ x^2 + gxy + ty^2 &= -1. \end{aligned}\right\}$$

Hence there cannot be more than four solutions in this case. If the form $f(x, y)$ is irreducible and if $k < 0$, i.e., $D < 0$, then by the fundamental theorem of §75 the number of solutions of $f(x, y)$ does not exceed 3, since

$$D = 108k \neq -23, -31, -44.$$

In $k > 0$, i.e., $D > 0$ we have by Siegel's theorem (see §70 for Faddeev's and Gel'man's improvements) that the number of solutions does not exceed 10. Thus we have that the number of solutions of (1) in case $k < 0$ does not exceed $4h$ and in case $k > 0$ does not exceed $10h$, where h is the number of classes of binary cubic forms of discriminant $108k$.

2. We now consider the inverse problem of how to reduce the solution of (2) to the solution of (1). We have Cayley's identity between the covariants of a binary cubic form

$$4H^3 - Q^2 = 27Df^2.$$

This identity follows readily from the expressions for the covariants given in Lemma II of § 32. From this it follows that if (x_0, y_0) is a solution of $f(x, y) = 1$ then the equation $U^3 - V^2 = 16 \cdot 27 \cdot D$ has the solution $U = 4H(x_0, y_0)$, $V = 4Q(x_0, y_0)$.

Therefore if all the solutions U, V of $U^3 - V^2 = 16 \cdot 27 \cdot D$ are found, then the solutions of $f(x, y) = 1$ can be found by solving the system

$$4H(x, y) = U,$$

$$4Q(x, y) = V.$$

The solution of this problem is trivial.

We give a short table of all the solutions of the equation $U^3 - V^2 = k$ for $k = -1, -2, -3, -4, -5$, and -6.

—1	—2	—3	—4	—5	—6
—1, 0 0, 1 2, 3	—1, 1	1, 2	0, 2	—1, 2	no solutions

The equation $U^3 - V^2 = -8$ has four solutions:

$$U = -2, 2, 46, 1,$$

$$V = 0, 4, 312, 3.$$

The first solution corresponds to a reducible class, the second and third to one irreducible class and the fourth to another irreducible class.

The equation $U^3 - V^2 = -17$ has discriminant $D = -108 \cdot 17 = -1836$. The ring defined by $\rho^3 = -6\rho + 6$ has this discriminant and we get at once the solution $U = -2$, $V = 3$. The fundamental unit of this ring is $\epsilon_0 = -\rho + 1$. Corresponding to this binomial unit we have the solution $U = 8$, $V = 23$. The fourth power of this unit is again a binomial unit $\epsilon_0^4 = 26\rho - 23$, which corresponds to $U = 5234$, $V = 378661$. This gives the nearby cube and square, 143 384 152 904 and 143 384 152 921, which were apparently first discovered heuristically by Verebrusov (Mat. Sb. vol. 26). It is interesting to note that the binomial unit which generates this large solution has small coefficients 26 and -23.

TABLE of all representations of 1 by all binary cubic forms of negative discriminant not exceeding 300 in absolute value

(Table computed by Delone [13])

$-D$	Equation	Fundamental Unit	Δ	Solutions	N.S.
23	$\varepsilon^3 = -\varepsilon^2 + 1$	ε	1	$\varepsilon^{-2} = \varepsilon + 1$; $\varepsilon^0 = 1$; $\varepsilon^1 = \varepsilon$; $\varepsilon^5 = -\varepsilon + 1$; $\varepsilon^{14} = 4\varepsilon - 3$	5
31	$\varepsilon^3 = -\varepsilon + 1$	ε	1	$\varepsilon^0 = 1$; $\varepsilon^1 = \varepsilon$; $\varepsilon^2 = -\varepsilon + 1$; $\varepsilon^8 = 3\varepsilon - 2$	4
44	$\varepsilon^3 = -\varepsilon^2 - \varepsilon + 1$	ε	1	$\varepsilon^0 = 1$; $\varepsilon^1 = \varepsilon$; $\varepsilon^4 = 2\varepsilon - 1$; $\varepsilon^{17} = -103\varepsilon + 56$	4
59	$\varepsilon^3 = -2\varepsilon + 1$	ε	1	$\varepsilon^0 = 1$; $\varepsilon^1 = \varepsilon$; $\varepsilon^3 = -2\varepsilon + 1$	3
76	$\varepsilon^3 = \varepsilon^2 - 3\varepsilon + 1$	ε	1	$\varepsilon^0 = 1$; $\varepsilon^1 = \varepsilon$; $\varepsilon^8 = -36\varepsilon + 13$	3
83	$\varepsilon^3 = -2\varepsilon^2 - 2\varepsilon + 1$	ε	1	$\varepsilon^0 = 1$; $\varepsilon^1 = \varepsilon$	2
87	$\varepsilon^3 = -\varepsilon^2 - 2\varepsilon + 1$	ε	1	$\varepsilon^0 = 1$; $\varepsilon^1 = \varepsilon$	2
104	$\rho^3 = \rho + 2$	$-\rho^2 + \rho + 1$	2	$\varepsilon^0 = 1$; $\varepsilon^2 = 2\rho - 3$	2
107	$\varepsilon^3 = 2\varepsilon^2 - 4\varepsilon + 1$	ε	1	$\varepsilon^0 = 1$; $\varepsilon^1 = \varepsilon$; $\varepsilon^4 = -7\varepsilon + 2$	3
108	$\rho^3 = 2$	$\rho - 1$	1	$\varepsilon^0 = 1$; $\varepsilon^1 = \rho - 1$	2
116	$\rho^3 = \rho^2 + 2$	$\rho^2 - \rho - 1$	2	$\varepsilon^0 = 1$	1
135	$\varepsilon^3 = -3\varepsilon + 1$	ε	1	$\varepsilon^0 = 1$; $\varepsilon^1 = \varepsilon$; $\varepsilon^3 = -3\varepsilon + 1$	3
139	$\varepsilon^3 = 4\varepsilon^2 - 6\varepsilon + 1$	ε	1	$\varepsilon^0 = 1$; $\varepsilon^1 = \varepsilon$	2
140	$\varepsilon^3 = 3\varepsilon^2 - 5\varepsilon + 1$	ε	1	$\varepsilon^0 = 1$; $\varepsilon^1 = \varepsilon$	2
152	$\rho^3 = \rho^2 + 2\rho + 2$	$-\rho^2 + \rho + 3$	2	$\varepsilon^0 = 1$	1
172	$\rho^3 = 2\rho + 2$	$-\rho^2 + 2\rho + 1$	2	$\varepsilon^0 = 1$	1
175	$\varepsilon^3 = -2\varepsilon^2 - 3\varepsilon + 1$	ε	1	$\varepsilon^0 = 1$; $\varepsilon^1 = \varepsilon$	2
176	$\varepsilon^3 = -\varepsilon^2 - 3\varepsilon + 1$	ε	1	$\varepsilon^0 = 1$; $\varepsilon^1 = \varepsilon$	2
199	$\varepsilon^3 = \varepsilon^2 - 4\varepsilon + 1$	ε	1	$\varepsilon^0 = 1$; $\varepsilon^1 = \varepsilon$	2
200	$\rho^3 = 2\rho^2 - 3\rho + 4$	$\rho^2 - \rho - 1$	2	$\varepsilon^0 = 1$	1
204	$\rho^3 = \rho^2 - \rho + 3$	$-\rho^2 + \rho + 1$	3	$\varepsilon^0 = 1$	1
211	$\varepsilon^3 = 6\varepsilon^2 - 10\varepsilon + 1$	ε	1	$\varepsilon^0 = 1$; $\varepsilon^1 = \varepsilon$	2
212	$\rho^3 = \rho^2 - 4\rho + 2$	$2\rho - 1$	8	$\varepsilon^0 = 1$; $\varepsilon^1 = 2\rho - 1$	2
216	$\rho^3 = -3\rho + 2$	$-\rho^2 - \rho + 1$	2	$\varepsilon^0 = 1$	1
231	$\varepsilon^3 = -4\varepsilon^2 - 5\varepsilon + 1$	ε	1	$\varepsilon^0 = 1$; $\varepsilon^1 = \varepsilon$	2
236	$\rho^3 = 2\rho^2 + \rho + 2$	$\rho^2 - 3\rho + 1$	4	$\varepsilon^0 = 1$	1
239	$\rho^3 = \rho + 3$	$\rho^2 - \rho - 1$	3	$\varepsilon^0 = 1$; $\varepsilon^2 = 3\rho - 5$	2
243	$\varepsilon^3 = -\varepsilon^2 - 12\varepsilon + 1$	ε	1	$\varepsilon^0 = 1$; $\varepsilon^1 = \varepsilon$	2

TABLE of all representations of 1 by all binary cubic forms of negative discriminant not exceeding 300 in absolute value

(Table continued)

$-D$	Equation	Fundamental Unit	Δ	Solutions	N.S.
244	$\rho^3=5\rho^2-4\rho+2$	$-2\rho^2+10\rho-7$	16	$\varepsilon^0=1$	1
247	$\varepsilon^3=-3\varepsilon^2-4\varepsilon+1$	ε	1	$\varepsilon^0=1$; $\varepsilon^1=\varepsilon$	2
255	$\varepsilon^3=5\varepsilon^2-8\varepsilon+1$	ε	1	$\varepsilon^0=1$; $\varepsilon^1=\varepsilon$	2
268	$\varepsilon^3=7\varepsilon^2-13\varepsilon+1$	ε	1	$\varepsilon^0=1$; $\varepsilon^1=\varepsilon$	2
279	$\varepsilon^3=2\varepsilon^2-5\varepsilon+1$	ε	1	$\varepsilon^0=1$; $\varepsilon^1=2$	2
283	$\varepsilon^3=-4\varepsilon+1$	ε	1	$\varepsilon^0=1$; $\varepsilon^1=\varepsilon$; $\varepsilon^3=-4\varepsilon+1$	3
300	$\rho^3=4\rho^2-2\rho+2$	$-\rho^2+5\rho-5$	9	$\varepsilon^0=1$	1

TABLE of all nonparallel cubic equations with least s of negative discriminant not exceeding 172 in absolute value

(Table computed by Delone [13])

D	s	q	n
−23	1	−2	1
	−1	0	1
	0	1	1
	−1	4	5
	0	55	157
−31	0	−1	1
	1	0	1
	1	2	1
	0	17	27
−44	−1	−1	1
	1	1	1
	1	11	11
	−1	31281	2139919
−59	0	−2	1.
	−1	1	2
	1	9	8
−76	1	−3	1
	0	2	2
	1	3077	64631
−83	1	−1	2
	−1	3	4
−87	−1	−2	1
	−1	2	3
−104	0	1	2
	1	46	106
−107	1	−3	2
	1	3	2
	−1	157	812
−108	0	0	2
	0	6	6
−116	1	0	2
−135	0	−3	1
	0	3	3
	0	33	73
−139	−1	−1	2
	0	8	9
−140	0	−2	2
	−1	5	7
−152	1	2	2
−172	2	0	2

PART B. THE SOLUTION OF CUBIC INDETERMINATE EQUATIONS IN TWO UNKNOWNS IN RATIONALS

§79. ON RATIONAL POINTS ON CUBIC CURVES

In Chapter V and in the preceding sections of this chapter we were concerned with the solution in integers of indeterminate equations of higher degree in two unknowns. From a geometrical point of view the solution of such equations is equivalent to finding points with integer coordinates on algebraic curves. We were mostly concerned with cubic equations. We were looking for solutions of equations of the type $f(x, y) = 1$ among the algebraic units, i.e., among the solutions of the equation

$$N(x_1, x_2, x_3) = 1,$$

where N is a Dirichlet form, all of whose solutions can be found by means of a certain periodic algorithm. The difficulty of finding the solutions consisted in selecting from the known infinite sequence of solutions some special solutions of a certain "degenerate" type.

In this section we are concerned with the solution of binary cubic equations in rational numbers. This problem differs materially from the foregoing one. For a wide class of these equations the form of the general solution, if a solution exists, is reminiscent of the form of the solution of

$$N(x_1, x_2, x_3) = 1$$

(N is the Dirichlet form), whose solution is determined in terms of the units of the region. Namely, all the solutions are obtained from the "basic solutions" by means of operations which are reminiscent of exponentiation and multiplication of fundamental units. The exceptions to the rule also represent a wide class of equations.

The solution of the binary equation $\Phi(u, v) = 0$, where $\Phi(u, v)$ is in general not homogeneous in u and v, in rational numbers u, v is obviously equivalent to the solution of homogeneous ternary equations in integers.

In fact, let the solution of $\Phi(u, v) = 0$ be

$$u = \frac{x}{z}, \quad v = \frac{y}{z},$$

where z is the common denominator of u and v. Multiplying by z^3, we see that x, y, z are integer solutions of the homogeneous ternary equation

$$z^3\Phi\left(\frac{x}{z}, \frac{y}{z}\right) = F(x, y, z) = 0.$$

Conversely, to every solution in integers of $F(x, y, z) = 0$ corresponds for $z \neq 0$ a solution in rationals of the binary equation

$$\Phi(u, v) = F(u, v, 1) = 0.$$

Thus to proportional solutions of the equation $F(x, y, z) = 0$ corresponds the same solution of $\Phi(u, v) = 0$ and conversely to every solution of the second equation correspond infinitely many proportional solutions of the first equation.

To the solutions of $F(x, y, z) = 0$ with $z = 0$ there actually corresponds no solution of $\Phi(u, v) = 0$. However, for simplicity and in order not to make exceptions, it is convenient to include among the rational solutions of $\Phi(u, v) = 0$ the solutions of the form $(x/0, y/0)$ with the understanding that they correspond to the solutions $(x, y, 0)$ of the equation $F(x, y, z) = 0$.

Such solutions will be called "infinitely distant." No solution of $\Phi(u, v)$ will correspond to the trivial solution $(0, 0, 0)$ of $F(x, y, z) = 0$.

In the geometrical interpretation the rational solutions of $\Phi(u, v) = 0$ are points with rational coordinates on certain curves. To the infinitely distant solutions correspond infinitely distant points with rational coordinates, i.e., the rational directions of the infinite branches of the curve. In what follows we will use the geometrical terminology.

The distribution of rational points on an algebraic curve depends on the genus of the curve, which is defined as $(m - 1)/2$, where m is the connectivity of the complex curve (more precisely of the Riemann surface) $\Phi(u, v) = 0$, which is a two-dimensional manifold in a four-dimensional space.

The genus of an indecomposable curve is given by the formula

$$p = \frac{(n - 1)(n - 2)}{2} - d,$$

where p is the genus, n is the degree of the curve and d is the number of double points (where a ν-fold point is counted as $\nu(\nu - 1)/2$ double points for obvious geometrical reasons).

A cubic curve can be of genus zero or one, depending on whether it has a double point or not. An indecomposable cubic curve cannot have more than one double point.

Curves of genus zero are also called unicursal curves.

We shall first solve the problem of the distribution of rational points on unicursal cubic curves by showing that a unicursal cubic curve whose equation has rational coefficients contains infinitely many rational points. We shall give a method for finding these points.

In fact, suppose that the cubic curve

$$\Phi(u, v) = 0$$

is unicursal, i.e., it has a double point.

The coordinates of the double point, as is well known, satisfy the equations

$$\left.\begin{aligned} \Phi\ (u, v) &= 0, \\ \Phi'_u (u, v) &= 0, \\ \Phi'_v (u, v) &= 0. \end{aligned}\right\} \qquad (*)$$

These equations have rational coefficients. Therefore the coordinates (u, v) must be algebraic. Let $R(u, v)$ be the field obtained by adjoining the numbers u and v to the rational field. Since the equations $(*)$ have rational coefficients, they are satisfied by the conjugates (u', v'), etc., of (u, v). From this it follows that if the field $R(u, v)$ differs from the field of rationals, then the curve $\Phi(u, v) = 0$ would have more than one double point, which is impossible. Therefore $R(u, v)$ coincides with the field of rationals and therefore u and v are both rational.

Hence we have shown that the double point of a unicursal cubic curve with rational coefficients has rational coordinates.

Consider the pencil of straight lines

$$v - v_0 = t(u - u_0)$$

passing through the double point with a rational slope t.

Every straight line of this pencil will intersect the curve $\Phi(u, v) = 0$ in another point besides the double point, and this point will also have rational coordinates. In fact the cubic equation with rational coefficients

$$\Phi(u, v_0 + t(u - u_0)) = 0,$$

which is the result of the simultaneous solution of the given curve and the straight line, has a rational double root u_0 and therefore the third root of this equation is also rational.

Hence to every rational value of t in the equation of the pencil of lines corresponds a rational point on the curve $\Phi(u, v) = 0$.

The converse is also obviously true; namely, that every rational point on the curve $\Phi(u, v) = 0$ corresponds to a rational value of t, since the slope of the line connecting any rational point on the curve with the rational double point is rational.

Hence we obtain all the rational points by solving simultaneously the equations

$$\Phi(u, v) = 0 \quad \text{and} \quad v - v_0 = t(u - u_0)$$

in general and then letting the parameter t assume all rational values.

Hence the problem of rational points on unicursal cubic curves is completely solved and we shall be concerned in what follows only with the more interesting case of curves of genus 1 without double points.

First of all we note two almost obvious theorems which, however, are very important in what follows.

THEOREM 1. *A tangent to a cubic curve at a rational point intersects the curve at another rational point.*

THEOREM 2. *A secant connecting two rational points of a cubic curve intersects the curve in a third rational point.*

PROOF. Let $v - v_0 = t(u - u_0)$ be the equation of the secant connecting two rational points of the curve $f(u, v) = 0$ or of a tangent at a rational point. In both cases this equation obviously has rational coefficients. The cubic equation

$$\Phi(u, v_0 + t(u - u_0)) = 0,$$

which is the result of the simultaneous solution of the given curve and a straight line, also has rational coefficients. This equation has two known rational roots if the line is a secant and a known rational double root if the line is a tangent, Therefore the third root u of this equation, which is the abscissa of the point of intersection under consideration, is also rational.

The ordinate v is also rational, since v is expressible rationally in terms of u. This proves both theorems.

H. Poincaré conjectured that all rational points on a cubic curve can be obtained from a finite number of basic points by means of the operation of constructing secants and tangents. Poincaré's conjecture was first proved by Mordell in 1922. Mordell's proof was somewhat simplified and considerably generalized by A. Weil in several papers on this subject.

We shall give here A. Weil's proof of Mordell's theorem, but will not take up its generalizations. For this we will need some auxiliary transformations which we shall take up in the next section.

§80. BIRATIONAL TRANSFORMATIONS

Two algebraic curves $f(u, v)$ and $f_1(u_1, v_1)$ are said to be connected by a birational transformation if all the coordinates of the second curve are rationally expressible in terms of the coordinates of the first and conversely. Obviously the problems of finding rational points on curves connected by a birational transformation are identical in case the coefficients in the transformation of points of one curve into the other are rational in both directions.

We shall show that every cubic curve whose equation has rational coefficients can be transformed by means of a birational transformation with rational coefficients into a special canonical form, provided the original curve contains at least one rational point.

In fact let the curve

$$f(u, v) = Au^3 + Bu^2v + Cuv^2 + Dv^3 + Eu^2 + Fuv + Gv^2 + Hu + Kv + M = 0$$

have a rational point (u_0, v_0).

We transform the origin into the point of intersection (u_1, v_1) of the curve $f(u, v) = 0$ with the straight line that is tangent to it at the point (u_0, v_0), and then rotate the coordinate axes so that the new axis Ou coincides with the tangent at the point (u_0, v_0). With a proper choice of scale this transformation will be birational with rational coefficients. The equation of the curve after this transformation will be

$$A'u^3 + B'u^2v + C'uv^2 + D'v^3 + E'u^2 + F'uv + G'v^2 + H'u + K'v = 0.$$

This equation has no constant term.

We next pass a pencil of lines through the new origin of coordinates. Every line in this pencil will intersect the curve at the origin and at two more points, whose coordinates can be found by solving a certain quadratic equation

In fact, letting $v = tu$, we get

$$(A' + B't + C't^2 + D't^3)\, u^3 + (E' + F't + G't^2)\, u^2 + (H' + K't)\, u = 0,$$

from which either

$$u = 0$$

or

$$u = \frac{-E' - F't - G't^2 \pm \sqrt{(E' + F't + G't^2)^2 - 4(H' + K't)(A' + B't + C't^2 + D't^3)}}{2(A' + B't + C't^2 + D't^3)}$$

Denoting $\pm\sqrt{(E' + F't + G't^2)^2 - 4(H' + K't)(A' + B't + C't^2 + D't^3)}$ by s we find that the given curve is connected by a birational transformation with rational coefficients to a quartic curve

$$s^2 = (E' + F't + G't^2)^2 - 4(H' + K't)(A' + B't + C't^2 + D't^3).$$

In fact

$$u = \frac{-E' - F't - G't^2 + s}{2(A' + B't + C't^2 + D't^3)},$$
$$v = tu$$

and conversely

$$t = \frac{v}{u},$$

$$s = E' + F't + G't^2 + 2u(A' + B't + C't^2 + D't^3).$$

Since the Ou axis is tangent to the given curve it follows that the quadratic equation defining u must have a double root at $t = 0$. This is possible if and only if

$$E'^2 - 4A'H' = 0.$$

Hence the constant term on the right-hand side of the quartic curve

$$s^2 = (E' + F't + G't^2)^2 - 4(A' + B't + C't^2 + D't^3)(H' + K't)$$

is zero.

We write this equation in a simpler form, denoting the coefficients of the right-hand side by a, b, c, d. Then

$$s^2 = at + bt^2 + ct^3 + dt^4.$$

Multiplying both sides by $4a^2/t^4$ and letting

$$\frac{2as}{t^2} = \eta', \quad \frac{a}{t} + \frac{b}{3a} = \xi',$$

we get a birational transformation.

After this transformation our curve becomes

$$\eta'^2 = 4\xi'^3 - g_2'\xi' - g_3',$$

where g_2' and g_3' are rational constants which are expressible simply in terms of a, b, c, d. Finally, making the birational transformation

$$\eta' = \alpha^3\eta, \quad \xi' = \alpha^2\xi,$$

where α is a suitably chosen rational number, we transform the equation into

$$\eta^2 = 4\xi^3 - g_2\xi - g_3,$$

where g_2 and g_3 are rational integers that cannot be divided by the fourth and sixth powers, respectively, of any number, other than 1.

The curve

$$\eta^2 = 4\xi^3 - g_2\xi - g_3$$

is connected by a birational transformation to the given curve

$$f(u, v) = 0.$$

The curve of the type

$$\eta^2 = 4\xi^3 - g_2\xi - g_3$$

is known as the canonical form of the Weierstrass cubic curve.

The right-hand side of the equation of the canonical form of the Weierstrass curve does not have a multiple root if we start with a curve of genus 1, for in the contrary case the canonical curve and therefore also the given curve would have a double root.

This transformation must be slightly modified in case the point of intersection of the tangent line with the curve is an infinitely distant point, as it makes no sense to transform the origin into the point at infinity. However the transformation is still possible, as can be seen by introducing homogeneous coordinates.

The transformation of cubic curves without double points to the canonical form introduces a useful analytic tool for studying the curve.

In fact the curve

$$\eta^2 = 4\xi^3 - g_2\xi - g_3$$

can be uniformized by means of the Weierstrass elliptic function

$$\xi = \wp(t),$$
$$\eta = \wp'(t).$$

The infinitely distant point on the curve corresponds to the value of the parameter $t = 0$.

It is known furthermore that the values t_1, t_2, t_3 of the parameter corresponding to three collinear points satisfy the congruence

$$t_1 + t_2 + t_3 \equiv 0 \pmod{\omega_1, \omega_2},$$

where ω_1 and ω_2 are the periods of the elliptic function $\wp(t)$. Therefore the operation of constructing rational points by means of secants and tangents through other points corresponds to the operations of addition and duplication of the argument of the elliptic function (with a change in sign).

Since addition is associative, the operation of constructing new points by means of the secant is also in a sense associative. In fact, let T_1, T_2, T_3 be three points on the curve corresponding to the values of the parameter t_1, t_2, t_3.

The point T corresponding to the value of the parameter $-t_1 - t_2 - t_3$ can be constructed in various ways.

Thus the construction of T based on the representation of $-t_1 - t_2 - t_3$ in the form $-(t_1 + t_2) - t_3$ is as follows.

1. Draw a secant through the points T_1 and T_2. The third point N' of intersection of the secant with the curve corresponds to the value of the parameter $-t_1 - t_2$.

2. Construct the point N that is symmetric with the point N' with respect to the $O\xi$-axis. The point N corresponds to the value of the parameter $t_1 + t_2$.

3. Draw a secant through the points N and T_3. The third point of intersection of the secant with the curve is the desired point T.

If we represent $-t_1 - t_2 - t_3$ as $-t_1 - (t_2 + t_3)$ we obtain a different method of construction of T.

1. Find the point of intersection M' of the curve with the secant T_2T_3.

2. Find the point M that is symmetric with M'.

3. Find the point of intersection T of the curve with MT_1.

These two methods must give the same point, a fact which is not immediately obvious. However, the associativity of the operation of constructing points by means of secants can be proved without using elliptic functions.

In what follows the construction of a point that is symmetric with the point of intersection of the curve with the secant T_1T_2 will be called the addition of the points T_1 and T_2, while the construction of a point that is symmetric with the point of intersection of the tangent at the point T_1 with the curve is called the duplication of the point T_1.

We repeat that the commutativity of the addition of points is geometrically obvious, while the associativity of addition can be proved by means of elliptic functions, but it can also be proved independently, for instance by actual computation.

In what follows it is not necessary to make use of elliptic functions as long as the commutativity and associativity of the addition of points is established. However elliptic functions will be used whenever they simplify the formulation.

§81. PROOF OF MORDELL'S THEOREM GIVEN BY WEIL

We now give a proof of the fundamental theorem of this theory, that all rational points on a cubic curve can be obtained from a finite number of basic points by constructing the secants and tangents, i.e., by means of successive additions of the arguments of the elliptic functions corresponding to rational points. It is sufficient to prove this theorem for curves given in a canonical form. It will be more convenient to choose a canonical form which differs slightly from the Weierstrass canonical form, namely

$$u^2 = v^3 - h_2 v - h_3,$$

which can be obtained from

$$\eta^2 = 4\xi^3 - g_2\xi - g_3$$

by the substitution $\eta = u/4$, $\xi = v/4$.

The numbers h_2 and h_3 can be taken as integers that are not divisible by the square and cube, respectively, of an integer different from 1.

The right-hand side of the canonical form

$$v^3 - h_2 v - h_3$$

has no multiple roots. Therefore the equation

$$v^3 - h_2 v - h_3 = 0$$

defines a certain reducible or irreducible cubic region. We will denote the roots of $v^3 - h_2 v - h_3 = 0$ by ρ, ρ', ρ''. The equation

$$u^2 = v^3 - h_2 v - h_3$$

can be written as

$$N(v - \rho) = u^2.$$

The solution of this equation is equivalent to finding all integer and rational numbers in a cubic field whose norms are perfect squares of special binomial numbers of the type $v - \rho$.

Among the numbers whose norms are perfect squares will be found all the squares of the elements of the cubic field, besides many other numbers.

We divide all these numbers into classes, uniting into one class all the numbers that differ from each other by a factor which is the square of a number in the field. The squares of all the numbers of the field go into a particular class, which we shall call the principal class. There are infinitely many classes for a given cubic field. The classes can be multiplied together, since the product of two numbers taken from two given classes belongs to a uniquely defined third class. The principal class plays the role of a unit class in this multiplication. The square of any class gives the principal class. As we have already mentioned, a cubic field has infinitely many classes of numbers whose norms are perfect squares. Nevertheless the following theorem holds.

THEOREM 1. *The binomial numbers* $v - \rho$ *whose norms are perfect squares belong to only a finite number of classes.*

PROOF. Let $N(v - \rho) = u^2$. We represent the rational number v by the fraction a/b in its lowest terms and show first of all that the denominator b must be a perfect square. Obviously $N(a - b\rho) = b^3u^2$ and so

$$bN(a - b\rho) = (b^2u)^2,$$

so that the product of two relatively prime numbers is a perfect square and therefore each of the factors must be a perfect square and we have

$$b = c^2 \qquad (a, c) = 1$$
$$N(a - c^2\rho) = n^2.$$

The numbers $v - \rho$ and $a - c^2\rho$ belong to the same class of numbers whose norms are perfect squares, so that it is sufficient to show that the numbers $a - c^2\rho$ belong to only a finite number of classes.

We now factor the integer $a - c^2\rho$ into prime ideals and exhibit the square factor, namely

$$a - c^2\rho = \mathfrak{a}\mathfrak{b}^2,$$

where the ideal $\mathfrak{a}$ is not divisible by the square of a prime ideal.

Consider the number $\lambda = (a - c^2\rho')(a - c^2\rho'')$. Since $\lambda(a - c^2\rho)$ is a square of a rational integer, λ must be divisible by the ideal $\mathfrak{a}$.

Combining the congruences

$$a - c^2\rho \equiv 0 \pmod{\mathfrak{a}},$$

$$\lambda = (a - c^2\rho')(a - c^2\rho'') \equiv 0 \pmod{\mathfrak{a}},$$

we obtain

$$c^4(\rho - \rho')(\rho - \rho'') \equiv 0 \pmod{\mathfrak{a}}.$$

But c and $\mathfrak{a}$ are relatively prime, therefore $\mathfrak{a}$ divides the different $(\rho - \rho')(\rho - \rho'')$ of ρ and hence there are only a finite number of choices for $\mathfrak{a}$. It is obvious that for numbers $\mathfrak{a}\mathfrak{b}^2$ belonging to the same class the ideals $\mathfrak{a}$ are equal and the ideals $\mathfrak{b}$ are equivalent. Conversely the numbers $\mathfrak{a}\mathfrak{b}^2$ for which the ideal $\mathfrak{a}$ is given and the ideals $\mathfrak{b}$ are equivalent can differ only by multipliers which are units and squares. Therefore the numbers $\mathfrak{a}\mathfrak{b}^2$ for a given ideal $\mathfrak{a}$ and for a given class of ideals $\mathfrak{b}$ can fall into two classes for fields with negative discriminants and into four classes for fields with positive discriminant.

The theorem is therefore proved, since for binomial numbers there is only a finite number of ideals $\mathfrak{a}$ and only a finite number of classes to which the ideal $\mathfrak{b}$ can belong. Therefore the numbers $\mathfrak{a}\mathfrak{b}^2$ with a given ideal $\mathfrak{a}$ and a given class of ideals for $\mathfrak{b}$ can be distributed at most in four classes.

Hence, although all the numbers with square norms are distributed in infinitely many classes, the binomial numbers $v - \rho$ with square norms are distributed in a finite number of classes. All the classes form a multiplicative group. This is not true for the binomial numbers $v - \rho$, since a product of two binomial numbers need not be binomial. However we can construct from two binomial numbers having a square norm a third number as follows. Every binomial number $v - \rho$ with a square norm u^2 corresponds to a point (u, v) with rational coordinates on the cubic curve

$$u^2 = v^3 - h_2 v - h_3.$$

Such points are "additive," i.e., we can add the arguments of the elliptic functions corresponding to these points.

THEOREM 2. *If two points (u_1, v_1) and (u_2, v_2) of the curve $u^2 = v^3 - h_2 v - h_3$ are "added," the classes to which $v_1 - \rho$ and $v_2 - \rho$ belong are multiplied.*

PROOF. As we know, the "sum" of two points (u_1, v_1) and (u_2, v_2) is the point symmetric with the point of intersection of the curve with the secant connecting (u_1, v_1) with (u_2, v_2). The abscissa v of the "sum" coincides with the abscissa of the point of intersection of the curve and the secant.

In order to determine v we eliminate u between the curve $u^2 = v^3 - h_2 v - h_3$ and the secant

$$u - u_1 = \frac{u_2 - u_1}{v_2 - v_1}(v - v_1).$$

Hence v is a root of the cubic equation

$$v^3 - h_2 v - h_3 = \left[u_1 + \frac{u_2 - u_1}{v_2 - v_1}(v - v_1)\right]^2,$$

whose roots are also v_1 and v_2.

If we set $v - \rho = \lambda$, $v_1 - \rho = \lambda_1$, $v_2 - \rho = \lambda_2$, the equation becomes

$$\lambda^3 + H_1\lambda^2 + H_2\lambda = \left[u_1 + \frac{u_2 - u_1}{\lambda_2 - \lambda_1}(\lambda - \lambda_1)\right]^2$$

The left-hand side has no constant term, since $v^3 - h_2 v - h_3$ is divisible by $v - \rho$. The roots of this equation are $v - \rho$, $v_1 - \rho$, $v_2 - \rho$. Since the product of the roots is equal to the constant term with the sign changed, we have

$$(v - \rho)(v_1 - \rho)(v_2 - \rho) = \left[u_1 - \lambda_1 \frac{u_2 - u_1}{\lambda_2 - \lambda_1}\right]^2 = \left[\frac{u_1\lambda_2 - u_2\lambda_1}{v_2 - v_1}\right]^2,$$

from which

$$v - \rho = (v_1 - \rho)(v_2 - \rho)\cdot\left[\frac{\frac{u_2}{\lambda_2} - \frac{u_1}{\lambda_1}}{v_2 - v_1}\right]^2$$

and the theorem follows.

THEOREM 3. *The number $v_2 - \rho$ corresponding to the point (u_2, v_2) which is the duplication of the point (u_1, v_1) belongs to the principal class, i.e., it is a square of an element of the field under consideration.*

PROOF. The equation

$$v^3 - h_2 v - h_3 = \left[u_1 + \frac{3v_1^2 - h_2}{2u_1}(v - v_1)\right]^2,$$

being the result of eliminating u from the equation of the curve and the tangent at the point (u_1, v_1), has a double root v_1 and a single root v_2.

Letting $v - \rho = \lambda$, $v_1 - \rho = \lambda_1$, we get an equation in λ having a double root λ_1 and single root $v_2 - \rho$. We have

$$\lambda^3 + H_1\lambda^2 + H_2\lambda = \left[u_1 + \frac{3v_1^2 - h_2}{2u_1}(\lambda - \lambda_1)\right]^2.$$

From this it follows that

$$(v_2-\rho)\lambda_1^2=\left[u_1-\frac{3v_1^2-h_2}{2u_1}\lambda_1\right]^2$$

and finally

$$v_2-\rho=\left[\frac{u_1}{\lambda_1}-\frac{3v_1^2-h_2}{2u_1}\right]^2,$$

from which the theorem follows.

THEOREM 4 (CONVERSE TO THEOREM 3). *If the number $v_2 - \rho$, corresponding to a rational point (u_2, v_2), belongs to the principal class of numbers with square norm, then the point (u_2, v_2) can be obtained as a duplication of another rational point (u_1, v_1).*

PROOF. Let $v_2 - \rho = (A + B\rho + C\rho^2)^2$, where A, B, and C are rational numbers. Equating the coefficients of $1, \rho, \rho^2$ on both sides of this equation (which must be done for reducible as well as irreducible regions), we obtain

$$\begin{aligned} A^2+2BCh_3 &= v_2, \\ 2AB+2BCh_2+C^2h_3 &= -1, \\ B^2+2AC+C^2h_2 &= 0. \end{aligned}$$

Eliminating A from the second and third equation, we get

$$B^3 - h_2BC^2 - h_3C^3 = C,$$

or dividing out C^3, we get

$$\left(\frac{1}{C}\right)^2 = \left(\frac{B}{C}\right)^3 - h_2\left(\frac{B}{C}\right) - h_3.$$

We see that $\left(\frac{1}{C}, \frac{B}{C}\right)$ is a rational point of the curve

$$u^2 = v^3 - h_2v - h_3.$$

Denoting $1/C = u_1$, $B/C = v_1$, we obtain after some simple calculation that

$$v_2-\rho=\left[\frac{u_1}{v_1-\rho}-\frac{3v_1^2-h_2}{2u_1}\right]^2,$$

from which the theorem follows.

THEOREM 5. *The result of "addition" of two points, for which the corresponding numbers $v - \rho$ belong to the same class, is a point which can be ob-*

tained by duplication of some other point.

The theorem follows from Theorems 2 and 4.

THEOREM 6. *All the rational points on the curve* $u^2 = v^3 - h_2 v - h_3$ *can be obtained from a finite number of basic rational points by the addition process.*

PROOF. We distribute all the rational points on the curve $u^2 = v^3 - h_2 v - h_3$ into classes by putting into the same class all the points for which $v - \rho$ belongs to the same class. As we already know, there are only a finite number of such classes. We select a representative of each class. Let $(u_1, v_1), (u_2, v_2), \cdots, (u_k, v_k)$ be the set of these representatives. We now apply to another rational point (u, v) an operation which we shall call reduction. We find among the representatives of all the classes the point (u_j, v_j) which belongs to the same class as (u, v). We then add the points (u_j, v_j) and (u, v), thus obtaining a new point, which by Theorem 5 will be the duplication of some other point (u', v').

We can next apply the reduction process to the point (u', v'), obtaining the point (u'', v''), and so on. We next show that by means of this reduction process we can "descend" in a finite number of steps to one of the points of a finite set. We denote by $t_1, t_2, \cdots, t_k$ the arguments of the representatives of all the classes and by $t'_1, t'_2, \cdots, t'_s$ the arguments of the finite set of points to which the reduction process leads, and we let t be the argument of the initial point. Then

$$t = -t_{i_1} + 2[-t_{i_2} + \cdots + 2[-t_{i_m} + 2t'_j] \cdots],$$

so that t is represented as a linear form with rational integer coefficients in terms of the arguments $t_1, t_2, \cdots, t_k, t'_1, t'_2, \cdots, t'_s$ of a finite set of points, which proves the theorem.

It remains to show that the reduction process leads in a finite number of steps to a point of some finite set.

In order to do this we need some estimates.

We replace the rational numbers, u, v by integers x, y, z as in Theorem 1 by the substitution $v = x/z^2$ with x and z relatively prime. Then $u = y/z^3$, where x, y, z satisfy the equation

$$y^2 = x^3 - h_2 x z^4 - h_3 z^6.$$

We call the *measure* of a rational point the maximum of x and z^2. Obviously there is only a finite number of points of bounded measure.

We show first of all that if L is the measure of a point (u_2, v_2) of the principal class, then the measure of (u_1, v_1), whose duplication gives (u_2, v_2), is less than $cL^{1/3}$, where c is a constant depending only on h_2 and h_3.

In fact the duplication formula gives

$$v_2-\rho=\left[\frac{u_1}{v_1-\rho}-\frac{3v_1^2-h_2}{2u_1}\right]^2.$$

Letting

$$v_2=\frac{x_2}{z_2^2};\qquad u_1=\frac{y_1}{z_1^3};\qquad v_1=\frac{x_1}{z_1^2};$$

$$x_1-z_1^2\rho=\lambda_1;\qquad x_1-z_1^2\rho'=\lambda_1';\qquad x_1-z_1^2\rho''=\lambda_1'',$$

we get after simple calculations

$$\frac{x_2}{z_2^2}-\rho=\frac{(\lambda_1\lambda_1'+\lambda_1\lambda_1''-\lambda_1'\lambda_1'')^2}{4y_1^2z_1^2},$$

$$\frac{x_2}{z_2^2}-\rho'=\frac{(\lambda_1'\lambda_1''+\lambda_1'\lambda_1-\lambda_1''\lambda_1)^2}{4y_1^2z_1^2},$$

$$\frac{x_2}{z_2^2}-\rho''=\frac{(\lambda_1''\lambda_1+\lambda_1''\lambda_1'-\lambda\lambda_1')^2}{4y_1^2z_1^2},$$

from which it follows that

$$z_2=\frac{1}{k}\cdot 2y_1z_1,$$

where k is a divisor of $\lambda_1\lambda_1'+\lambda_1\lambda_1''-\lambda_1'\lambda_1''$, $\lambda_1'\lambda_1''+\lambda_1'\lambda_1-\lambda_1''\lambda_1$, $\lambda_1''\lambda_1+\lambda_1''\lambda_1'-\lambda\lambda_1'$. Obviously $(k, z_1)=1$, since

$$\lambda_1\lambda_1'+\lambda_1\lambda_1''-\lambda_1'\lambda_1''\equiv x_1^2 \pmod{z_1},$$

and x_1 and z_1 are relatively prime. Moreover k divides $2\lambda_1\lambda_1'$, $2\lambda_1'\lambda_1''$, $2\lambda_1''\lambda_1'$, and hence also

$$2\lambda_1\lambda_1'(\lambda_1-\lambda_1')+2\lambda_1'\lambda_1''(\lambda_1'-\lambda_1'')+2\lambda_1''\lambda_1(\lambda_1''-\lambda_1)$$
$$=-2(\lambda_1-\lambda_1')(\lambda_1'-\lambda_1'')(\lambda_1''-\lambda_1)=-2z_1^6\sqrt{\Delta},$$

where Δ is the discriminant of ρ. Since $(k, z_1)=1$ it follows that k divides $2\sqrt{\Delta}$. Therefore k is a constant bounded from above and depending only on h_2 and h_3.

Hence

$$z_2^2=\frac{4}{k^2}y_1^2z_1^2=\frac{4}{k^2}z_1^2\lambda_1\lambda_1'\lambda_1'',$$

and

$$\begin{aligned}
\lambda_2 &= x_2 - z_2^2\rho = \frac{1}{k^2}(\lambda_1\lambda_1' + \lambda_1\lambda_1'' - \lambda_1'\lambda_1'')^2,\\
\lambda_2' &= x_2 - z_2^2\rho' = \frac{1}{k^2}(\lambda_1'\lambda_1'' + \lambda_1'\lambda_1 - \lambda_1''\lambda_1)^2,\\
\lambda_2'' &= x_2 - z_2^2\rho'' = \frac{1}{k^2}(\lambda_1''\lambda_1 + \lambda_1''\lambda_1' - \lambda_1\lambda_1')^2.
\end{aligned} \qquad (*)$$

Suppose first that z_1 is small, so that $z_1^2 < L^{1/6}$.

If we assume now that $|x_1| > cL^{1/3}$ we arrive at a contradiction if c is sufficiently large. In fact if $|x_1| > c_1 L^{1/3}$, then

$$|x_1 - z_1^2\rho_1| > c_2 L^{1/3}; \quad |x_1 - z_1^2\rho_1'| > c_2 L^{1/3}; \quad |x_1 - z_1^2\rho_1'| > c_2 L^{1/3}$$

and therefore

$$z_2^2 = \frac{4}{k^2} z_1^2 (x_1 - z_1^2\rho_1)(x_1 - z_1^2\rho_1')(x_1 - z_1^2\rho_1'') > \frac{4}{k^2} c_2^3 L,$$

which is impossible with a sufficiently large c_2.

Suppose next that $z_1^2 > L^{1/6}$. In this case we proceed differently.

It follows from $(*)$ that

$$\lambda_1'\lambda_1'' = \frac{k}{2}\left(\sqrt{x_2 - z_2^2\rho'} + \sqrt{x_2 - z_2^2\rho''}\right),$$

from which

$$\begin{aligned}
\lambda_1 &= \frac{k^2}{4}\cdot\frac{z_2^2}{z_1^2}\cdot\frac{1}{\lambda_1'\lambda_1''} = \frac{k}{2}\cdot\frac{z_2^2}{z_1^2\left(\sqrt{x_2 - z_2^2\rho'} + \sqrt{x_2 - z_2^2\rho''}\right)}\\
&= \frac{k}{2}\cdot\frac{\sqrt{x_2 - z_2^2\rho'} - \sqrt{x_2 - z_2^2\rho''}}{z_1^2(\rho'' - \rho')}
\end{aligned}$$

and therefore

$$|\lambda_1| < c\frac{L^{1/2}}{z_1^2} < cL^{1/3},$$

where c is a constant depending only on h_2 and h_3. This gives $|\lambda_1'| < cL^{1/3}$, from which follow the same estimates for x_1 and z_1^2.

We now consider the measure of the sum of two points. Let the measure of (u_1, v_1) be M and the measure of (u_2, v_2) be L.

From the addition formula it follows that

$$\frac{x}{z^2} - \rho = \frac{[y_2 z_1(x_1 - z_1^2\rho) - y_1 z_2(x_2 - z_2^2\rho)]^2}{(x_2 z_1^2 - x_1 z_2^2)^2 (x_1 - z_1^2\rho)(x_2 - z_2^2\rho)},$$

from which

$$z \leq x_2 z_1^2 - x_1 z_2^2,$$

since the numerator is obviously divisible by $(x_1 - z_1^2 \rho)(x_2 - z_2^2 \rho)$. From this it follows that the measure of the point (u, v) which is the sum of (u_1, v_1) and (u_2, v_2) does not exceed cM^2L^2, where c is a constant.

We apply these results to estimate the measure of the points arising in the descent. Let M_0 be the greatest measure of all the representatives of the classes of points. Let L be the measure of the initial rational point. Taking the sum of the initial point and one of the representative points we obtain a point of measure not exceeding $cM_0^2L^2$. This point is the duplication of a point (u', v') whose measure is less than $c'M_0^{2/3}L^{2/3}$. This measure will be in general less than the measure L of the initial point. But after a finite number of steps this diminution of measure must stop, since otherwise there would be an infinity of points with measure less than L. The measure will not diminish only if $c'M_0^{2/3}L^{2/3} \geq L$, which can happen only if $L < c'^3 M_0^2$.

Hence from any given point one can descend in a finite number of steps to a point with measure $\leq c'^3 M_0^2$. There are only a finite number of such points. This proves the theorem.

§82. ON THE EQUATION $x^3 + y^3 = Az^3$

The equation in the title of this section is a special case of the equations considered in the preceding section. However, it is convenient to consider it separately, using the same idea of descent but dividing the arguments by 3 instead of 2. By doing so it is possible for us to obtain rather accurate estimates for the number of solutions of the equation.

1. Consider the curve

$$x^3 + y^3 = A \tag{1}$$

and its parametric representation

$$x = x(t) = \frac{9A + \wp'(t)}{6\wp(t)},$$

$$y = y(t) = \frac{9A - \wp'(t)}{6\wp(t)}.$$

It is known that the function $\wp(t)$ and therefore also $x(t)$ and $y(t)$ have a real period ω and a complex period $\omega' = \omega \cdot e^{2\pi i/3}$

The point (x, y) traverses the curve (1) as t goes from 0 to ω. The value $t = 0$ corresponds to an infinitely distant point on the curve. To the point $t = \omega/2$ corresponds the point $P(\sqrt[3]{A/2}, \sqrt[3]{A/2})$, to $t = \omega/3$ and $t = 2\omega/3$ correspond the points of inflection of the curve $Q_1(\sqrt[3]{A}, 0)$ and $Q_2(0, \sqrt[3]{A})$. The point P is rationally only for $A = 2k^3$ and the points Q are rational only for $A = k^3$. For all other values of A the values of the argument giving rational points are incommeasurable with the period.

Simple algebraic operations with the argument t correspond to simple geometric operations with the points of the curve. For instance:

1) If the point $M(x, y)$ corresponds to the argument t, then the point $M(y, x)$ corresponds to the argument $-t$.

2) If t_1 corresponds to the point $M_1(x_1, y_1)$ and t_2 to the point $M_2(x_2, y_2)$, then $-t_1 - t_2$ corresponds to the point of intersection M_3 of the curve with the secant M_1M_2.

3) If t corresponds to M, then $-2t$ corresponds to the point of intersection N of the curve with the tangent at the point M.

From this it is easy to give formulas for calculating new solutions of $x^3 + y^3 = A$ from the known solutions.

I. If the solution (x, y, z) corresponds to the argument t, then to $-t$ corresponds the solution (y, x, z).

II. If t_1 corresponds to (x_1, y_1, z_1) and t_2 to (x_2, y_2, z_2), then (X, Y, Z) corresponds to $-t_1 - t_2$, where

$$\left.\begin{aligned} X &= Az_1z_2(x_2z_1 - x_1z_2) + y_1y_2(x_1y_2 - x_2y_1), \\ Y &= Az_1z_2(y_2z_1 - y_1z_2) + x_1x_2(y_1x_2 - y_2x_1), \\ Z &= x_1x_2(x_2z_1 - x_1z_2) + y_1y_2(y_2z_1 - y_1z_2). \end{aligned}\right\} \tag{2}$$

("addition formulas").

If $t_1 = t_2$, then the addition formulas do not hold. In this case we have "duplication formulas."

III. If t_1 corresponds to (x_1, y_1, z_1), then $-2t_1$ corresponds to (X_2, Y_2, Z_2), where

$$\left.\begin{aligned} X_2 &= -x_1(x_1^3 + 2y_1^3), \\ Y_2 &= y_1(2x_1^3 + y_1^3), \\ Z_2 &= z_1(y_1^3 - x_1^3). \end{aligned}\right\} \tag{3}$$

Besides this we need the "triplication formulas."

IV. If t_1 corresponds to (x_1, y_1, z_1), then $3t_1$ corresponds to (X_3, Y_3, Z_3), where

$$\left.\begin{aligned} X_3 &= x_1^9 + 6x_1^6 y_1^3 + 3x_1^3 y_1^6 - y_1^9, \\ Y_3 &= y_1^9 + 6 y_1^6 x_1^3 + 3 y_1^3 x_1^6 - x_1^9, \\ Z_3 &= 3x_1 y_1 z_1 (x_1^6 + x_1^3 y_1^3 + y_1^6). \end{aligned}\right\} \tag{4}$$

It is not hard to verify the following relations:

$$3(x_1 + y_1)(x_1 - z_1\rho)(y_1 - z_1\rho) = (x_1 + y_1 - z_1\rho)^3, \tag{1'}$$

$$3(x_1 - z_1\rho)(x_2 - z_2\rho)(X - Z\rho) = [y_1(x_2 - z_2\rho) - y_2(x_1 - z_1\rho)]^3, \tag{2'}$$

$$3(x_1 + y_1)(x_2 + y_2)(X + Z) = A[z_2(x_1 + y_1) - z_1(x_2 + y_2)]^3, \tag{2''}$$

$$3(x_1\zeta + y_1\zeta^2)(x_2\zeta + y_2\zeta^2)(X\zeta + Y\zeta^2) = A[z_2(x_1\zeta + y_1\zeta^2) - z_1(x_2\zeta + y_2\zeta^2)]^3, \tag{2'''}$$

$$X_2 - Z_2\rho = (x_1 - z_1\rho)(x_1 + z_1\rho)^3, \tag{3'}$$

$$X_2 + Y_2 = (x_1 + y_1)(y_1 - x_1)^3, \tag{3''}$$

$$X_2\zeta + Y_2\zeta^2 = (x_1\zeta + y_1\zeta^2)(y_1\zeta^2 - x_1\zeta)^3, \tag{3'''}$$

$$X_3 - Z_3\rho = (-y^2x + x^2z\rho - yz^2\rho^2)^3, \tag{4'}$$

$$X_3 + Y_3 = 9Ax_1^3 y_1^3 z_1^3, \tag{4''}$$

$$X_3\zeta + Y_3\zeta^2 = \zeta(1 - \zeta)(x_1^3 - y_1^3\zeta^2)^3. \tag{4'''}$$

Formulas (1′) to (4‴) have $\rho = \sqrt[3]{A}$, $\zeta = e^{2\pi i/3}$, the other notation being the same as in (2), (3) and (4).

2. In what follows we shall need the following results from the theory of the field $\Omega(\sqrt[3]{A})$.

If A has no cubic factors and if $A = fg^2$, where f is the product of the primes which divide A to the first power, and g the product of those primes whose squares divide A, then a basis of integers in the field $\Omega(\sqrt[3]{A})$ can be written as $[1, \rho, \bar{\rho}]$ in case $A \not\equiv \pm 1 \pmod 9$, or as $[1, \rho, (1 \pm \rho \pm \bar{\rho})/3]$ in case $A \equiv \pm 1 \pmod 9$, where $\rho = \sqrt[3]{A}$ and $\bar{\rho} = \sqrt[3]{\bar{A}}$, with $\bar{A} = f^2 g$.

In the first case $\Omega(\sqrt[3]{A})$ is called a field of the first kind and in the second, a field of the second kind. In fields of the first kind $3 = \pi_3^3$, while in fields of the second kind $3 = \pi_3^2\pi_1$, where π_3 and π_1 are prime ideals in $\Omega(\rho)$.

We shall assume that A has no cubic factors.

The equation $x^3 + y^3 = Az^3$ can be written as

$$N(x - z\rho) = -y^3.$$

From this it follows that if the binomial number $x - z\rho$ is the cube of some number λ in $\Omega(\rho)$, then $(x, y = -N(\lambda), z)$ is a solution of

$$x^3 + y^3 = Az^3.$$

We prove the following theorem.

THEOREM 1. *If $X - Z\rho = \lambda^3$, where λ is an element of the field $\Omega(\rho)$ and X is relatively prime to A, then the solution $(X, Y = -N(\lambda), Z)$ can be obtained by triplication of the argument of some other solution (x_1, y_1, z_1).*

PROOF. Without loss of generality we can assume that

$$\lambda = a + b\rho + c\bar{\rho},$$

where a, b, c are integers having no common factor.

Then

$$\begin{aligned} X - Z\rho &= (a + b\rho + c\bar{\rho})^3 \\ &= a^3 + Ab^3 + \bar{A}c^3 + 6fgabc + 3\rho(a^2b + fgb^2c + fc^2a) \\ &\quad + 3\bar{\rho}(gab^2 + fgbc^2 + ca^2), \\ Y &= -N(a + b\rho + c\bar{\rho}) = -a^3 - Ab^3 - \bar{A}c^3 + 3fgabc. \end{aligned} \tag{5}$$

From this

$$X = a^3 + Ab^3 + \bar{A}c^3 + 6fgabc, \tag{5'}$$

$$Y = -a^3 - \bar{A}b^3 - Ac^3 + 3fgabc, \tag{5''}$$

$$Z = 3(a^2b + fgb^2c + fc^2a), \tag{5'''}$$

$$gab^2 + fgbc^2 + ca^2 = 0. \tag{6}$$

It follows from (5′) that $(a, A) = 1$ and from (6) that ca^2 is divisible by g. Therefore c is divisible by g, so that $c = gc_1$.

Substituting into (6) and dividing by g, we get

$$ab^2 + Abc_1^2 + c_1a^2 = 0. \tag{6'}$$

We denote $(b, c_1) = d$, $b = db_1$, $c_1 = dc_2$.

Then $(a, d) = 1$, $(b_1, c_2) = 1$.

Substituting into (6′), we obtain

$$ab_1^2d + b_1c_2^2d^2A + c_2a^2 = 0, \tag{6''}$$

from which $c_2 = dc_3$. Substituting into (6″), we get

$$ab_1^2 + b_1 c_3^2 d^3 A + a^2 c_3 = 0. \tag{6'''}$$

From (6''') it follows that $a = c_3^2 a_1$ and therefore

$$a_1 b_1^2 + b_1 A d^3 + a_1^2 c_3^3 = 0, \tag{6''''}$$

and finally $b_1 = a_1^2 b_2$ and hence

$$a_1^3 b_2^2 + A b_2 d^3 + c_3^3 = 0. \tag{7}$$

From (7) we see that c_3^3 is divisible by b_2. On the other hand, $(c_3, b_2) = 1$. Therefore $b_2 = e = \pm 1$.

We rewrite (7) in the form

$$a_1^3 + c_3^3 = A(-ed)^3, \tag{7'}$$

from which it follows that $(a_1, c_3, -ed)$ is a solution of $x^3 + y^3 = Az^3$. Letting $a_1 = x_1$, $c_3 = y_1$, $-ed = z_1$, we obtain

$$a = x_1 y_1^2, \quad b = -x_1^2 z_1, \quad c = g z_1^2 y_1$$

and from (5'), (5'') and (5''') it follows that

$$\left.\begin{aligned} X &= -(x_1^9 + 6x_1^6 y_1^3 + 3x_1^3 y_1^6 - z_1^9), \\ Y &= -(y_1^9 + 6y_1^6 x_1^3 + 3y_1^3 x_1^6 - x_1^9), \\ Z &= -3x_1 y_1 z_1 (x_1^6 + x_1^3 y_1^3 + y_1^6). \end{aligned}\right\} \tag{8}$$

Combining (8) with (6) establishes Theorem 1. This theorem was proved by B. Delone in papers devoted to the equation $ax^3 + y^3 = 1$ in 1916.

THEOREM 2. *In order that the argument of the solution* (X, Y, Z) *be the triple of the argument of some other solution* (x, y, z) *it is necessary and sufficient that* $9(X+Y)^2(X - Z\rho)$ *be the cube of an element of* $\Omega(\rho)$.

PROOF. The necessity of these conditions follows directly from relations (4') and (4'').

To prove the sufficiency we show that we can find X_1, Y_1, Z_1 proportional to X, Y, Z such that $X_1 - Z_1\rho = \lambda^3$ with X_1 relatively prime to A.

Let

$$9(X+Y)^2(X - Z\rho) = \lambda^3. \tag{9}$$

Without loss of generality we can assume that X and Y are relatively prime. Since $X^3 + Y^3 = AZ^3$ and A has no cubic factors, it follows that if $(X, Y) = 1$, then also $(X, AZ) = 1$ and $(Y, AZ) = 1$.

We have

$$9(X+Y)^2(X-Z\rho)=(a+b\rho+c\bar{\rho})^3$$
$$=a^3+Ab^3+\bar{A}c^3+6fgabc+3\rho(a^2b+fgb^2c+fc^2a)$$
$$+3\bar{\rho}(a^2c+gb^2a+fgc^2b)$$

and

$$N[9(X+Y)^2(X-Z\rho)]=-9^3(X+Y)^6\cdot Y^3=[a^3+Ab^3+\bar{A}c^3-3fgabc]^3$$

Thus

$$9X(X+Y)^2=a^3+Ab^3+\bar{A}c^3+6fgabc,$$
$$9Y(X+Y)^2=-a^3-Ab^3-\bar{A}c^3+3fgabc.$$

Adding, we get

$$(X+Y)^3=fgabc.$$

From this it follows that $X+Y$ is divisible by fg. On the other hand the equation $X^3+Y^3=AZ^3$ can be written as

$$(X+Y)[(X+Y)^2-3XY]=fg^2Z^3. \tag{10}$$

Suppose that A is not divisible by 3. Since in this case $3XY$ is relatively prime to A and $(X+Y)^2$ is divisible by all the prime factors of A, the expression $(X+Y)^2-3XY$ is relatively prime to A. Therefore $X+Y$ is divisible by A.

It is obvious that $X+Y$ and $(X+Y)^2-3XY$ are either relatively prime or else have the factor 3 in common. Therefore, either $X+Y=Av^3$ or $X+Y=9Av^3$.

In the first case it follows from (9) that $9(X-Z\rho)=\lambda_1^3$, and the solution $(9X, 9Y, 9Z)$ satisfies the conditions of Theorem 1.

In the second case $X-\rho Y=\lambda_1^3$ and therefore the solution (X, Y, Z) itself satisfies the conditions of Theorem 1.

Suppose that A is divisible by 3. Then $A=3^\sigma f_1g_1^2$, where $\sigma=1$ or 2. In this case $X+Y=3^{\sigma-1}f_1g_1^2v^3$ by (10) and therefore from (9) we have $X-Z\rho=\lambda_1^3$, i.e., again the solution (X, Y, Z) satisfies the conditions of Theorem 1.

REMARK. It is not hard to see that if A is divisible by 3, then the equations

$$(X+Y)^2(X-Z\rho)=\lambda^3 \text{ and } 3(X+Y)^2(X-Z\rho)=\lambda^3$$

are impossible.

THEOREM 3. *In order that the difference of the arguments of the solutions* (x_1, y_1, z_1) *and* (x_2, y_2, z_2) *be the triplication of the argument of some other solution* (x_3, y_3, z_3) *it is necessary and sufficient that*

$$\frac{(x_1 + y_1)^2 (x_1 - z_1\rho)}{(x_2 + y_2)^2 (x_2 - z_2\rho)} = \lambda^3, \tag{11}$$

where λ *is an integer or fractional number of the field* $\Omega(\rho)$.

PROOF. We first prove the sufficiency of the condition. To do this, construct a solution (X, Y, Z) whose argument is the difference of the arguments of

$$(x_1, y_1, z_1) \text{ and } (x_2, y_2, z_2).$$

The solution (X, Y, Z) can be obtained by the addition formulas from (x_1, y_1, z_1) and (x_2, y_2, z_2). Therefore from (2′) and (2″) we have

$$3(y_1 - z_1\rho)(x_2 - z_2\rho)(X - Z\rho) = \alpha^3, \qquad 3(x_1 + y_1)(x_2 + y_2)(X + Y) = \beta^3,$$

from which

$$27(x_1 + y_1)^2 (y_1 - z_1\rho)(x_2 + y_2)^2 (x_2 - z_2\rho)(X + Y)^2 (X - Z\rho) = (\alpha\beta)^3. \tag{12}$$

From (1′)

$$3(x_1 + y_1)^4 (x_1 - z_1\rho)(y_1 - z_1\rho) = \nu^3. \tag{13}$$

Dividing (12) by (13) we get

$$9(X + Y)^2 (X - Z\rho) \cdot \frac{(x_2 + y_2)^2 (x_2 - z_2\rho)}{(x_1 + y_1)^2 (x_1 - z_1\rho)} = \left(\frac{\alpha\beta}{\nu}\right)^3,$$

From this, taking into account condition (11), we have

$$9(X + Y)^2 (X - Z\rho) = \left(\frac{\alpha\beta\lambda}{\nu}\right)^3 = \mu^3.$$

This proves the sufficiency of condition (11) by Theorem 2.

In order to prove the necessity we must carry out the same steps in reverse order.

REMARK. It is not hard to establish, bearing in mind the remark after Theorem 2, that in case A is not divisible by 3 the equations

$$\frac{(x_1 + y_1)^2 (x_1 - z_1\rho)}{(x_2 + y_2)^2 (x_2 - z_2\rho)} = 3^\sigma \lambda^3,$$

are impossible with $\sigma = 1$ and 2.

3. We write the equation $X^3 + Y^3 = AZ^3$ in the form

$$3(X + Y)(X - Z\rho)(Y - Z\rho) = (X + Y - Z\rho)^3. \tag{1'}$$

If X, Y, Z are relatively prime in pairs, so are $X + Y$, $X - Z$ and $Y - Z$.

In case the field $\Omega(\rho)$ is of the first kind it follows from (1′) and from the fact that 3 is the cube of an ideal that $X+Y$, $X-Z$, and $Y-Z$ are also cubes of ideals and therefore $9(X+Y)^2(X-Z\rho)$ is also a cube of an ideal.

In the case that $\Omega(\rho)$ is a field of the second kind, we have

$$9(X+Y)^2(X-Z\rho)=j^3 \text{ or } 3j^3 \text{ or } 9j^3,$$

where j is an ideal in the field $\Omega(\rho)$.

It follows from group theory that the number of classes of ideals whose cubes give the principal class is $s=3^k$.

Let $a_1, a_2, \cdots, a_s$ be the representatives of such classes. Let the numbers corresponding to their cubes be $\mu_1, \mu_2, \cdots, \mu_s$. Then every number which is a cube of an ideal will differ only by a factor which is the cube of an integer or of a fractional number of the field $\Omega(\rho)$ from one of the $3s$ numbers

$$\mu_1, \mu_1\epsilon, \mu_1\epsilon^2;\ \mu_2, \mu_2\epsilon, \mu_2\epsilon^2, \cdots, \mu_s, \mu_s\epsilon, \mu_s\epsilon^2, \tag{A}$$

where ϵ is the fundamental unit of the field $\Omega(\rho)$. Therefore the numbers $9(X+Y)^2(X-Z\rho)$ will differ only by factors which are cubes of numbers in $\Omega(\rho)$ from the numbers in (A) in case $\Omega(\rho)$ is of the first kind, or from the numbers

$$\mu_1, \mu_1\epsilon, \mu_1\epsilon^2;\ 3\mu_1, 3\mu_1\epsilon, 3\mu_1\epsilon^2;\ 9\mu_1, 9\mu_1\epsilon, 9\mu_1\epsilon^2;\ \cdots, \tag{B}$$

in case $\Omega(\rho)$ is of the second kind.

We shall call two solutions of $X^3+Y^3=AZ^3$ equivalent if the numbers $9(X+Y)^2(X-Z\rho)$ corresponding to them differ by a factor which is a cube of a number in $\Omega(\rho)$. Equivalent solutions are put into one class. Relations (2′), (2″) (3′) and (3″) show that the classes of solutions form a group which is a subgroup of the group (A) or (B). Therefore the number of classes of solutions is 3^m, where

$$m \le k+1 \text{ in case } \Omega(\rho) \text{ is of the first kind,}$$

$$m \le k+2 \text{ in case } \Omega(\rho) \text{ is of the second kind.}$$

It is not hard to show from the remark to Theorem 3 that

$$m \le k \quad \text{in case } \Omega(\rho) \text{ is of the first kind, } (A, 3)=1,$$

$$m \le k+1 \text{ in case } \Omega(\rho) \text{ is of the second kind.}$$

We know that the set of arguments t giving the solutions of $x^3+y^3=Az^3$ has a finite basis.

We also know that if we exclude from consideration the cases $A=1$ and $A=2$, which do not interest us, then the values of the argument t are incomıensurable with the period ω. In this case it is easily seen that there exists a basis $t_1, t_2, \cdots, t_p$ for which the relation $r_1t_1+r_2t_2+\cdots+r_pt_p=n\omega$ is impossible for any integer values of $r_1, r_2, \cdots, r_p, n$.

We shall show that $p=m$, where 3^m is the number of classes of solutions of $x^3+y^3=Az^3$. In fact the solutions which correspond to the 3^p values of the arguments

$$t=\alpha_1t_1+\alpha_2t_2+\cdots+\alpha_pt_p \quad (\alpha_i=0,\ 1,\ 2)$$

cannot be equivalent, since if they were, then by Theorem 3 the difference of two such arguments would be, up to a period, a triplication of the argument of some third solution and we would have

$$(\alpha_1'-\alpha_1'')t_1+(\alpha_2'-\alpha_2'')t_2+\ldots+(\alpha_p'-\alpha_p'')t_p=3\beta_1t_1+3\beta_2t_2+\ldots+3\beta_pt_p+n\omega,$$

which is obviously impossible.

Conversely, an argument of any solution $t=\gamma_1t_1+\gamma_2t_2+\cdots+\gamma_pt_p$ can be written in the form $t=\alpha_1t_1+\alpha_2t_2+\cdots+\alpha_pt_p+3(\beta_1t_1+\beta_2t_2+\cdots+\beta_pt_p)$, where $\alpha_i=0, 1, 2$, from which it follows by virtue of Theorem 3 that every solution is equivalent to one of the 3^p solutions corresponding to the values of the arguments $\alpha_1t_1+\alpha_2t_2+\cdots+\alpha_pt_p$. Hence $3^p=3^m$ and therefore $p=m$.

Although we already know that there exist only a finite number of basic solutions, it is of some interest to find out how quickly the size of the solutions diminishes in the descent based on dividing the argument by 3.

Let

$$(x_1, y_1, z_1), (x_2, y_2, z_2), \cdots, (x_s, y_s, z_s) \qquad \text{(C)}$$

be the representatives of all the classes of solutions of $x^3+y^3=Az^3$ and let $t_1, t_2, \cdots, t_s$ be the corresponding values of the arguments. Let L be the upper bound of the numbers $|x_i|, |y_i|, |z_i|$ for $i=1, 2, \cdots, s$. Let (X, Y, Z) be any solution of the equation not contained in (C). We denote by T the argument corresponding ot this solution. Among the solutions (C) there will be a solution (x_i, y_i, z_i) equivalent to (X, Y, Z). Then the solution (X_3, Y_3, Z_3) corresponding to the argument $T-t_i$ will be the triplication of some solution (x, y, z). We can determine X_3, Y_3, Z_3 by the formulas

$$X_3=AZz_i(x_iZ-z_iY)+Xy_i(Yy_i-Xx_i),$$
$$Y_3=AZz_i(y_iZ-z_iY)+Yx_i(Xx_i-Yy_i),$$
$$Z_3=x_iY(x_iZ-z_iY)+y_iX(y_iZ-z_iX),$$

from which

$$|Z_3| < 2L^2\cdot[|X| + |Y|]^2. \tag{14}$$

Without violating the inequality (14) we can assume that X_3, Y_3, Z_3 are relatively prime, since if we divide out their common factor this will only decrease their absolute value.

But the solution (X_3, Y_3, Z_3) is the triplication of some solution (x, y, z). Hence either X_3, Y_3, Z_3 or $9X_3, 9Y_3, 9Z_3$ can be obtained from (x, y, z) by the triplication formulas (4)

$$3^\sigma X_3 = x^9 + 6x^6y^3 + 3x^3y^6 - y^9,$$
$$3^\sigma Y_3 = y^9 + 6y^6x^3 + 3y^3x^6 - x^9,$$
$$3^\sigma Z_3 = 3xyz\,(x^6 + x^3y^3 + y^6),$$

from which

$$|xyz|\cdot(x^6 + x^3y^3 + y^6) < 3Z_3.$$

Furthermore $x^6 + x^3y^3 + y^6 \geqslant \frac{3}{4}x^6$, and since $x^3 = Az^3 - y^3$, we have

$$|Az^3| + |y|^3 \geqslant |x|^3,$$

from which

$$(A+1)|yz|^3 > |x^3| \text{ и } |yz| > \frac{|x|}{\sqrt[3]{A+1}} > \frac{|x|}{2\sqrt[3]{A}}.$$

Hence,

$$\frac{3}{8\sqrt[3]{A}}|x|^8 < 3|Z_3|;\ |x|^8 < 8A^{\frac{1}{3}}|Z_3| < 16A^{\frac{1}{3}}L^2[|X| + |Y|]^2,$$

from which

$$|x| < 2^{1/2}A^{1/24}L^{1/4}[|X| + |Y|]^{1/4}.$$

Similarly

$$|y| < 2^{1/2}A^{1/24}L^{1/4}[|X| + |Y|]^{1/4} \text{ and } |x| + |y| < 2^{2/3}A^{1/24}L^{1/4}[|X| + |Y|]^{1/4}.$$

Hence the sum of the absolute values of x and y for the new solution is in general less than the corresponding sum for the given solution (X, Y, Z). Repeating this operation on (x, y, z) we arrive at a still smaller solution, etc., until we come to one of the solutions (x_i, y_i, z_i) or to a solution for which the above operation will not lead to a smaller value of $|x| + |y|$.

This will happen when $|x| + |y|$ becomes less than $M = (2^{3/2}A^{1/24}L^{1/4}) = 4A^{1/18}L^{1/3}$. Hence by means of the operation of descent one can arrive at a solution for which $|x| + |y| < 4A^{1/18}L^{1/3}$.

Let us give a resumé of our results.

The number m of basic solutions of the equation $x^3 + y^3 = Az^3$ is finite. In fact

$$m \leq k + 1 \text{ if } A \text{ is divisible by } 3 \text{ or if } A = \pm 1 \pmod 9,$$

$$m \leq k \qquad \text{if } A \equiv \pm 2, \ \pm 4 \pmod 9,$$

where $3^k = s$ is the number of classes of ideals in the field $\Omega(\sqrt[3]{A})$ whose cubes form the principal class.

4. In case A is a prime or a square of a prime it is possible to obtain sharper estimates for the number of basic solutions; namely, that there are not more than two basic solutions. We shall limit ourselves to the case when A is a prime and $A \neq 2$ and $A \neq 3$.

THEOREM 4. *In order that the solution* (X, Y, Z) *be a triplication of another solution* (x, y, z) *it is necessary and sufficient that* $(X + Y)^2 (X\zeta + Y\zeta^2)$ *be the product of* A^2 *by the cube of an integer in the field* $\Omega(\zeta)$, *where* $\zeta = e^{2\pi i/3}$.

PROOF. The necessity follows immediately from (4″) and (4‴). We prove the sufficiency. Let

$$(X + Y)^2 (X\zeta + Y\zeta^2) = A^2 (a + b\zeta)^3. \tag{15}$$

Without loss of generality we can assume that X, Y, Z are relatively prime in pairs. It follows from (15) that

$$X(X + Y)^2 = A^2(-a^3 + 3a^2b - b^3), \quad Y(X + Y)^2 = A^2(-a^3 + 3ab^2 - b^3),$$

from which

$$(X + Y)^3 = A^2(-2a^3 + 3a^2b + 3ab^2 - 2b^3),$$

and therefore $X + Y$ is divisible by A.

On the other hand, $(X + Y)(X\zeta + Y\zeta^2)(X\zeta^2 + Y\zeta) = AZ^3$. The numbers $X + Y$, $X\zeta + Y\zeta^2$, $X\zeta^2 + Y\zeta$ are either relatively prime or have a common factor $\eta = 1 - \zeta$, where in the latter case $X\zeta + Y\zeta^2$ and $X\zeta^2 + Y\zeta$ are divisible by η but not by $3 = -\zeta^2\zeta^2$.

Therefore $X + Y = 3^\sigma A\nu^3$, where $\sigma = 0$ or 2.

Substituting into (15), we obtain

$$3^{\sigma_1}(X\zeta + Y\zeta^2) = (a_1 + b_1\zeta)^3, \text{ where } \sigma_1 = 0 \text{ or } 1,$$

from which

$$3^{\sigma_1} X = - a_1^3 + 3a_1^2 b_1 - b_1^3, \quad 3^{\sigma_1} Y = - a_1^3 + 3a_1 b^2 - b_1^3. \tag{16}$$

Since X and Y are relatively prime, $(a_1, b_1) = 1$. Adding the two equations in (16), we get

$$3^{\sigma_1}(X+Y) = - 2a_1^3 + 3a_1^2 b_1 - 3a_1 b_1^2 - 2b_1^3 = (2b_1 - a_1)(2a_1 - b_1)(a_1 + b_1).$$

But $3^{\sigma_1}(X+Y) = 3^{\sigma+\sigma_1} Av^3 = A(3^{\sigma_1} v)^3$.

Hence

$$(a_1 - 2b_1)(b_1 - 2a_1)(a_1 + b_1) = A(3^{\sigma_1} v)^3. \tag{17}$$

The numbers $a_1 - 2b_1$, $b_1 - 2a_1$, $a_1 + b_1$ are either relatively prime in pairs or else they have a common factor 3. One of them is divisible by A, since A is a prime. We denote this one by t, and the others by p and q. Obviously

$$t + p + q = 0.$$

On the other hand, $p = \delta x_1^3$, $q = \delta y_1^3$, $t = - A\delta z_1^3$, where $\delta = 1$ or 3 by (17). Therefore $x_1^3 + y_1^3 = Az_1^3$.

It is not hard to check that for all possible ways of assigning t, p and q, the solution (X, Y, Z) can be obtained by means of triplication of (x_1, y_1, z_1).

THEOREM 5. *In order that the difference of the arguments of* (x_1, y_1, z_1) *and* (x_2, y_2, z_2) *be a triplication of the argument of some third solution it is necessary and sufficient that*

$$\frac{(x_1+y_1)^2(x_1\zeta+y_1\zeta^2)}{(x_2+y_2)^2(x_2\zeta+y_2\zeta^2)} = \lambda^3,$$

where λ *is an integer or a fraction of the field* $\Omega(\zeta)$.

The proof is based on (3′) and on Theorem 4 and proceeds in the same way as the proof of Theorem 3.

5. Let A be a prime of the form $6n - 1$. Then A is a prime in the field $\Omega(\zeta)$, and $x\zeta + y\zeta^2$, if $(x, y) = 1$, is relatively prime to A.

From the equation $(x+y)(x\zeta + y\zeta^2)(x\zeta^2 + y\zeta) = Az^3$ we conclude that there are six possibilities for the numbers $x + y$ and $x\zeta + y\zeta^2$; namely,

$$\begin{aligned}
x+y &= Av^2, & x\zeta+y\zeta^2 &= (a+b\zeta)^3,\\
x+y &= Av^2, & x\zeta+y\zeta^2 &= \zeta(a+b\zeta)^3,\\
x+y &= Av^2, & x\zeta+y\zeta^2 &= \zeta^2(a+b\zeta)^3,\\
x+y &= 9Av^2, & x\zeta+y\zeta^2 &= \eta(a+b\zeta)^3,\\
x+y &= 9Av^2, & x\zeta+y\zeta^2 &= \zeta\eta(a+b\zeta)^3,\\
x+y &= 9Av^2, & x\zeta+y\zeta^2 &= \zeta^2\eta(a+b\zeta)^3,
\end{aligned}$$

ıd therefore three possibilities for the number $(x+y)^2(x\zeta+y\zeta^2)$:

$$(x+y)^2(x\zeta+y\zeta^2) = A^2 \quad (a_1+b_1\zeta)^3,$$
$$(x+y)^2(x\zeta+y\zeta^2) = A^2\zeta \quad (a_1+a_1\zeta)^3,$$
$$(x+y)^2(x\zeta+y\zeta^2) = A^2\zeta^2 (a_1+b_1\zeta)^3.$$

From this it readily follows (as in subsection 3) that the equation $X^3 + Y^3 = Z^3$ cannot have more than one basic solution.

If A is a prime of the form $6n+1$, then A is decomposable into the prime .ctors $A = \pi_1\pi_2$ in the field $\Omega(\zeta)$.

In this case there are nine possibilities for the number $(x+y)^2(x\zeta+y\zeta^2)$; ımely,

$$(x+y)^2(x\zeta+y\zeta^2) = A^2 \quad (a+b\zeta)^3, = \pi_1 \quad (a+b\zeta)^3, = \pi_2 \quad (a+b\zeta)^3,$$
$$= A^2\,\zeta\,(a+b\zeta)^3, = \pi_1\zeta\,(a+b\zeta)^3, = \pi_2\zeta\,(a+b\zeta)^3,$$
$$= A^2\zeta^2(a+b\zeta)^3, = \pi_1\zeta^2(a+b\zeta)^3, = \pi_2\zeta^2(a+b\zeta)^3,$$

ıd hence the equation $X^3 + Y^3 = AZ^3$ cannot have more than two basic solutions.

We can improve our estimates of the number of basic solutions as follows. In ıse $(x+y)^2(x\zeta+y\zeta^2) = A^2\zeta(a+b\zeta)^3$, either $x\zeta+y\zeta^2$ or $3(x\zeta+y\zeta^2)$ is of e form $\zeta(a_1+b_1\zeta)^3$, and hence $x+y = Av^3$ or $9Av^3$, respectively.

But then

$$3^{\sigma_1}x = a_1^3 - 3a_1b_1^2 + b_1^3, \quad 3^{\sigma_1}y = 3a_1^2b_1 - 3a_1b_1^2,$$

om which

$$3^{\sigma_1}(x+y) = a_1^3 + 3a_1^2b_1 - 6a_1b_1^2 + b_1^3 \text{ and } a_1^3 + 3a_1^2b_1 - 6ab_1^2 + b_1^3 = A(3^{\sigma_1}v)^3.$$

The form $a_1^3 + 3a_1^2b_1 - 6ab_1^2 + b_1^3$ can have only prime factors which are de- ımposable into ideals in a real subfield of the field $\Omega(e^{2\pi i/3})$ i.e., prime fac- ɪrs of the form $18n \pm 1$.

Hence if $A \not\equiv \pm 1 \pmod{18}$ this possibility does not exist and the number of ısic solutions is one less.

Hence for primes $A \neq 2 \neq 3$ the equation $x^3 + y^3 = Az^3$ has

for $A = 18n + 1$ not more than 2 basic solutions,

„ $A = 18n + 7$
„ $A = 18n + 13$ } not more than one basic equation,
„ $A = 18n + 17$

„ $A = 18n + 5$
„ $A = 18n + 11$ } no solutions.

For $A = A_1^2$, where A_1 is a prime, the same estimates hold.

TABLE of basic solutions of the equation

$$x^3 + y^3 = Az^3 \quad \text{for} \quad A \leq 50$$

A	Number of Basic Solutions	Basic Solutions	A	Number of Basic Solutions	Basic Solutions
6	1	(37, 17, 21)	28	1*	(3, 1, 1)
7	1	(2,—1, 1)	30	2	(289, — 19, 93); (163, 107, 57)
9	1	(2, 1, 1)			
12	1	(89, 19, 39)	31	1	(137, — 65, 42)
13	1	(7, 2, 3)	33	1	(1853, 523, 582)
15	1	(397, 683, 294)	34	1	(631, — 359, 182)
17	1	(18, — 1, 7)	35	1*	(3, 2, 1)
19	2	(8, 1, 3); (5, 3, 2)	37	2	(4, — 3, 1); (19, 18, 7
20	1	(19, 1, 7)	42	1*	(449, — 71, 129)
22	1	(25469, 17299, 9954)	43	1	(7, 1, 2)
26	1*	(3, —1, 1)	49	1	(11, — 2, 3)
			50	1	(23417, —11267, 6111).

* For $A = 26, 28, 35, 42$ the application of results of subsection 3 gives the numbe of solutions ≤ 2, but it can be easily shown by considerations similar to those in subse tion 4 that it is ≤ 1. For the values of $A \leq 50$ not listed it is known that the equation has no nontrivial solutions.

APPENDIX

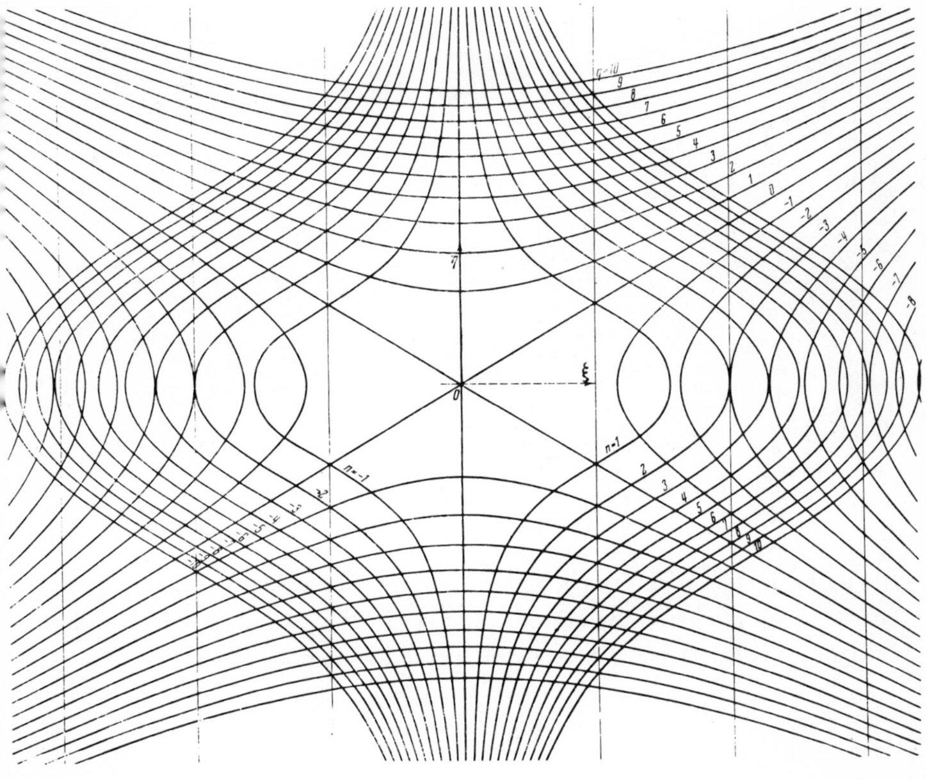

$D < 0$. Projection onto the $\xi\eta$-plane parallel to the rational direction of the lattice of the integer equations $x^3 - sx^2 + qx - n = 0$, with $s = 0$. The thin straight lines are those which contain reducible points.

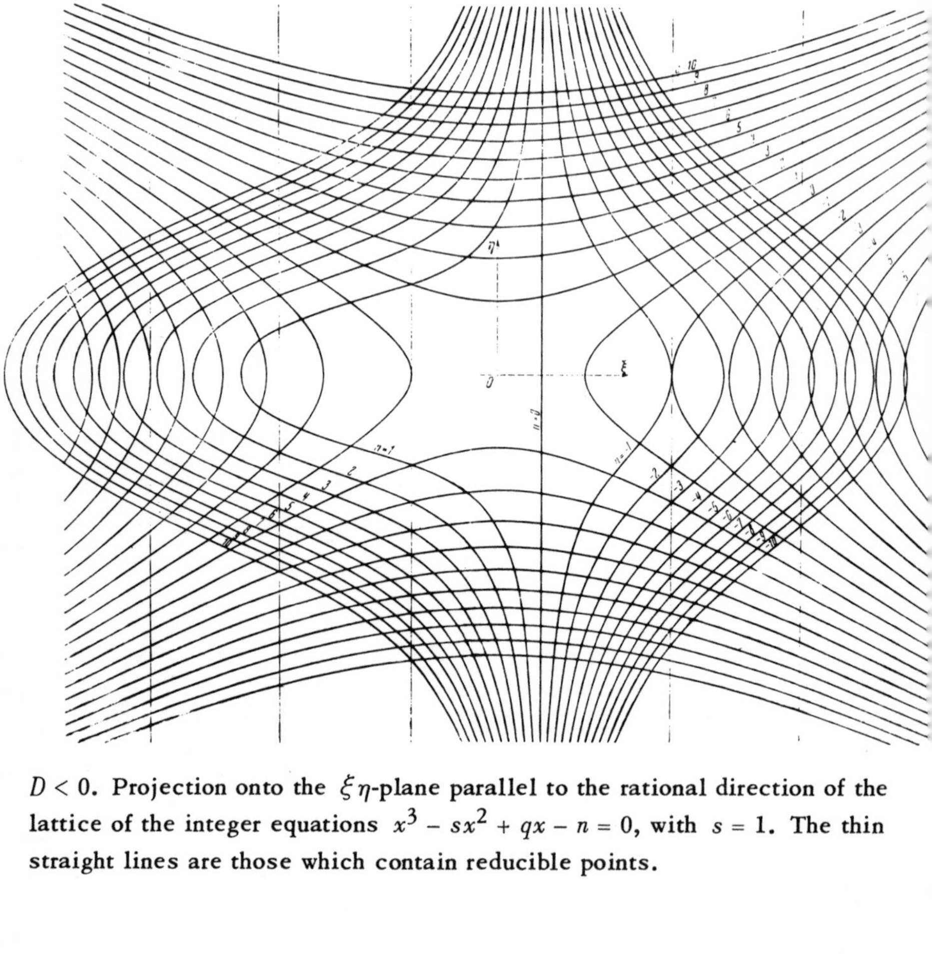

$D < 0$. Projection onto the $\xi\eta$-plane parallel to the rational direction of the lattice of the integer equations $x^3 - sx^2 + qx - n = 0$, with $s = 1$. The thin straight lines are those which contain reducible points.

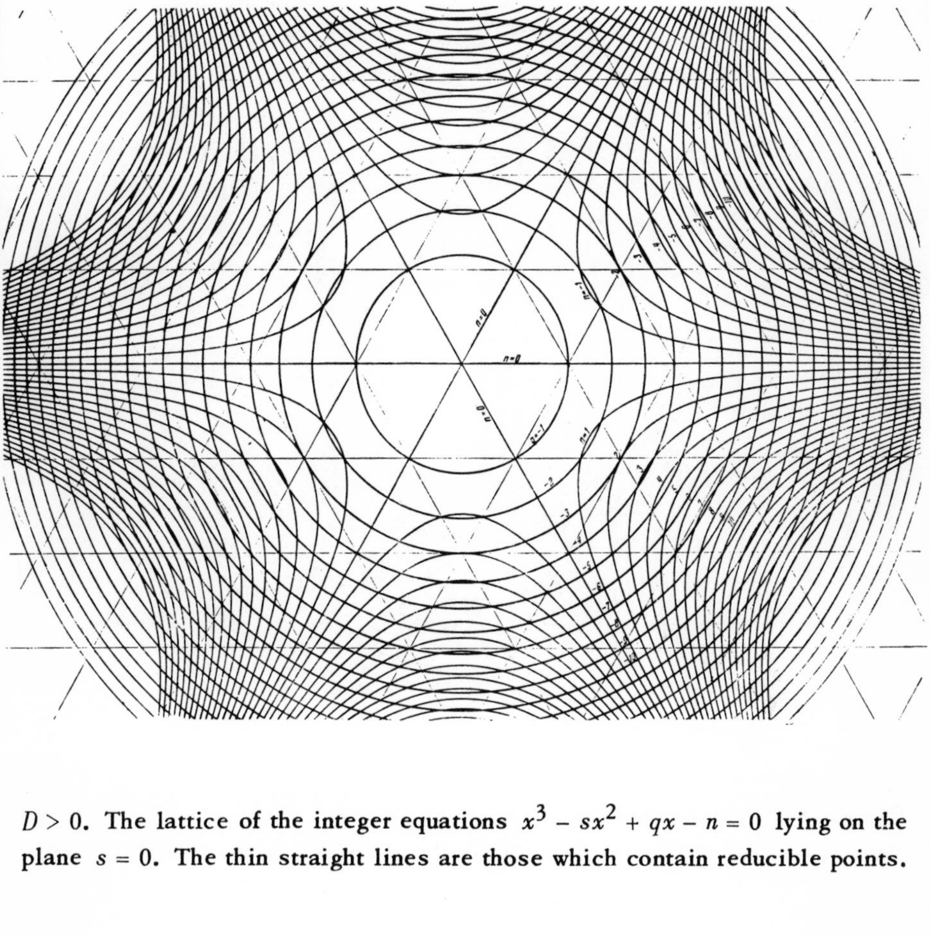

$D > 0$. The lattice of the integer equations $x^3 - sx^2 + qx - n = 0$ lying on the plane $s = 0$. The thin straight lines are those which contain reducible points.

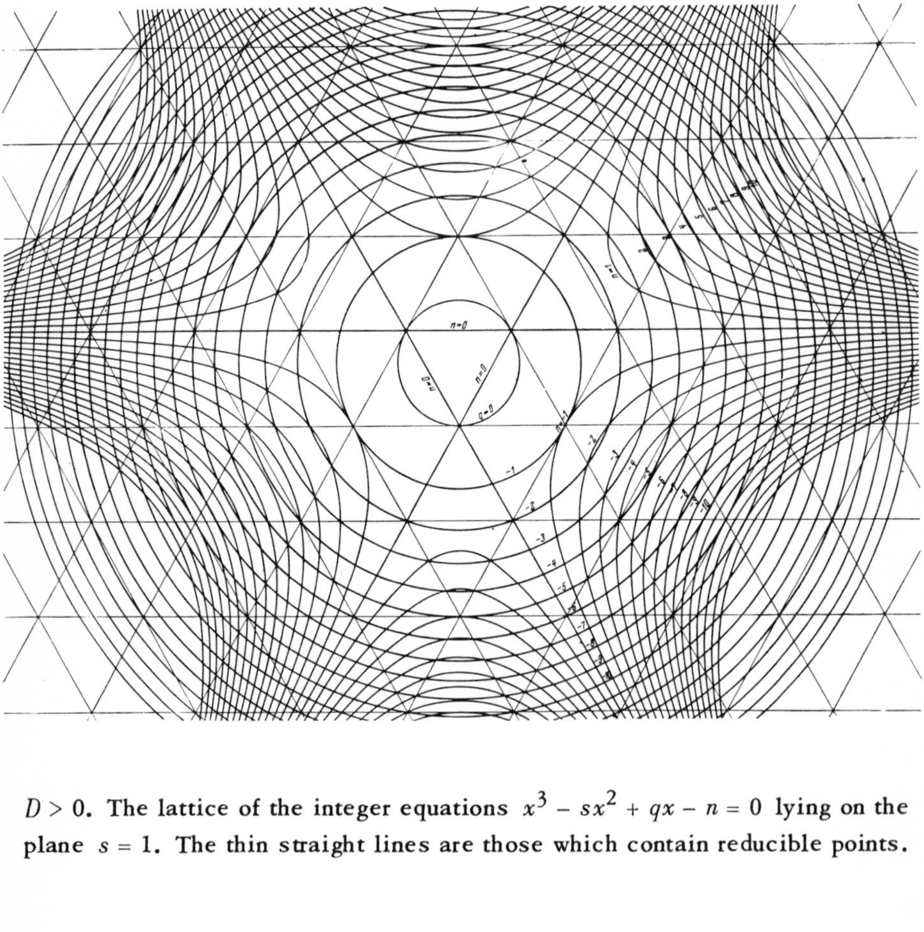

$D > 0$. The lattice of the integer equations $x^3 - sx^2 + qx - n = 0$ lying on the plane $s = 1$. The thin straight lines are those which contain reducible points.

SUPPLEMENT I

INTRODUCTION TO DIRICHLET'S LECTURES ON THE THEORY OF NUMBERS: THE GEOMETRY OF BINARY QUADRATIC FORMS [1)]

B. N. DELONE

§1. DEFINITIONS AND SOME GENERAL THEOREMS ABOUT LATTICES

1. DEFINITION. A uniform sequence of points on a straight line in which the distance between two neighboring points is equal to a will be called a *sequence of points* with parameter a or a *one-dimensional lattice*, and will be denoted by E_1.

Let $\overrightarrow{OP}$ and $\overrightarrow{OQ}$ be two vectors of a given length forming a given angle POQ. The figure OPQ will be called a *vector-pair*, the point P being called the *end of the first vector*, and the point Q the *end of the second vector*. The collection of points of the plane OPQ whose coordinates are rational integers *with respect to the vector-pair* OPQ, i.e., with respect to the oblique-angled coordinate system with origin at the point O, with axes OP and OQ, and with scalar units on these axes equal to OP and OQ, will be called a *two-dimensional lattice* and will be denoted by E_2. The vector-pair OPQ will be said to be a *basic vector-pair* and the parallelogram constructed on it will be called a *basic parallelogram* of the lattice E_2.

In the same way, three given vectors $\overrightarrow{OP}$, $\overrightarrow{OQ}$, and $\overrightarrow{OR}$ forming a given angle in space will also be called a *vector-triple*. The collection of points of space whose coordinates are integers *with respect to the vector-triple* $OPQR$, i.e., with respect to the oblique-angled coordinate system with origin at the point O, with axes OP, OQ, and OR, and with scalar units on these axes equal to OP, OQ, and OR, will be called a *three-dimensional lattice*, and will be denoted by E_3.

---

1) This section is taken from the Introduction by B. N. Delone to the Russian translation of P. G. L. Dirichlet, *Vorlesungen über Zahlentheorie*, herausgegeben von R. Dedekind (4 Auflage, Braunschweig, Vieweg, 1894).

The vector-triple $OPQR$ will be said to be a *basic vector-triple* and the parallelepiped constructed on it will be called a *basic parallelepiped* of the lattice E_3.

If we are given an arbitrary system of points, then by a *parallelogram of the system* and by a *parallelepiped of the system* we will mean a parallelogram or parallelepiped all of whose vertices are points of the system. A parallelogram or parallelepiped of the system will be said to be *empty* if it contains no points of the system other than its vertices.

These definitions may be extended to lattices of any dimension.

2. THEOREM I. *A lattice contains no pair of points situated closer together than some given distance r. If D, E, and F are three arbitrary points of a lattice, and the segment FG is equal and parallel to the segment DE, then G is also a point of the lattice.*

The last property is called the *property of parallel translation* and follows easily from the definitions.

We will call two figures or two systems of points *homologous* with respect to a given lattice if one of them may be obtained from the other by a parallel translation of the lattice.

3. THEOREM II. *A parallelogram of some lattice E_2 or a parallelepiped of some lattice E_3 is a basic parallelogram of E_2 or a basic parallelepiped of E_3 if and only if it is empty.*

PROOF. That a basic parallelogram of a lattice E_2 is empty follows directly from its definition. If, conversely, a parallelogram of the lattice E_2 is empty, then in view of the property of parallel translation in E_2 the lattice E_2 contains the lattice E_2' constructed on this parallelogram. But E_2 cannot contain any other points; for otherwise, again by the property of parallel translation, the given lattice would have to contain points of the lattice E_2 other than its vertices. But this is impossible since the parallelogram was assumed to be empty. Hence the lattice E_2' is identical with E_2 and the given empty parallelogram is a basic parallelogram of the lattice E_2.

The proof is analogous for the case of a three-dimensional parallelepiped.

4. REMARK. A *triangle* of a lattice E_2 will be a *fundamental triangle* of this lattice (a triangle constructed on the basic vector-pair of the lattice E_2) if and only if it is empty, for then the parallelegram constructed on it will also be empty. However, a *tetrahedron* of the lattice E_3 may be empty, while the parallelepiped of this lattice constructed on it may turn out to be not empty, i.e., it will

not be a basic parallelepiped for the lattice.

5. THEOREM III. *If in an arbitrary system of points* 1) *there is at least one point such that the distance between the given point and any other point of the system is not less than some given value* r *and* 2) *the system possesses the property of parallel translation, then the system is a lattice.*

This fundamental theorem is, so to speak, a converse of Theorem I.

PROOF. Let O be the point of the given system that is such that no other point of the system is situated at a distance less than r from it. Then by the property of parallel translation no two points of the system can be closer than the distance r to each other. Hence, no bounded region can contain an unbounded collection of points of the system.

If the system does not consist of only the one point O (a case which, strictly speaking, does not contradict the theorem), then let $\bar{P}$ be some point of the system other than O. On the segment $O\bar{P}$ there is only a finite number of points of the system, and thus there is a point closest to O. Let this be the point P. If the segment $O\bar{P}$ contains no points of the system, then this point P will be the point $\bar{P}$. The straight line $O\bar{P}$ contains, in view of the property of parallel translation, all the points of the point sequence OP (if we take for the points D, E, and F the points O, P, and $\bar{P}$, and so on), and it contains no other points of the system; for in the contrary case, again by the property of parallel translation, such points would then belong also to the segment OP, which would contradict the assumption that P is the point closest to O on the segment $O\bar{P}$. Hence, if the given system is one-dimensional, it is identical with the sequence of points OP and is thus a one-dimensional lattice.

If the system is not one-dimensional, i.e., it possesses points that do not lie on the straight line OP, then in view of the property of parallel translation there emanates from each of these points a sequence of points equal and parallel to the sequence OP, the so-called sequence of points homologous to the sequence OP. Let $\bar{Q}$ be some point of the system that does not lie on the straight line OP, and let $\bar{Q}\bar{Q}'$ be the sequence of points passing through $\bar{Q}$ that is homologous to the sequence OP. If in the plane $OP\bar{Q}$ there is a sequence of points $\bar{\bar{Q}}\bar{\bar{Q}}'$ of the given system that is homologous to the sequence of points OP, and whose straight line $\bar{\bar{Q}}\bar{\bar{Q}}'$ passes between the lines OP and $\bar{Q}\bar{Q}'$, then the straight line $\bar{\bar{Q}}\bar{\bar{Q}}'$ has a segment in common with the parallelogram $OP\bar{Q}$ that is equal in magnitude and direction to the segment $\bar{\bar{Q}}\bar{\bar{Q}}'$. Thus, the sequence of points $\bar{\bar{Q}}\bar{\bar{Q}}'$ undoubtedly contains a point belonging to this parallelogram (lying either within it or on its boundary). Hence, there can be only a finite number of such intervening sequences (if they exist at all). This means that there is some sequence QQ' that is closes to the sequence OP with no sequence parallel to it passing between the straight lines OP and QQ'. Then in the plane OPQ, by the property of parallel translation of the given system, there exists a two-dimensional lattice with the basic parallelogram OPQ. No points of the given system other than the points of this lattice can lie in this plane for otherwise, again because of the property of parallel translation, the parallelogram OPQ would contain points of the system other than its vertices. But this would contradict the assumption that P is the point of the straight line OP that is closest to O, while QQ' is the parallel sequence of points of the plane OPQ that is closest to OP.

Hence if the system is two-dimensional, it is identical with this two-dimensional lattice.

Finally, if the system is three-dimensional, then it possesses points that do not lie in the plane OPQ. Let $\overline{R}$ be one of these points. By the property of parallel translation, there passes through this point a lattice equal and parallel to the two-dimensional lattice OPQ, namely, the so-called lattice homologous to OPQ. Let $\overline{R}\overline{R}'\overline{R}''$ be this two-dimensional lattice. If there exists in the system a lattice $\overline{\overline{R}}\overline{\overline{R}}'\overline{\overline{R}}''$ homologous to OPQ whose plane passes between the planes OPQ and $\overline{R}\overline{R}'\overline{R}''$, then the plane $\overline{\overline{R}}\overline{\overline{R}}'\overline{\overline{R}}''$ has a parallelogram in common with the parallelepiped $OPQ\overline{R}$, and this parallelogram is equal in magnitude and direction to the parallelogram $\overline{\overline{R}}\overline{\overline{R}}'\overline{\overline{R}}''$. Thus, there is undoubtedly a point of this parallelogram in the lattice $\overline{\overline{R}}\overline{\overline{R}}'\overline{\overline{R}}''$, and hence also in the parallelepiped $OPQ\overline{R}$. In any case, there may be only a finite number of such intervening lattices (if they exist at all). This means that there is some two-dimensional lattice $RR'R''$ of our system that is homologous to the lattice OPQ and which is closest to OPQ, so that there is no two-dimensional lattice of our system parallel to it between the planes OPQ and $RR'R''$. Thus the given system of points belongs to the three-dimensional lattice with basic vector-triple $OPQR$. Moreover, there cannot be any other points in the lattice under consideration, for otherwise, again by the property of parallel translation, the parallelepiped $OPQR$ would also have to contain points of the system other than its vertices, which would contradict the assumption that no other points of the system in the plane OPQ belong to the parallelogram OPQ and that $RR'R''$ is the closest homologous lattice of our system to the lattice

OPQ. Thus the given system is identical with the three-dimensional lattice $OPQR$ and the theorem is proved.

6. Theorem III shows that, conversely, a lattice may be defined as a system of points possessing the properties of *discreteness* (i.e., the distance between any two points is not less than some determined finite number r) and parallel translation. Given the property of parallel translation, we can weaken the first condition, requiring only the existence of one point of the system such that a sphere or circle with center at this point and a positive radius r contains no other point of the system. From this point of view a lattice may be characterized differently: it is a system of all the points into which a point of a plane (or of a space) may go under some discrete group of parallel translations.

A group of parallel translations of a space, if it is not merely the identity, is clearly infinite and abelian, but in general it may be either discrete or not discrete. In other words, it may or may not contain infinitely small translations. Clearly the set of all parallel translations of a lattice forms a discrete group of parallel translations. Theorem III shows, conversely, that the set of all points *homologous* to a given point of a space with respect to a given discrete group of parallel translations, i.e., obtained from this point by all the translations of this group, is a lattice. An n-dimensional lattice is a model of the most general infinite Abelian group with n independent generators, all the elements of which, other than zero, are of infinite order.

7. One may make the following remark about the freedom of choice of a basic vector-pair in the lattice E_2 or in the lattice E_3.

The concept of a *lattice* includes only a system of points, and does *not* include the straight lines on which these points lie. The same lattice E_2 or E_3 may be given by means of very different basic vector-pairs or vector-triples.

From the proof of the preceding theorem it is easy to see that necessary and sufficient conditions for the vector-pair OPQ to be a basic vector-pair in a given lattice E_2 are as follows: 1) O is an arbitrary point of the lattice E_2; 2) P is another point of E_2 satisfying the one condition that there is no point of the lattice E_2 within the segment OP; 3) Q is an arbitrary point of one of the two sequences of points of the lattice E_2 that are homologous to the sequence of points OP and that are closest to it. Necessary and sufficient conditions for a vector-triple $OPQR$ to be a basic vector-triple of some given lattice E_3 are as follows: 1) O is an arbitrary point of E_3; 2) P is another point of E_3 satisfying the one condition that the segment OP is empty; 3) Q is a point of E_3 belonging in the plane OPQ to one of the two sequences of points of the lattice E_3 that lie in this plane, are homologous to the sequence of points OP, and are closest to it; 4) R is an arbitrary point of one of the two two-dimensional lattices of the lattice E_3 that are homologous to the two-dimensional lattice OPQ and are closest to it.

8. THEOREM IV. *All the basic parallelograms of the same lattice E_2 have the same area and all the basic parallelepipeds of the same lattice E_3 have the same volume.*

PROOF. Since the method of proof used for the lattice E_2 is the same as for the lattice E_3, we will prove this theorem only for the lattice E_3.

Let $OPQR$ and $O\overline{P}\overline{Q}\overline{R}$ be two different basic vector-triples of the same lattice E_3, and let v and $\overline{v}$ be the volumes of basic parallelograms constructed on them. It is easy to calculate that $\overline{v} = \Delta v$, where Δ is the absolute value of the determinant $\begin{vmatrix} p, & q, & r, \\ p', & q', & r', \\ p'' & q'' & r'' \end{vmatrix}$, whose rows (p, q, r), (p', q', r') and (p'', q'', r'') are the coordinates of the points $\overline{P}$, $\overline{Q}$ and $\overline{R}$ with respect to the vector-triple $OPQR$. But these coordinates are *integers*. Thus Δ is a nonzero integer. Since $O\overline{P}\,\overline{Q}\,\overline{R}$ is in its turn a basic vector-triple, the coordinates of the points P, Q and R with respect to the vector-triple $O\overline{P}\,\overline{Q}\,\overline{R}$ are also integers, and this means that we have analogously $v = \overline{\Delta}\overline{v}$, where $\overline{\Delta}$ is again a rational integer different from zero. Hence we have

$$v = \overline{\Delta}\overline{v} = \overline{\Delta}\Delta v,$$

from which it follows that $\overline{\Delta}\Delta = 1$, i.e., $\Delta = 1$, and thus $v = \overline{v}$.

Another proof of the same theorem. Let us take a large sphere of radius R, and let it include N points of our lattice E_3. Let A and B be two different basic parallelepipeds of the lattice E_3, i.e., such that B cannot be obtained from A by a parallel translation. To each of the N given points we assign a parallelepiped A, for instance that parallelepiped for which the given point is the lower left front vertex. All these parallelepipeds are contained in a sphere of radius R without being one inside the other. Moreover, some of them protrude outside the sphere, while a portion of the sphere near its surface is not completely filled. If the volume of such a parallelepiped is V_A, then the volume of the sphere V_R is approximately equal to NV_A, $V_R \approx NV_A$, i.e., $V_A \approx V_R/N$. Analogously, we find that $V_B \approx V_R/N$. Increasing the radius of the sphere R

nboundedly

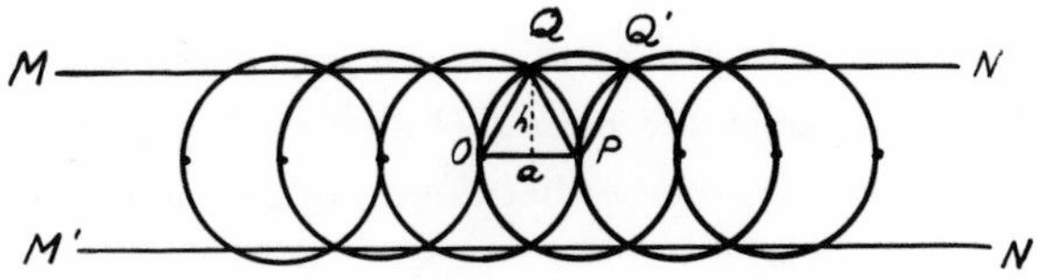

Figure 1

nd taking the limit, we find that $V_A = V_B$.

REMARK. All the definitions, theorems and proofs given in this section are lso true for lattices of any dimension considered in n-dimensional Euclidean pace.

§2. FURTHER THEOREMS ABOUT LATTICES IN A PLANE

9. THEOREM V. *If the area of a basic parallelogram of the lattice* E_2 *is qual to* s, *then the distance between the point* O *of the lattice* E_2 *and the losest point to it of the same lattice does not exceed the value* $\sqrt{2s/\sqrt{3}}$.

PROOF. Let P be the point of the lattice E_2 closest to the point O (Figre 1). In other words, within the circle of radius $a = OP$ described about the oint O, there is no other point of the lattice E_2. The same is true for similar ircles described around all the remaining points of the sequence OP. If through he points of intersection of these circles we now draw the straight lines MN and $I'N'$, then within the band MN, $M'N'$ there lie no points of the lattice E_2 other han points of the sequence OP, since each interior point of this band lies within t least one of our circles. The sequence homologous and closest to the sequence $)P$ consequently lies at least at a distance of $h = a\sqrt{3}/2$. Hence, the area s f a basic parallelogram of the lattice E_2 can not be less than $a^2\sqrt{3}/2$, from which we get that $a \leq \sqrt{2s/\sqrt{3}}$. Clearly, equality will hold if and only if the oints of the homologous sequence closest to OP coincide with the points Q, $)'$, $\cdots$, i.e., when the fundamental triangle OPQ is equilateral. That is, the xact limit is obtained in this case only.

10. If we describe around each point of the lattice E_2 a circle of radius $a/2$, vhere a is the least distance between two points of the lattice E_2, then these ircles will not intersect, since no two points of the lattice E_2 are within a disance less than a of each other. Thus, the lattice just found with basic vectorair OPQ gives the *closest packing of equal circles* of diameter a, where no two ircles intersect and where the centers of the circles form a lattice.

11. THEOREM VI. *In each lattice* E_2 *there is in general one and only one*

acute-angled fundamental triangle (if we do not count the triangle symmetric to it

PROOF. Let P be one of the points of the lattice E_2 that are closest to O. If there are constructed through the points O and P perpendiculars to the segment OP, λ and μ (Figure 2), then either there is one point of each of the two

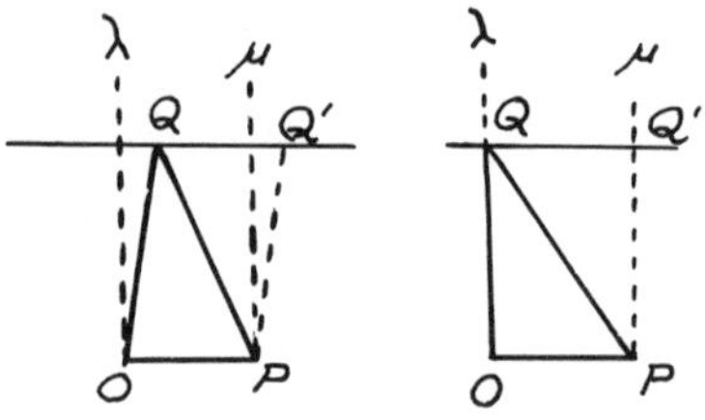

Figure 2

homologous sequences closest to the sequence OP within the band formed by these perpendiculars, or there are in each of these sequences two points lying on the perpendiculars λ and μ themselves. Let Q be one of these points. The triangle OPQ will then be empty and thus will be a fundamental triangle of the lattice E_2. This triangle has no obtuse angles. In fact, the angle Q is in any case acute, for the side OP of the triangle OPQ is the shortest segment in the lattice E_2, and thus can certainly be no longer than the other sides of this triangle. The angles O and P are not obtuse because the point Q lies either between the perpendiculars λ and μ or on one of these perpendiculars. The triangle PQQ' is also a fundamental triangle without obtuse angles, but it is symmetric to the triangle OPQ.

12. We must still decide the question of whether there are any other such nonobtuse fundamental triangles in the lattice E_2.

That part of the plane of the lattice E_2 in which each point lies as close to the point O as to any other point of the lattice is called the *Dirichlet region* of the point O in the lattice E_2. Let OPQ be an acute fundamental triangle of the lattice E_2. We consider the six triangles OPQ, OQR, ORP', $OP'Q'$, $OQ'R'$, and $OR'P$ (Figure 3). Three of these triangles are equal and the remaining three are symmetric to them. If we construct inside any one of these triangles perpendiculars at the midpoints of its sides, then they will intersect within the triangle since it is acute, and they will divide the triangle into three quadrangles. We construct such triangles for all the points of the lattice E_2, for which we need only divide into two equal parts all the basic parallelograms of the lattice E_2 homologous to the basic parallelogram $OPQR$, using diagonals homologous to the iagonal OQ. We divide all these triangles into the small quadrangles shown in e figure. Each point of the lattice E_2 will then be surrounded by six such

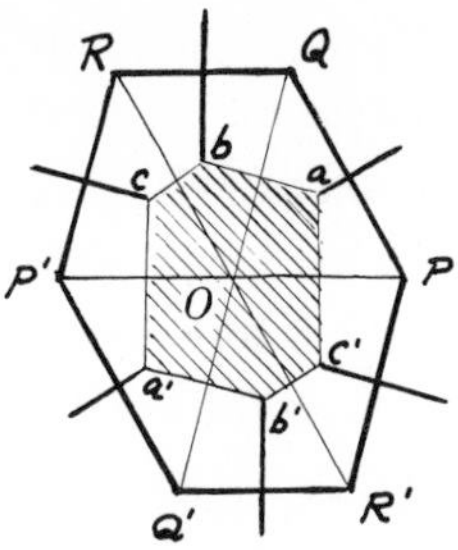

Figure 3

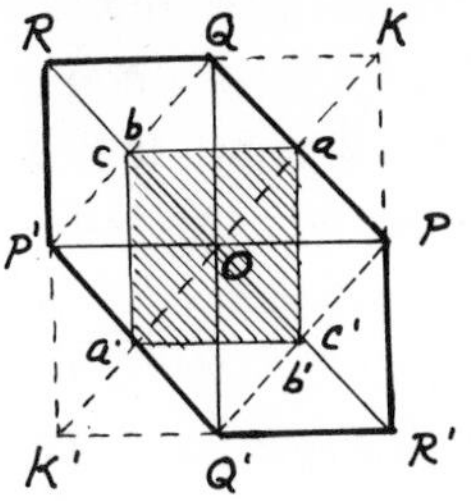

Figure 4

uadrangles, forming together a hexagon homologous to the hexagon $abca'b'c'$. hese hexagons thus cover the whole plane without overlapping each other. The irichlet region of the point O lies in any case within the hexagon $abca'b'c'$, ince each of its points is closer, for example, to O than P, i.e., lies on the interior side'' of the straight line ac', and further, is closer to O than to Q, e., lies on the ''interior side'' of the straight line ab, and so on. The Dirichlet egions of other points of the lattice E_2 have a similar position inside their cor-esponding hexagons. But by definition, the Dirichlet regions cover the whole lane, since for each point of the plane there is a point of the lattice E_2 that the iven point is as close to as it is to any other. Hence a Dirichlet region cannot ill only a part of a hexagon; it must identically coincide with the hexagon. Thus e hexagon $abca'b'c'$ is the Dirichlet region of the point O in the lattice E_2.

By its definition the Dirichlet region is uniquely determined by the lattice $_2$. As we saw, however, the acute fundamental triangles are uniquely associated ith these ''Dirichlet hexagons'': the vertices of the triangle are the centers of hose three Dirichlet regions that have a common vertex inside the triangle. Thus n acute fundamental triangle is uniquely determined by the lattice E_2.

13. In the limiting case, when the triangle OPQ is right-angled, the Dirichlet egion is also degenerate: it is not a hexagon, but a quadrangle (Figure 4). Two f the sides of the hexagon, bc and $b'c'$, become equal to zero. In this case, esides the previous six nonobtuse fundamental triangles, six other triangles also eet at the point O; namely, OPQ, OKQ, OQP', $OP'K'$, $OK'Q'$, $OQ'P$.

14. THEOREM VII. *The sides of an acute fundamental triangle are the three hortest parameters of the lattice* E_2.

Parameters of a lattice are segments connecting two points of the lattice but not containing any other points of the lattice.

PROOF. Let OPQ be an acute fundamental triangle of the lattice E_2, wher $PQ \leq OP \leq OQ$ and OD is a perpendicular dropped from the point O onto the straight sequence of points II (Figure 5). Then the angle PQO is greater than $45°$. In fact, the angle POQ is less than or equal to the angle PQO and if the angle PQO were less than $45°$, then the angle OPQ would have to be greater than $90°$; but the triangle OPQ has no obtuse angles. It follows from this that the angle OQD is greater than $90°$, i.e., that $OD > OQ$.

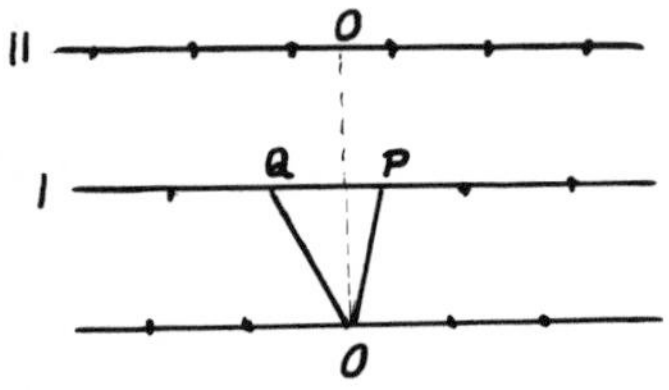

Figure 5

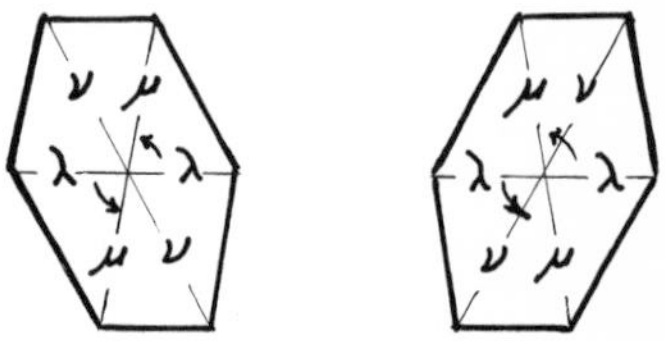

Figure 6

It is understood that OP and OQ are the two smallest parameters going from the point O to the points of the sequence I. All the parameters going to the points of the sequences II, III, and so on, are larger than OD, and thus larger than OQ. Thus PQ, OP, and OQ are the three least parameters of the lattice E_2

15. In the future we will call a certain direction of rotation in the plane of the lattice E_2 *right* in contradistinction to rotation in the opposite direction, which will be said to be *left*. Corresponding to this, we will speak of *right* and *left vector-pairs*, meaning by the *angle of a vector-pair* that angle between its vectors which is less than $180°$, always considering the direction of rotation of the angle of the vector-pair as being from its first vector to its second.

16. We will say that a vector-pair is *reduced* if 1) its first vector is the smallest and the second the next smallest parameter of the lattice and 2) the vector-pair is a right vector-pair. The three least parameters $\lambda \leq \mu \leq \nu$ may be situated in two different ways with respect to the established positive direction of rotation: either in the order λ, μ, ν or in the order λ, ν, μ. In the first case the reduced vector-pair will be acute, while in the second it will be obtuse (Figure 6).

If the vector-pair OPQ is reduced, then, in general it follows directly from Theorems VI and VII that only the reflected vector-pair $OP'Q'$ will also be educed (Figure 8).

17. The only exceptions are the following three cases: 1) when $\lambda = \mu < \nu$; 2) when $\lambda < \mu = \nu$; 3) when $\lambda = \mu = \nu$. In these cases there are respectively 4, 4, and 12 reduced vector-pairs, which are pairwise reflections of each other (Figure 7).

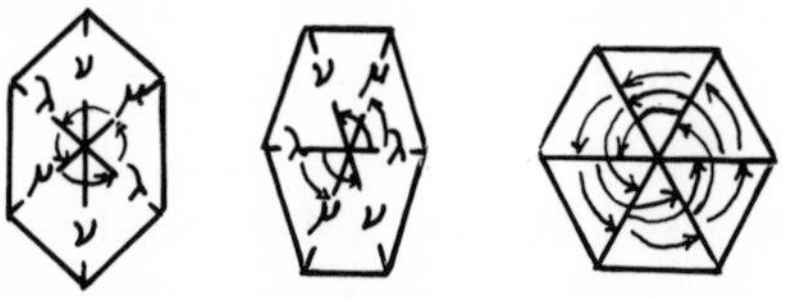

Figure 7

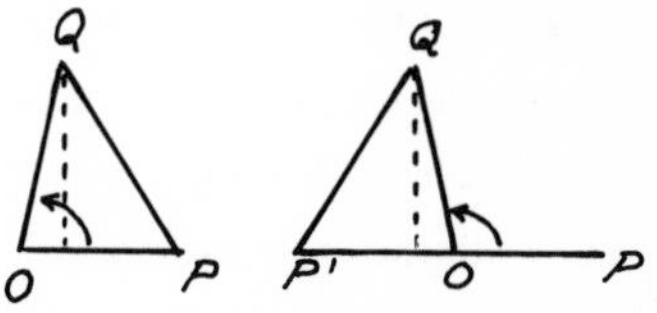

Figure 8

The case of a right-angled or square Dirichlet region is not an exception in this sense.

18. THEOREM VIII. *A basic vector-pair OPQ will be reduced if and only if* 1) *the projection of its second side OQ onto the straight line of its first side OP is in absolute value less than or equal to half of its first side*; 2) *its first side OP is less than or equal to its second side OQ*; 3) *it is a right vector-pair.*

PROOF. In fact, if these conditions are satisfied and the angle of the vector-pair is not obtuse, then in the fundamental triangle $PQ \geq OQ \geq OP$ (Figure 8). This means that its largest angle is located at the point O, i.e., the triangle is not obtuse, from which it follows by Theorem VII that the vector-pair OPQ is reduced. If the angle of the vector-pair is obtuse, then the triangle OQP' has the indicated properties, from which it is again clear that the vector-pair OPQ is reduced.

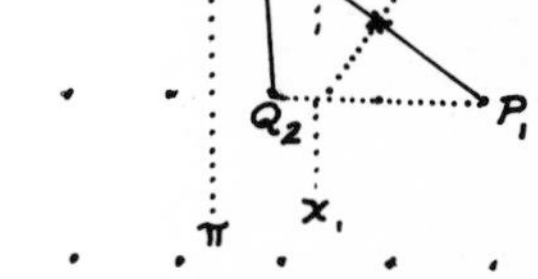

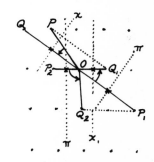

Figure 9

19. **Algorithm of reduction.** Let there be given a vector-pair OPQ. If the point Q' is symmetric to the point Q with respect to O and if R is an arbitrary point of the sequence passing through P parallel to the sequence OQ, then we will say that the vector-pair $OQ'R$ is adjacent on the right to the vector-pair OPQ. This vector-pair has the same direction of rotation as the vector-pair OPQ.

The transition from an arbitrary basic vector-pair of the lattice (the direction of rotation of which is taken to be positive) to a reduced vector-pair may be made (following Gauss) in the following manner (see Figure 9).

We construct the vector-pair OP_1Q_1 adjacent on the right to the given vector pair OPQ so that the projection of its second vector OQ_1 onto the first vector OP_1 is less than or equal to the first vector in absolute value, i.e., so that the point Q_1 lies between the perpendiculars π and κ. There is always one such point, or two (if they lie on the perpendiculars π and κ themselves). Further, we again construct a vector-pair OP_2Q_2 adjacent on the right to the vector-pair OP_1Q_1, possessing the same property, i.e., it is such that the point Q_2 lies between the perpendiculars π_1 and κ_1, and so on.

For each such vector-pair condition 1) of Theorem VII is satisfied, and it cannot happen that condition 2) is never satisfied. In fact, it would then be true that $OQ_1 > OQ_2 > OQ_3 > \cdots$. But only a finite number of points of the lattice are situated in the circle of radius OQ_1 with center at O. Consequently, condition 2) must be satisfied after a finite number of such transformations. Then the vector-pair will be reduced.

20. The Pell angle of a lattice. Every lattice coincides with itself after rotation by 180° around its point O. But it may occur that a lattice will coincide with itself under rotation by a smaller angle. Since the Dirichlet region is a rectangle or a hexagon with center of symmetry at the point Q, this may occur only when the Dirichlet region is a square or a regular hexagon, and then this angle is 90° or 60°. We will call this least angle of repetition the *Pell angle* of the lattice.

21. The vector-pair corresponding to a given parameter of a lattice. Every parameter OM of the lattice may be taken for the first side of some basic vector-pair of the lattice. That one of these vector-pairs which has a right direction of rotation and which satisfies condition 1) of Theorem VIII will be called the *vector-pair corresponding to the parameter* OM, and the vector-pair itself will be said to be *semireduced.*

In the general case there are in all two distinct semireduced vector-pairs, while in the case when the Pell angle is 90° or 60°, there are always four or six such distinct vector-pairs respectively, but there can not be more since if there were a vector-pair equal to the given one, i.e., obtained from it by means of a rotation around the point O, then the lattice would coincide with itself under this rotation, since the given vector-pair is a basic one.

§3. THEORY OF THE DISTRIBUTION OF THE POINTS OF A LATTICE WITH RESPECT TO GIVEN ASYMPTOTES

We turn now to lattice theorems of a slightly different character, namely relating to the distribution of points of the lattice E_2 with respect to some infinite straight line.

22. DEFINITION. Let there be given in the plane of some given lattice E_2 two straight lines $O\xi$ and $O\eta$ passing through the point O of the lattice and irrational with respect to the lattice E_2, i.e., meeting no other points of the lattice. We will call these lines *axes* or *asymptotes*.

Let P be an arbitrary point of the lattice E_2. In the future a *coordinate parallelogram of a point* P will be taken to mean a parallelogram which has its center at the point O, one of its vertices at the point P, and sides parallel to the axes $O\xi$ and $O\eta$. Since the axes are irrational, no side of the coordinate parallelogram can contain two points of the lattice E_2, since otherwise there would be a point of the lattice other than the point O lying on the corresponding axis. Hence if P is a point of the lattice E_2, then there lies on the boundary of its coordinate parallelogram only one more point P' of the lattice, symmetric to P with respect to the point O, and located at the opposite vertex of the parallelogram.

A point P of the lattice E_2 whose coordinate parallelogram contains within itself no points of the system other than the point O is called a *relative minimum* of the lattice E_2 with respect to the asymptotes $O\xi$ and $O\eta$.

23. THEOREM IX. *The given lattice* E_2 *has infinitely many relative minima with respect to the given asymptotes* $O\xi$, $O\eta$.

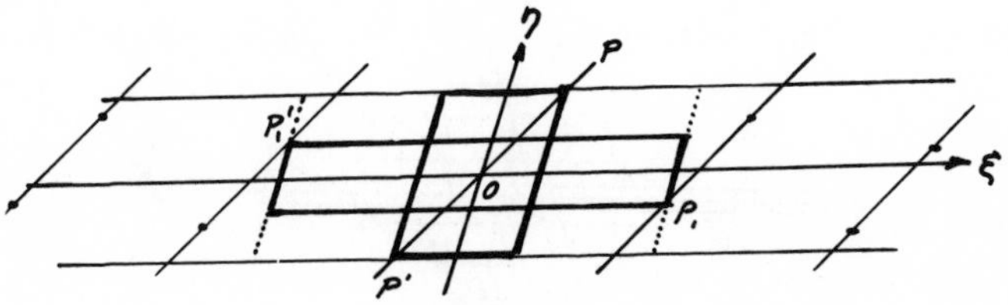

Figure 10

PROOF. It is first necessary to show that there exists at least one such relative minimum. This is clear; for example, if the point Q of the lattice E_2 is not a relative minimum, i.e., if there are other points of the lattice within its coordinate parallelogram, then it is possible to apply the argument to one of these points, and so on. In the end we are led in this manner to a relative minimum, since there are only a finite number of points of the lattice E_2 in the coordinate parallelogram of the point Q.

24. Now let P be a relative minimum, with a positive abscissa ξ for example, (Figure 10). If we extend indefinitely the sides ot the coordinate parallelogram of the point P parallel to the axis ξ, we will obtain a band containing the axis ξ. The right side of the coordinate parallelogram of the point P parallel to the axis η is now allowed to slide inside this band, remaining constantly parallel to itself, in the direction of increasing abscissa. Eventually, it will necessarily cross some point of the lattice E_2, since every sequence of points of the lattice E_2 parallel to the sequence of points OP has two points within the band. In fact the segment of the straight line of such a sequence of points lying within the band has length $PP' = 2OP$, and there are no points of the lattice E_2 other than O on the axis ξ.

Let P_1 be the first point through which this sliding side passes. Then only this point lies on it, since the axis η also contains no points of the lattice other than the point O. Thus P_1 is clearly a relative minimum. We may now repeat this step, starting with the point P_1, and so on. We thus obtain an infinite set of relative minima $P_1, P_2, P_3, \cdots$ lying along the positive semi-axis ξ.

25. The points $P_1', P_2', P_3', \cdots$ symmetric to these minima with respect to the point O are also relative minima, but they lie along the negative semi-axis ξ

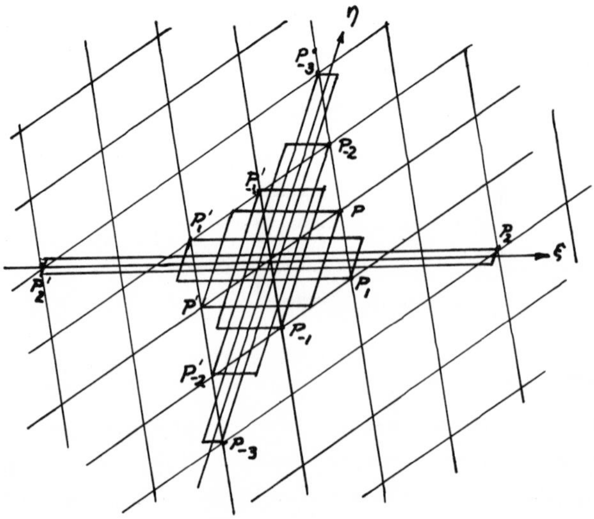

Figure 11

If, remaining in the half-plane $\xi > 0$, we apply this method, starting from the same point P and in the direction of the axis η, we obtain a chain of relative minima $P_{-1}, P_{-2}, P_{-3}, \cdots$ which approach the axis η. There are also relative minima $P'_{-1}, P'_{-2}, P'_{-3}, \cdots$ symmetric to them with respect to the point O (Figure 11).

26. THEOREM X. *The method of Theorem IX yields all of the relative minima of the lattice* E_2.

PROOF. In fact, every relative minimum that has an abscissa larger than that of P must have an ordinate larger in absolute value than the ordinate of the point P; in the contrary case P would lie in its coordinate parallelogram. Hence, each such relative minimum must lie in the band considered in Theorem IX.

But P_1 was the first point of the lattice E_2 that had an abscissa larger than that of the point P. The same is true for P_2 with respect to P_1 and so on.

Two relative minima situated with respect to each other in the same way as the points P and P_1 will be said to be *successive* and P_1 will be said to be the *first successor* with respect to the minimum P along the semi-axis $+\xi$. Thus for example, P'_{-2} and P'_{-3} are successive relative minima and P'_{-3} is the first successor with respect to the minimum P'_{-2} along the semi-axis $-\xi$.

27. THEOREM XI. *A vector-pair constructed on two successive relative minima is a basic vector-pair of the lattice* E_2.

PROOF. The triangle OPP_1 (Figure 12) lies in the parallelogram $abcd$, and this parallelogram is empty except for the point O. The triangle OPP_1 is thus empty, and hence a fundamental triangle. This means that the vector-pair OPP_1 is a basic vector-pair of the lattice E_2.

It follows from this theorem that P_1 lies in the parallel sequence of points of the lattice E_2 that is closest to the sequence OP.

28. THEOREM XII. *Successive minima lie on different sides of the corresponding axis.*

PROOF. In fact, the two points of the sequence parallel to the sequence OP that are included within the band of Theorem IX lie on different sides of the axis ξ, and both are situated to the right of the right side of the coordinate parallelogram of the point P since it is empty.

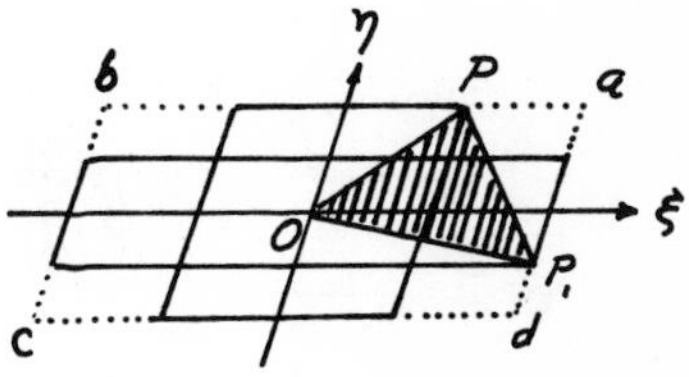

Figure 12

Under the application of the method used in the proof of Theorem IX, this side clearly first meets that one of the two points that lies on the other side of the axis ξ with respect to the point P.

29. DEFINITION. By the *angle of a vector-pair* we will again mean the angle formed by the vectors that is less than 180°.

We will say that a vector-pair *includes* a given axis or asymptote (these terms are synonymous) parallel to one of the two chosen axes if this asymptote passes within the angle of the vector-pair. It is clear that there can be only three possibilities: the vector-pair may include one, two, or no asymptotes.

Which of the ends of the vector-pair we will call *first* and which *second* is arbitrary; but in the symbol for the vector-pair we will always place the letter denoting the end of its first vector immediately after the O that designates its vertex.

A segment drawn from the end of the *first* vector of the vector-pair in a direction parallel to its second vector will be called the *beak* of the vector-pair. Thus the beak always proceeds from the first side of the vector-pair. Its length may be measured by taking the second side for unit length. If it is positive, it is directed inside the angle of the vector-pair, while if it is negative, it goes outside this angle. We will say that we *extend* the beak only when we draw it inside the frame.

A basic vector-pair of the lattice E_2 will be said to be *reduced* with respect to some asymptote if the ends of its vectors are successive minima such that the second is the successor with respect to the first along this asymptote.

THEOREM XIII. *A basic vector-pair of the lattice* E_2 *is reduced if and only if* 1)· *it includes one and only one asymptote and* 2) *the end of its second vector lies further along this asymptote, but closer to it, than the end of its first vector.*

PROOF. The necessity of these conditions follows from the constructions of Theorem IX and Theorem XI. However, they are also sufficient.

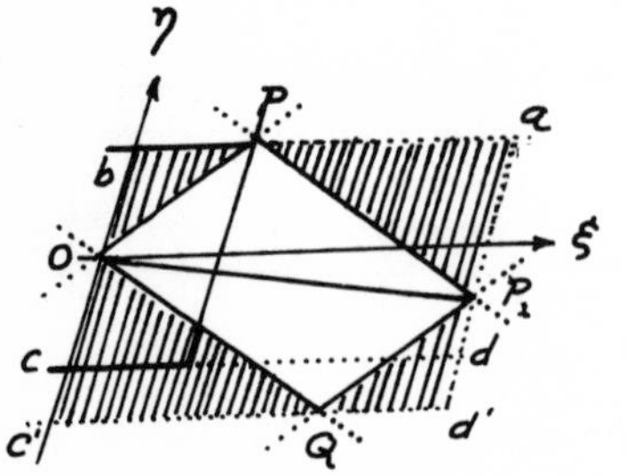

Figure 13

In fact, we continue all four of the sides of the parallelogram OPP_1Q (Figure 13). Then we obtain two empty intersecting bands, since OPP_1Q is a basic parallelogram. As is easy to see, these two bands cover the parallelogram $abc'd'$ which means that they also cover $abcd$, since the latter contains only the points

O, P, and P_1 of the lattice E_2. Thus P and P_1 are successive minima and the second is the successor with respect to the first. Thus conditions 1) and 2) are also sufficient.

31. Let OPP_1 be a reduced frame, and let $P_2, P_3, P_4, \cdots$ be a sequence of relative minima following one another after the minimum P_1 along the axis included in the vector-pair. Then all the vector-pairs $OP_1P_2, OP_2P_3, OP_3P_4, \cdots$ are also reduced basic vector-pairs. We call them *successors* with respect to the reduced vector-pair OPP_1. The collection of all these vector-pairs will be called a *chain* of the reduced vector-pair OPP_1. Starting with the first frame, this chain may also proceed in the opposite direction along the same semi-axis, where the vector-pairs $OP_{-1}P, OP_{-2}P_{-1}, OP_{-3}P_{-2}, \cdots$ are predecessors of the vector-pair OPP_1 (see Figure 11).

The fundamental problem is the following: given an arbitrary basic vector-pair of the lattice E_2, to find a method of going from it to some reduced vector-pair (it is immaterial to us along which axis it will be reduced), and further to go step by step to all the successive vector-pairs in its chain.

32. **Preliminary transformation of the given vector-pair.** If the given vector-pair OPP_1 contains no asymptotes, then we go from it to the vector-pair OPP_1' containing two asymptotes (Figure 14). If it is necessary at all, this preliminary transformation will be made only once, at the very beginning of the proposed algorithm. Thus we may confine ourselves in the future to the consideration of vector-pairs including at least one asymptote. For simplicity, we will say that such vector-pairs are prepared.

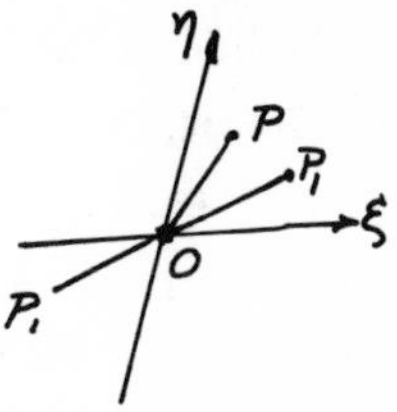

Figure 14

33. **Transformation of an arbitrary prepared vector-pair into a chain of reduced vector-pairs, and progress along this chain.** Assume that we are given the vector-pair OPP_1 of the lattice E_2 already prepared, i.e., such that it includes at least one asymptote. Then the reduction algorithm consists of the following.

We extend the beak of the vector-pair OPP_1 to the last point P_2 for which the vector-pair OP_1P_2 still includes at least one asymptote. We then extend the beak of the basic vector-pair OP_1P_2 thus obtained to the last point P_3 for which the vector-pair OP_2P_3 still includes at least one asymptote, and so on.

We will now show that by this process we always go from the given vector-pair to some reduced one, and then step by step to all its successors in its chain.

34. CASE I. The prepared vector-pair is already reduced, i.e., it includes one and only one axis, and the end of its second side lies further along this axis, but closer to it, than the end of its first side (Figure 15).

Since the point P is further from the asymptote than P_1, the length of the beak to the point of its intersection with the included asymptote is greater than unity. This means that the last point P_2 on the beak which still lies on the same side as the point P, and hence forms another vector-pair OP_1P_2 which includes the asymptote, is different from P. The positive integer δ showing how many

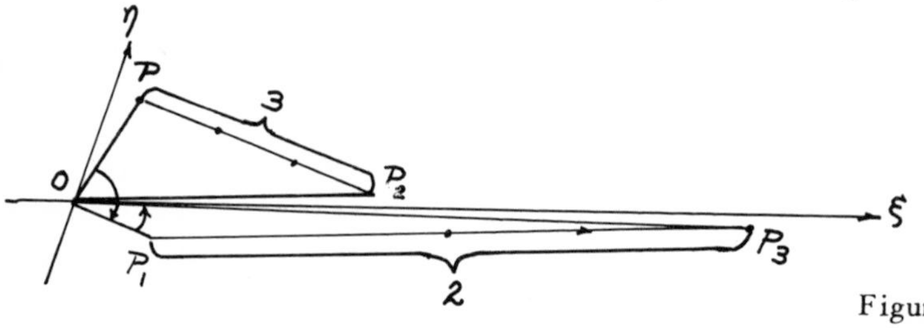

Figure 15

times it is necessary to lay off the segment OP_1 from the point P to the point P_2, i.e., the *length* of the beak PP_2, is equal to 3 in our drawing. The vector-pair OP_1P_2 is once more reduced, since again 1) it includes the asymptote $O\xi$ and 2) the end of its second side lies further along this asymptote, but closer to it, than the end of its first side.

We now consider the vector-pair OP_1P_2 and extend its beak in the same way as we did the beak of the vector-pair OPP_1. This second beak P_1P_3 has length 2 in our drawing. We continue this operation with the vector-pair OP_2P_3, and so on. Thus extending the beaks alternately, first on one side, and then on the other side of the asymptote, we will obtain, one after the other, successive vector-pairs of the chain of the vector-pair OPP_1.

35. CASE II. The prepared vector-pair, although including only one asymptote is not reduced. Here there may be three possibilities; shown respectively in the drawings α), β) and γ) of Figure 16.

α) The end of the first side, but not of the second, lies further along the included asymptote, but closer to it. The beak, proceeding as always from the end of the first side, i.e., from the point P to the point of its intersection with the included asymptote, is shorter than the second side OP_1 of the vector-pair. The point P_2 is the point P, and $\delta = 0$. The first step in the algorithm consists simply in going from the vector-pair OPP_1 to the vector-pair $OP_1P_2 = OP_1P$, i.e., in the permutation of successive sides of the vector-pair. The vector-pair OP_1P_2 will already be reduced.

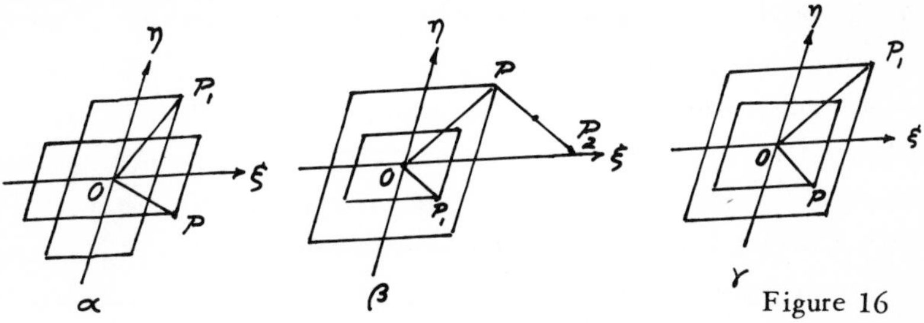

Figure 16

β) The end of the second side lies within the coordinate parallelogram of the end of the first side. The beak continued to the point of intersection from the included asymptote is longer than OP_1. Hence δ is at least equal to unity and the point P_2 is distinct from the point P. The vector-pair OP_1P_2 is already reduced.

γ) The end of the first side lies within the coordinate parallelogram of the end of the second side. The point P_2, as in case α), is the point P. The first step of the algorithm gives $\delta = 0$ and leads only to changing the places of the sides of the vector-pair. Then we obtain step β, and consequently only one more step of the algorithm is needed to give a reduced vector-pair.

Thus we see that in Case II the algorithm is applied without change, and one, or at most two, steps make the vector-pair reduced. If we continue to repeat these steps we will obtain one after another successive vector-pairs which follow this reduced vector-pair and are members of its chain, since we find ourselves already in the position of Case I.

36. CASE III. The prepared vector-pair includes two asymptotes. Here again there may be three distinct possibilities.

α) The points P and P_2 lie on opposite sides of the first asymptote (Figure 17). Of the two asymptotes covered by the vector-pair, we will take as the first one that which first intersects the positive beak, extended as always from the end of the first side of the vector-pair under consideration.

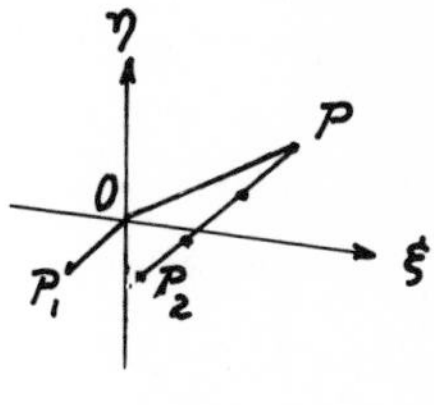

Figure 17

In case α) the vector-pair OP_1P_2 already includes only one asymptote. Thus after the first step of our algorithm we will obtain Case I or II.

β) The point P_2 does not coincide with the point P although it lies in front of the first asymptote. This occurs when there are points of the lattice E_2 on the positive beak between P and the first asymptote, but there are no points of the lattice on the segment of the beak between both asymptotes (Figure 18).

In this case the point P_2 lies inside the parallelogram $OaPb$. If the following step of our algorithm yields the same result, the point P_3 lies within the parallelogram OcP_1d. If the next step of the algorithm again leads to the same situation, then the point P_4 lies inside the analogous parallelogram of the point P_2, and thus within the parallelogram $OaPb$, and so on.

But since the parallelograms $OaPb$ and OcP_1d contain only a finite number of points of the lattice E_2, it will eventually turn out that one of the successive points will lie *between* the asymptotes, and we will arrive at one of the cases that have already been considered.

γ) The point P_2 is the point P, i.e., the first point Q of the lattice E_2 on the positive beak lies already on that side of the second asymptote (Figure 19).

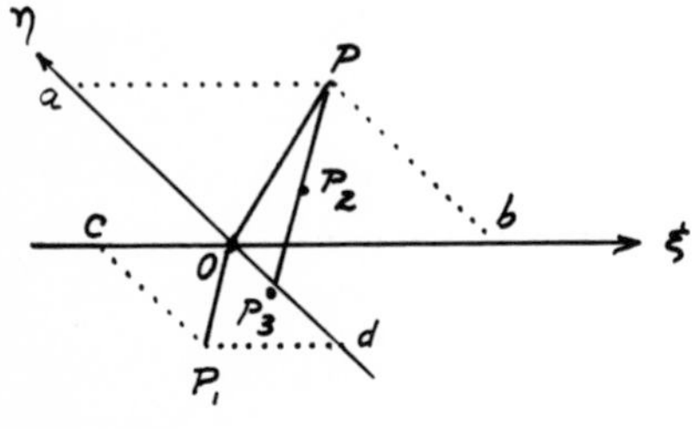

Figure 18

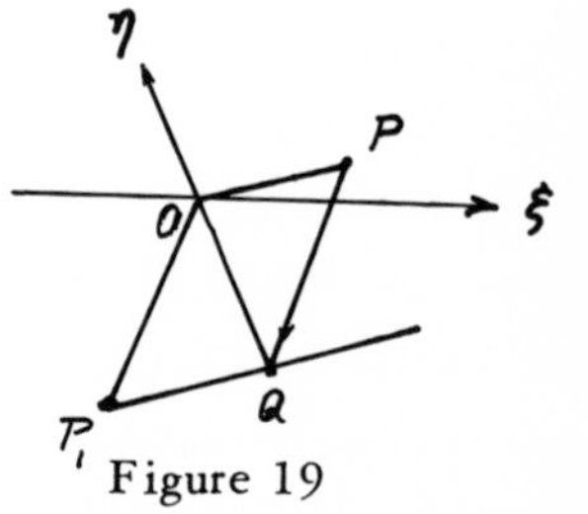

Figure 19

In our algorithm we again obtain $\delta = 0$ and the first step leads simply to an interchange of the vectors of the vector-pair, i.e., to the transition from the vector-pair OPP_1 to the vector-pair $OP_1P_2 = OP_1P$. At the next step the beak will no longer be equal to zero, i.e., $\delta_1 \neq 0$, since the first point Q on this beak which is extended now from the point P_1 still lies in front of the first asymptote. Thus after the second step we return to one of the cases that have been considered

Thus, by means of our algorithm we can finally arrive from an arbitrary prepared vector-pair to a vector-pair covering only one asymptote. And then, repeating the algorithm without any change, we obtain a reduced vector-pair and subsequently, one after another, the successive vector-pairs of the chain following it.

37. REMARK. All the definitions and theorems concerning the properties of lattices with respect to asymptotes are *invariant* with respect to any affine trans-

formation. For example, a relative minimum remains a relative minimum, and so on.

38. **Hyperbolic rotation.** Let ρ be an arbitrary positive number. The transition from points (ξ, η) to points $(\rho\xi, \rho^{-1}\eta)$ is an affine transformation which takes the asymptotes into themselves. We will call this transformation a *hyperbolic rotation* and the magnitude ρ, the *parameter* of the rotation. Under such a rotation each point slides along the hyperbola (with asymptotes $O\xi$, $O\eta$) on which it lies.

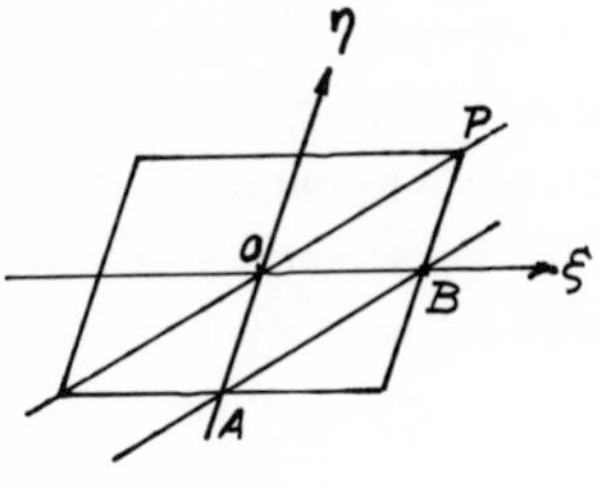

Figure 20

39. THEOREM XIV. *The area of the coordinate parallelogram of a relative minimum is less than* 4s, *where* s *is the area of a basic parallelogram of the lattice under consideration.*

PROOF. In fact, if the point P is a relative minimum, then the parallelogram $OPAB$ must be empty (Figure 20). But this may occur only if its area, which is equal to the area of the parallelogram $OBPC$, is less than s.

40. THEOREM XV. *If all the relative minima lie on a finite number of hyperbolas, then the lattice periodically coincides with itself under a hyperbolic rotation.*

PROOF. In fact, by a suitable hyperbolic transformation, the end of the first side of the reduced vector-pair may once and for all be taken on a fixed straight line η_0 parallel to the axis η (Figure 21). But this straight line has only a finite number of points of intersection with the possible hyperbolas. Thus there are only a finite number of possible positions for the end of this side. But since s is given and does not change under hyperbolic rotation, for each such position of the end of the first vector of the reduced vector-pair, the end of the second vector must lie on some fixed straight line δ parallel to the first vector of the vector-pair. This straight line has only a finite number of points of intersection with the finite number of possible

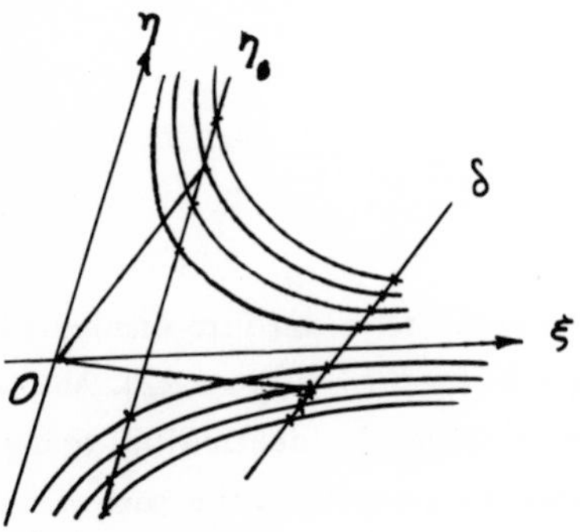

Figure 21

hyperbolas on which the end of the second vector must lie.

Thus in this case there is only a finite set of such distinct *normed* reduced basic vector-pairs. But since there is an infinite set of reduced basic vector-pairs in a lattice, there is undoubtedly an infinite set of such reduced vector-pairs that give the same normed vector-pair. In other words, there exists a hyperbolic rotation as a result of which the lattice coincides with itself. Under further rotations by the same "angle" the lattice periodically coincides with itself.

41. The Pell angle of a lattice with respect to given asymptotes. We will call the least of the indicated angles the *Pell angle*. In the same way that an arbitrary lattice coincides with itself under a usual rotation around its point O by each 180°, here the lattice coincides with itself after a hyperbolic rotation by its Pell angle.

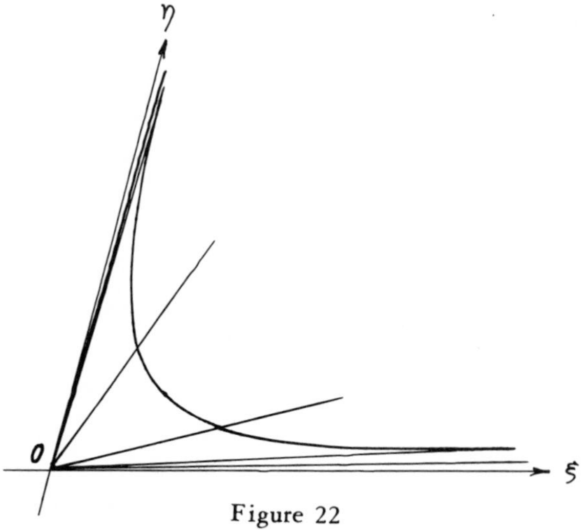

Figure 22

Each angle between asymptotes can be divided into an infinite number of such angles, where this division may begin with an arbitrary ray (Figure 22). Moreover, that part of the lattice which lies in one of these angles is identical up to a hyperbolic rotation by a corresponding multiple of this Pell angle, to the part of the lattice lying in each other such angle.

42. REMARK. It follows from the last two theorems that if a lattice does not periodically coincide with itself under hyperbolic rotation, then among the hyperbolas whose coordinate parallelograms have an area less than $4s$, there is at least one limiting hyperbola which is a position of condensation for the hyperbolas on which the points of the lattice lie.

43. THEOREM XVI. *Conversely, if a lattice periodically coincides with itself under a hyperbolic rotation, then its points, being situated under a definite hyperbola, lie on only a finite number of hyperbolas, where each hyperbola that contains at least one point contains an infinite number of points of the lattice.*

PROOF. This follows from the fact that a part of the plane lying under a given hyperbola in one of the Pell angles has a finite diameter. Consequently, there are in it only a finite number of points of the lattice, which are therefore situated on a finite number of hyperbolas. But because of the periodicity under hyperbolic rotation, the points of the lattice lie on the same hyperbolas in the other Pell angles.

Below we will see that in fact both these cases, which are so different from one another, do actually occur: there exist lattices which repeat infinitely under hyperbolic rotation with respect to a given asymptote, and there exist lattices without this property.

44. The vector-pair corresponding to a given parameter of a lattice in the hyperbolic case. Each parameter OM of a lattice may be taken for the first vector of some basic vector-pair. In subsection 21 we defined a "vector-pair corresponding to a given parameter OM" of a lattice, or a "semireduced vector-pair," for the usual case when the Pell angle is equal to 180°. We may further say the following: a vector-pair will be said to correspond to the parameter OM when 1) it is a right vector-pair, 2) OM is its first vector, and 3) the orthogonal projection of its second vector onto the first vector has the least possible absolute value.

We will call two directions *hyperbolically orthogonal* if they are parallel to two diameters conjugate with respect to the given asymptotes. Then we will again say that a vector-pair *corresponds to a given parameter* OM in the hyperbolic case when 1) it is a right vector-pair, 2) OM is its first vector, and 3) the orthogonal projection (in the hyperbolic sense) of its second vector onto the first vector has the least possible absolute value, i.e., the end of the second vector of the vector-pair is chosen from the one of the two closest parallel sequences to the sequence OM that gives a right vector-pair, and it is chosen in this sequence so that its projection onto the straight line OM parallel to the direction conjugate with OM lies at a minimal distance from the point O.

45. There cannot exist two distinct points M for which the corresponding vector-pairs are identical, up to a hyperbolic rotation by an angle less than the

Pell angle, for it is clear that the hyperbolic angle of two such vector-pairs would also be an angle of periodicity of the lattice (Figure 23).

§4. THE THEORY OF POSITIVE BINARY QUADRATIC FORMS

We turn now to methods that will enable us to introduce calculations into the theory of lattices.

46. The positive binary quadratic form corresponding to a given vector-pair. A particular lattice E_2 can be defined by the length of the sides of its basic vector-pair OPQ and the magnitude of the angle formed by them. However, another method is more convenient. We are given the squares A and C of the magnitude of the vectors of the basic vector-pair and the product B of these magnitudes by the cosine of the angle ϕ between the vectors. By the well-known formula for the square of the side of an oblique triangle, we find that the square of the distance from the point O to a point of the lattice E_2 that has coordinates x and y with respect to the basic vector-pair is

$$Ax^2 + 2Bxy + Cy^2.$$

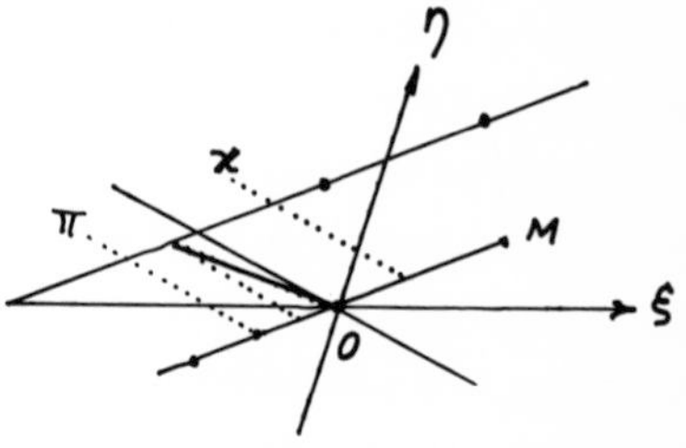

Figure 23

This connection between the quadratic form and the vector-pair OPQ may be represented in a different way. Let ξ and η be arbitrarily chosen rectangular coordinates and let the vector-pair OPQ lie in their plane so that the point O coincides with the origin of coordinates. Then if the points P and Q have the coordinates (ξ_1, η_1) and (ξ_2, η_2) clearly $\xi_1\xi_2 + \eta_1\eta_2 = \overline{OP} \cdot \overline{OQ} \cos\phi$ (i.e., is equal to the scalar product of the vectors $\overrightarrow{OP}$ and $\overrightarrow{OQ}$). Thus we have

$$(x\xi_1 + y\xi_2)^2 + (x\eta_1 + y\eta_2)^2$$
$$= (\xi_1^2 + \eta_1^2)x^2 + 2(\xi_1\xi_2 + \eta_1\eta_2)\,xy + (\xi_2^2 + \eta_2^2)y^2 = Ax^2 + 2Bxy + Cy^2.$$

Among other things it follows from this that the form $Ax^2 + 2Bxy + Cy^2$, which we will also abbreviate to (A, B, C), is positive.

From the point of view of vectors the form (A, B, C) is simply the scalar square of the linear vector expression $px + qy$, i.e., $Ax^2 + 2Bxy + Cy^2 = (px + qy)^2$, where p and q are the vectors $\overrightarrow{OP}$ and $\overrightarrow{OQ}$; in fact

$$A = \xi_1^2 + \eta_1^2 = p^2, \quad B = \xi_1\xi_2 + \eta_1\eta_2 = (pq), \quad C = \xi_2^2 + \eta_2^2 = q^2.$$

47. It is not difficult to see that if the form (A, B, C) undergoes a permutation $\begin{bmatrix}\alpha, & \beta\\ \gamma, & \delta\end{bmatrix}$, i.e., x and y are interchanged in the expressions $\alpha x + \beta y$ and $\gamma x + \delta y$, where α, β, γ, and δ are real numbers, we obtain the form $(\bar{A}, \bar{B}, \bar{C})$, whose vector-pair $O\bar{P}\bar{Q}$ has the ends of its vectors $\bar{P}$ and $\bar{Q}$ at the points with coordinates (α, γ) and (β, δ) with respect to the vector-pair OPQ. If α, β, γ, and δ are rational integers and $\alpha\delta - \beta\gamma = \pm 1$, then the vector-pair $O\bar{P}\bar{Q}$ is again a basic vector-pair of the lattice E_2. In fact, the points $\bar{P}$ and $\bar{Q}$ are then points of this lattice and the area of the parallelogram $O\bar{P}\bar{Q}$ is equal to the area of the parallelogram OPQ. In this case the forms (A, B, C) and $(\bar{A}, \bar{B}, \bar{C})$ are said to be *equivalent*; they are *properly equivalent* if $\alpha\delta - \beta\gamma = 1$, and *improperly equivalent* if $\alpha\delta - \beta\gamma = -1$. Properly equivalent forms correspond to basic vector-pairs with the same direction of rotation, while improperly equivalent forms correspond to vector-pairs with opposite directions of rotation.

Thus lattices E_2 and classes of properly equivalent binary positive quadratic forms correspond to each other in the sense that to each such class there corresponds a definite lattice E_2, and to each lattice E_2 there correspond in general two such classes, depending on which of the two directions of rotation is considered positive. The determinant of the form $D = B^2 - AC$ is equal to $-(\xi_1\eta_2 - \xi_2\eta_1)^2$, which is equal to $-s^2$, where s is the area of a basic parallelogram of the given lattice E_2.

48. The form (A, B, C) is said to be *reduced* (following Gauss) if its vector-pair is reduced in the sense of §2, subsection 16. The conditions indicated in Theorem VIII yield the following *conditions of reduction* expressed in terms of the quantities A, B, and C:

$$C \geq A \geq 2|B|.$$

49. The *reduction algorithm* (following Gauss) presented in §2, subsection 19 is translated into the language of calculation in the following way. The form (A', B', A'') is found, which is adjacent on the right to the given form (A, B, A'): $(A', B', A'') = (A, B, A')\begin{bmatrix}0, & 1\\ -1, & \delta\end{bmatrix}$, where the number δ is chosen so that $B' = -B + A'\delta$ is between $-A'/2$ and $A'/2$. Then the form (A'', B'', A''') adjacent on the right to the form (A', B', A'') is found in exactly the same way, and so on until finally one of the forms, for example the form $(A^{(n)}, B^{(n)}, A^{(n+1)})$, does not satisfy the conditions of reduction.

50. If the form (A, B, C) is reduced and $B \geq 0$, then its vector-pair determines a nonoblique triangle; but if $B < 0$, then such a triangle is given by the form $(A, B, C)\begin{pmatrix}0, & -1\\ 1, & 0\end{pmatrix} = (C, -B, A)$. If the form (A, B, C) determines an acute triangle, then the transformation for going from this vector-pair to itself and to the other vector-pairs corresponding to the five remaining acute triangles surrounding the point O are the following:

$$\begin{pmatrix}1, & 0\\ 0, & 1\end{pmatrix}, \begin{pmatrix}0, & -1\\ 1, & 1\end{pmatrix}, \begin{pmatrix}-1, & -1\\ 1, & 0\end{pmatrix}, \begin{pmatrix}-1, & 0\\ 0, & -1\end{pmatrix}, \begin{pmatrix}0, & 1\\ -1, & -1\end{pmatrix}, \begin{pmatrix}1, & 1\\ -1, & 0\end{pmatrix}.$$

The following forms correspond to them:

$$(A, B, C), (C, -B+C, A-2B+C), (A-2B+C, A-B, A);$$
$$(A, B, C), (C, -B+C, A-2B+C), (A-2B+C, A-B, A).$$

51. Tabulation of positive binary quadratic forms with integer coefficients. The discussion of positive forms (A, B, C) has up to now referred to the case of completely arbitrary real coefficients A, B, C. However, one often considers forms whose coefficients A, B, C are ordinary rational integers. For forms with rational integer coefficients the following fundamental theorem holds: *The number of classes of such forms with the same discriminant D is finite.*

For the proof of this theorem we note that, from the conditions of reduction for a reduced form there follow the inequalities $A^2 \leq AC$, $4B^2 \leq A^2$, from which we have $4B^2 \leq AC$, or $3B^2 \leq AC - B^2 = |D|$, i.e., $|B| \leq \sqrt{|D|/3}$. Thus if the discriminant of a positive form with integer coefficients is equal to D, then B may take on only the values $0, \pm 1, \pm 2, \cdots, \pm \lambda$, where λ is the greatest integer $[\sqrt{|D|/3}]$, in $\sqrt{|D|/3}$. If B is now given one of these values, then $AC = B^2 + |D|$. Thus it is necessary to factor the number $B^2 + |D|$ in all possible ways into two positive factors (in the case of a positive form A and C are both always positive) and take each time for A that factor which does not exceed the other, which will be taken for C. If it turns out that $A \geq 2|B|$, then the form thus obtained is reduced and is to be recorded; in the contrary case it is omitted. By this method we necessarily obtain all the reduced forms.

By subsection 16 of §2 we may decide whether there are equivalent forms among them. Subsections 16 and 17 of §2 show that the only cases when two nonidentical reduced forms are properly equivalent are the cases 1) $\lambda = \mu$ and 2) $\lambda < \mu = \nu$ (the case $\lambda = \mu = \nu$ is not an exception with respect to forms, for it also gives only two distinct reduced forms). In case 1) one of the reduced forms is the form (A, B, A) and the other is the form $(A, -B, A)$ obtained from the first by the transformation $\begin{pmatrix} 0, & -1 \\ 1, & 0 \end{pmatrix}$; in case 2) the forms are $(A, \frac{1}{2} A, C)$ and $(A, -\frac{1}{2} A, C)$, where the first goes into the second under the transformation $\begin{pmatrix} 1, & -1 \\ 0, & 1 \end{pmatrix}$.

In §67 we present three examples of the determination of all nonequivalent reduced forms for a given negative determinant $D = -\Delta$.

52. The resolution of the question of whether two given positive binary quadratic forms with integer coefficients are properly equivalent. If the determinants are not equal the forms are not equivalent. If they are equal, we find two reduced forms of which the first is properly equivalent to the first of the given forms and the second to the second. It is clear that the given forms are properly equivalent if and only if these reduced forms are identical or if one of the exceptional cases just indicated takes place. Let S and T be the transformations by means of which the two forms are transformed into identical reduced forms. Then the first form goes into the second by means of the transformation ST^{-1}.

53. The representation of numbers by means of positive binary forms with integer coefficients. Let m be a given positive rational integer, and let A, B, C also be rational integers. It is required to solve the equation $Ax^2 + 2Bxy + Cy^2 = m$ in rational integers x, y. Each such solution x, y is said to be a *representation* of the number m in terms of the form (A, B, C). The determination of all these representations is the determination of all the points M of the lattice corresponding to the forms that lie on the circle of radius $\sqrt{m}$ with center at the point O.

It is sufficient to give a method for the determination of all the representations in which x and y are relatively prime. In fact, if their greatest common divisor were μ, for example, then the number m would be divisible by μ^2, and the determination of all such representations reduces to the determination of the representation of the number m/μ^2 in terms of numbers x, y that have no common divisor.

In order to find all the representations with relatively prime x and y it is only necessary to list, as in subsections 20 and 21 of §2, all the forms (m, N, L) with $N^2 - mL = D$ and $m \geq 2|N|$ (there will be as many such forms as there are solutions N of the congruence $D \equiv N^2 \pmod{m}$ for which $-m/2 \leq N \leq m/2$), since such forms correspond to all the vector-pairs with parameter OM (where

$\overline{OM}^2 = m$). Thus for each vector-pair corresponding to each listed form it is necessary to decide whether it is located in the lattice of the given form. In other words, for each of the listed forms it is necessary to decide whether it is properly equivalent to the given form (since by definition of the corresponding vector-pair we always consider it to be right, i.e., with the same direction of rotation as the given form). If

$$(A,\ B,\ C)\begin{pmatrix} x_1, & \beta \\ y_1, & \delta \end{pmatrix} = (m,\ N,\ L),$$

then x_1, y_1 is a representation of the number m.

In view of what was said in subsection 20 of §2, the representation thus obtained, together with the associated representations $-x_1, -y_1$ give in the general case all the relatively prime representations of the number m. If the Pell angle is $90°$, then there are the further representations

$$-\frac{x_1B + y_1C}{\sigma},\quad \frac{x_1A + y_1B}{\sigma}$$

and the ones associated with them, and in the case when it is equal to $60°$ the representations

$$\frac{1}{2}x_1 - \frac{x_1B + y_1C}{\sigma},\quad \frac{1}{2}y_1 + \frac{x_1A + y_1B}{\sigma};$$

$$\frac{1}{2}x_1 + \frac{x_1B + y_1C}{\sigma},\quad \frac{1}{2}y_1 - \frac{x_1A + y_1B}{\sigma}$$

and the representations associated with them; here σ designates the greatest common divisor of the numbers A, $2B$ and C.

We do not derive these formulas here, for they are easily obtained on the basis of what was said in subsection 21 of §2.

§5. THE THEORY OF INDEFINITE BINARY QUADRATIC FORMS

54. The indefinite binary quadratic form corresponding to a given vector-pair. A form (A, B, C) with positive determinant D is said to be indefinite. Each such form may be interpreted in the following way. Let $O\xi$, $O\eta$ be arbitrarily chosen asymptotes and let

$$Ax^2 + 2Bxy + Cy^2 = (\xi_1x + \xi_2y)\,(\eta_1x + \eta_2y)$$

(if $D = B^2 - AC > 0$, then ξ_1, ξ_2, η_1, and η_2 are real); then we may put in correspondence to this form the vector-pair OPQ, the ends P and Q of whose vectors have coordinates (ξ_1, η_1) and (ξ_2, η_2) with respect to the chosen asymptotes.

Thus to a given vector-pair there will correspond a unique indefinite form, and to the given form, a continuum of such vector-pairs depending on one parameter. In fact, if ρ is an arbitrary real number, then $(\rho\xi_1 x + \rho\xi_2 y)\,(\eta_1 x/\rho + \eta_2 y/\rho)$ will also be a decomposition of the same form, and there will be no other decompositions.

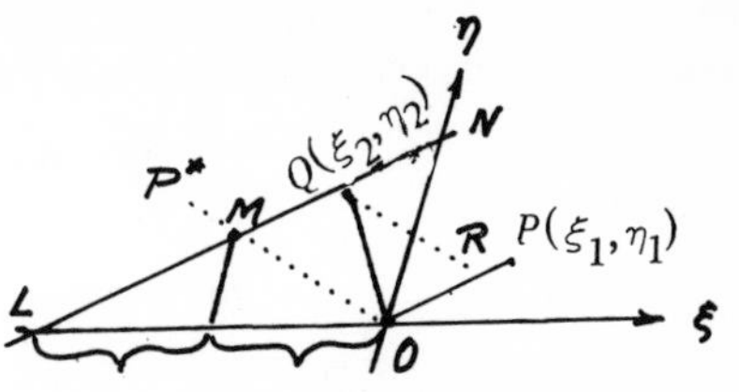

Figure 24

Such a multiplication by ρ, where ρ is positive, is a hyperbolic rotation. Under this rotation the end P of the first vector of the vector-pair OPQ of the form will slide along the hyperbola $\xi\eta = A$, and the end Q of the second vector, along the hyperbola $\xi\eta = C$, while the square of the area of the parallelogram constructed on this vector-pair will remain equal to $(\xi_1\eta_2 - \xi_2\eta_1)^2 = 4(B^2 - AC) = 4D$. But if ρ is negative, the reflected vector-pair will be obtained.

As was already mentioned, $A = \xi_1\eta_1$, $2B = \xi_1\eta_2 + \xi_2\eta_1$, $C = \xi_2\eta_2$. If the square root of the parameter of the hyperbola on which the point lies is now called the *hyperbolic distance* from this point to the point O, then A and C will be the squares of the hyperbolic lengths of the vectors OP and OQ of the vector-pair. The geometric meaning of B is the following. This B is the product of the hyperbolic length of the first vector OP by the hyperbolic length of the orthogonal projection (in the hyperbolic sense) OR of the second vector onto the first vector (Figure 24). Here again, as in subsection 44 of §3, the straight line QR is said to be hyperbolically orthogonal to the straight line OP if it is parallel to the direction of OP^* conjugate with the direction of OP with respect to the asymptotes $O\xi$, $O\eta$ (where OP^* is the diameter conjugate with OP, or, in other words, $LM = MN$, where LN is the chord parallel to OP). In fact, direct calculation gives for the coordinates of the point R the values $k\xi_1$, $k\eta_1$, where $k = \xi_1\eta_2 + \xi_2\eta_1/2\xi_1\eta_1$. From this the product of the hyperbolic lengths of OP and OR is equal to $\sqrt{\xi_1\eta_1}\,\sqrt{k\xi_1 k\eta_1} = k\xi_1\eta_1 = B$.

When translated into the language of vectors this means that the indefinite form $Ax^2 + 2Bxy + Cy^2 = (px + qy)^2$, where the expression $(px + qy)^2$ is the scalar square in the ordinary sense, the length of a vector is understood to be its hyperbolic length, and the length of an orthogonal projection of one vector onto another is understood to be the hyperbolic length of the hyperbolically orthogonal projection.

The point with coordinates x, y with respect to the frame OPQ has coordinates $\xi_1 x + \xi_2 y, \eta_1 x + \eta_2 y$ with respect to the asymptotes $O\xi$, $O\eta$, i.e., it lies on the hyperbola $\xi\eta = Ax^2 + 2Bxy + Cy^2$ with respect to these asymptotes, or on the hyperbola whose parameter is equal to the value of the form for the pair x, y. Hence this value is equal to the square of the hyperbolic distance from the point x, y to the point O.

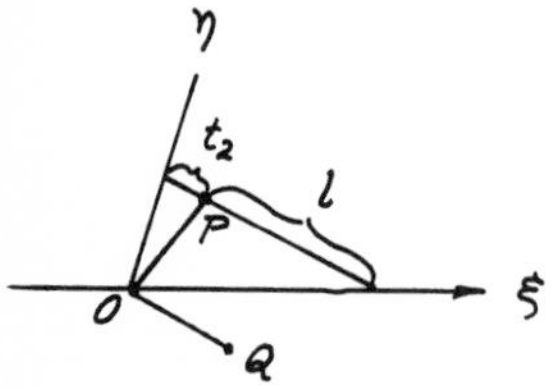

Figure 25

55. *If we want to obtain a form corresponding to the vector-pair for which the ends of the sides have the coordinates* α, γ *and* β, δ *with respect to the vector-pair* OPQ *of a given indefinite form* (A, B, C) *then in exactly the same way as for positive forms we must transform this form by the transformation* $\begin{pmatrix} \alpha, & \beta \\ \gamma, & \delta \end{pmatrix}$. If α, β, γ, and δ are integers and $\alpha\delta - \beta\gamma = \pm 1$, then the second form is also said to be *equivalent* to the first, *properly*, if $\alpha\delta - \beta\gamma = 1$, and *improperly*, if $\alpha\delta - \beta\gamma = -1$. To distinct basic vector-pairs of the same lattice E_2 with respect to the same asymptotes there correspond equivalent forms, i.e., there corresponds to the lattice E_2 with fixed asymptotes and a right direction in its plane a class of forms, whereby a class we mean a collection of properly equivalent forms.

56. Reduced indefinite binary quadratic forms. We will call such a form reduced if its vector-pair is reduced with respect to one of the asymptotes in the sense of subsection 29 of §3, i.e., by Theorem XIII of §3, if it covers one asymptote and the end of its second vector lies further along but closer to it than the end of the first vector. In order to obtain reduction conditions and methods of calculation for the case under consideration it is convenient to consider the geometrical significance of the roots of the equation $A + 2Bt + Ct^2 = 0$, which we will call the *roots of the form* (A, B, C).

If the length of the beak is t, then the coordinates of its end with respect to the vector-pair are $(1, t)$. The parameter of the hyperbola on which this point lies is equal to $A + 2Bt + Ct^2$. Thus the roots t_1 and t_2 of the form are numbers showing how many times it is necessary to lay out the second vector OQ of the form on the beak, starting from the end of its first side P, in order to reach the asymptote (Figure 25). From this we see directly that the vector-pair of the form will include two, one, or no asymptotes depending on whether the form has two, one or no positive roots. The vector-pair includes one and only one asymptote if its roots have opposite signs, i.e., if $AC < 0$. It is easy to see that the form will be reduced if and only if the positive root $t_1 > 1$, while the negative root t_2 is in absolute value less than unity, $|t_2| < 1$. The *reduction conditions* are consequently the following:

$$0 < B + \sqrt{D} < C < -B + \sqrt{D} \quad \text{for } C > 0,$$

$$0 < -B + \sqrt{D} < |C| < B + \sqrt{D} \quad \text{for } C < 0.$$

The number C can not be equal to zero, for then the point Q would lie on the asymptote, while the asymptotes are assumed to be irrational.

57. In order to pass from an arbitrary indefinite form to the form equivalent to it (properly or improperly) and then to carry out the calculation of a chain of reduced forms following it, we need only to translate the algorithm of subsections 32 and 33 of §3 into the language of calculation.

If the form covers no asymptotes so that both its roots are negative, i.e., $AC > 0$ and $BC > 0$, then by subsection 32 of §3 it is necessary to use the transformation $\begin{pmatrix} 1, & 0 \\ 0, & -1 \end{pmatrix}$ to pass to the form $(A, -B, C)$ that already covers two asymptotes. This is the preparatory transformation. The further transformations of the algorithm of subsection 33 of §3 clearly consist in transformations of the type $\begin{pmatrix} 0, & 1 \\ 1, & \delta \end{pmatrix}$, where δ is the greatest positive integer which is less than the greatest positive root of the form. Hence, if $C > 0$, then $\delta = [(-B + \sqrt{D})/C]$, and for $C < 0$, $\delta = [(B + \sqrt{D})/|C|]$, where [ ], as always, designates the greatest integer less than or equal to the expression enclosed in the brackets.

These calculations are most simply carried out in the following way. If (A, B, A') is the prepared form and (A', B', A'') is the transformed form, then $B' = B + A'\delta$, where δ has the indicated value. Thus B' satisfies the inequalities $\sqrt{D} - A' \leq B' \leq \sqrt{D}$, if $A' > 0$, and $-\sqrt{D} \leq B' \leq -\sqrt{D} - A'$ for $A' < 0$; or assuming $\lambda = [\sqrt{D}\,]$, we obtain for B' the inequalities

$$\left.\begin{aligned} \lambda + 1 - A' \leq B' &\leq \lambda, && \text{if } A' > 0, \\ -\lambda \leq B' &\leq -\lambda - 1 - A', && \text{if } A' < 0. \end{aligned}\right\} \qquad (*)$$

Consequently, it is necessary to look for a $B' = B + A'\delta$ satisfying the corresponding one of the inequalities (*), but this can be at once determined by a glance at the form. Clearly there is always one and only one such B'. We obtain δ in the same way. To obtain A'' we note that $B'^2 - A'A'' = B^2 - AA'$; setting here $B' = B + A'\delta$, we find

$$A'' = A + (B + B')\delta. \qquad (**)$$

EXAMPLE. Let $(A, B, A') = \phi_0 = (3, 1, -4)$. Here $AC < 0$, i.e., the form ϕ_0 is already prepared. We have $D = B^2 - AC = 13$, $\lambda = [\sqrt{13}] = 3$. Since $A' = -4 < 0$, it is necessary to use the second of the inequalities of (*). We obtain $-3 \leq B' \leq -4 + 4 = 0$, and $B' = 1 - 4\delta$, from which it follows that $\delta = 1$, $B' = -3$; this means, in view of formula (**), that $A'' = 3 + (1 - 3)\delta = 1$. Thus the transformed form (A', B', A'') is the form $\phi_1 = (-4, -3, 1)$.

To obtain the next transformed form $(A'', B'', A''') = \phi_2$, we use the first of the inequalities of (*), since $A'' = 1 > 0$. We obtain $4 - 1 \leq B'' \leq 3$ and $B'' = -3 + 1 \cdot \delta$, from which it follows that $\delta = 6$ and $B'' = 3$. Consequently, on the basis of formula (**), $A''' = -4 + (-3 + 3)6 = -4$, and hence $\phi_2 = (1, 3, -4)$. Further calculations give the forms $\phi_3 = (-4, -1, 3)$, $\phi_4 = (3, 2, -3)$, $\phi_5 = (-3, -1, 4)$, $\phi_6 = (4, 3, -1)$, $\phi_7 = (-1, -3, 4)$, $\phi_8 = (4, 1, -3)$, $\phi_9 = (-3, -2, 3)$ and $\phi_{10} = (3, 1, -4)$, i.e., again ϕ_0.

58. The tabulation of indefinite binary quadratic forms with integer coefficients. Up to now no special assumptions have been made concerning the coefficients of indefinite forms. Now let A, B and C be rational integers, i.e., we are considering indefinite forms with integer coefficients. It turns out that the following fundamental theorem is also true for them: the number of distinct classes of forms with the same discriminant D is finite.

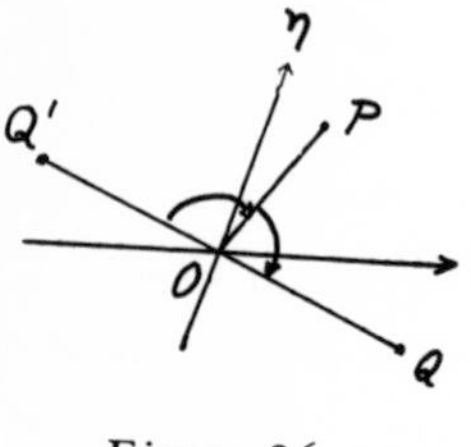

Figure 26

This quickly follows from the fact that each class contains reduced forms. In fact, if one of the reduced forms is improperly equivalent to a given one, then the form following it will be properly equivalent to the given form since two successive forms have opposite directions of rotation. If the form is reduced, then its coefficients A and C are of opposite sign, i.e., $AC < 0$. But $D = B^2 - AC > 0$, i.e., $B^2 < D$, and consequently there are only a finite number of possible values that may be taken on by the coefficient B in the reduced form with given determinant D; and for each such B there are only a finite number of values for A and C since $|A| \cdot |C|$ must be equal to $D - B^2$.

If (A, B, C) is a reduced form of a class and OPQ is its vector-pair, then the vector-pair $OQ'P$ is also reduced and has the same direction of rotation as the vector-pair OPQ (Figure 26). This means that the form $(C, -B, A)$ corresponding to it will again be a reduced form of the same class. Thus in each class there will be reduced forms for which $B > 0$. B cannot be zero, for then we would obtain from the reduction inequalities that $\sqrt{D} = C$, and the asymptotes would not be irrational. We see from the reduction inequalities that if $B > 0$ for the reduced form, then $A > 0$ and $C < 0$. Hence for such a reduced form we have

$$A = \frac{D - B^2}{|C|} = \frac{(\sqrt{D} + B)(\sqrt{D} - B)}{|C|},$$

$$0 < \frac{-B + \sqrt{D}}{|C|} < 1 \text{ and } 1 < \frac{B + \sqrt{D}}{|C|}.$$

Consequently, for such a reduced form with $B > 0$ we have

$$\sqrt{D} - B < A < \sqrt{D} + B \text{ and } \sqrt{D} - B < |C| < \sqrt{D} + B.$$

Thus, in order to obtain all possible forms with integer coefficients for a positive determinant D and $B > 0$, for each value of B from the sequence 1, 2, 3, $\cdots$, λ, where $\lambda = [\sqrt{D}]$, it is necessary to factor $D - B^2$ in all possible ways into two positive factors lying between $\lambda - B + 1$ and $\lambda + B$ inclusive. Then one of these factors is taken for A, while the other, taken with a negative sign, is set equal to C.

EXAMPLE.

$D = 13,$		$\lambda = [\sqrt{13}] = 3,$	
$B = 1,$		$2,$	$3,$
$D - B^2 = 12,$		$9,$	$4,$
$A \cdot \lvert C \rvert =$	$(1 \cdot 12),$	$(1 \cdot 9),$	$\boxed{1 \cdot 4},$
	$(2 \cdot 6)$	$\boxed{3 \cdot 3},$	$\boxed{2 \cdot 2},$
	$\boxed{3 \cdot 4},$	$(9 \cdot 1),$	$\boxed{4 \cdot 1}.$
	$\boxed{4 \cdot 3},$		
	$(6 \cdot 2),$		
	$(12 \cdot 1),$		

The factorizations enclosed in brackets do not satisfy the inequalities for A and $|C|$. Thus we obtain for $D = 13$ six reduced forms with the coefficient $B > 0$:

$$(3, 1, -4), (4, -1, 3), (3, 2, -3), (1, 3, -4), (2, 3, -2), (4, 3, -1).$$

However, it is impossible to conclude from this that there are six classes of forms with integer coefficients and determinant $D = 13$, since in the case of an indefinite form some of the reduced forms with $B > 0$ may be equivalent to one another.

59. **The periodicity of a chain of reduced forms in the case of a form with integer coefficients.** This periodicity follows directly from Theorems XIV and XV (subsections 39 and 40 of §3), since a form with integer coefficients for integer x and y is itself an integer. This means that the parameters of all the hyperbolas containing the points of the lattice E_2 that correspond to the form are integers. Thus, by Theorem XIV all the relative minima lie on a finite number of hyperbolas.

This also follows from the fact just proven, that there are in general only a finite number of reduced forms with integer coefficients and the same determinant D.

If the period consists of k members and OPP_1 is a reduced vector-pair, then under the transformation $\begin{Bmatrix} \alpha_1, & \beta_1 \\ \gamma_1, & \delta_1 \end{Bmatrix}$ that takes the vector-pair OPP_1 into the vector-pair OP_kP_{k+1} the form (A, B, C) corresponding to the vector-pair OPP_1 goes into itself. All the remaining transformations which take the form into itself are clearly of the form $\pm \begin{Bmatrix} \alpha_1, & \beta_1 \\ \gamma_1, & \delta_1 \end{Bmatrix}^s$ with positive and negative integer exponents s. These tranformations are called *automorphisms* of the form.

60. **The resolution of the question of whether there are two properly equivalent indefinite binary quadratic forms with integer coefficients.** If the determinants of the forms under consideration are different the forms will not be equivalent. If the determinants are equal, then by means of the reduction algorithm we find a reduced form properly equivalent to the first of the given forms. It is necessary to note that all the transformations of this algorithm, including the preparatory one if it is necessary, are improper transformations. Thus if we pass to a reduced form by means of an odd number of transformations, it is necessary to calculate the next reduced form in order to obtain a reduced form properly equivalent to the given one.

Then we turn to the second form and calculate for it the whole period of reduced forms. If the reduced form (A, B, C) properly equivalent to the first form, or the reduced form $(C, -B, A)$ properly equivalent to the form (A, B, C), occurs in the indicated period and is therefore obtained from the second form by an even number of transformations, then the two given forms are properly equivalent; in the contrary case they are improperly equivalent.

In fact, each form possesses reduced forms equivalent to it, and all reduced forms properly equivalent to some form are located either in the chain of its reduced forms or in a chain along another asymptote. But the form of the second chain can be obtained by interchanging the outermost coefficients of the form and changing the sign of the middle coefficient.

61. **The representation of numbers by an indeterminate binary quadratic form with integer coefficients.** Let m be a given rational integer and let A, B, and C also be rational integers. It is required to find all the representations of the number m in terms of the form (A, B, C). The determination of all such representations is exactly the same problem as the determination of all the points M of the lattice corresponding to the form (A, B, C) that lie on the hyperbola $\xi\eta = m$. As in the case of positive forms it is sufficient again to indicate the method for the determination of all representations with relatively prime values x, y.

In view of subsections 44 and 45 of §3, we will in any case find *all* the relatively prime representations x, y, the points M of which lie on one branch of the hyperbola $\xi\eta = m$, if we find all the distinct vector-pairs corresponding to the parameter OM and then rotate each of these by all the angles which are multiples of the Pell angle of the given form. Other than these representations x, y, there exist only the relatively prime representations $-x$, $-y$ corresponding to the points symmetric to the points M with respect to the point O and lying on the other branch of the hyperbola $\xi\eta = m$.

The middle coefficient N of the form (m, N, L) corresponding to one of the vector-pairs set into correspondence with the parameter OM satisfies, in view of its geometric interpretation and of the property of the corresponding vector-pair, the inequality $-m/2 < N < m/2$ (in general, there are a finite number of such forms with integer coefficients and with determinant D, namely, as many as the number of roots N of the congruence $D \equiv -N^2 \pmod{m}$ satisfying the condition $-m/2 < N < m/2$).

Thus in order to find *all* the representations of the number m with relatively prime values of x and y, it is necessary to write out all such forms (m, N, L), and then to decide for each of these whether or not it is properly equivalent to the fiven form (A, B, C). Those of them for which this is true give the *fundamental* solutions of the equation $(A, B, C) = m$, since if $(A, B, C) \begin{pmatrix} x_1, & \beta \\ y_1, & \delta \end{pmatrix} = (m, N, L)$, then x_1, y_1 is a solution, namely that one which corresponds to the end of the first side of the form (m, N, L). In order to obtain all the solutions, it is necessary to find for each such solution the solutions x_s, y_s "homologous" to it in all the remaining Pell angles. For this it is necessary to transform the solution x_1, y_1 by all the automorphisms of the forms (A, B, C), i.e., by all the powers $\begin{pmatrix}\alpha_1, \beta_1\\ \gamma_1, \delta_1\end{pmatrix}$ of the basic automorphism.

If $\begin{pmatrix}\alpha_1, \beta_1\\ \gamma_1, \delta_1\end{pmatrix}^s = \begin{pmatrix}\alpha_s, \beta_s\\ \gamma_s, \delta_s\end{pmatrix}$, then all these representations obtained by transformation of a basic representation x_1, y_1 have the form $x_s = \alpha_s x_1 + \beta_s y_1$, $y_s = \gamma_s x_1 + \delta_s y_1$. Besides these representations homologous to the representation x_1, y_1 with respect to the periodicity of the hyperbolic rotation, there are associated with the representation x_1, y_1 the further representations $-x_s, -y_s$ symmetric with them with respect to the point O.

62. **Connection with the Pell equation.** All the automorphic transformations $\begin{pmatrix}\alpha_s, \beta_s\\ \gamma_s, \delta_s\end{pmatrix}$ and all the representations x_s, y_s homologous to the representation x_1, y_1 may be calculated much more conveniently if we turn to the parameter ρ of the Pell angle of the given form.

We consider an arbitrary nonzero point Q on the asymptote and let its coordinates with respect to the vector-pair OPP_1 be x, y. Then with respect to the vector-pair OP_kP_{k+1} (here we again assume that the period consists of k members) it has coordinates $x' = x/\rho$, $y' = y/\rho$, where ρ is the parameter of the Pell angle. From this we obtain $x/y = (\alpha_1 x + \beta_1 y)/(\gamma_1 x + \delta_1 y)$ or $\gamma_1 x^2 + (\delta_1 - \alpha_1)\, xy - \beta_1 y^2 = 0$. But since the point Q lies on the asymptote we have the further relation $Ax^2 + 2Bxy + Cy^2 = 0$. Hence $A : 2B : C = \gamma_1 : \delta_1 - \alpha_1 : -\beta_1$.

Among other things we here obtain the converse to the theorem about the periodicity of a lattice of a form with integer coefficients.

THEOREM XVII. *If a chain of reduced forms is periodic, then the coefficients A, B and C of the form are proportional to rational integers.*

In other words, if a lattice periodically repeats under hyperbolic rotation with respect to a given asymptote, then its form is proportional to a form with integer coefficients.

Let σ be the greatest common divisor of the numbers A, $2B$, and C. Then $\gamma_1 = Au_1/\sigma$, $\delta_1 - \alpha_1 = 2Bu_1/\sigma$, and $-\beta_1 = Cu_1/\sigma$, where u_1 is a rational integer.

f we have $\alpha_1 + \delta_1 = 2t_1/\sigma$, then we get $\alpha_1 = (t_1 - Bu_1)/\sigma$, $\beta_1 = -Cu_1/\sigma$, $\gamma_1 = Au_1/\sigma$, and $\delta_1 = (t_1 + Bu_1)/\sigma$. Or, since $\alpha_1\delta_1 - \beta_1\gamma_1 = 1$ (namely $+1$, since the two vector-pairs OPP_1 and OP_kP_{k+1} are identically oriented), we have $t_1^2 - Du_1^2 = \sigma^2$, i.e., we obtain the Pell equation. If (ξ_1, η_1) and (ξ_2, η_2) are the coordinates of the points P and P_1, while (ξ_1', η_1') and (ξ_2', η_2') are the coordinates of the points P_k and P_{k+1}, then $\xi_1' = \alpha_1\xi_1 + \gamma_1\xi_2$ and $\xi_2' = \beta_1\xi_1 + \delta_1\xi_2$. Moreover, we have $\xi_1' = \rho\xi_1$ and $\xi_2' = \rho\xi_2$; thus we obtain

$$(\alpha_1 - \rho)\,\xi_1 + \gamma_1\xi_2 = 0, \quad \beta_1\xi_1 + (\delta - \rho)\,\xi_2 = 0,$$

from which it follows that

$$\rho^2 - (\alpha_1 + \delta_1)\,\rho + (\alpha_1\delta_1 - \beta_1\gamma_1) = 0.$$

If we substitute here the expressions just obtained for α_1, β_1, γ_1, and δ_1 the equation will take the form $\rho^2 - 2t_1\rho/\sigma + (t_1^2 - Du_1^2)/\sigma^2 = 0$ or $\rho = (t_1 \pm \sqrt{D}\,u_1)/\sigma$.

The transition from the vector-pair OPP_1 to the vector-pair $OP_{sk}P_{sk+1}$ corresponds to the parameter ρ^s which is associated with the magnitudes of α_s, β_s, γ_s, and δ_s in the same way that the parameter ρ is associated with the magnitudes of α_1, β_1, γ_1 and δ_1. From this we obtain first, that in the relation

$$\left[\frac{t_1 + \sqrt{D}\,u_1}{\sigma}\right]^s = \frac{t_s + \sqrt{D}\,u_s}{\sigma}$$

t_s and u_s are integers, and secondly, that

$$\alpha_s = \frac{t_s - Bu_s}{\sigma}, \quad \beta_s = \frac{-Cu_s}{\sigma}, \quad \gamma_s = \frac{Au_s}{\sigma}, \quad \delta_s = \frac{t_s + Bu_s}{\sigma}.$$

Hence all the solutions homologous to the solution x_1, y_1 are obtained in the following form:

$$x_s = \frac{1}{\sigma}\,[x_1t_s - (x_1B + y_1C)\,u_s],$$
$$y_s = \frac{1}{\sigma}\,[y_1t_s + (x_1A + y_1B)\,u_s].$$

63. The case of a form with integer coefficients whose determinant is a perfect square. This case is not covered by the above theorem since the asymptotes are rational. It is possible to show that all the different classes of such forms for which $D = d^2$ have as their representatives the forms

$$(0, d, -d+1),\ (0, d, -d+2), \cdots, (0, d, 0), \cdots, (0, d, d-1),\ (0, d, d).$$

Since

$$Ax^2 + 2Bxy + Cy^2 = \left[\frac{-B+d}{C}\,x - y\right]\left[\frac{-B-d}{C}\,x - y\right]C,$$

the representation of the number m in terms of such a form leads simply to the solution of the determinate system of equations

$$(-B+d)x-Cy=m_1, \quad (-B-d)x-Cy=m_2$$

in integers x, y for all factorizations of the number mC into integer factors m_1, m_2.

SUPPLEMENT TWO

INVESTIGATIONS IN THE GEOMETRY OF GALOIS THEORY [1)]

B. N. DELONE and D. K. FADDEEV

§1. THE THEORY OF R-ALGEBRAS

1. **The space K_n as an algebra.** Let there be given a completely arbitrary (commutative) field K and an n-dimensional vector space over it. We choose in the field a basis $\mathbf{E}_n$ and besides the operations of vector addition and subtraction and multiplication by scalars (elements of K), we introduce the operation of multiplication of vectors (points). The product of two vectors will be the vector whose coordinates with respect to the chosen basis (the initial basis) are equal to the products of the corresponding coordinates of the vectors being multiplied. Under the introduction of this operation the vector space becomes a commutative algebra, which we will denote by K_n. Among the K-linear subspaces of K_n we note the *coordinate subspaces* spanned by a subset of the vectors of the initial basis, and the *bisectrices*, namely the sets of all points having equal coordinates with respect to complexes of vectors into which all the vectors of the initial basis can be decomposed. By the *initial basis of a bisectrix* we mean the collection of all vectors, each of whose coordinates is equal to 1 in one of the complexes of vectors of the initial coordinate basis $\mathbf{E}_n$ characterizing the bisectrix, and is equal to zero in the remaining axes. Correspondingly, the *initial basis of a coordinate subspace* will be the collection of vectors from the initial basis $\mathbf{E}_n$ by which the subspace is spanned. Bisectrices and coordinate subspaces are subalgebras of K_n, while multiplication of points of a bisectrix (coordinate subspace) with respect to the initial basis of the whole K_n coincides with multiplication defined for the bisectrix (coordinate subspace) with respect to its initial basis.

LEMMA 1. *Any K-subalgebra Q of the algebra K_n is either a coordinate*

---

1) This Supplement is a translation of the first four sections of the article in Mat. Sb. (N.S.) 15 (57) (1944), 244–254.

subspace, a bisectrix of $\mathbf{E}_n$*, or a bisectrix of a coordinate subspace.*

PROOF. We choose a numbering of the axes so that points with nonzero first coordinates are located in Q. Among these points we choose a point ω, with the least number of nonzero coordinates. Then all the nonzero coordinates of the point ω are equal. In fact, if we assume that ω has a coordinate $\omega^{(2)}$ different from the first coordinate $\omega^{(1)}$ and different from zero, then the point $\omega' = \omega^2 - \omega^{(2)} \cdot \omega$, belonging to Q, would have a nonzero first coordinate and a smaller number of nonzero coordinates then ω. Together with the point ω, Q contains the point $\epsilon_1 = \omega^{(1)-1} \cdot \omega$, whose coordinates with the given numbering of axes are $(\underbrace{1, 1, \cdots, 1}_{n_1}, 0, 0, \cdots, 0)$. Moreover, the first n_1 coordinates of any point τ in Q are equal, for if there were a coordinate $\tau^{(2)}$ of the point τ, taken from among the first n_1 coordinates and not equal to the first coordinate $\tau^{(1)}$, then the point $\tau' = \tau \cdot \epsilon_1 - \tau^{(2)} \cdot \epsilon_1$ would have a nonzero first coordinate and would have fewer nonzero coordinates than ω. Applying the same argument to each coordinate axis for which there exist points of Q with the corresponding coordinate different from zero, we see that all the points of Q have coordinates

$$(\underbrace{\omega^{(1)}, \cdots, \omega^{(1)}}_{n_1}, \cdots, \underbrace{\omega^{(m)}, \cdots, \omega^{(m)}}_{n_m}, \underbrace{0, \cdots, 0}_{n'}),$$

where the points

$$\epsilon_1 = (\underbrace{1, \cdots, 1}_{n_1}, 0, \cdots, 0), \cdots, \epsilon_m = (0, \cdots, 0, \underbrace{1, \cdots, 1}_{n_m}, \underbrace{0, \cdots, 0}_{n'})$$

belong to Q, and therefore $\omega^{(1)}, \cdots, \omega^{(m)}$ are arbitrary elements of K. If $n_1 = \cdots = n_m = 1$, then Q is a coordinate subspace, and if $n' = 0$ then Q is a bisectrix of K_n; in the remaining cases Q is the bisectrix of a coordinate subspace. The lemma is proved.

2. R-algebras of the space K_n. Decomposition into a direct sum. Let there be given some field R contained in K, and let a basis $\mathfrak{E}_n$ be selected in K_n, which is, in general, not the initial one. By an R-module we will mean a collection of all points of K_n having elements of the field R as coordinates with respect to $\mathfrak{E}_n$. An R-module whose points are reproduced under multiplication will be called an R-algebra. An example of an R-algebra is an R-module constructed on the initial basis $\mathbf{E}_n$.

A linear subspace of K_n that is a K-linear envelope of some collection of vectors of an R-algebra $\mathbf{A}$ will be called an $\mathbf{A}$-*complete* subspace, and the collecion of points of **A** included in it will be called its **A**-*completion*. In particular, ll of K_n is **A**-complete. The dimension of an **A**-complete subspace is equal to he dimension (with respect to R) of its **A**-completion for, as it is easy to see, ectors of any R-module which are linearly independent with respect to R remain inearly independent with respect to K. Clearly, the vector sum of two **A**-complete ubspaces is **A**-complete. It is also easy to see that the intersection of two -complete subspaces is **A**-complete, since the dimension (with respect to K) of his intersection and the dimension of the completions contained in it are equal o the same number, namely, to the amount by which the sum of the dimensions of he given subspaces exceeds the dimension of their vector sum. A linear trans- ormation of K_n which takes all the points of an R-algebra **A** into points of **A** vill be said to be *rational* with respect to **A**. Clearly, linear transformations ational with respect to **A**, singular or nonsingular take any **A**-complete sub- pace of K_n (in particular all of K_n) into an **A**-complete subspace.

LEMMA 1$'$. *Subalgebras (over R) of an R-algebra* **A** *are* **A**-*completions of* -*complete subalgebras of K_n, i.e., they are bisectrices, coordinate subspaces,* *r bisectrices of coordinate subspaces.*

In fact, if **B** is a subalgebra of **A**, then its K-linear envelope $\overline{\mathbf{B}}$ is a sub- lgebra of K_n. Any m-dimensional subalgebra of the R-algebra **A** may be con- idered as an R-algebra of the space K_m, put into the corresponding coordinate ubspace or bisectrix, i.e., as an R-algebra of this subspace with respect to its nitial basis.

A *zero divisor* will be any point that has both zero and nonzero coordinates. t is easy to see that in any R-algebra it is possible to divide by any of the oints that are not zero or zero divisors. In fact, multiplication of K_n by such a oint λ is a nonsingular linear transformation rational with respect to **A** which akes all of **A** into all of **A**. Hence, for each point μ in **A** there is a point μ' n **A** such that $\mu'\lambda = \mu$, i.e., $\mu' = \mu/\lambda$. It further follows from this that any R- lgebra that contains at least one point that is not a zero-divisor and is not equal o zero will contain the identity $(1, 1, \cdots, 1)$.

If the R-algebra **A** can be represented in the form of a direct sum of two -algebras, i.e., in the form of the vector sum of two algebras completing the omplementary coordinate subspaces, then **A** is said to be a reducible algebra, hile if such a representation is impossible, **A** is said to be irreducible. Any educible R-algebra contains zero-divisors; for example, all the points of the lgebras which are being added. The very important converse also holds.

LEMMA 2. *If an R-algebra contains a zero-divisor ω, then it is reducible and decomposes into the direct sum of two R-algebras, one of which is in the coordinate subspace K_{n_1} which includes those axes for which the coordinates of ω are different from zero, while the other R-algebra is in the complementary coordinate subspace.*

PROOF. We multiply K_n by the point ω. When this is done, K_n goes into K_{n_1}. Since multiplication by a point $\omega \in \mathbf{A}$ is a rational transformation with respect to $\mathbf{A}$, therefore K_{n_1} will be $\mathbf{A}$-complete. The completion of K_{n_1} is clearl an algebra and will be denoted by $\mathbf{A}_1$. The point ω belongs to it and is not a zero-divisor in it; hence A_1 includes a unit ϵ_1 of the space K_{n_1}. Further, the transformation $\alpha' = \alpha - \alpha\epsilon_1$ is rational with respect to A and takes K_n into the space K_{n_2} that is complementary to K_{n_1}. This subspace is also $\mathbf{A}$-complete. It completion forms in its turn an algebra $\mathbf{A}_2$. Since for any $\alpha \in \mathbf{A}$, it is true that $\alpha = \alpha\epsilon_1 + (\alpha - \alpha\epsilon_1)$, $\alpha\epsilon_1 \in \mathbf{A}_1$, $\alpha - \alpha\epsilon_1 \in \mathbf{A}_2$ and $K_{n_1} \cap K_{n_2} = 0$, the algebra $\mathbf{A}$ is the direct sum of $\mathbf{A}_1$ and $\mathbf{A}_2$.

It is now easy to prove the following important theorem:

THEOREM 1. *Each R-algebra $\mathbf{A}$ is either irreducible or uniquely decompos able into the direct sum of irreducible algebras.*

PROOF. If $\mathbf{A}$ is reducible we decompose it into the direct sum of two algebras; if one or both of these is reducible we continue the decomposition, and so on. The process of decomposition must terminate, since the number of direct sum mands of $\mathbf{A}$ cannot exceed its dimension. Thus $\mathbf{A}$ is decomposed into the direct sum of irreducible R-algebras $\mathbf{A}_1, \mathbf{A}_2, \cdots, \mathbf{A}_k$. Since an irreducible algebra can not contain a zero-divisor, the complexes of vectors of the initial basis pertainin to the subspaces containing $\mathbf{A}_1, \mathbf{A}_2, \cdots, \mathbf{A}_k$ may be characterized by the fact that the coordinates of all of the points of $\mathbf{A}$ that correspond to each separate complex either vanish or do not vanish simultaneously. This holds for every complex of coordinate vectors of each subspace containing an irreducible summand o the algebra $\mathbf{A}$, and hence such a summand must coincide with one of the $\mathbf{A}_1$, $\mathbf{A}_2, \cdots, \mathbf{A}_k$. The theorem is proved.

We note that it follows from this theorem that any R-algebra contains a unit of K_n. In fact, each irreducible R-algebra contains a unit because of the possibility of division by any one of its points other than zero, while the sum of units of all the subspaces containing irreducible summands of the algebra is clearly a unit of the whole K_n.

3. The direct product of algebras. Let there be given points α and β

n the spaces K_m and K_n with coordinates $(\alpha^{(1)}, \alpha^{(2)}, \cdots, \alpha^{(m)})$ and $(\beta^{(1)}, \beta^{(2)}, \cdots, \beta^{(n)})$. We associate with them a point of the space K_{mn} with coordinates $(\cdots, \alpha^{(i)} \cdot \beta^{(j)}, \cdots)$, $i = 1, \cdots, m$; $j = 1, \cdots, n$. The point constructed in uch a manner will be called the *composite point* of α and β and will be denoted y $\alpha * \beta$. It is easy to convince oneself of the validity of the following rules for perations:

(1^1) $\alpha * (\beta_1 + \beta_2) = (\alpha * \beta_1) + (\alpha * \beta_2)$,

(1^2) $(\alpha_1 + \alpha_2) * \beta = (\alpha_1 * \beta) + (\alpha_2 * \beta)$,

(1^3) $\alpha * (a\beta) = (a\alpha) * \beta = a(\alpha * \beta)$,

where a denotes any scalar;

(2) $\alpha_1\alpha_2 * \beta_1\beta_2 = (\alpha_1 * \beta_1)(\alpha_2 * \beta_2)$.

The *composite of two point collections* **A** and **B** will be the collection of he composites of all the points of **A** with the points of **B**. Finally, the *direct roduct* **A** $*$ **B** of the collections **A** and **B** (which are assumed to be additive and ubtractive) will be the collection of all points obtained from the composites of **A** and **B** by addition and subtraction.

THEOREM 2. *The direct product of two R-algebras is an algebra.*

PROOF. From the definition of the direct product and from properties (1^1), (1^2), and (1^3) for composites of points, it follows that the direct product of linear nvelopes (with respect to the field K or to one of its subfields) of two collecions is the linear envelope of their composites. In particular, $K_m * K_n = K_{mn}$, or the composite of the initial basis of K_m and K_n is the initial basis of K_{mn}. Further, the composite of any coordinate systems $\mathfrak{E}_m$ and $\mathfrak{E}_n$ of the spaces K_m nd K_n is always the basis of K_{mn}, since its K-linear envelope is equal to $K_m * K_n = K_{mn}$ and it consists of exactly mn vectors. From this it follows that he direct product of R-algebras is an R-module based on the composites of its ases. This R-module, in view of rule (2), is reproduced by multiplication, i.e., s an R-algebra, which is what we wanted to show.

§2. THE GALOIS GROUP OF AN R-ALGEBRA

By *axial-superpositions* we will mean linear transformations of K_n by which he vectors of the initial coordinate basis are only permuted among themselves. An *axial-superposition into itself* of an R-algebra will be an axial-superposition hat takes the R-algebra into itself. Axial-superpositions of an R-algebra into tself are automorphisms of the R-algebra and clearly form a group. There exist

R-algebras admitting all $n!$ possible axial-superpositions; an example is an R-algebra constructed on the initial basis. The other extreme case is also possible, when the R-algebra does not have any axial-superpositions into itself other than the identity. For an irreducible R-algebra the number of axial-superpositions into itself cannot exceed its dimension; namely, the following assertion is true.

LEMMA 1. *Among the axial-superpositions of an irreducible R-algebra into itself there exists not more than one taking some vector of the initial basis into a particular other vector of the initial basis, i.e., there are no more than n axial superpositions.*

PROOF. Let us assume the contrary, namely, that two distinct axial-superpositions into itself σ_1 and σ_2 of an R-algebra $\mathbf{A}$ take a vector $\mathbf{e}_1$ of the initial basis into the same vector $\mathbf{e}_2$. Then the axial-superposition $\sigma_3 = \sigma_2\sigma_1^{-1} \neq 1$ takes $\mathbf{e}_1$ into itself. Here there exists a point α of $\mathbf{A}$ such that $\alpha^{\sigma_3} = \beta \neq \alpha$, since $\sigma_3 \neq 1$. The first coordinates of the points α and β are equal, since $\mathbf{e}_1^{\sigma_3} = \mathbf{e}_1$ and hence the point $\beta - \alpha$ of $\mathbf{A}$ turns out to be a zero-divisor, which is impossible in view of the irreducibility of $\mathbf{A}$. The lemma is proved.

We will say that an R-algebra of the space K_n is *normal* if it is irreducible and has n axial-superpositions into itself.

THEOREM 1. *Every irreducible R-algebra of* $\mathbf{A}$ *is a subalgebra of some normal algebra.*

PROOF. We take n copies of the algebra $\mathbf{A}$, denoting them by $\mathbf{A}_1, \mathbf{A}_2, \cdots, \mathbf{A}_n$ and we form their direct product $\mathbf{D}$. It is an R-algebra in a space of dimension n^n. We will number the vectors of the initial coordinate system of this space with sets of indices $(j_1, j_2, \cdots, j_n)$, where we lay out on the axes $\mathbf{e}_{j_1 j_2 \cdots j_n}$ the products of the j_1th coordinates of the points of $\mathbf{A}_1$, the j_2th coordinates of the points of $\mathbf{A}_2$, and so on to the j_nth coordinates of the points of $\mathbf{A}_n$ and the sums of such products. We consider now the $n!$ axes whose "numbers" do not include identical indices, and we show that $\mathbf{D}$ has a direct summand $\mathbf{C}$ which is contained in the coordinate subspace $K_{n!}$ based on these axes. We introduce into the algebra $\mathbf{A}$ the basis $\omega_1, \cdots, \omega_n$; we denote by $\omega_{1,i}, \cdots, \omega_{n,i}$ the corresponding bases of the algebras $\mathbf{A}_i$, and we construct the point β, represented symbolically in the form of the determinant

$$\beta = \begin{vmatrix} \omega_{11} & \omega_{12} & \cdots & \omega_{1n} \\ \omega_{21} & \omega_{22} & \cdots & \omega_{2n} \\ \cdot & \cdot & \cdot & \cdot \\ \omega_{n1} & \omega_{n2} & \cdots & \omega_{nn} \end{vmatrix}.$$

In the calculation of this determinant it is necessary to consider its individual elements as composites of points of the algebras $\mathbf{A}_1, \cdots, \mathbf{A}_n$, while addition must be understood as addition in the algebra $\mathbf{D}$. Clearly, the coordinate of the point β that corresponds to the axis $\mathbf{e}_{j_1 j_2 \cdots j_n}$ is equal to the determinant whose columns are composed respectively of the $j_1, j_2, \cdots, j_n$th coordinates of the points $\omega_1, \omega_2, \cdots, \omega_n$. Hence all the coordinates of the point β that correspond to axes whose "numbers" contain equal indices are equal to zero, while the coordinates corresponding to axes without equal indices are equal, up to the sign, to the determinant consisting of all the coordinates of the points $\omega_1, \omega_2, \cdots, \omega_n$, and are thus different from zero. Hence, in view of Lemma 2, the algebra $\mathbf{D}$ actually has a direct summand $\mathbf{C}$ that is contained in the coordinate subspace $K_{n!}$. We now rearrange in some manner $\mathbf{A}_1, \mathbf{A}_2, \cdots, \mathbf{A}_n$. Then their direct products will not change while the axis with the number $(j_1, j_2, \cdots, j_n)$ will go into the axis with the number in which the indices $j_1, j_2, \cdots, j_n$ undergo the corresponding permutation. The algebra $\mathbf{C}$ is transformed into itself and any axis of its initial basis may be taken into any other axis of the same basis by means of the appropriate choice of the permutation of $\mathbf{A}_1, \mathbf{A}_2, \cdots, \mathbf{A}_n$. The algebra $\mathbf{C}$ may turn out to be reducible; clearly, in this case it is the direct sum of identical normal algebras. In fact, let σ be an axial-superposition into itself of the algebra $\mathbf{C}$ (induced by some permutation of $\mathbf{A}_1, \mathbf{A}_2, \cdots, \mathbf{A}_n$), which takes some axis of the subspace containing an irreducible summand of $\mathbf{B}$ into another axis of the same subspace. This axial-superposition takes $\mathbf{B}$ into some irreducible summand of the algebra $\mathbf{D}$ which must coincide with $\mathbf{B}$, for coordinate subspaces containing distinct irreducible summands of algebras intersect only in zero. Hence, such an axial-superposition of $\mathbf{C}$ induces an axial-superposition of $\mathbf{B}$ into itself, where any axis of the initial basis of the algebra $\mathbf{B}$ may be taken into any other axis of its initial basis, i.e., $\mathbf{B}$ is normal. Having considered an axial-superposition taking some axis of an irreducible summand $\mathbf{B}$ into an axis of another irreducible summand $\mathbf{B}'$, we see that it takes $\mathbf{B}$ into $\mathbf{B}'$. Thus we see that all the direct summands of $\mathbf{C}$ are normal and may be obtained from one of the $\mathbf{B}$ by axial-superpositions, i.e., they are equal to each other.

Further, the algebra $\mathbf{D}$ contains the composite $\mathbf{A}_1 * 1 * \cdots * 1 = \widetilde{\mathbf{A}}_1$, which is nothing other than the algebra $\mathbf{A}$ based on some bisectrix; namely, the first coordinates of points of $\mathbf{A}$ are laid out on the complex of axes, the first index of which is equal to 1, the second on the complex of axes, the first index of which is equal to 2, and so on. Let e be a unit of the space $K_{n!}$. Then clearly $e \in \mathbf{C}$ and $\widetilde{\mathbf{A}}_i e \subset \mathbf{C}$ is again an algebra $\mathbf{A}$ put into the corresponding bisectrix of $K_{n!}$. Thus, $\mathbf{A}$ is a subalgebra of $\mathbf{C}$, based on the bisectrix of all of $K_{n!}$. But, in any case, $\mathbf{A}$ is also a subalgebra for $\mathbf{B}$, which follows from the following lemma:

LEMMA 2. *If an irreducible R-algebra* $\mathbf{A}$ *is a subalgebra of an R-algebra* $\mathbf{C}$ *and is located on the bisectrix of all of its space, then* $\mathbf{A}$ *is a subalgebra of each irreducible summand of* $\mathbf{C}$.

PROOF. Let $\mathbf{C} = \mathbf{B}_1 + \cdots + \mathbf{B}_k$ be the decomposition into irreducible summands, let $K_{n_1}, \cdots, K_{n_k}$ be the subspaces containing $\mathbf{B}_1, \cdots, \mathbf{B}_k$, let $K_{n'_1}, \cdots, K_{n'_k}$ be the subspaces complementary to them, and let $\epsilon_1, \cdots, \epsilon_k$ be units of the algebras $\mathbf{B}_1, \cdots, \mathbf{B}_k$. Then clearly the collection $\epsilon_j \mathbf{A}$ is a subalgebra of $\mathbf{B}_j$, the coordinate points of which coincide with the coordinates of the corresponding points of $\mathbf{A}$, where all the coordinates will be represented unless multiplication by ϵ_j annihilates some vector of the initial coordinate system of the bisectrix containing $\mathbf{A}$. But this situation would be possible only if the bisectrix containing $\mathbf{A}$ had an intersection with the space $K_{n'_j}$ other than zero, which is impossible. In fact, if there were a bisectrix containing $\mathbf{A}$ with a nonzero intersection with $K_{n'_j}$, then this intersection, being the intersection of $\mathbf{C}$-complete subspaces, would be $\mathbf{C}$-complete, and points of this intersection would be zero-divisors and would be included in $\mathbf{A}$, which is impossible, in view of the irreducibility of $\mathbf{A}$. Thus each algebra $\epsilon_j \mathbf{A}$ is equal to $\mathbf{A}$ based on some bisectrix K_{n_j} in a corresponding way, i.e., $\mathbf{A}$ is a subalgebra of each $\mathbf{B}_j$. Lemma 2 and Theorem 1 are now proved in full.

We note that, starting with the reducible algebra $\mathbf{A}$, by the same construction we could have constructed a normal algebra $\mathbf{B}$. Having generalized Lemma 4 in a corresponding manner, it is easy to see that the normal algebra so constructed contains all the irreducible summands of $\mathbf{A}$ as subalgebras. Further, it is possible to show that the normal algebra $\mathbf{B}$ thus constructed is minimal among all the normal algebras that contain all the irreducible summands.

§3. BASIC THEOREMS OF GALOIS FOR R-ALGEBRAS

Let $\mathfrak{G}$ be the group of axial-superpositions of a normal algebra **A** and let $\mathfrak{H}$ be one of its subgroups. We decompose all the axes of the initial coordinate system into complexes, putting into one complex all the axes that can be obtained from one another by means of axial-superpositions from the group $\mathfrak{H}$. It is easy to see that such complexes do not have common axes, that the number of axes in each complex is equal to the order of $\mathfrak{H}$, and hence that the number of complexes is equal to the index of $\mathfrak{H}$. The bisectrix of the space K_n determined by such a decomposition of the initial coordinate system will be called the bisectrix *belonging to the subgroup* $\mathfrak{H}$. Its points may be characterized by the fact that they and only they remain fixed under all the axial-superpositions from $\mathfrak{G}$.

THEOREM 1. *Any R-subalgebra of a normal R-algebra* **A** *is the completion of a bisectrix belonging to some subgroups of the group of axial-superpositions* $\mathfrak{G}$ *of the algebra* **A** *into itself. Conversely, a bisectrix belonging to some subgroups of the group* $\mathfrak{G}$ *is* **A**-*complete and its completion is a subalgebra of* **A**.

PROOF. Let there be given a subalgebra **B** of a normal algebra **A**. It completes some bisectrix $\overline{\mathbf{B}}$ of the whole K_n. Let this bisectrix be characterized by the equality of coordinates in the complexes of axes

$$(\mathbf{e}_1, \dots, \mathbf{e}_m), \quad (\mathbf{e}_{m+1}, \dots), \dots .$$

We consider the collection $\mathfrak{H}_1$ of all axial-superpositions taking the axis $\mathbf{e}_1$ into the axes of the first complex. These axial-superpositions do not change all the points of **B**, for if one of these axial-superpositions $\omega \in \mathbf{B}$ went into a different point ω', then, in view of the normality of $\omega' \in \mathbf{A}$, **A** would contain the zero divisor $\omega - \omega'$. Each axial-superposition taking $\mathbf{e}_1$ into the axis $\mathbf{e}_k$ of another complex changes at least one point of the subalgebra **B**, since there exist in it points that have unequal coordinates in the axes $\mathbf{e}_1$ and $\mathbf{e}_k$. Thus the collection $\mathfrak{H}_1$ coincides with the collection $\mathfrak{H}$ of all the axial-superpositions that do not change all the points of the subalgebra **B**. From these considerations we conclude that the collection of all axial-superpositions taking any axis into all the axes of the complex containing it coincides with the collection $\mathfrak{H}$. Clearly $\mathfrak{H}$ is a group, and the bisectrix containing **B** belongs to this group.

Let there now be given some subgroup $\mathfrak{H}$ of the group $\mathfrak{G}$ of axial-superpositions into itself of the normal algebra **A**. We associate with each point $\alpha \in K_n$ the sum of all the points obtained from α by axial-superpositions from the group $\mathfrak{H}$. This determines a linear transformation of K_n which is rational with respect to **A** because of its normality, and which takes all of K_n into a bisectrix belonging to $\mathfrak{H}$. Hence this bisectrix is **A**-complete and its completion is clearly a subalgebra of the algebra **A**. The theorem is proved in full.

THEOREM 2. *If $\mathfrak{H}$ is a normal divisor of the group $\mathfrak{G}$ of axial-superposition of a normal R-algebra* **A**, *then the subalgebra* **B** *belonging to $\mathfrak{H}$ is normal and its group of axial-superpositions is isomorphic to $\mathfrak{G}/\mathfrak{H}$.*

PROOF. Let $\mathfrak{G} = \mathfrak{H} + \sigma_2\mathfrak{H} + \cdots + \sigma_k\mathfrak{H}$ and let $\mathbf{e}_1$ be one of the vectors of the initial coordinate system of K_n. Then the vectors of the initial coordinate system belonging to $\mathfrak{H}$ are $e_k = \sum_{\tau\in\sigma_k\mathfrak{H}} \mathbf{e}^{\tau}$. It is easy to see that if $\mathfrak{H}$ is a normal divisor of $\mathfrak{G}$, then each axial-superposition of $\mathfrak{G}$ takes into itself the initial basis of the bisectrix belonging to $\mathfrak{H}$ and consequently the whole bisectrix. In fact

$$e_k^{\sigma} = \sum_{\tau\in\sigma_k\mathfrak{H}} \mathbf{e}_1^{\tau\sigma} = \sum_{\tau'\in\sigma_k\mathfrak{H}\sigma} \mathbf{e}_1^{\tau'} = \sum_{\tau'\in\sigma_k\sigma\mathfrak{H}} \mathbf{e}_1^{\tau'}.$$

Axial-superpositions induced in the bisectrix form a group homomorphic to $\mathfrak{G}$ with the kernel of the homomorphism being $\mathfrak{H}$. Hence this group is isomorphic to $\mathfrak{G}/\mathfrak{H}$. Its order is equal to the dimension of the bisectrix. Under all these superpositions **B** goes into itself, and hence, being irreducible since it is a subalgebra of an irreducible algebra **A**, it is normal. The theorem is proved.

§4. CONNECTION WITH THE PRESENT-DAY PRESENTATION OF GALOIS THEORY

1. On generic points. A generic point of the space K_n is a point whose coordinates are distinct and different from zero.

LEMMA 1. *Any irreducible R-algebra* **A** *contains a generic point.*

PROOF. Let us consider separately the cases when R consists of a finite and of an infinite number of elements.

Let the field R be finite. Then any irreducible R-algebra **A** will also be a finite field. As is well known, all the nonzero elements of a finite field form a *cyclic* group with respect to multiplication. Let α be a generator of this group. Then α is a generic point, for if two of its coordinates were equal, i.e., if α lay in some bisectrix, then all the elements of **A** would lie in the same bisectrix and, except for zero, would all be powers of α, which is impossible.

Now let R be infinite. We find first of all in the R-algebra **A** points $\alpha_2, \alpha_3, \cdots, \alpha_n$ such that the ith coordinate $\alpha_i^{(i)}$ of the point α_i is different from its first coordinate $\alpha_i^{(1)}$. Such points may be found, for otherwise **A** would be in some bisectrix. We now construct successively the points $\beta_2, \beta_3, \cdots, \beta_n$ such that all the coordinates from the second to the ith of the points β_i are different from its first coordinate. As β_2 we take α_2, constructing the successive points inductively. Let β_i be already constructed. We look for β_{i+1} in the form $\beta_{i+1} = \beta_i + x\alpha_{i+1}$, where $x \in R$. For our purpose we must choose x so that none of the following equalities are fulfilled:

$$\beta_i^{(2)} + x\alpha_{i+1}^{(2)} = \beta_i^{(1)} + x\alpha_{i+1}^{(1)},$$
$$\cdots\cdots\cdots\cdots\cdots$$
$$\beta_i^{(i)} + x\alpha_{i+1}^{(i)} = \beta_i^{(1)} + x\alpha_{i+1}^{(1)},$$
$$\beta_i^{(i+1)} + x\alpha_{i+1}^{(i+1)} = \beta_i^{(1)} + x\alpha_{i+1}^{(1)}.$$

None of these equalities is an identity (the last in view of the choice α_{i+1}, the remaining in view of the construction of the point β_i). Hence each of these equalities can be satisfied for not more than one value of x. Taking x different from this finite number of excluded values, we construct the point $\beta_{i+1} = \beta_i + x\alpha_{i+1}$, satisfying the given requirement. The last point β_n, which we denote by γ_1, has the property that its first coordinate is different from all the remaining coordinates.

In the same way we construct points $\gamma_2, \cdots, \gamma_n$ so that the ith coordinate of the point γ_i is different from all the remaining coordinates of that point. Then we pass to the inductive construction of the points $\delta_2, \delta_3, \cdots, \delta_n$ such that the first i coordinates of the point δ_i are distinct. As δ_2 we take γ_2. Let δ_i be already constructed. We look for the point δ_{i+1} in the form $\delta_i + x\gamma_{i+1}$ for $x \in R$. We must choose x so that none of the following equalities is satisfied:

$$\delta_i^{(j)} + x\gamma_{i+1}^{(j)} = \delta_i^{(k)} + x\gamma_{i+1}^{(k)}, \qquad j, k \leq i,$$
$$\delta_i^{(j)} + x\gamma_{i+1}^{(j)} = \delta_i^{(i+1)} + x\gamma_{i+1}^{(i+1)}, \qquad j = 1, 2, \cdots, i.$$

The equalities in the first set are not satisfied identically because of the choice of δ_i, while the last are not satisfied identically because of the choice of γ_{i+1}. Hence we may again take for x any member of R other than a finite number of values.

The last of the points δ_n thus constructed will not have equal coordinates, and in view of the irreducibility of **A** all of its coordinates will be different from 0, i.e., δ_n is a generic point. The lemma is proved.

REMARK. If R is infinite the requirement of the irreducibility of **A** is not essential. It is used only to check that no coordinate of the point δ_n is equal to zero, which may be avoided by adding, when necessary, a properly chosen scalar multiple of the unit. If R is finite the requirement of irreducibility is essential, for in this case it is easy to construct an example of a reducible algebra that does not have any generic points.

2. **Content of the theory thus constructed.** We have the following theorem:

THEOREM. *Any irreducible R-algebra is a separable finite algebraic extension of the field R. Conversely, any separable finite algebraic extension of degree n of the field R may be represented in the form of an irreducible R-algebra in the field K_n for a suitably chosen field K.*

PROOF. Let α be a generic point of an irreducible R-algebra **A** of the space K_n. Then the points $1, \alpha, \cdots, \alpha^{n-1}$ are linearly independent with respect to K, i.e., they form a coordinate system for the space K_n. In fact, if they were linearly dependent, that is if we had $c_1\alpha^{n-1} + \cdots + c_n = 0$ with coefficients from K, then the polynomial $\phi(x) = c_1x^{n-1} + \cdots + c_n$ would have n distinct roots, namely the coordinates of the point α, which is impossible. The basis $1, \alpha, \cdots, \alpha^{n-1}$ belongs to **A**, and hence all the points of **A** are representable in terms of the basis with coordinates in R. In particular, there exist $a_1, a_2, \cdots, a_n \in R$ such that $\alpha^n = a_1\alpha^{n-1} + \cdots + a_n$. The roots of the polynomial $f(x) = x^n - a_1x^{n-1} - \cdots - a_n$ are the coordinates of the point α; they are all distinct. The polynomial $f(x)$ is irreducible in R. In fact, if we had $f(x) = \phi_1(x) \cdot \phi_2(x)$, where ϕ_1, ϕ_2 are nonconstant polynomials with coefficients from R, then the point $\phi_1(\alpha)$, being different from zero, would have zero coordinates corresponding to those coordinates of α which are roots of $\phi_1(x)$. Thus $\mathbf{A} = R(\alpha)$, where α is a root of a polynomial that is irreducible in R and which does not have multiple roots, i.e., it is a separable finite algebraic extension of R.

Conversely, let there be given a field $\tilde{\mathbf{A}}$, which is a finite separable algebraic extension of R, let $\tilde{\alpha}$ be a primitive element of it, and let $f(x)$ be an irreducible polynomial determining $\tilde{\alpha}$. We take for K a field in which $f(x)$ may be decomposed into linear factors, for example, an algebraically closed field containing R. In K let $f(x) = (x - \alpha^{(1)})(x - \alpha^{(2)}) \cdots (x - \alpha^{(n)})$. In view of the separability of $\tilde{\mathbf{A}}$, all the $\alpha^{(1)}, \alpha^{(2)}, \cdots, \alpha^{(n)}$ will be distinct. We associate with the element $\tilde{\alpha}$ the point α of the space K_n with coordinates $\alpha^{(1)}, \alpha^{(2)}, \cdots, \alpha^{(n)}$. Since α is a generic point in K_n, the points $1, \alpha, \cdots, \alpha^{n-1}$ form a coordinate system in K_n. Clearly, an R-module based on this coordinate system is an R-algebra $\mathbf{A}$, isomorphic with the field $\widetilde{\mathbf{A}}$. It will be irreducible, since, in view of the isomorphism with the field $\widetilde{\mathbf{A}}$, it will contain no zero-divisors. The theorem is proved.

BIBLIOGRAPHY

[1] F. Arndt, *Versuch einer Theorie der homogenen Funktionen des dritten Grades mit zwei Variabeln,* Arch. Math. Phys. 17 (1851), 1–85.

[2] ——, *Untersuchungen über die Anzahl der kubischen Klassen, welche zu einer determinirenden quadratischen Klasse gehören,* Arch. Math. Phys. 19 (1852), 408–418.

[3] ——, *Tabellarische Berechnung der reducirten binären kubischen Formen und Klassification derselben für alle succesiven negativen Determinanten* $(-D)$ *von* $D = 3$ *bis* $D = 2000$, Arch. Math. Phys. 31 (1858), 335–448.

[4] ——, *Zur Theorie der binären kubischen Formen,* J. Reine Angew. Math. 53 (1857), 309–321.

[5] W. E. H. Berwick, *The classification of ideal numbers that depend on a cubic irrationality,* Proc. London Math. Soc. (2) 12 (1913), 393–429.

[6] B. A. Venkov, *Classification of cubic regions by quadratic regions,* Proc. 2nd all-Union Math. Congress (Leningrad, 1934). (Russian)

[7] A. Weil, *Sur un théorème de Mordell,* Bull. Sci. Math. (2) 54 (1930), 182–191.

[8] G. Voronoĭ, *Concerning algebraic integers derivable from a root of an equation of the third degree,* Master's Thesis, St. Petersburg, 1894. (Russian)

[9] ——, *On a generalization of the algorithm for continued fractions,* Doctoral Thesis, Warsaw, 1896. (Russian)

[10] R. Dedekind, *Ueber die Anzahl der Idealklassen in reinen kubischen Zahlkörpern,* J. Reine Angew. Math. 121 (1900), 40–123.

[11] B. N. Delone, *Solution of the indeterminate equation* $X^3q + Y^3 = 1$, Izv. Akad. Nauk SSSR (6) 16 (1922), 273–280. (Russian)

[12] ——, *On the number of representations of a number by a cubic binary form with negative determinant,* Izv. Akad. Nauk SSSR (6) 16 (1922), 253–272. (Russian)

[13] ——, *Vollständige Lösung der unbestimmten Gleichung* $X^3q + Y^3 = 1$ *in ganzen Zahlen,* Math. Z. 28 (1928), 1–9; *Über die Darstellung der Zahlen durch die binären kubischen Formen von negativer Diskriminante,* Math. Z. 31 (1930), 1–26. (German translations of [11] and [12])

[14] ——, *Ueber den Algorithmus der Erhöhung*, Ž. Leningrad. Fiz.-Mat. Obšč. 1 (1927), no. 2, 257–267.

[15] ——, *Solution of the problem of equivalence and tabulation of cubic binary forms with negative determinant*, Ž. Leningrad. Fiz.-Mat. Obšč. 1 (1926), no. 1, 40–55. (Russian)

[16] ——, *Interprétation géometrique de la généralisation de l'algorithme des fractions continues donné par Voronoĭ*, C. R. Acad. Sci. Paris (1923).

[17] ——, *On indeterminate equations*, Proc. all-Russian Math. Congress (Moscow, 1927), pp. 148–161. (Russian)

[18] ——, *A table of purely real domains of the fourth order* (in collaboration with I. Sominski and K. Billevič), Izv. Akad. Nauk SSSR Otd. Mat. i Estest. Nauk (1935), 1267–1310. (Russian. French summary)

[19] ——, *On the geometry of Galois theory*, Memorial volume dedicated to D. A. Grave, pp. 52–62, Moscow, 1940. (Russian)

[20] G. Eisenstein, *Théorèmes sur les formes cubiques et solution d'une équation du quatrième degré à quatre indeterminées*, J. Reine Angew. Math. 27 (1844), 75–79.

[21] ——, *Untersuchungen über die cubischen Formen mit zwei Variabeln*, J. Reine Angew. Math. 27 (1844), 89–104.

[22] ——, *Eigenschaften und Beziehungen der Ausdrücke, welche bei der Auflösung der allgemeinen cubischen Gleichungen erscheinen*, J. Reine Angew. Math. 27 (1844), 319–329.

[23] ——, *Allgemeine Untersuchungen über die Formen dritten Grades mit drei Variabeln, welche der Kreistheilung ihre Enstehung verdanken*, J. Reine Angew. Math. 28 (1844), 289–374.

[24] O. Žitomirskiĭ, *Sur la classification des formes cubiques*, Izv. Akad. Nauk SSSR Otd. Mat. i Estest. Nauk (1935), 1299–1312.

[25] E. I. Zolotarev, *On an indeterminate equation of third degree*, St. Petersburg, 1869. (Russian)

[26] ——, *Theory of integral complex numbers with applications to the integral calculus*, Doctoral Dissertation, St. Petersburg, 1874. (Russian)

[27] F. Klein, *Ausgewählte Kapiteln der Zahlentheorie*, Göttingen, 1896–97.

[28] F. Levi, *Kubische Zahlkörper und binäre kubische Formenklassen*, Ber. Sachs. Akad. Wiss. Leipzig Mat.-Nat. Kl. 66 (1914).

[29] A. Markov, *Sur les nombres entiers dépendants d'une racine cubique d'un nombre entier ordinaire,* Mem. l'Acad. Imp. Sci. St. Pétersbourg (7) 38 (1892), no. 9, 1–37.

[30] G. B. Mathews and W. E. H. Berwick, *On the reduction of arithmetical binary cubics which have a negative discriminant,* Proc. London Math. Soc. (2) 10 (1911–1912), 48–53.

[31] G. B. Mathews, *On the reduction and classification of binary cubics which have a negative discriminant,* Proc. London Math. Soc. (2) 10 (1911–1912), 128–138.

[32] H. Minkowski, *Diophantische Approximationen,* Leipzig, 1907.

[33] ———, *Généralisation de la théorie des fractions continues,* Ann. Sci. École Norm. Sup. (3) 13 (1896), 41–60.

[34] L. J. Mordell, *Note on the integer solutions of the equation* $Ey^2 = Ax^3 + Bx^2 + Cx + D$, Messenger of Math. 51 (1922), 169–171.

[35] ———, *On the integer solutions of the equation* $ey^2 = ax^3 + bx^2 + cx + d$, Proc. London Math. Soc. (2) 21 (1922–23), 415–419.

[36] ———, *On the rational solutions of the indeterminate equations of the third and fourth degrees,* Proc. Cambridge Philos. Soc. 21 (1922), 179–192.

[37] ———, *Indeterminate equations of the third degree,* Science Progress (1923).

[38] T. Nagell, *Vollständige Lösung einiger unbestimmten Gleichungen dritten Grades,* Vid.-Selsk. Skr. I. Mat. Nat. Kl. 1922, no. 14.

[39] ———, *Über die Einheiten in reinen kubischen Zahlkörpern,* Vid.-Selsk. Skr. I. Mat. Nat. Kl. 1923, no. 11.

[40] ———, *Solution complète de quelques équations cubiques à deux indéterminées,* J. Math. Pures Appl. (9) 4 (1925), 209–270.

[41] ———, *Über einige kubische Gleichungen mit zwei Unbestimmten,* Math. Z. 24 (1925), 422–447.

[42] ———, *Darstellung ganzer Zahlen durch binäre kubische Formen mit negativer Diskriminante,* Math. Z. 28 (1928), 10–29.

[43] ———, *Zur Theorie der kubischen Irrationalitäten,* Acta Math. 55 (1930), 33–65.

[44] ———, *L'analyse indéterminée de degré supérieur,* Mémor. Sci. Math. Vol. 39, Paris, 1929.

[45] L. W. Reid, *Tafel der Klassenanzahlen für kubische Zahlkörper,* Inaugural Dissertation, Göttingen, 1899.

[46] C. L. Siegel, *Über einige Anwendungen diophantischer Approximationen,* Sitz. Preuss. Akad. Wiss. Phys.-Math. Kl. 1929, 508.

[47] ——, *Die Gleichung* $ax^n - by^n = c$, Math. Ann. 114 (1937), 57–68.

[48] V. Tartakovskiĭ, *Auflösung der Gleichung* $x^4 - \rho y^4 = 1$, Izv. Akad. Nauk SSSR (6) 20 (1926), 301–324.

[49] A. Thue, *Bemerkungen über gewisse Näherungsbrüche algebraischer Zahlen,* Vid.-Selsk. Skr. I. Mat. Nat. Kl. 1908.

[50] ——, *Ueber rationale Annäherungswerte der reellen Wurzeln der ganzer Functionen dritten Grades* $x^3 - ax - b$, Vid.-Selsk. Skr. I. Mat. Nat. Kl. 1908.

[51] ——, *On an equation which is in general insoluble,* Vid.-Selsk. Skr. I. Mat. Nat. Kl. 1908. (Norwegian)

[52] ——, *Über Annäherungswerte algebraischer Zahlen,* J. Reine Angew. Math. 135 (1910), 284–305.

[53] ——, *Eine Lösung der Gleichung* $P(x) - Q(x) = (x - \rho)^n \cdot Pr(x)$ *in ganzen Functionen P, Q und R für jede beliebige ganze Zahl, wenn* ρ *eine Wurzel einer beliebigen ganzen Function bedeutet,* Vid.-Selsk. Skr. I. Mat. Nat. Kl. 1909.

[54] ——, *Ein Fundamentaltheorem zur Bestimmung von Annäherungswerten aller Wurzeln gewisser ganzen Funktionen,* J. Reine Angew. Math. 138 (1910), 96–108.

[55] J. V. Uspensky, *A method for finding units in cubic orders of a negative discriminant,* Trans. Amer. Math. Soc. 33 (1931), 1–22.

[56] D. K. Faddeev, *Tabulation of Galois domains and rings of the third order,* Trudy Fiz.-Mat. Inst. Steklov. V (1934)), 19–24. (Russian)

[57] ——, *On the equation* $x^4 - Ay^4 = \pm 1$, Trudy Fiz.-Mat. Inst. Steklov. V (1934), 41–52. (Russian)

[58] ——, *On the equation* $x^3 + y^3 = Az^3$, Trudy Fiz.-Mat. Inst. Steklov. V (1934), 25–40. (Russian)

[59] ——, *Classification of algebraic domains by their cubic resolvents,* Proc. 2nd all-Union Math. Congress (Leningrad, 1934), Vol. 2, pp. 32–35. (Russian)

[60] ———, *On a property of the group of classes of ideals for a domain of third degree*, Proc. 2nd all-Union Math. Congress (Leningrad, 1934), Vol. 2, pp. 42–44. (Russian)

[61] ———, *On a class of indeterminate equations of the third degree*, Proc. 2nd all-Union Math. Congress (Leningrad, 1934), Vol. 2, pp. 36–41. (Russian)

[62] ———, *The structure of algebraic domains whose Galois group is the quaternion group*, Leningrad. Gos, Univ. Učen. Zap. (1937), no. 17, 17–24. (Russian)

[63] P. Furtwängler, *Kubische Zahlkörper und Zahlengitter*, Dissertation, Göttingen.

[64] H. Hasse, *Arithmetische Theorie der kubischen Zahlkörper auf Klassenkörpertheoretischer Grundlage*, Math. Z. 31 (1930), 565–582.

[65] N. G. Čebotarev, *Foundations of Galois theory*. I, II, GITTL, Moscow, 1934, 1936. (Russian)

[66] ———, *The problem inverse to the Tschirnhausen problem*, Vestnik Čist. i Prikl. Znan. 1 (1922), no. 2, 1–8. (Russian)

[67] L. Charve, *De la réduction des formes quadratiques ternaires positives et de son application aux irrationnelles du troisième degré*, Ann. Sci. École Norm. Sup. (2) 9 (1880), 3–156. (Supplement)